# OUTLINE OF HISTORICAL GEOLOGY

# OUTLINE OF
# HISTORICAL GEOLOGY

*by*

A. K. WELLS D.SC

*and*

J. F. KIRKALDY D.SC

Fifth Edition

WITH 133 ILLUSTRATIONS

*London*

THOMAS MURBY & CO

40 MUSEUM STREET W.C.1

FIRST PUBLISHED IN 1937
SECOND REVISED EDITION 1948
THIRD REVISED EDITION 1951
FOURTH REVISED EDITION 1959
FIFTH IMPRESSION 1960
FIFTH REVISED EDITION (SIXTH IMPRESSION) 1966



George Allen & Unwin Ltd.,
40 Museum Street, London, W.C.1
are proprietors of
Thomas Murby & Co.

MADE AND PRINTED IN GREAT BRITAIN BY
MORRISON AND GIBB LIMITED, LONDON AND EDINBURGH

# PREFACE TO THE FIRST EDITION

THE author is one of the many who are firmly convinced of the high cultural value of Geology, particularly of Historical Geology. Quite apart from its stimulating effect upon the imagination, even a limited familiarity with this branch of Science adds a new significance to the countryside and a new interest to natural scenery. The professional geologist, however, has not done all he might do to allow the man in the street to share the benefits that arise from his training. Largely for this reason the present volume has been made less of a textbook than an effort to cater for the requirements of the general reader who is not content to remain in ignorance of the history of his country prior to the year 55 B.C. At the same time it will serve adequately for the undergraduate with no geological background who is about to embark on a course of Stratigraphy.

So far as practicable, abstruse technicalities have been suppressed; but the principles involved are introduced as occasion arises, and the 'why and wherefore' are carefully explained.

It has been thought best to concentrate upon the special aspects of each successive chapter of geological history. This could be done in a book of limited size only at the expense of the less significant and less interesting facts that would naturally find a place in a more comprehensive work. For similar reasons it has been thought unnecessary, at this stage, to quote references and authorities, except in a few cases, for the statements made.

In preparing the book the author has drawn freely upon the work of others. He has received valuable assistance from his colleague, Mr. J. F. Kirkaldy, who has constructively criticized the manuscript and has read the proofs; also from his son, M. K. Wells, who has drawn some of the illustrations and has lettered many others. Mr. A. N. Thomas has kindly drawn some of the illustrations of the Lower Palaeozoic faunas.

A. KINGSLEY WELLS

KING'S COLLEGE
UNIVERSITY OF LONDON
*October* 1937

# PREFACE TO THE FIFTH EDITION

SINCE the publication of the last Edition rapid developments in a number of specialized branches of Geology have affected our understanding and teaching of Historical Geology. In particular the rise of Sedimentology has made available several new lines from which may be deduced the environments in which sediments, particularly those which are unfossiliferous or sparsely fossiliferous, were deposited. The close attention now being paid to structures in sedimentary rocks, especially when metamorphosed, has greatly increased, though not in all cases, clarified, our knowledge of their post-depositional history. 'Radiometric' methods of dating minerals and rocks promise to place the geologists' time-scale on a firm chronological, as distinct from a relative, basis.

The geology of the seas surrounding the British Isles is being actively explored; while on land the steadily increasing number of deep borings sunk in the search for oil and gas has greatly increased our knowledge of deeper-seated geology. In addition to all these new lines of investigation, substantial advances in our knowledge of rocks and structures have been made in many parts of the British Isles by the application of long-established conventional methods of geological study.

In the new Edition considerable changes have been made. Two entirely new chapters have been added: in the one the principles of Geochronology are introduced to the reader; the other deals with underground and under-sea Geology. Several of the original chapters, particularly in the first half of the book, have been substantially re-written. As in previous Editions, rather than filling the pages with technical data, we have concentrated on the conclusions that may reasonably be inferred from them and have stressed the interpretation of the facts. This has involved us in indicating some of the current problems of Stratigraphy, without always supplying the solution. We have not always accepted uncritically everything that is newly recorded; wherever the interpretation of the evidence seems to us unproven or ambiguous, we have commented to this effect.

We anticipate that the reader will soon become puzzled by the inaccuracy and inadequacy of stratigraphical nomenclature: we have had to devote considerable space to explaining away wrong impressions conveyed by some terms in common—even official—use. The trouble arises largely from the fact that many of the terms go back to times when Stratigraphy was in its infancy. The pioneer geologists named distinctive groups of strata from their broad lithological character as displayed in a particular type area. The range of lithological terms was then much more limited than at present, and none was precisely defined. Thus 'shale' was applied to any megascopically fine-grained sedimentary rock, irrespective of the proportion of material of clay grade to silt. When these formations were traced into other areas, their lithology was found to change, in some cases drastically, yet the original name was retained, with the result that we are still burdened with 'Old Red Sandstone' which is neither red nor sandstone; with 'Upper Coal Measures' which, in many areas, bear no resemblance to the typical coal-bearing strata of the coal-mining districts and contain no coal; and with 'Bunter Pebble Beds' which in some localities contain no pebbles.

In fossiliferous strata it is possible to divide Systems into Series and these, in turn into Stages and sub-Stages, each defined by its distinctive faunal assemblage and bearing names which are independent of lithological variations. The term 'Soudley Sandstone' to make sense, must refer to a particular sandstone occurring at Soudley in Shropshire; but 'Soudleyan'—the Stage name based on the old term—may be sandstone, siltstone, mudstone, conglomerate or limestone, in *any* area where strata of this age occur. Ideally the whole Stratigraphical Column should be treated in this way; but we have a very long way to go before up-to-date methods of classification and nomenclature have been applied to all the Geological Systems.

Quite a large number of stratigraphical place-names are based on Welsh or Scottish localities. Many of these names look quite impossible to pronounce. In some cases we have attempted to indicate how they should be pronounced—with due apologies to those whose native tongues are Welsh or Gaelic.

In the present revision we have been forced to alter the names of many of the fossils referred to, and in some cases figured. Many palaeontologists have no inhibitions where changing the name of a fossil is concerned, no matter how long it may have been in vogue. Many of these fossil names have become household words in geological circles, many are on the short lists of types which even elementary students are expected to identify on sight. As generic identification only is required in early stages of training, when revision suggests that a new name is really necessary, it is a very great help if the new name bears some resemblance to the old. Thus the trilobite '*Ogygia*' of the last generation of students will probably be recognised in '*Ogygiocarella*'; and the familiar '*Asaphus*' in '*Asaphiscus*', or '*Agnostus trisectus*' in '*Lotagnostus trisectus*';

but who except the palaeontological expert can be expected to pierce the disguises of *Dunbarella* (formerly *Pterinopecten*), *Dictyoclostus* (formerly *Productus*) or *Strapellus* (formerly *Euomphalus*)—all these are common fossils, well within the vocabulary of the elementary student. When the original specific name is retained, though the generic name is altered, there is a link between the present and the past; but when both are changed there is no such connection, and both teachers and students are faced with a dilemma: should the old, established name, or the new, revised one, or both, be used? The brachiopod *Chonetes striatella*, one of the best known and most widely collected of the Silurian fossils became in 1963 *Protochonetes ludloviensis*. This fossil, under its old name, was characteristic of the topmost beds in the Silurian of Shropshire which were therefore called '*Chonetes* Beds'. The complete fossil assemblage was termed the '*Chonetes striatella* fauna'; but the re-christening has made both these convenient terms obsolete. Unfortunately this process is continuous and where fossil names are concerned the students' 'lot is not a happy one'.

As on former occasions we have derived considerable benefit from discussion of knotty points with our colleagues, among them the senior author's son, Dr. M. K. Wells, who also helped in preparing the new illustrations in the text.

A. K. WELLS
J. F. KIRKALDY

# CONTENTS

There rolls the deep where grew the tree.
O Earth, what changes hast thou seen!
There, where the long street roars, hath been
The stillness of the central sea.

The hills are shadows, and they flow
From form to form, and nothing stands;
They melt like mists, the solid lands,
Like clouds they shape themselves and go.

ALFRED, LORD TENNYSON

# ILLUSTRATIONS IN THE TEXT

# GENERAL WORKS OF REFERENCE

BRITISH REGIONAL GEOLOGY. Well-illustrated accounts of the geology, topography and scenery of the natural regions of Britain. By various Authors, published by the Geological Survey and Museum, in separate parts.

**M. Black.** *Petrology of the Sedimentary Rocks.* Revised by J. T. Greensmith.

**A. W. Grabau.** *Principles of Stratigraphy.*

**A. Holmes.** *Principles of Physical Geology*, 1964.

**L. J. Wills.** *Physiographical Evolution of the British Isles*, 1929; *Palaeogeographical Atlas*, Blackie, 1952.

**S. W. Wooldridge and R. S. Morgan.** *The Physical Basis of Geography: an Outline of Geomorphology.*

Detailed accounts of the geology of a particular district in which a reader may be interested will be found in one or other of the Memoirs of the Geological Survey, of which a list is published by the Department of Scientific and Industrial Research.

Among the publications of the Geologists' Association, London, are excursion handbooks, prepared for use in the areas visited by the Association, and a series of 'Guides' published to commemorate the centenary of the Association in 1958. Each Guide includes detailed itineraries covering areas around university towns, selected coastal and 'classic' areas such as Snowdonia, S. Shropshire and the Dorset Coast. Particulars are published in the 'Proceedings' of the Association.

Geological maps of the British Isles (scale 1 inch to 25 miles) or of Great Britain (scale 1 inch to 10 miles) are published by the Geological Survey.

Messrs. T. Murby & Co., 40 Museum St., W.C.1, publish outline geological maps of the British Isles. These are very useful for making outcrop- and locality-maps or palaeogeographical maps of the different Systems.

## CHAPTER I

# INTRODUCTION

THE earth has been likened to a projectile of nickel-iron with a thin skin of slag upon its surface. The latter, termed the lithosphere by geologists, consists of two chief parts: a lower (inner) continuous shell of basaltic composition—the basaltic shell—and a higher (outer) discontinuous granitic shell. The former underlies the oceans as well as the existing continents, while the latter forms the major portion of the continents themselves, but is almost completely absent from the ocean-floors. Our knowledge of the nature and disposition of these earth-shells is based to a limited extent upon direct observation, but is largely inferred from earthquake phenomena and geophysical observations and measurements. Direct observation is necessarily limited to things seen at the surface and in mines; in this connection it should be remembered that the deepest mines penetrate only to a depth of some 7000 feet into the lithosphere—a mere pinprick in the skin of a sphere 8000 miles in diameter.

In the process of smelting a sample of ore the metal is separated from the dross—the rock matrix in which it is embedded—by fusion. In the process the matrix material, which cools into slag, rises and floats on the surface of the much heavier molten metal. It is difficult to resist the conclusion that the comparable relationship between the core and the 'crust' of the earth (the lithosphere) is due to an analogous operation on a gigantic scale. Further, the lithosphere is, as stated above, itself stratified. From a large number of carefully studied examples it is known that when molten rock material, the *magma* of geologists, cools, it tends to become stratified, as the minerals which crystallize first, at high temperatures, are relatively heavy and therefore sink through the fluid and become concentrated in a basal layer. These minerals of early formation include those of which basalt, the commonest of all lavas, is composed. Their separation leaves a relatively light residue from which ultimately the minerals composing granite crystallize. These facts inevitably lead to the belief that the stratiform nature of the lithosphere implies a molten condition at the time when the separation of the shells was effected, that is, at the end of the 'Formative Period.'

Since that time the exposed portions, particularly of the granitic shell, have been subjected to wastage, to wear and tear, to disintegration caused by temperature changes, and by the rasping action of sand suspended in running water or blown by wind. The products of this continuous wastage have been spread out in the depressions on the earth's surface as sheets of sediment deposited one upon another as time progressed. These constitute the sedimentary 'skin,' which is the special province of the student of stratigraphy who is concerned with the materials of which it is composed, with their arrangement and structure, with their origins and modes of accumulation. The study of the actual processes of degradation, disintegration, transportation and sedimentation falls within the province of physical geology, rather than stratigraphy. It will be useful, however, to realize the truth of the geological adage that 'the present is the key to the past.' The degradation of the hills, the transport of the sediment and its deposition elsewhere are going on now before our eyes in exactly the same ways, we believe, as in the past. Sir A. Geikie stated that the Thames carries seawards half a million tons of mineral salts in solution every day, more than two-thirds of this being calcium bicarbonate, which must have been derived from the limestone areas within the drainage basin of the river. The area of the latter being known, it is a matter of simple arithmetic to prove that the removal of this material would result in lowering the surface by one inch in 13,000 years. Of course in the short span of a lifetime no change can be seen; but that such a lowering does in fact take place is strikingly shown in the Pennines, where the surface of the uplands is strewn with erratic boulders carried into the area by the great ice-sheets in the Pleistocene Period and deposited on the surface (which is of limestone) when the ice melted, perhaps half a million years ago. The boulders are now raised upon pedestals of limestone, the height of which is a measure of the extent to which the land surface has been lowered by solution, that is, by the work of rain (Fig. 1).

Reverting for a moment to the Thames, the material carried in solution is only a small portion of its total load of sediment: a vast amount is transported in suspension and is dumped on the floor of the estuary and of the North Sea. What is true of this one river is true of all, and what is true of the present is true of all past geological periods. In this way the upland areas are lowered and the seas in like measure are silted up, both processes taking place imperceptibly slowly, but in the course of ages producing the most far-reaching changes in the face of the earth, and by degrees building up the stratified sedimentary 'skin.' The material laid under contribution has varied from time to time, and the variations are reflected in the nature of the sediments themselves. We can understand their nature best, perhaps, by considering in some little detail a typical section through them (Fig. 2).

If a boring were made vertically downwards through Central London, first a small thickness (some 30 feet) of river gravel would be passed through, then the well-known London Clay would be entered. The highest part of this is a brown tenacious clay, familiar to many of us, and it passes down into the less frequently seen blue clay, which would persist for a thickness of some 50 feet. Next, a score or two feet of variable sediments, 'the Lower London Tertiaries,' would be encountered, including the Thanet Sand, which

FIG. 1.
Perched boulder of Silurian Grit resting on Carboniferous Limestone at Norber, near Clapham, Yorkshire.
(*From a photograph by Godfrey Bingley.*)

lies upon the Chalk—the first real rock we should encounter—and this would persist through a thickness of nearly 700 feet. Some of us will have seen the Chalk at the surface, in quarries and road-cuttings, in the North Downs, for example, where the planes of stratification are seen to be inclined northwards at a small angle—some 3 or 4 degrees only. Again, some of us will have seen the same rock under the same conditions to the north-west, in the Chiltern Hills (Fig. 3); but here the Chalk is inclined to the south-east and is seen to plunge underground beneath a cover of clay, sand and gravel. We have seen that it underlies London at a depth of several hundred feet, and it is evident that the Chalk is a thick sheet—a torn and crumpled sheet—of rock of unique type, which maintains its character over a very wide area, extending over many hundreds of square miles. This is equally true of the London Clay and of the other layers mentioned above, and it is evident that the sedimentary skin of the granitic shell is a stratified complex of sheets of rock, some thoroughly hard and compacted, others still soft and unconsolidated, but all more or less distinctive in appearance, in composition and, as we may deduce, in mode of origin.

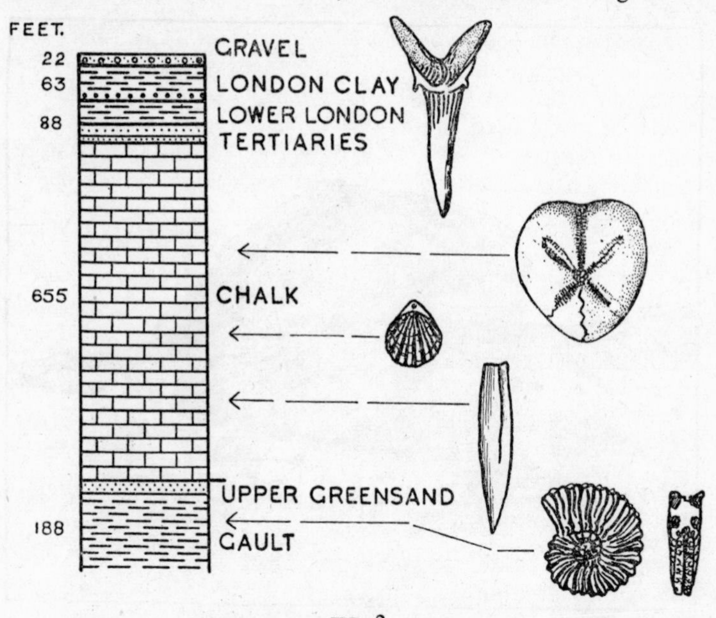


FIG. 2.
Diagram showing the order of the strata and their approximate thickness beneath Central London.

The fossils shown are, from above downwards:
Shark's tooth, London Clay.
Sea-urchin, *Micraster*, Chalk.
Brachiopod, *Rhynchonella*, Chalk.
Belemnite, Chalk.
Ammonite (*Euhoplites*), Gault.

Turning to another aspect, the Chalk yields to careful search a variety of fossils—the hard parts of the creatures living at the time of accumulation of the Chalk (Fig. 2). Many of them are the remains of extinct marine animals, including ammonites, the nearest living representative of which is the nautilus of existing southern seas. The ammonites, like the latter, were free-swimming 'shell-fish,' and after death the shells sank and were entombed, when the conditions were favourable, in the accumulating ooze. Again, there are numbers of sea-urchins quite similar in general appearance to those which live on the sea-floors at the present time. Were there no other evidence that such is the case, the occurrence of these fossils at many levels in the Chalk would make it abundantly clear that it is of marine origin throughout: each level at which the sea-urchins occur must represent the then-existing sea-floor. The Chalk is a singularly pure type of limestone. We have seen that the limestones drained by the Thames and its tributaries are being removed in solution at the rate of one inch in 13,000 years; that the material in solution is transported to the sea and becomes available, by chemical precipitation or through the activities of organisms, for the formation of limestone, as it were, of the next generation. Now if we could assume, for the sake of simplicity, that the whole of the material were deposited on a part of the sea-floor of the same area as the

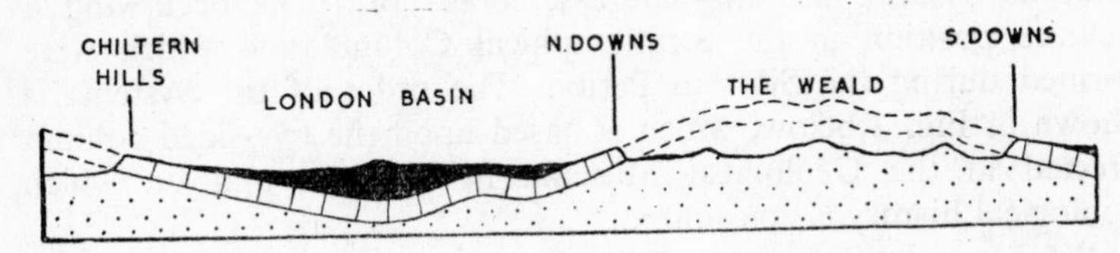


FIG. 3.

Diagram-section from the Chiltern Hills to the South Downs. The Chalk *outcrops* (occurs at the surface) in the Chilterns and North and South Downs. It is concealed by newer strata (black) in the London Basin; it has been destroyed over the Weald, where rocks older than the Chalk (dotted) are exposed.

tract from which it was removed, the figure quoted above would be the rate of accumulation of the new limestone. Is this figure applicable to the Chalk? If so, it is a matter of simple arithmetic to calculate the period of time required for the accumulation of the full thickness of 700 feet. It is a vast period of time: if the Chalk accumulated a hundred or even a thousand times faster than we have assumed (and it is difficult to conceive of any conditions in Nature which would account for so rapid a rate of accumulation), it still represents the passage of millions of years: and it is only one member and represents only a small fraction of the total thickness of the sedimentary skin! If the thicknesses of the Chalk, of the London Clay, and of all the other units are added together, the total of 500,000 feet is obtained, and this figure may be taken as the maximum thickness of the **Stratigraphical Column.** As a fact the total thickness in any one place is found to be very much less than this: even in North America, where some parts of the column are vastly thicker than anywhere else, the total is twenty-six miles, while the average thickness is only one and a quarter miles. The striking disparity between the maximum total and the average thickness is due to the imperfection of the geological record. The stratigrapher is able to read into the rocks their geological history, and in the complete stratigraphical column the whole of geological history is written: each stratum is a chapter, a page, or a paragraph, according to its thickness and the time it represents. When the details of the stratigraphical column preserved at any place are examined, however, it becomes clear that the story is not continuous, sometimes whole chapters, invariably many pages, are missing.

Just as the history of this country is divided up into named periods, the Plantagenet, the Tudor, for example, so geological history comprises a succession of conveniently defined Periods, while the rocks which were formed during any one Period constitute a Geological System. Thus one may speak, for example, of the Silurian System, meaning an assemblage of rocks occupying a definite position in the Stratigraphical Column and which were formed during the Silurian Period. The order of the Systems is shown in Fig. 4 below, which is based upon the five-sided column erected in the Geological Museum in London, and on which geological history is epitomized.

We have already seen that on the existing mountains and hills relatively rapid wastage is taking place, and at the same time vast loads of detritus are being transported by running water and deposited on the existing sea-floors. In due course these processes should inevitably result in the smoothing out of all the surface irregularities on the earth: it must tend to reduce the hills to a plain, while the shallow seas at least must be silted up. How is it then, that after the passage of so much time, mountains probably as high as at any past time, and 'shelf-seas' of the epicontinental type still exist? The Chalk itself can provide the answer. Each fossiliferous layer represents a one-time sea-floor; but Chalk sea-urchins and other fossils can be collected to-day from Chalk standing at nearly 1000 feet above sea-level. Add a reasonable figure to allow for the depth of the Chalk sea—say at most 200 fathoms, and we obtain a figure of about 2200 feet as an approximation to the change of level since the Chalk was in process of deposition. What applies to this one instance is equally true of the marine sedimentary rocks of any past age, which often occur to-day on the mountain tops. This kind of evidence establishes the fact that, in time past, long periods of wastage at high levels and sedimentation at low levels have been punctuated, as it were, by phases of intense change in the configuration of the earth's surface. These periods of remoulding and renovation formerly referred to as 'revolutions,'

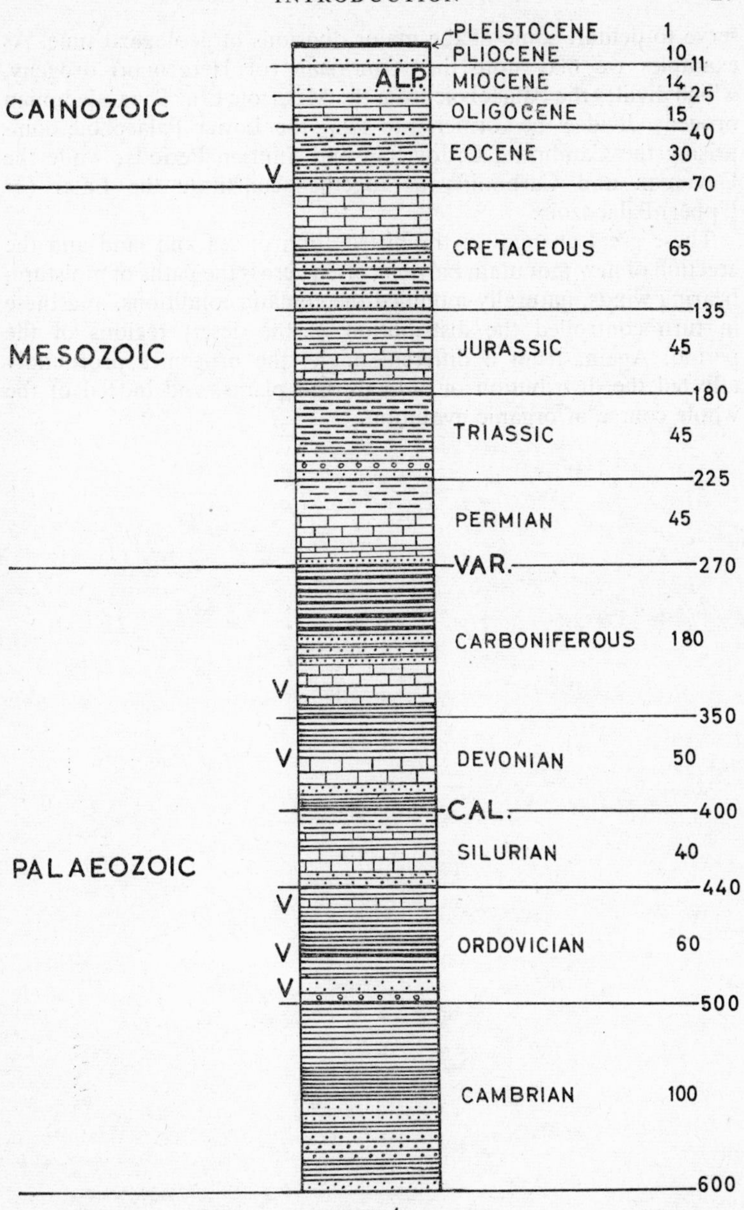


FIG. 4.

The Stratigraphical Column showing the geological Systems and the approximate duration of the Periods in millions of years. The figures are those of A. Holmes in *Trans. Geol. Soc. Edin.*, **17** (1960).

Major earth movements indicated by ALP. (Alpine); VAR. (Variscan); CAL. (Caledonian); V (volcanic episodes).

serve to delimit some of the major divisions of geological time. As examples we may note the Armorican (or Hercynian) orogeny, which divides the Palaeozoic from the Mesozoic Era. The Caledonian orogeny divides the former into two; the Lower Palaeozoic comprising the Cambrian, Ordovician and Silurian Periods; while the Devonian and Carboniferous together constitute the Later (or Upper) Palaeozoic.

These great changes in the distribution of sea and land and the erection of new mountain barriers, often across the paths of moisture-bearing winds, naturally modified the climatic conditions, and these in turn controlled the distribution of the desert regions of the period. Again, from a different angle, the orogenies profoundly affected the distribution of animals and plants, and indeed of the whole course of organic evolution.

## CHAPTER II

# THE CAMBRIAN PERIOD

It is a matter of convenience to commence our systematic study with the Cambrian, but it must be realized that this is not the true base of the stratigraphical column. The true base lies so far below the Cambrian that most geologists believe Post-Cambrian time to be far less than the much longer span between the end of the Formative Period and the opening of the Cambrian. Be that as it may be, the Precambrian rocks are so varied in type, so vast in thickness, and their relationships are such as to justify the belief that the time interval they represent is several times longer than the whole of the rest of geological time. From calculations based on measurements of the radioactivity of certain minerals in the Precambrian of the Canadian Shield, Holmes estimates that these rocks were formed 3,000,000,000 years ago. The corresponding figures for the duration of geological time between the opening of the Cambrian Period and the present is, perhaps 600,000,000 years. These phenomenal figures are not of importance in themselves; but the impression they convey of the immensity of geological time is important in the appreciation of the account which follows. But though they are undoubtedly stimulating to the imagination on these accounts, the Precambrian suffer from one serious disability which renders them quite unsuitable to illustrate the general principles of stratigraphy: they are almost completely devoid of fossils. Thus, though they offer to the specialist an almost unlimited field of research, and though they are admittedly of immense economic value on account of the precious metals which are sealed up within them, they may well be regarded at this stage of our studies as merely the foundations upon which the edifice of historical geology is erected. For our present purpose this history may be taken as commencing at the opening of the Cambrian Period, believed to date from 600 million years ago.

Although some of the fundamental principles of geology were understood by the philosophers of Greece and Rome, the real study of the science, and particularly of stratigraphy, commenced little more than a century ago. The way was paved by William Smith, the 'father of Stratigraphy,' who, as a civil engineer engaged chiefly in canal construction, had unique opportunities of observing the relations between the different strata through which these new cuttings were driven. Even before Smith's day John Strange had been impressed by the persistence of the curious oyster-like shell *Gryphaea* (Fig. 88), in the blue clay occurring at the foot of the Cotswold Hills, and known as the Lias. But it was William Smith who went one step farther and first enunciated the principle which is the very foundation of stratigraphy: that the strata may be identified by the fossils they contain. He observed that in passing across southern England from west to east a succession of strata is traversed, inclined more or less uniformly eastwards, and by applying the obvious rule that in strata which have been tilted the older must dip under the newer, he established the order of the strata between the Old Red Sandstone and the London Clay. His pioneer work culminated in the production, in 1815, of a geological map of England, in itself a remarkable achievement. The principles established by William Smith were quickly put to the test and were applied in different parts of this and other countries by others eager to follow the route he had indicated, and in a short time the succession of rocks, their structure and the faunas they contain had been worked out down to the Old Red Sandstone. But for a long time the Lower Palaeozoic remained a closed book. Partly on account of the inaccessibility of the areas within which they occur, but largely because of the complicated geological structure of these areas and of the difficulty of obtaining fossils from them, these ancient rocks were neglected.

More than a century has passed since Adam Sedgwick in 1831, in search of new geological worlds to conquer, carried out a pioneer survey of a part of North Wales. Shortly afterwards, when the results of his studies were made public, he introduced the name Cambrian System for some of these ancient rocks, reminding us that the original type locality for the rocks of this system is in the Cambria of the ancient Britons. In South Wales also, in the Malvern Hills, the Bristol district, Shropshire, Nuneaton in Warwickshire, the Lickey Hills near Birmingham, the English Lake District, the Isle of Man, the North-West Highlands of Scotland and at several localities in Ireland, Cambrian rocks now appear at the surface of the ground. Further, their extension beneath a cover of newer rocks southwards and eastwards from the visible outcrops is proved by their occurrence in borings, for example, at Leicester, at Calvert in Buckinghamshire and at Fobbing in Essex. It is clear that, towards the end of the Cambrian Period, rocks of this age must have formed a continuous sheet over most of the area now occupied by the British Isles. Further, we are justified in believing the sheet to have spread far beyond these confines, as Cambrian rocks very similar in appearance and fossil contents to those occurring at the localities named above are found also on the eastern seaboard of North America on the one hand, and in the Baltic regions on the other; they persist but little changed in character through Belgium and France to Spain and Sardinia. In like manner the countries at present bordering the Pacific Ocean have their Cambrian rocks, notably China and Siberia, western North America and Australia.

Without exception the Cambrian rocks of these areas originated as sheets of sediment on the floors of the Cambrian seas; and the first significant event in the history of the period was an advance of the seas over the bordering lands on a scale possibly not equalled at any subsequent time. This first **marine transgression** resulted in the submergence of tens of thousands of square miles that had formerly been dry land. It was not an instantaneous process, but rather a progressive inundation, punctuated by periods of still-stand, and occasionally by retreats. The maximum submergence was effected late in Cambrian time.

To appreciate the value of the evidence upon which these bald statements of facts are based, we must first understand how the Cambrian rocks are recognized as such, and we must next be able to place them on the Cambrian time-scale; that is, at least to recognize them as of early-, middle- or late-Cambrian age. In the first place, the Cambrian rocks are recognized as such by the fossils they contain, which are distinctive—so much so in fact that there is no possibility of error—they are unique in that they represent the first **fauna,** the first definite assemblage of living creatures whose remains have been preserved as fossils, and from which have been evolved the multitudes of creatures which inhabit our planet to-day. One outstanding fact in connection with the Cambrian fauna is the wide range of types of creatures represented: nearly all the main branches of the invertebrate animal kingdom from jelly-fish to crustaceans are there; but there is not a single back-boned creature (vertebrate) among them, neither are there any land plants. Further, the Cambrian fossils include the simplest, most primitive representatives of the classes to which they belong. Many shell-fish, whose remains are found in much younger rocks or which are even living forms, begin life as small embryonic shells, the shape of which is the same as their Cambrian ancestors in the mature, full grown condition. Of the many races represented, two are of predominant importance: the trilobites (Fig. 5), which were the masters of the Cambrian seas, and the brachiopods, which are bivalve shell-fish. The former are the oldest marine crustaceans known and have long been completely extinct. They probably originated in the Precambrian forerunner of the Pacific Ocean to the west of North America, whence they spread into all the then-existing seas. It is well to remember that the span of Cambrian time is estimated at ninety to a hundred million years: is it to be wondered at that in

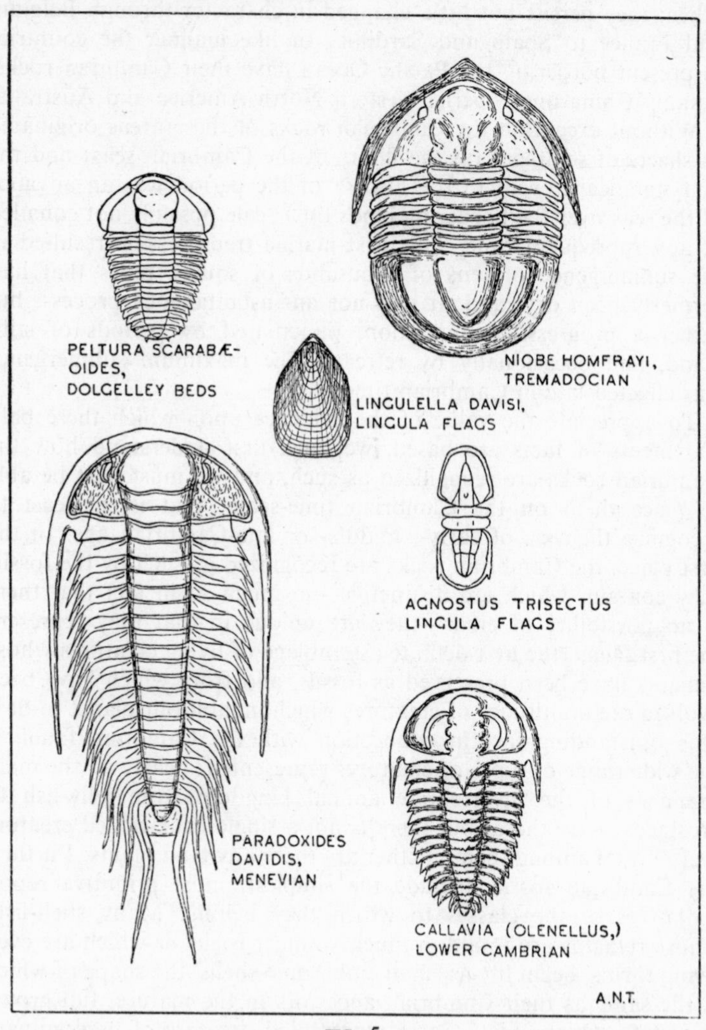


FIG. 5.

Cambrian fossils, including the largest trilobite, *Paradoxides* (11″) and the smallest, *Agnostus* (¼″).

They are in correct stratigraphical order, the oldest at the bottom, the youngest at the top. *Agnostus trisectus* is now *Lotagnostus trisectus.*

the course of that period the organization of the trilobite underwent drastic change, so much so that the later Cambrian forms bear only the most general family likeness to those which first appeared?

The lowest fossiliferous rock in the Cambrian of western North America has yielded only two trilobite species; but at higher levels new forms appear in increasing abundance, while the original ones disappear. This is, of course, the normal result of the march of evolution, and it leads us to the following important generalization: each type of trilobite existed for a certain limited space of time—a short space in the case of the less successful, but longer in the case of the more successful, the more robust and the more adaptable members of the race. Consequently each is likely to be discovered in the rocks formed from the sediments that were in the process of accumulation during this space of time. It follows that if the succession of trilobite faunas is studied in the Cambrian rocks of some type area, it will serve as a standard of reference, by comparison with which it will be possible to 'date' the Cambrian rocks exposed in some other locality. In point of fact the succession of trilobite (and brachiopod) faunas has been carefully studied and described in great detail, so that the expert is able to place a stratum in its correct systematic position, sometimes from the examination of a single specimen, or at most after examination of the fauna yielded by the rock. Thus the System is capable of subdivision into a number of faunal units, each defined by the fossils it contains, and frequently named after a particularly characteristic form. On the broadest scale the Cambrian is divided into three major units, corresponding with early, middle and late Cambrian times, spoken of as Lower, Middle and Upper Cambrian respectively, and containing as fossils members of the great trilobite families, the *Mesonacidae* in the case of the first, the *Paradoxidae* in the case of the second, and the *Olenidae* in that of the third division. So we speak, for example, of the *Paradoxides* Series, meaning those rocks which contain the remains of different species of *Paradoxides*, occurring in the middle of the Cambrian System, and of Middle Cambrian age.

In some parts of the world Cambrian rocks occur resting directly upon Precambrian strata, but containing in their *basal* layers various types of *Paradoxides*. The inference is that such areas stood above sea-level in early Cambrian times, but were inundated by the Middle Cambrian Sea. Similarly, there are other still more extensive tracts where the Upper Cambrian alone is present: these were reached by the marine transgression still later, and give point to the statement made above, that the advance of the sea was slow and progressive. These general facts are represented diagrammatically in Fig. 6, and the technical name for the resulting geological arrangement or structure is 'overlap.' In the diagram section the Cambrian rocks overstep the Precambrian, and higher divisions overlap lower ones. The surface of separation between the two series of rocks, which differ in age and perhaps markedly in attitude, is known as an *unconformity*.

Normally around existing coastlines a narrow zone of pebbles or shingle beach is followed outwards by a belt of sand, becoming finer in grain as the distance from the shore increases, and finally passing through silt into sediment of the clay grade. During a marine transgression these belts migrate inland, and at the period of maximum submergence it might well be that clay would be deposited upon the sand laid down when the water was less deep,

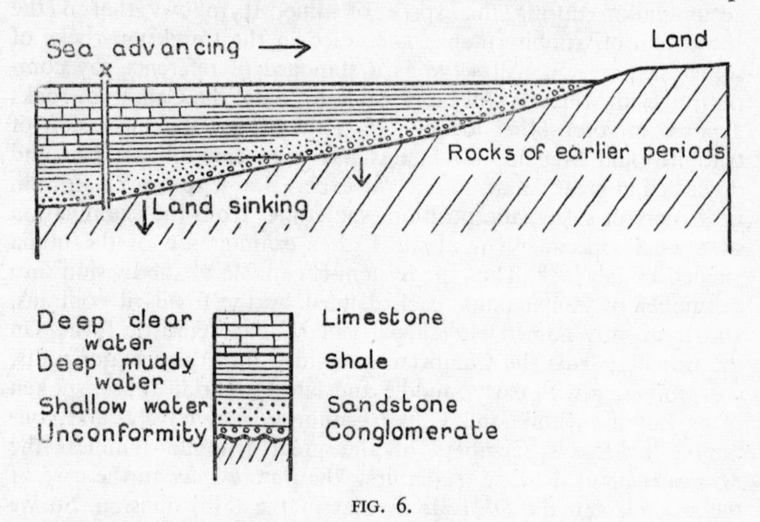


FIG. 6.

Diagram-section of overlapping series. The horizontal section shows distribution of different rock-types; the vertical section below shows the order of the strata met with in a boring at X.

and this in turn we might expect to pass downwards into shingle representing the beach deposits of the early advance (Fig. 6). In general the Cambrian rocks conform to this general plan.

The **Lower Cambrian.**—The base of the System is marked by an accumulation of pebbles, formed from the harder underlying strata, embedded in a sandy matrix, now thoroughly indurated. This is the 'basal conglomerate,' and is, in effect, the fossil beach of the initial transgression. It is not invariably present in all Cambrian outcrops: in fact the succession commonly commences with a clean, white sand converted by pressure and induration into the toughest and most durable of all sedimentary rock-types, termed quartzite. The quartz grains are particularly well rounded; the sand was of the 'millet-seed' type and accumulated on an irregular wind-swept land surface. It was reworked by the transgressive early Cambrian sea. It can be examined in Shropshire where it flanks the Wrekin and Caer Caradoc; in the Nuneaton district in Warwickshire where the outcrop is scarred with great open workings, in which the rock is extensively quarried for road metal; on the flanks of the Malvern Hills, though it is not well exposed there; in the Lickey Hills on the outskirts of Birmingham; and in the North-West Highlands of Scotland, where spectacular cliffs of white-weathering quartzite rise above the red and chocolate coloured sandstones of the underlying formation. In none of these localities is the age of the basal beds proved palaeontologically, as fossils are absent; but in all areas they are shown to be Lower Cambrian by the occurrence of the typical trilobites (*Olenellus*, *Callavia*, etc.) in the immediately overlying rocks which follow without a break, and which are usually impure greenish sandstones and sandy limestones, such as the Comley Sandstone in Shropshire.

As it was in **Wales** that the System was first recognized and named, it is appropriate to look more closely into the nature of the rocks, first in the north of the country. Here they occur in two areas, the more southerly, in Merionethshire, forming the Harlech Dome, so called on account of its essentially dome-like structure. The more northerly occurrence lies near Llanberis in Carnarvonshire (Fig. 7).

Much of the **Harlech Dome** is wild and desolate in the extreme, especially in the centre where the Rhinog Mountains stand. The rocks in the Dome consist of alternating clay-rocks now slates and shales, and so-called grits. The details of the succession on the coast are shown in Fig. 8. The Rhinog and Barmouth Grit Groups are all but identical in lithology: they are coarse-grained, massive bedded, grey-green rocks, often arkosic,[1] sometimes false-bedded, sometimes conglomeratic, the pebbles being well-rounded quartz in the main. Both Grits are poorly sorted: the pebbles are scattered irregularly in the sandy matrix which contains an appreciable clay fraction. Rocks of this kind are termed greywackes, a slightly Anglicized version of an old German rock-name. A detailed study, using modern techniques, has been made of the Rhinog Grits occurring at the tip of St. Tudwal's Peninsula in Carnarvonshire. Here they bear the local name, Hell's Mouth Grits, and contain rock- and mineral fragments which can be matched in the Mona (Precambrian) Complex exposed to the north, particularly in Anglesey. The Grits display a rhythmic repetition of massive greywackes, each up to 12 feet thick, graded from coarse to fine upwards, succeeded by siltstone and this in turn by mudstone. The

[1] arkose = feldspathic sandstone containing more than 10 per cent of feldspar.

greywacke-grits make up some five-sixths of the total thickness of 600 feet.

The chief interest of the Manganese Shale Group lies in the manganese ore, which is part of the bedded succession—a prettily colour-banded rock containing very minute crystals of spessartine, the manganese garnet. Although inaccessibility of the outcrops

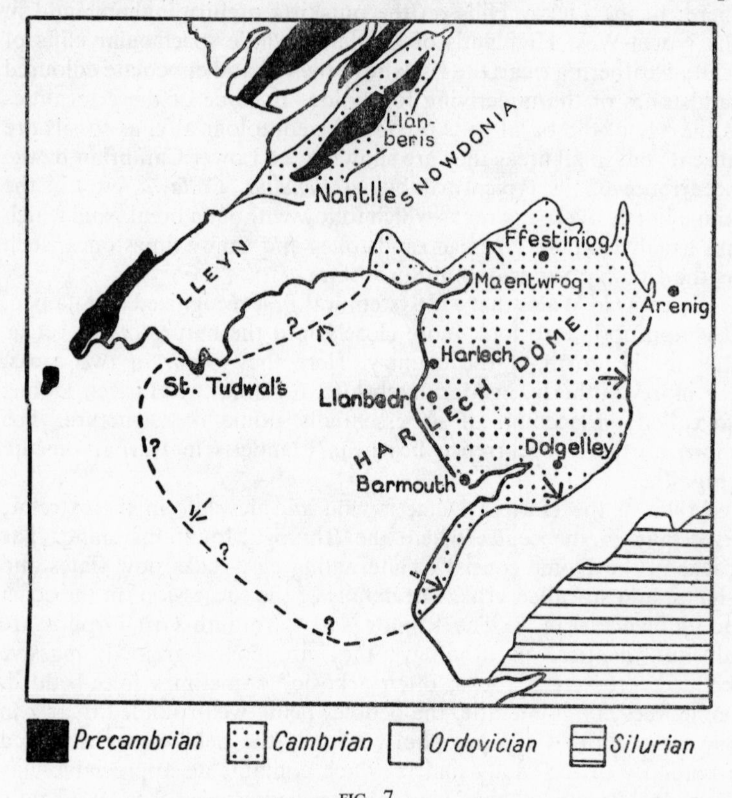


FIG. 7.
Geological sketch-map of part of North Wales, showing distribution of Lower Palaeozoic rocks.

prevents the rock being successfully exploited as an ore of manganese, it is valuable to the stratigrapher for quite another reason: it has been tested in trial levels at many points, and this makes it very easy to follow in the field, and with its aid to decipher the geological structure. It is a valuable 'marker horizon.' The Manganese Shale conforms to its name in the western parts of the Harlech Dome; but towards the east 'grit' tends to replace shale. In its typical development this formation is unique in Britain, especially the ore body itself. Although uncertainty still exists concerning its mode of origin, apparently the manganese was deposited as carbonate (rhodochrosite); and deposits of this kind have been discovered in stagnant deeps in the Central Baltic.

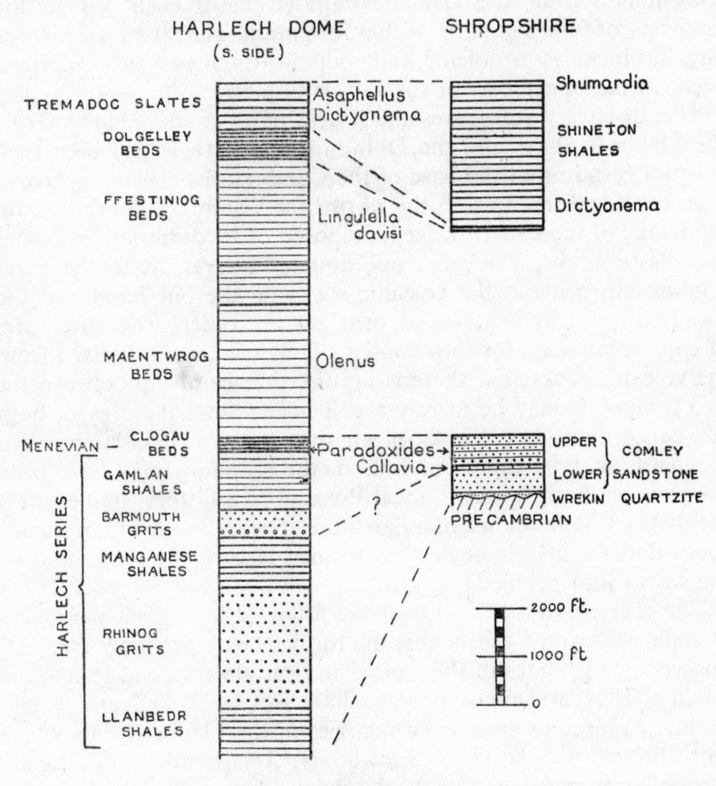


FIG. 8.

Vertical sections through the Cambrian strata of the Dolgelley (=Dolgellau) district, Merionethshire, and South Shropshire.

Stratigraphical names in capitals; fossil names in small type.
The lithological types are indicated conventionally; shales and slates ruled horizontally; sandstones and grits dotted; limestone—oblong 'bricks.'

In the centre of the Dome, immediately east of the Rhinog Mountains occurs an outcrop of a third 'grit'—the Dolwen Grit—which appears to represent part of the Llanbedr Slates of the coastal area. It is quite unlike the other (Barmouth and Rhinog) Grits in its topographical expression as it forms a low-lying swampy area, while the others form rugged, steep-sided mountains.

For over a century the age of the Harlechian was in doubt, as no fossils were discovered below the Clogau Beds which contain a

Middle Cambrian (*Paradoxidian*) fauna. In 1915 Middle Cambrian fossils were discovered in the Carnarvonshire equivalents of the Gamlan Beds which rest upon and grade down into the Barmouth Grits, which are also, presumably, Middle Cambrian. In 1960 re-examination of the Hell's Mouth (Rhinog) Grits led to the discovery of fossils in parts of that formation. The fauna is a meagre one, but includes protolenid and eodiscid trilobites which elsewhere occur in the upper part of the Lower Cambrian.

This discovery still leaves the lowest parts of the Rhinog Grits, the Llanbedr Slates and the Dolwen Grit undated; and even then it is not certain that the base of the Cambrian has been reached.

In the **Llanberis area** to the north, the Cambrian is exposed on the flanks of the Padarn ridge, composed of Precambrian lavas and pyroclastic rocks. There is some doubt, however, as to the exact relationship between the volcanic rocks on the one hand and the Cambrian conglomerates and grits on the other. The latter are, of course, younger, for they consist chiefly of material derived from the volcanic rocks; but there is no discordance of dip between the two groups. It may be merely a coincidence that the dips of both are concordant; but it may mean that the time-interval between them was of brief duration. Indeed, the eruptions may have been the last significant event in local Precambrian history, immediately before the Cambrian Sea inundated the area and buried the volcanic rocks under a mantle of detritus formed largely of lava ground by the waves into pebbles and grit.

The coarse-grained basal beds are followed by a great succession of slates with some grit bands, the former being probably the best-known roofing slates in the world, and certainly second to none in quality. They are approximately 3000 feet thick and are magnificently exposed in great open quarries in the Llanberis Pass which cuts through the heart of Snowdonia. The Llanberis Slates are succeeded by massive, completely unfossiliferous Bronllwyd[1] Grits, and these in turn are overlain by Maentwrog Beds,[1] the lowest member of the Upper Cambrian succession. As long ago as 1887 quarrymen discovered the head-shield of a trilobite in the highest slates at a point where bedding and cleavage coincide. Since that date at very infrequent intervals other fragments of fossils have been found; but the faunal evidence of age is inconclusive. The most significant fossil is apparently that which was first discovered. Originally it was named *Conocoryphe viola*, but has recently been

[1] These Welsh names on first acquaintance look unpronounceable. It is useful to remember that 'Ll' is pronounced Thl, so 'Llan' becomes 'Thlan'; 'w' has a vowel sound, 'oo', so that 'Maentwrog' becomes Minetoorog; 'Bronllwyd' is pronounced Bron-thloo-id

renamed *Pseudatops viola*. It is accompanied by *Hyolithus*. In the view of some experts the age indicated is Lower Cambrian. The vertical range of '*Conocoryphe viola*' in the Llanberis Slates is unknown. So is that of the protolenid trilobite from the Rhinog (Hell's Mouth) Grits; but it has been suggested that they are both of approximately the same age. The palaeontological evidence is very slender, however, and much more evidence will be needed before a firm correlation is justified.

In **Shropshire** it was demonstrated at an early date that the Cambrian System was represented by rocks of three different lithologies: from below upwards, (1) quartzite, (2) glauconitic sandstone and (3) shales. In due course these were termed the Wrekin Quartzite, Comley Sandstone and Shineton Shales, after type localities. Later, fossils were discovered in the Comley Sandstone, including *Callavia* ('*Olenellus*') by Charles Lapworth, and *Paradoxides* by Groom, proving that both Lower and Middle Cambrian are represented. The Comley Sandstone was therefore divided into two parts termed Lower and Upper respectively. Subsequently more detailed study has shown that although glauconitic sandstone is present in both divisions, especially the Lower, the omnibus term 'Comley Sandstone' is a misnomer for much of the formation. To-day it is convenient to divide the beds into three groups of strata, varying in lithology and defined palaeontologically. Clearly 'Comley' should be retained and 'Comley Sandstone' is an appropriate name for the lowest division. Above come several thin limestones about 6 feet in total thickness containing a succession of faunas, which can be closely matched in the Lower Cambrian of Eastern N. America, where, however, they are separated by considerable thicknesses of strata. In Shropshire over the same period of time the amount of sediment which accumulated was insignificantly small; but life went on all the time and consequently the successive faunas are closely packed in a small thickness of strata. This is our first example of a **condensed sequence.**

The Middle Cambrian of Shropshire commences with a breccia, the included fragments in which contain *Lower* Cambrian fossils. The matrix, of typical Comley Sandstone aspect, contains indigenous *Middle* Cambrian trilobites. From careful observation of the relationships in different localities it is evident that compacted Comley Sandstone and Limestones had been folded, laid bare and denuded during a post-Lower, pre-Middle Cambrian erosion interval. The possibility of some of the Lower Cambrian fossils having been separated from their matrix and embedded in the accumulating sediment in close association with living Middle Cambrian trilobites proved a reality in the area: it must have been extremely disconcerting to discover fossils of two different ages in one and the same bed. It is certain, too, that some of the Middle Cambrian sediment was derived, second hand, by the destruction of the Lower Cambrian rocks.

A summary statement of the features shown by the Lower and Middle Cambrian in Shropshire is appended:

| | |
|---|---|
| Upper Comley Group (Paradoxidian) | a varied succession of shales, flags and glauconitic grits divided into seven *Paradoxides* zones, including *P. davidis* and *P. hicksii* and with an *Agnostus* horizon at the top. |
| | unconformity |
| Lower Comley Group (Mesonacidian) | Comley Limestones, shallow water, nodular and phosphatic, 6 feet, with *Protolenus*, *Strenuella*, *Eodiscus*, etc. and with *Callavia* at the base. |
| | Comley Sandstone, 500 feet, glauconitic, yielding Ostracod genera at the top, and *Hyolithus* and *Obolella groomi* at the base. |
| Wrekin Quartzite | 150 feet., conglomeratic at the base. A residual deposit formed on a wind-swept land area and reworked by the Lower Cambrian Sea. |
| | unconformity |
| Precambrian | Uriconian volcanics |

The middle Cambrian, Upper Comley Group can be matched almost bed by bed with their age-equivalents in southern Sweden, while the fauna includes also forms with Bohemian affinities, proving free communication between these widely separated areas.

The **Middle Cambrian** of the British Isles commonly comprises two members, a lower arenaceous, and an upper, argillaceous group. The former constitutes the Lower Solva Beds in the classic outcrops at St Davids; while the latter includes the Upper Solva Beds (Fig. 9). The Menevian Beds are almost black, of exceedingly fine grain, and undoubtedly of deep-water origin, representing the culmination of the marine transgression. In North Wales these rocks have attracted much attention, as in the Dolgellau district under the local name, Clogau Beds, they are cut by a number of gold-bearing quartz lodes, which have been spasmodically exploited since early historic periods. Although there appears to be no discordance of dip between the Clogau Beds and the underlying Harlech Series, it may be significant that in the easterly parts of the Harlech Dome, where the individual members of the succession tend to become less distinct as the argillaceous rocks become more gritty, a mappable grit comes in at the base of the Clogau Beds. This is the Cefn Coch Grit which indicates shallowing of the sea, if not actual emergence at this time.

The age of these Middle Cambrian beds is amply proved by a distinctive trilobite fauna, including various species of *Paradoxides*.

The most easterly surface exposures of Cambrian rocks in England occur near Nuneaton in Warwickshire, and include above the basal (Hartshill) quartzite, a succession of argillaceous beds ranging in age from Middle to Upper Cambrian, known collectively as the Stockingford Shales. A large trilobite fauna, consisting chiefly of

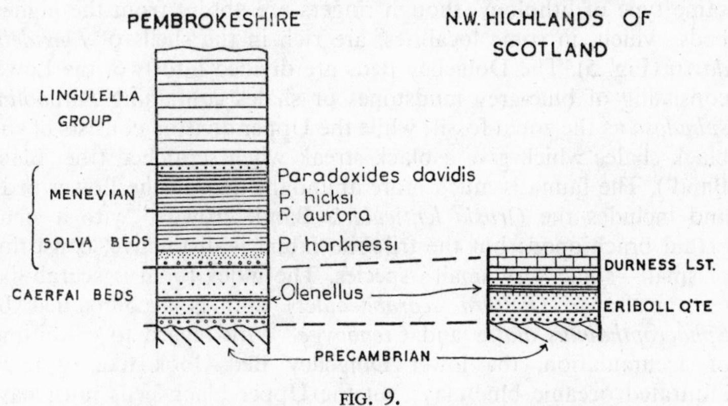


FIG. 9.

Vertical sections through the Cambrian strata of South Wales and North-West Highlands of Scotland to same scale as Fig. 8.
The bracket encloses the Middle Cambrian of South Wales.

species of *Paradoxides* and *Agnostus*, and obtained from artificial trenches rather than natural exposures, has enabled very detailed comparison to be made with the Middle Cambrian of Scandinavia and elsewhere, and it must be admitted that these beds provide a much better standard of comparison than Cambria itself, where the rocks are but poorly fossiliferous and imperfectly known.

The **Upper Cambrian** appears to mark a return to shallower water conditions: much of the rock falling into this division is shale interbedded with thin tough sheets of quartzite or sandstone. Certain of the bedding planes of these 'flags' are literally crowded with brachiopod shells, *Lingulella davisi*, together with an occasional specimen of the typical Upper Cambrian trilobite, *Olenus*.

These were originally called the 'Lingula Flags', and many years ago were divided into three lithological units which are very constant in their development round the Harlech Dome and even farther afield. The name is a bad one, however, on two counts: firstly, the horny brachiopod that gives the beds their name has been shown to belong to the genus *Lingulella*; and secondly, the highest part of the middle division and the whole of the upper division are definitely not flaggy. There is nothing to be gained by perpetuating this misnomer: they should be termed the 'Lingulella Group', and are so called in this account. The three divisions take their names from small towns on the flanks of the Harlech Dome (Figs. 7 and 8). The Maentwrog Beds are rusty-weathering shales interbedded with tough, resistant, siliceous bands termed 'ringers', and are noteworthy on account of the extraordinary abundance of cubes of pyrite that occur in some layers. The Ffestiniog Beds above show much the same type of lithology, though ringers are absent from the highest beds, which, in some localities, are rich in the shells of *Lingulella davisi* (Fig. 5). The Dolgelley Beds are divided into two, the Lower consisting of blue-grey mudstones or shales containing *Parabolina spinulosa* as the zonal fossil; while the Upper division consists of soft black shales which give a black streak when scratched (the 'Black Band'). The fauna is much more abundant than in the Lower beds, and includes the *Orusia lenticularis* Band, crowded with a small orthid brachiopod; but the trilobite fauna is distinctive, consisting of small—some very small—species. The index fossil is scarab-like in appearance (*Peltura scarabaeoides*) and is accompanied by *Sphaeropthalmus alatus* and *Ctenopyge*. With regard to conditions of accumulation, the lower Dolgelley Beds look like ordinary indurated oceanic blue clay; but the Upper black beds must have accumulated in a special environment. Their high sulphide content and their presumably pelagic fauna have suggested deposition under poisonous conditions caused by defective circulation and covered by the term 'euxenic'. It may be significant that the black Dolgelley Beds contain uranium and thorium in higher than average amounts.

The highest thousand feet of the Cambrian in the Harlech Dome are referred to the **Tremadoc Series (Tremadocian).** Although on casual acquaintance they impress one as a monotonous series of grey slates, in the type area they were proved to include several distinctive groups of slates, shales and flags, yielding, all too rarely, trilobites including *Asaphellus*, *Niobella* (*Niobe*) and *Shumardia*, all of which give their names to one of these groups. In addition, and of outstanding importance, is a relatively narrow band (there appear to be two in the Dolgellau district) crowded with the remains of the dendroid graptolite, *Dictyonema*. True graptolites first appear in force in the Arenig Series. Among the trilobites are some genera which occur at lower levels in the Cambrian; but there are more with Ordovician affinities. It may reasonably be claimed that the Tremadoc fauna as a whole is intermediate in character between the

Cambrian and the Ordovician, and therefore the systematic position of the Tremadocian must be decided on other grounds. Lithologically the Series forms a natural continuation of the underlying Upper Cambrian strata: the argillaceous Tremadoc Slates (as they were originally called) rest without visible break on argillaceous Upper Dolgelley Beds; but they are succeeded by completely different rock-types nowhere more convincingly displayed than in South Shropshire, though in Wales too the contrasts at the Tremadoc—Arenig boundary are almost as striking, both as regards lithology and topographical expression. In Britain, therefore, the Tremadocian marks the *end* of a chapter of geological history, *not* the beginning of a new one. An unconformity, inferred in Shropshire, proved in North Wales and visible in South Wales separates the Tremadoc from the Arenig Series. It is logical on these several grounds to follow historical precedent and include the Tremadoc Series in the Upper Cambrian. In parts of Scandinavia, however, an unconformity lies *beneath* the Series, which is therefore regarded as the basal member of the Ordovician. This view is shared by the majority of Continental geologists and by an increasing number of British geologists, who appear to have lost sight of the fact that the type locality is Tremadoc in Cambria—not Scania.

In Shropshire no representatives of the typical flags of the Lingulella Group are visible, though the Dolgelley Beds are represented locally. The important member of the Upper Cambrian succession, however, is the **Shineton Shales,** the local representatives of the Tremadocian, which occur on both sides of the Longmynd. In the western outcrop the Shales are estimated at some 3000 feet in thickness. What lies below them is unknown.

The Upper Cambrian is more fully represented in the Nuneaton district where it is believed all three divisions of the Lingulella Group occur, as well as the lower part of the Tremadocian. The Upper Cambrian rocks of the Malvern Hills resemble those of Shropshire, in that only the Dolgelley and Tremadoc Beds seem to be represented. The most southerly outcrop lies a few miles north of Bristol, at Tortworth, where fossiliferous Tremadocian are known to occur.

Northwards from Wales and the English Midlands no rocks of proved Cambrian age occur until the Scottish Highlands are reached. In the **North-West Highlands** a narrow band of Cambrian and Ordovician rocks occurs, even thin beds being singularly constant from one end of the hundred-mile-long outcrop to the other. The lowest member of the succession is the Eriboll Quartzite resting with strong unconformity on Precambrian rocks. The most distinctive stratum in the Eriboll Quartzite is the Pipe Rock, so named as it is riddled with worm burrows and was evidently deposited on an inter-tidal flat. The quartzites become muddy upwards and pass into the Fucoid Beds, largely dolomitic mudstones containing worm tracks which were originally thought to be fucoids (sea-weeds). The more arenaceous Serpulite Grit follows, and this is succeeded by the Durness Limestone consisting dominantly of dolomitic limestones containing abundant chert. Formerly the succession was thought to be unbroken; but recently (1960) it was shown to include several nonsequences: the record is evidently incomplete; but the time-significance of the breaks remains uncertain. The Fucoid Beds have yielded the remains of Lower Cambrian trilobites—*Olenellus* (true) and an interesting form, *Olenelloides*, which resembles a very early stage in the development of a trilobite, but here in the adult condition. Neither of these trilobites has been recorded from British Cambrian rocks in other areas: they appear to belong to a different faunal province which includes Greenland and eastern North America. The overlying and main part of the Durness Limestone contains early Ordovician fossils and is discussed in due course.

Farther to the south beyond the Central Highlands and close to the great Highland Boundary Fault in the neighbourhood of Callander some years ago John Pringle[1] discovered a trilobite fauna in the Leny Limestone, usually regarded as belonging to the Upper Dalradian. This was a momentous discovery as until that time not a single fossil had been found in the Dalradian. Further, the fauna consists of *Pagetia* (not known elsewhere from British Cambrian rocks), and eodiscids, and is of Middle Cambrian age. It may well be significant that these fossils occur in a limestone, and that real limestones do not occur in other British Cambrian areas, though they do in the North-West Highlands, where, however, Middle Cambrian rocks are not known.

It is necessary to refer at this point to the **Highland Border Series** as the term is used in two different senses. The strata covered by the term are shales associated with cherts and occur in the near neighbourhood of the Highland Boundary Fault at intervals from the Clyde estuary to Stonehaven, where they have been named the Margie Series and include pillow lavas. In the absence of diagnostic fossils they have been regarded as early Ordovician in age, largely because of the occurrence of spilitic pillow lavas associated with shales and chert. This is the lithological association characteristic of the Arenig Series in the Girvan area on the south side of the Midland Valley Trough. On the other hand the Leny Limestone

[1] Pringle, J., 'The discovery of Cambrian trilobites . . . near Callander, Perthshire,' *Advanc. Sci.*, **1** (for 1939), 252.

and associated strata were regarded by Pringle and others as belonging to the Highland Border Series and this usage is accepted by some modern writers. We believe that it is undesirable to attempt to include rocks known to be of Middle Cambrian age with others believed on good grounds to be early Ordovician in one named Series: it is not in accordance with first principles (see p. 130).

The formations commonly ascribed to the Cambrian in **Ireland** are problematical, as so far they have failed to yield satisfactory evidence of their age. Fossils are not completely absent; but those which have been collected belong to lowly organisms of doubtful status and of no diagnostic value. The rocks constitute the **Bray Series,** named from Bray Head south of Dublin, whence they extend southwards into Wicklow and Wexford. In places greywackes are dominant; but elsewhere shales or slates, purple and green in colour, are associated with greywackes, current-bedded sandstones and pure quartzites which form prominent features in the landscape. Like the early Cambrian quartzites of the English Midlands, those in the Bray Series consist of aeolian sand-grains. The relationship of these formations to older and younger strata is uncertain: the floor on which they rest is a thrust plane along which they were transported from the east across the Ordovician including part of the metamorphic aureole of the Leinster Granite. It may well be significant that the Bray Series is aligned with the Manx Slates of the Isle of Man with which they may be correlated.

The greater part of the **Isle of Man** consists of rocks tentatively ascribed to the Cambrian and termed the **Manx Slate Group** estimated to be 25,000 feet thick and consisting of siltstones, greywackes, slates and subordinate quartzites deposited under geosynclinal conditions. A special feature of the succession is the occurrence of penecontemporaneous slump-breccias consisting of large unsorted fragments, usually tabular in shape and embedded in a matrix of dark-coloured pelite. These breccias represent sediment deposited on a submarine slope which periodically exceeded the angle of rest appropriate to the sediment. Consequently the latter slid or 'slumped' down the slope and accumulated where the gradient flattened out. Such slumping has been described from several horizons in the Palaeozoic, and in different localities; but the phenomena are perhaps most characteristic of the Silurian of the Welsh Borderlands and are given fuller consideration in the appropriate chapter.

Evidence of the age of the Manx Slate Group is meagre and, indeed, is suspect. Worm tracks and burrows have been recorded from the more flaggy members of the series, and specimens of *Dictyonema flabelliforme*, of zonal value in the Tremadoc Series in

Wales and Shropshire, are thought to have been collected many years ago (1899) from a slate quarry high up in the succession; but later search has failed to bring to light other specimens. If we accept the evidence at its face value, this isolated record would indicate that the upper part of the succession is Tremadocian; but the note on p. 50 suggests otherwise.

A comparison of the four vertical sections shown in Figs. 8 and 9 reveals marked differences in the thicknesses of the Cambrian rocks in different areas. This is due partly to the fact that in none of these districts is the Cambrian complete; the base is not seen at Dolgellau, the top part of the succession is missing in South Wales,

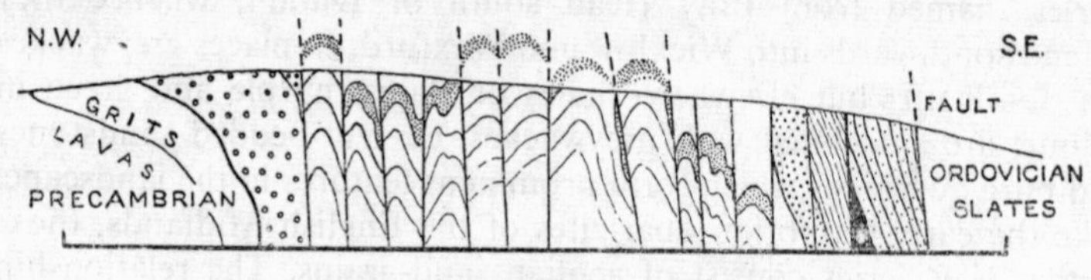


FIG. 10.
The Cambrian Slate Belt near Nantile, Carnarvonshire.
Grits, dotted; slates, plain.
The thicker nearly vertical lines are faults.
Length of base-line, 1 mile.
(*After W. G. Fearnsides and T. O. Morris.*)

the Tremadoc Slates being absent; the greater part of the Lingulella Group is absent from Shropshire; while only Lower Cambrian fossils have been recognized in the North-West Highlands of Scotland. Even in North Wales the thickness is far from constant. It is possible to obtain an almost complete view of the type-area of the System from the mountains of Snowdonia. Southwards lies the Harlech Dome, in which the System attains to the maximum thickness in Britain (12,000 feet); northwards, in the middle distance, lies the Cambrian Slate Belt, within which the rocks have been strongly folded, faulted and cleaved, enabling them to be split readily into extensive thin sheets, this property rendering them the finest roofing slates in the world. Here, in the neighbourhood of Llanberis, Bethesda and Nantlle the thickness is reduced by half (Fig. 10). Farther north, within a few miles, the Cambrian rocks thin out altogether. The explanation of the dramatically sudden disappearance of the whole System involves the study of the relations of the Cambrian to the overlying Ordovician rocks and is considered in the next chapter.

We revert to two subjects touched upon in the foregoing account, but more conveniently expanded at this point. The first concerns the whereabouts of the base of the Cambrian, which in Britain is nowhere synonymous with the beginning of Cambrian time. Opinion is divided as to how it should be defined and where it should be drawn. In a few favoured places the *local* base of the System is visible even from a considerable distance: in the North-West Highlands of Scotland, for example, no problem arises on account of the striking lithological differences between the white Cambrian quartzites lying unconformably upon the red Precambrian arkoses. Wherever an unconformity separates the Cambrian from older rocks the former is necessarily incomplete and the local base does not correspond with the beginning of Cambrian time. The latter is recorded only where the accumulation of sediments was continuous over the late Precambrian—early Cambrian interval of time. Even in such areas the base must be chosen arbitrarily. Some people advocate drawing the line at the base of the lowest biozone; but that leaves the matter far too indefinite. As time goes on obscure traces of life are discovered at lower and lower horizons in the younger Precambrian (the Proterozoic) and what is the lowest biozone to-day becomes the lowest-but-one to-morrow. There is no finality on these lines. On the other hand, the Cambrian System is subdivided on the basis of successive trilobite faunas, and therefore it seems rational to draw the base of the Cambrian at a selected *mappable* horizon below the oldest bed containing trilobites.

Except in a strictly geochronological sense no problem arises. Thus much of the Comley Sandstone and the whole of the underlying Wrekin Quartzite lie beneath the lowest stratum containing trilobite remains; but their inclusion in the Cambrian System is automatic and unquestioned. The dated trilobite-bearing *Callavia* Limestone in the Lower Comley Group grades downwards into the Wrekin Quartzite with no semblance of a break; but the latter rests with violent discordance on the underlying Precambrian. In Shropshire therefore the *local* base of the Cambrian coincides with that of the Wrekin Quartzite; but how far up in the continuous Time Scale this horizon lies we have at present no means of knowing.

There are really three significant events which one would like to date accurately: (1) the appearance of life on the Earth, though this is a matter of no stratigraphical significance; (2) the occurrence of recognizable fossils although of lowly organization and without hard parts. This marks the base of the Phanerozoic Time Scale; and (3) the advent of the clearly defined Lower Cambrian fauna, which on general grounds one would expect to be much more recent than (2). Some Russian scientists date the lowest biozone at 550 m.y. ago and this coincides with the base of the Phanerozoic. Holmes places the base of the Cambrian at 600 m.y. Obviously both of these figures cannot be correct. If the Russian date is accurate, Holmes must be far too remote; if the date chosen by Holmes is correct the Russian figure must be correspondingly far too recent.

Finally we may profitably look more closely at the conditions under which the Harlech (Rhinog and Barmouth) Grits are thought to have been deposited. Opinions are sharply divided on this matter. Some people believe these rocks to have originated as sediments deposited under shallow-water, in-shore conditions; but others claim them to be deep-water deposits. Since early days it has been customary to accept the principle that in normal marine sediments coarseness of grain is proportional to shallowness of water, and conversely, the finer the sediment, the deeper the water, and the greater the distance from the then-existing coastlines. This must still be true of many instances; but not all. In about 1950 it became known that coarse-grained sediment may be carried long distances seawards and deposited in deep water. The agents of transport are density or **turbidity currents.** A characteristic of sediments carried by turbidity currents is lack of sorting; and the most typical of such rocks are the greywackes. Matters in this country were brought to a head by the reading of a paper, concerned with the Harlech Grits, in which it was claimed that these rocks were transported by turbidity currents and deposited in deep water. Since that time turbidity currents and turbidites have been much in vogue. Recognition of the latter depends upon palaeocurrent data, particularly structures of a directional kind which indicate the direction of flow. As they are normally exposed on the under-surfaces of strata they are termed sole structures and include 'flute-casts' or 'flute-moulds', 'gouge channnels' and 'groove-casts'. To obtain acceptable and trustworthy results a large number of these directional features must be recorded, corrected for the existing structure and studied statistically. Such sedimentological studies form an essential part of modern stratigraphical research; but in some cases conflicting conclusions have been reached by different people studying the same formation, but using different techniques. The most probable sources of error are: (1) too few field observations, (2) too wide extrapolation in both areal (horizontal) and vertical senses, and (3) failure to comprehend the limitations of the several methods used. These currents naturally flow in the direction of steepest slope, which will be normal to the coastline at first; but when the continental slope flattens out, they may turn roughly at right angles and flow parallel to the coast. The flow-direction after the current has passed may be quite different from that during the peak period.

Further, a strong current flowing in a trough may induce secondary currents oblique to the main direction. It will be realized that if all the observed directions are plotted on a map, the resulting picture may appear complicated, particularly if the three-dimensional aspect has been ignored. Local current-directions relating to one bedding plane may have little or no bearing on the general direction of transport for the whole formation, and do not necessarily indicate, by a back-bearing, the whereabouts of the source of supply.

The material of which the Rhinog Grits is composed has been derived by different authorities from the SW., W., NW., N., NE. and E. It obviously would be absurd to look for one single direction which was operative throughout the period of accumulation of the whole 2000 feet of rock over all 400 square miles of outcrop. Several, possibly all of these directions may have been correct at a particular time somewhere within the area of outcrop.

With regard to the depth of the Rhinog Grit Sea, or in fact any other 'fossil' sea, the terms 'deep' and 'shallow' are relative only: there are no criteria by which the depth can be accurately assessed. That currents may carry coarse sediment into the deeper parts of the existing seas is an observed fact; but that does not prove that the Rhinog Grits are deep-water deposits. Those who believe this to be the case base their conclusion on certain structural features, in the interpretation of which there is room for difference of opinion, and to some 'these researches fail to carry conviction in the belief that the Harlechian sediments were deposited in deep rather than shallow water.'[1]

One final point connected with the subject of turbidity currents may be noted: the need to trigger-off the process by some external agent—earthquake shocks were suggested. But in several areas of greywackes of different ages repeated cycles of graded greywackes occur, and this would involve cyclic earthquake activity, of which there is no evidence.

## REFERENCES

For additional reading the student is recommended to study the appropriate parts of the British Regional Geologies, published by the Geological Survey and Museum on:

North Wales; South Wales (for the classical area of St Davids); Central England (for Nuneaton); North-West Highlands of Scotland; Welsh Borderland (for Shropshire, Malvern Hills, etc.).

[1] C. J. Stubblefield in 'Cambrian Palaeogeography in Britain,' *C. R. Int. Geol. Cong.* **(XX)**, Mexico (1956), **1**, 1.

Fuller accounts of selected areas will be found in papers listed below:

BASSETT, D. A. 'The Welsh Geosyncline . . .' in *The British Caledonides*, 1963, 35–70.

BASSETT, D. A., and WALTON, E. K. 'The Hell's Mouth Grits: . . .,' *Q.J.G.S.*, **116** (1960), 85.

GEORGE, T. N. 'Palaeozoic Growth of the British Caledonides' in 'The British Caledonides,' a Symposium (1963), 1–34.

JONES, O. T. 'On the evolution of a geosyncline,' *Q.J.G.S.*, **94** (1938), 60, for a discussion of the lithology and of the conditions of sedimentation.

MATLEY, C. A., and WILSON, T. STACEY. 'The Harlech Dome north of the Barmouth Estuary,' *Q.J.G.S.*, **102** (1946), 1. The latest account of this classical area gives full details of the succession and structure, and is illustrated by a detailed geological map.

STUBBLEFIELD, C. J. 'Cambrian Palaeogeography in Britain,' *C. R. Int. Geol. Cong.* (XX), Mexico (1956), **1**, 1.

WHITTARD, W. F. 'A Geology of South Shropshire,' *Proc. Geol. Assoc.*, **63** (1952), 143. The writer states the case, from the palaeontological angle for including the Tremadocian in the Ordovician System.

*Q.J.G.S.* = *Quarterly Journal of the Geological Society of London.*

## NOTE

A recent (1965) announcement[1] of the discovery of microfossils in siltstone low down in the succession came too late to be incorporated in the account of the Manx Slates. The microfossils are stated to indicate the zone of *D. extensus* in the Arenig Series of the Ordovician System. Therefore it would appear that the Manx Slates must be largely, if not entirely early Ordovician in age; and instead of underlying the Skiddaw Slate Series, they must be their age-equivalents.

[1] Downie, C., 'Microfossils from the Manx Slate Series', *Proc. Geol. Soc. Lond.*, No. 1625 (Aug. 1965).

## CHAPTER III

# THE ORDOVICIAN PERIOD

IN 1831, the year when Sedgwick commenced unravelling the geological structure of North Wales, and thus laid the foundations of the Cambrian System, a famous contemporary, R. I. Murchison, discovered fossiliferous mudstones underlying the Old Red Sandstone of the Welsh borderland in the neighbourhood of the Wye Valley. In the following few years these were incorporated in his newly established Silurian System, named after the country inhabited in ancient times by the Silures. Later both Sedgwick and Murchison extended their investigations, the former including newer rocks, which he termed 'Upper Cambrian', in the System that he had founded; and the latter working downwards into older strata, to which he gave the name 'Lower Silurian'. Inevitably the two systems thus extended overlapped, and it became evident in the course of time that Sedgwick's Upper Cambrian was equivalent to Murchison's Lower Silurian. The knowledge caused bitterness of feeling between the two pioneers. Both occupied high positions: Sedgwick occupied the Chair of Geology at Cambridge University, while Murchison was the newly appointed Director of the Geological Survey. Neither would give way; but after their deaths, Professor Charles Lapworth, of Birmingham University, himself a great authority on these ancient rocks, suggested that the strata involved should be given the status of a System, for which he proposed the name Ordovician, 'after the last and most valiant of the old Cambrian tribes' whose geographical location was halfway between Cambria (North Wales) and Siluria (South Wales).

Within the area of the British Isles the Ordovician sedimentary rocks are entirely marine, and the period may be regarded as the continuation of the marine sedimentation which commenced in the Cambrian and was brought to a close at the end of Silurian time. Up to a point there is a distinct similarity between the main events in the history of both periods: both commenced with a marine transgression; in both periods there is clear evidence of a late readvance, causing the inundation of wide areas which had stood above sea-level for the greater part of the period. There are, however, notable differences: in the Ordovician, active volcanoes sprang into existence in many parts of our area—there had been none in the Cambrian period. Further, after comparing the Cambrian rocks of

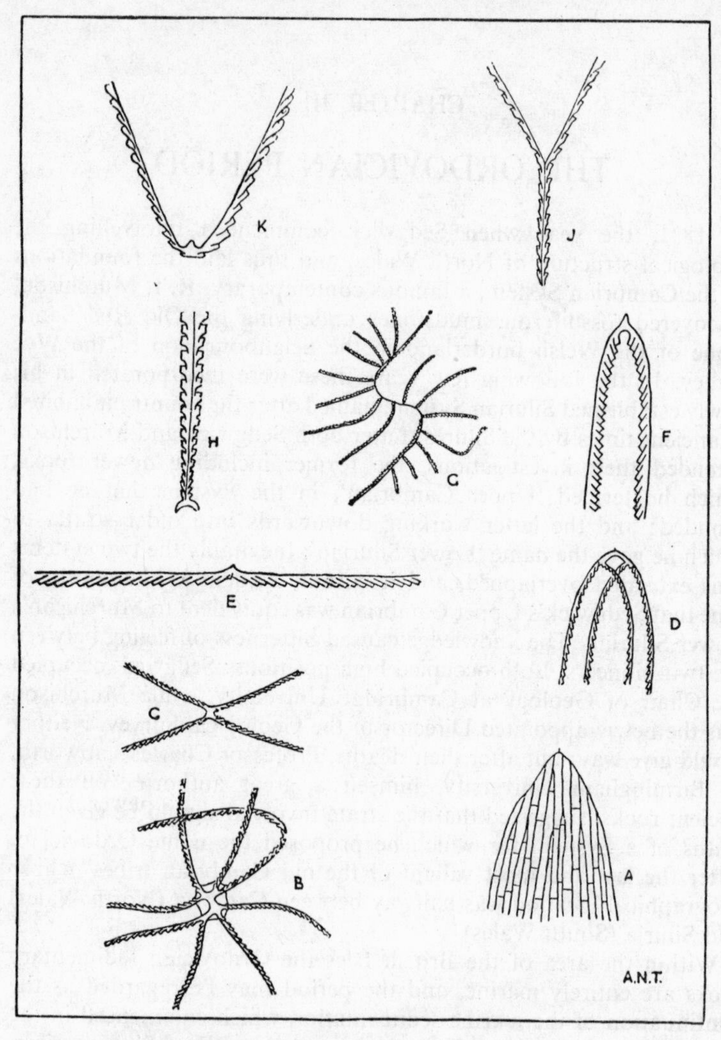


FIG. 11. Characteristic Ordovician graptolites, mostly zonal forms.

A. *Dictyonema sociale*. Tremadoc Slates.
B. *Dichograptus octobrachiatus*. Arenig Series.
C. *Tetragraptus amii*. Arenig Series.
D. *Tetragraptus fruticosus*. Arenig Series.
E. *Didymograptus hirundo*. Top of Arenig Series.
F. *Didymograptus murchisoni*. Upper Llanvirn Series.
G. *Nemagraptus gracilis*. Caradoc Series.
H. *Mesograptus multidens*. Caradoc Series.
J. *Dicranograptus clingani*. Caradoc Series.
K. *Dicellograptus complanatus*. Ashgill Series.

different localities, one is left with the general impression of uniform conditions over wide areas; but in the Ordovician System we are impressed by the evidence of diversity of conditions, so much so, in fact, that it is impossible to describe the System concisely, and in general terms.

In certain localities the Ordovician rocks comprise boulder beds, conglomerates, coarse-grained grits, sandstones and greywackes, largely of shallow-water formation, and containing an abundance of so-called 'shelly fossils', including brachiopods and other shell-fish, corals, crinoids and notably trilobites, which, though deposed from the dominant position they had occupied in the preceding Period, are still among the most valuable fossils from the point of view of the stratigrapher. By contrast, in other areas, the rocks are less diversified, comprising dark-coloured, fine-grained shales and mudstones—that is, rocks representing the clay grade of sediment, formed under deep water, remote from the then-existing coastlines. Shelly fossils are typically absent from rocks of these kinds, their place being taken by a new group of creatures, the graptolites. Dendroid graptolites had made their first appearance in Tremadoc (Upper Cambrian) times. The general aspect of a group of strata is spoken of concisely as its **'facies'**: and the term may have reference to either lithological characters or fossil contents. Clearly, if rocks of a certain age exhibit a lateral change of lithological facies, in other words, if changes can be traced in the mineral fragments of which the rocks are composed, in their grain-size, in the nature and amount of matrix, and in any other characters which give the rocks a degree of distinctiveness, a change in conditions of formation is implied. Equally clearly, if the change in lithological facies is striking, it is reasonable to anticipate finding just as marked differences in the kinds of fossils entombed in the rocks, for at the present time totally different assemblages of creatures inhabit the several 'depth zones' of the seas which are recognized by biologists. One of the chief attractions of the Ordovician System as a field of research is the almost endless succession of problems that confront the geologist who attempts to link up or 'correlate' these rocks of different facies occurring in isolated outcrops.

The System is divided into:

5. The Ashgill Series }
4. The Caradoc Series } = The Bala Series.
3. The Llandeilo Series.
2. The Llanvirn Series.
1. The Arenig (or Skiddaw) Series.

These series, in turn, are divided into stages and even smaller

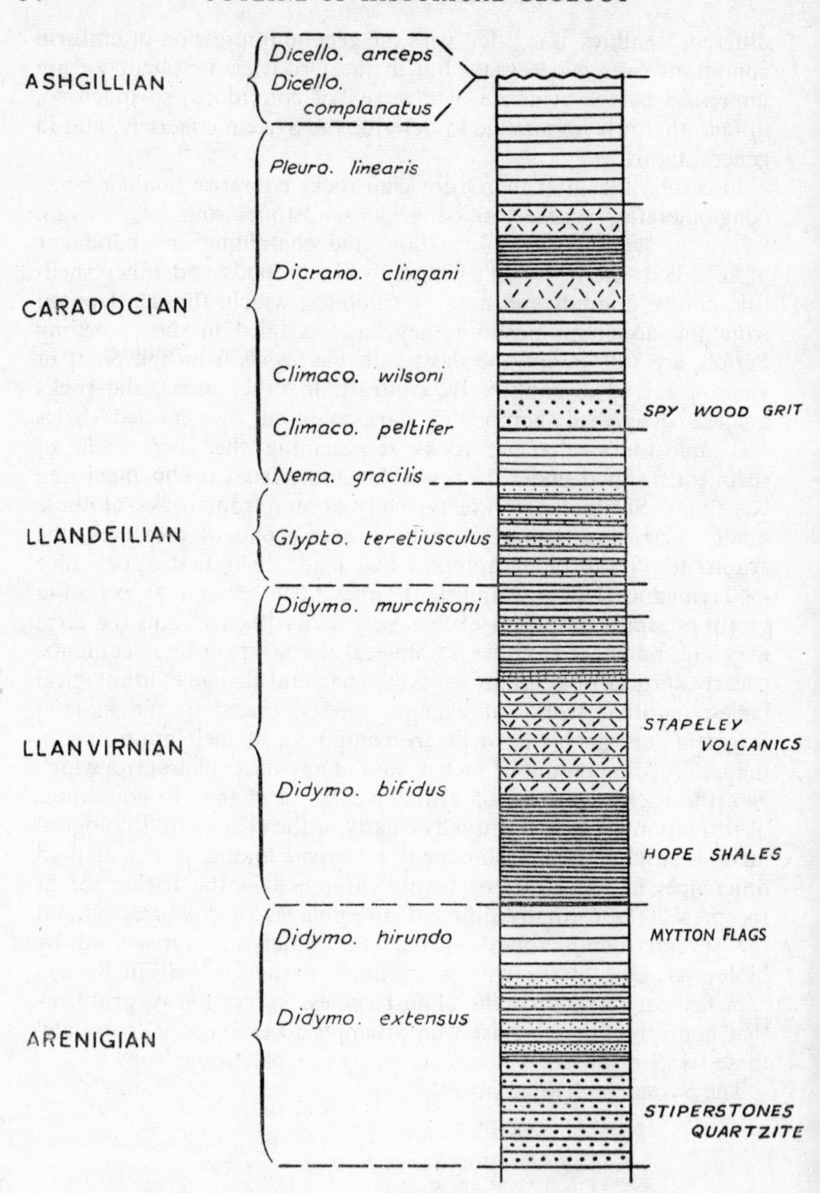


FIG. 12.

Vertical section of the Ordovician of the Shelve area, Shropshire, showing the graptolite zones and the limits given to the five series in the Welsh Borderland.

divisions which generally will not concern us. Most of the series- and stage-names were applied long ago by the pioneer workers on these rocks, others are much later introductions. The type-areas of Bala and Caradoc, Llandeilo and Arenig are places where the series which bear their names are essentially of the shelly facies, and the original limits to the series were fixed without regard to changes in the contemporary graptolite faunas. Subsequently Charles Lapworth proved the graptolites to be most delicate time indices, and therefore of the highest stratigraphical value. He showed that throughout the whole period of their existence these creatures were continuously and rapidly evolving. Further, although possessing no means of locomotion of their own, winds, waves and currents made good this deficiency, so that migration of the successive types was rapid: the graptolites approach very closely to the ideal group of organisms, as each member covered a wide geographical range, but the rapidity with which they evolved ensured that their remains would successively be restricted to small vertical thicknesses of rock.

The dendroid graptolite, *Dictyonema*, from the Tremadoc Slate, consisted of a large number of delicate branches, the so-called stipes, suspended from floating seaweed. Each stipe consisted of many small conical 'cells', each of which housed a polyp, so that a *Dictyonema* was a veritable colony, comprising several hundred individuals. In the true graptolites overcrowding and under-nourishment gave impetus to the gradual development of improvements in the housing scheme, first by decreasing the number of stipes, then by altering their attitude, and by spacing the individuals more widely apart. By taking note of these facts the different genera, species and varieties may be recognized and named. Their distribution in the Ordovician column has been minutely studied by Lapworth, Marr, Miss G. Elles, Bulman and others, who have divided the system into a series of *zones*, each of which is a group of strata characterized by a distinctive assemblage of graptolites, and bearing the name of a specific graptolite (the zonal index) which reached its maximum development in the rocks comprised in the zone. Further, attempts have been made to group the zones into series; but these zone-groups cannot easily be made to correspond with the original series named above, for obvious reasons.

The succession of graptolite zones is well established, and the order in which they occur is not in question; but there are wide differences of opinion as to how they should be grouped into series. So that there shall be no dubiety as to the exact meaning of the series-names in this account, the full list of zones and their grouping are shown in Fig. 12. The same sequence of graptolite zones is applicable over a wide area; but in certain parts of Britain it proves necessary to substitute some zonal indices for others. Thus, although the Cardocian zones of *C. peltifer* and *Cl. wilsoni* apply in southern Scotland, the two together are equivalent to the single zone of *Mesograptus multidens* in Shropshire and Wales.

The Ordovician Period, according to one authoritative estimate, may have extended over 60,000,000 years; the System is divided into twelve zones. Assuming that these were of equal duration the figures suggest that the average period of time represented by one graptolite zone was of the order of five million years. One tends to forget the enormous period of time represented when one is examining Ordovician rocks of the graptolitic shale type. The lithological uniformity conveys an impression of unchanging conditions, and it is difficult to think in terms of the correct time-scale. This becomes less difficult when dealing with the rocks in areas more sensitive to change, where a single zone may bear evidence of a long series of significant geological events. This is particularly true of shallow-water, coastal areas of course, and we may refer in anticipation, to the variations shown by the *D. murchisoni* Zone in Wales, which is considered in due course.

### THE RELATION OF THE ORDOVICIAN TO THE UNDERLYING ROCKS

Ordovician rocks outcrop in Wales, the Lake District, Shropshire, Cornwall, the Southern Uplands and the North-West Highlands of Scotland, also in small inliers at Sedbergh, Cross Fell and Austwick. In Ireland Ordovician strata occur in three main areas: (1) in the north-east, together with the Silurian they form the pre-Carboniferous massif of Longford—Co. Down which is a direct continuation of the Southern Uplands of Scotland; (2) a much more extensive area in the south-east invaded by the great Leinster Granite and forming the Leinster massif; (3) in that part of Ireland analogous with the Midland Valley of Scotland Ordovician rocks are important in the neighbourhood of Pomeroy and in Cos. Mayo and Galway.

In **North Wales** the Ordovician rocks rest *unconformably* upon older strata: upon different levels in the Cambrian, here on Tremadoc Slate, as at Dolgellau and Tremadoc; there on Lingulella Flags, as in Pembrokeshire; elsewhere, as at St Tudwals, upon the lower members of the Harlech Series, and in western Carnarvonshire and in Anglesey directly on the Precambrian. These relationships prove that the deposition of the highest Cambrian sediments was followed by uplift of the area of sedimentation, accompanied by tilting and folding. Then followed a period of erosion, in the course of which the crests of the folds especially suffered wear and tear, amounting to thousands of feet in parts of Carnarvonshire, so that rocks low down in the Cambrian were exposed at the surface. Originally, it is believed, Cambrian rocks stretched far over Anglesey, though now no rocks of this age intervene between the Arenig Series and the Precambrian floor upon which they directly rest. Fig. 13 shows in diagram form the sequence of events outlined above. It is not a section through any actual part of Wales, but represents in the simplest way the relationship between the Precambrian, Cambrian and basal Ordovician in North Wales.

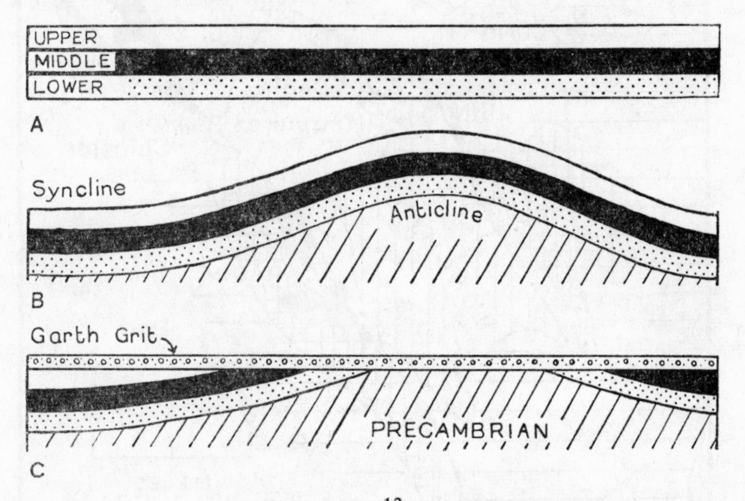


FIG. 13.

Diagram showing stages in the development of the unconformable relationship between the Ordovician and older rocks in North Wales.

*Top Section:* Lower, Middle and Upper Cambrian shown as uniform bands.
*Middle Section:* the same, folded with the underlying Precambrian.
*Bottom Section:* immediately after deposition of the Garth Grit (the basal conglomerate of the Ordovician).

The Ordovician lies unconformably on older rocks in **South Wales** also. The Lingulella Flags (Upper Cambrian) look much like the typical development in the Harlech Dome area; but the Tremadocian, if ever deposited here (it probably was), is unrepresented and the Arenig Series is seen to rest with slight angular discordance on the Upper Cambrian. This relationship is visible in a gully on the Pembrokeshire coast at one point only.

It is apparent that at the opening of the Ordovician Period the sea swept rapidly over a large area covering Wales as far north as peninsular Carnarvonshire and southern Anglesey, depositing the basal Arenigian sediments. Thereafter it slowly encroached upon a land-mass lying north-west of Wales, younger formations overlapping older ones, so that first the Llanvirnian and then the Caradocian (in the north of Anglesey) come to rest directly upon the Precambrian floor.

On this evidence a strip of the Ordovician coastline is located in

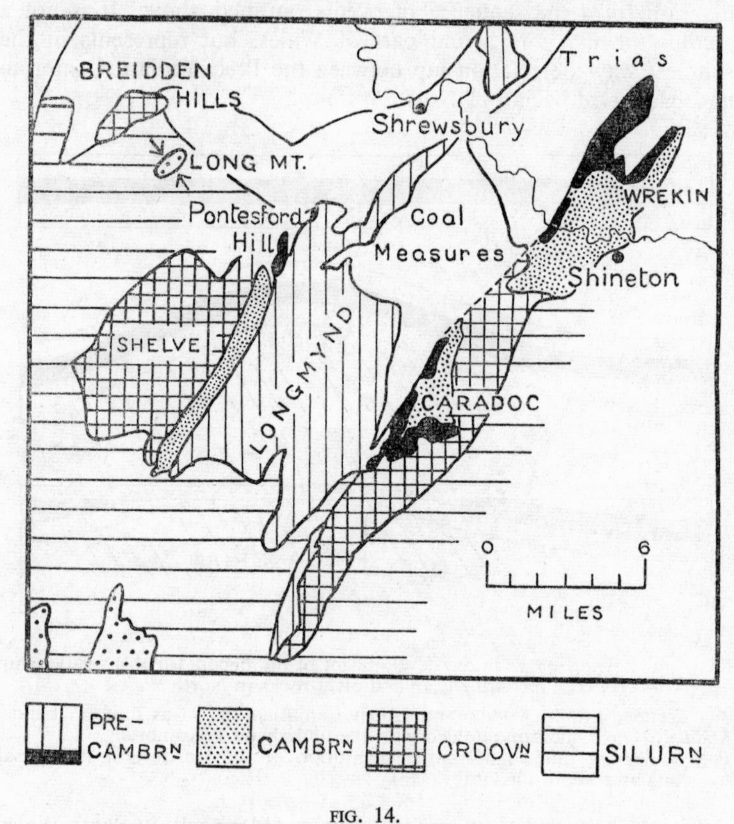


FIG. 14.
Sketch-map showing the rock-groups of South Shropshire.
(*After C. Lapworth, W. W. Watts and others.*)
Precambrian igneous rocks, solid black; large dots, O.R.S.

the extreme north of Wales, with land lying on the site of the present Irish Sea.

Another strip of coastline may be inferred to have existed on the other side of this basin, in Shropshire or a little farther to the east. The evidence in **Shropshire** is examined in some detail, for it is of more than passing interest. Ordovician rocks occur in the three main areas shown in Fig. 14: (1) the Breidden Hills on the borders of Shropshire and Montgomeryshire; (2) the Shelve area to the west; (3) the Caradoc area, east of the Longmynd. In addition there is a small tract at the north-west corner of the Longmynd, immediately east of Pontesford Hill (Fig. 63), which is very important.

In the Breidden Hills the Caradocian rocks only are exposed, and it is unknown how much of the lower Ordovician succession is concealed.

In the **Shelve area,** separated from the Breiddens by the Long Mountain syncline of Silurian and lowest Devonian rocks, the Ordovician is complete up to the Ashgillian in a variable succession totalling 9000 feet of strata (Fig. 12).

In a part of Shropshire lying south and east of the Longmynd and usually referred to as the **Caradoc area** (after Caer Caradoc, one of the prominent Church Stretton hills), the Ordovician is limited to the Caradocian, which rests unconformably on older rocks. A small patch of graptolitic Caradocian rests unconformably on very steeply dipping Precambrian rocks in the extreme north-western corner of the Longmynd (see Fig. 63). Therefore the boundary between the region where the Ordovician is restricted to the Caradoc Series and that in which the System is complete must coincide with the *western* boundary of the Longmynd. This boundary is a fault, the Western Boundary Fault. Its importance may be gauged from the fact that it separates a tract of country in which the Caradocian rocks lie some 10,000 feet above the Precambrian basement from one in which the former rest directly on the latter. For the moment we leave the fascinating possible interpretations to the imagination of the reader.

At no point east of the Caradoc area do Ordovician rocks occur at or below the surface, though both Cambrian and Silurian strata do occur in inliers in the English Midlands. Farther southward, on the western flanks of the Malverns, the same relations are seen: the Cambrian and Silurian are both present, but no Ordovician. This is surely the result of non-deposition, and indicates that the Midlands formed part of another land area lying eastward of the Ordovician Sea that covered Wales and latterly parts of Shropshire. It may be noted that there is evidence in other parts of the country of a great extension of the area of sedimentation in Caradocian times. This is notably the case in the Southern Uplands of Scotland, the English Lake District and at Crossfell; while evidence of an unusual kind was forthcoming near Austwick. Here, Precambrian (Ingletonian) rocks, with gaping joints, formed the local floor to the deposits of the Caradocian Sea. Later denudation has completely removed the sheet of Caradocian sediments except for material which percolated down into one of the joint-fissures. This constitutes a 'Neptunean dyke', which can be dated by the fossils it contains. It proves that the Caradocian Sea invaded the north Midlands as far as the western flank of the present Pennines. These relationships are duplicated near Church Stretton where quarrying for road-metal in Uriconian volcanics uncovered a Neptunian dyke filled with sandstone from which Caradocian fossils were obtained.

The evidence in the **Lake District** indicates that the Welsh basin was in direct communication with the area, for the graptolitic successions are closely similar. The relation of the Ordovician to the older rocks is unknown. It has been claimed that the lowest part of the great Skiddaw Group, which is definitely in the main of Arenig age, is Upper Cambrian (Tremadocian), on the evidence of the occurrence of certain fossils, notably species of the dendroid graptolite, *Bryograptus*. The validity of this evidence has been questioned by some authorities, on the grounds of the very close association of the alleged Tremadocian, with undoubted Arenigian graptolites; and it seems almost certain that the Skiddaw Group is wholly Ordovician in age.

Ordovician strata are met with next in the **Southern Uplands** of Scotland, where they occur as long, narrow inliers in the Silurian strata which occupy the greater part of this tract of country. Arenigian rocks occur, but their relation to, and the nature of, the underlying rocks is unknown. The basin in which the Ordovician was deposited in southern Scotland was elongated north-east to south-west with its axial parts occupying a belt of country passing through Moffat (Fig. 18) and extending south-westward into North-East Ireland—Co. Down and beyond. That the two 'basins' of deposition—the Anglo-Welsh and the Southern Uplands—North-East Ireland basins—were in direct communication, at least at intervals, is proved by the all-but identity of the graptolite-successions in beds of the same lithology; but the details of their geological histories were very different, as the sequel will show.

The **Highland Border Series** is of doubtful status and age. As the name implies, these rocks occupy a narrow belt of country adjacent to the great Highland Boundary Fault extending north-eastwards from the Clyde Estuary through the southern end of Loch Lomond and ultimately reaching the sea near Stonehaven, where the strata are sometimes termed the Margie Series. The rocks are dark-coloured shales with cherts, and locally include spilitic pillow lavas. They have been folded and torn during earth-movements which can only be vaguely dated as post-Arenig, pre-Lower O.R.S. The lithology is similar to that of the Arenig Series in the Girvan area, and it is widely believed that these rocks are also Arenigian. Formerly they have been termed Cambro-Ordovician, and some people include in the Series the proved Middle Cambrian strata from which J. Pringle obtained a trilobite fauna. (See p. 130.)

Finally, in the **North-West Highlands** of Scotland Cambro-Ordovician strata occupy a narrow belt extending from the north coast at Durness south-south-westwards into Skye. These Lower Palaeozoic rocks lie with strong unconformity on the Precambrian (Torridonian), and disappear eastwards under the strongly metamorphosed rocks of the Moine, which have been driven over them along low-lying thrust-planes. The basal member is the Lower Cambrian Eriboll Quartzite. This is followed upwards by the Durness Limestone Group, essentially a thick group of dolomitic limestones, somewhat argillaceous below, and locally containing much chert, originally colloidal silica. From the lowest of the seven divisions of the Durness Limestone Group, Lapworth obtained Lower Cambrian fossils, so different in type from those obtained from beds of the same age in England and Wales, that it must be concluded that they belonged to different faunal provinces. The second division is quite unfossiliferous, which is little short of a tragedy, for this is the critical part of the whole succession. The remaining five divisions are similar in their fossil-contents, which are completely dissimilar to those yielded by beds of the same age elsewhere in Britain; but they are almost identical with fossils occurring in Arenigian (Beekmantown) and later limestones in the Appalachians in North America. This Scottish succession therefore contains beds of proved Lower Cambrian age below, and of Ordovician age above. It remains for the future to discover what has happened to the missing Middle and Upper Cambrian rocks: this is one of the unsolved problems of the Lower Palaeozoic. The common interpretation placed on the facts stated above is that the North-West Highlands, by reason of its completely distinctive Arenig-Llandeilo fauna, must have been cut off from the Anglo-Welsh basin. In this connection one question must be asked. If the conditions of sedimentation in the Anglo-Welsh basin had been suitable for the development of chert-bearing dolomitic limestones during Arenig times, would the beds have contained the Beekmantown—or Durness-Limestone fauna? The question cannot be answered by direct comparison, for such beds occur in the North-West Highlands only; but it should be remembered that the Arenig age of the Beekmantown Limestone was demonstrated by tracing the limestones into the Hudson Valley, where they pass laterally into graptolitic shales of typical Anglo-Welsh lithology and fauna!

## THE ORDOVICIAN SUCCESSION

In general the lowest rocks of the **Arenig Series** bear evidence of accumulation under shallow-water conditions: in Anglesey these attain to their maximum development, and comprise no less than 3000 feet of coarse beach deposits, including wave-worn boulders up to 4 feet across. In the belt of country south and east of the Harlech Dome including Dolgellau and Arenig, the basal member of the Ordovician succession is a thin quartzose conglomerate, the Garth Grit, which is followed upwards by a thick series of massive, sometimes cross-bedded feldspathic grits consisting essentially of broken feldspar crystals, presumably similar in origin to the 'feldspar-sands' occurring in Mid-Wales on a higher horizon and referred to below. Especially towards the base irregular lenticles of dark-coloured shaly material are intercalated giving a very distinctive appearance which caused W. G. Fearnsides to call them 'streaky bacon beds'. The feldspathic massive 'grits' are succeeded abruptly by graptolitic shales, which, however, are developed to a much greater extent in other parts of Britain, notably in South Wales (Pembrokeshire) and the English Lake District, where in the Skiddaw Slates, the succession is most complete. At low levels the beds contain *Dichograptus* (an eight-branched form). Higher in the succession this is joined and ultimately replaced by the four-branched *Tetragraptus*. Similarly, higher still two-branched didymograptids appear, two of them being zonal forms: *D. extensus* below and *D. hirundo* above. In both of these forms the two stipes are extended horizontally (Fig. 11, E).

The upper shaly portion of the Arenig Series is named the **Tetragraptus Shales.** There was considerable volcanic activity[1] throughout this period in Wales and Scotland, with probably the maximum development in the neighbourhood of Skomer Island, lying off the western coast of Pembrokeshire. Here, although the base is not exposed and the basal Silurian rocks follow unconformably, a thickness of 3000 feet of Arenig beds includes lavas covering a wide range of composition (from acid to basic), interbedded with conglomerates, quartzites and finer grained sedimentary material.

The Arenig Series in Shropshire is well exposed west of the Longmynd. The succession commences with a coarse-grained, white-weathering quartzite, some 800 feet in thickness. This **Stiperstone Quartzite** forms a very prominent feature, capped by

[1] The Series takes its name from the Arenig Mountains in North Wales; but detailed mapping has shown that the igneous rocks building the mountain belong to later episodes in the Ordovician.

tor-like crags. The underlying Tremadocian shales are, naturally, indifferently exposed; but there appears to be no angular discordance between the highest Cambrian and the lowest Ordovician, though the abrupt change in lithology is significant, and indicates a drastic change in environment.

The Stiperstone Quartzite, which is extensively quarried, dips steeply under the Mytton Flags, of greywacke facies and containing a mixed fauna of shelly fossils and graptolites, dendroid types being locally abundant. The formation reaches 3000 feet in thickness, so that the Arenig Series in this district totals 4000 feet.

In the Lake District the **Skiddaw Slate Series** conforms to the general pattern of the Arenigian stated above: the lower portion is coarser-grained than the higher part—the former are differentiated as the Loweswater Flags, upwards of 4000 feet in thickness, and the latter as the Mosser-Kirkstile Slates, some 2500 feet thick. Graptolites occurring at different levels have enabled a succession of graptolite zones to be established and these match up well with those of South Wales. The rocks are difficult to study on account of structural complexities: they are often tightly folded, strongly faulted and cleaved.

The highest part of the Series has yielded tuning-fork grapolites (proving their Llanvirnian age) close up underneath the base of the overlying Borrowdale Volcanic Series which appear to follow conformably.

Arenigian strata occur in two Scottish areas, in the North-West Highlands where they are of calcareous facies and unique in Britain; and in the Southern Uplands where they consist largely of spilitic pillow lavas associated with variously coloured cherts and rare graptolitic mudstones. They are considered in more detail later (p. 73).

The **Llanvirn Series.**—In rocks of much the same lithological type as the Tetragraptus Shales, the characteristic fossils of the latter group give place to a new assemblage which includes several forms of the so-called tuning-fork graptolites, whose range is co-extensive with the Llanvirn Series, named from a locality near St Davids, South Wales.

A point of minor difficulty has arisen in connection with fixing the exact horizon of the boundary between the Tetragraptus Shales and the Bifidus Beds. Not long ago the discovery of a small tuning-fork graptolite would have been accepted as proof of the Lower Llanvirn age of the rock containing it. Recently, however, an early form of *D. bifidus*, distinguished as *D. protobifidus*, has come to light in beds which, on the balance of the palaeontological evidence, have been referred to the top of the Tetragraptus Shales. If this interpretation is accepted, the statement that the Llanvirnian is co-extensive with the range of the tuning-fork graptolites is no longer wholly true. It must be decided which is the lesser evil: to move the boundary down so as to include the Protobifidus Beds with the Llanvirnian; or to allow tuning-fork graptolites in the Arenigian. Growth of knowledge has in this case complicated a formerly simple matter.

It appears that the conditions of accumulation must have been uniform over a wide area in Lower Llanvirnian times: there is little variation in lithology wherever the beds occur—in North and South Wales, Shropshire and the Lake District. The sedimentary part of the Llanvirnian consists of dark, blue-black shales with a prolific graptolite fauna, and with a rather more flaggy type of lithology above. These strata constitute two graptolite zones of very unequal thickness, the lower (*Bifidus* Zone) being the thicker and more uniformly developed. In addition to the normal sediments, volcanic tuffs and lavas locally increase the thickness enormously. The most widely distributed volcanic group in the whole System occurs in the *Bifidus* Zone. Although so uniform in lithological characters, the Llanvirnian beds vary considerably in thickness: in South Wales, for example, the *Bifidus* Beds reach a maximum of 2000 feet at St Clears, but diminish rapidly to only 400 feet at Llandeilo. These variations reflect the general instability of the crust during this period of intense volcanic activity.

In the Shelve area (Fig. 14) the *Bifidus* Zone reaches its fullest development (4500 feet) and exhibits more variation in both lithology and fauna than elsewhere in Britain. In addition to the characteristic graptolites the rocks contain an important trilobite fauna, including *Cyclopyge*, *Placoparia* and *Barrandia* together with certain species occurring in beds of this age in Bohemia, proving free communication between these widely separated areas. Much coarser sediment appears in the upper part of the zone, shales and mudstones below giving place to richly fossiliferous flags and greywackes, containing many lamellibranchs, gasteropods and inarticulate brachiopods as well as trilobites including members of the *Ogyginae* family. In the Shelve the *Bifidus* Beds grade up into the *Murchisoni* Zone: the boundary between them is arbitrarily fixed by the first appearance of the younger fauna.

The Upper Llanvirnian (*Murchisoni* Zone) shows considerable variation, largely as a consequence of the fact that the period was one of great volcanic activity and crustal instability. The zone is represented by somewhat flaggy graptolitic shales in places, such as western Pembrokeshire in South Wales. The material which comes from Abereiddy Bay is well known and noteworthy on account of the great abundance of graptolites that it contains—the zonal index form (Fig. 11, F) associated with *D. murchisoni* var. *geminus* (in effect a short-branched *murchisoni*) and *Orthograptus calcaratus*.

Elsewhere, as in parts of North Wales, the shale-facies does not occur; but the zone is certainly represented among the volcanic lavas and tuffs. In the area around Builth and Llandrindod in mid-Wales this is proved to be the case as two separate volcanic series—the Builth Series above and the Llandrindod Series below—are sandwiched between lower and upper graptolitic shales containing fossils typical of the zone. The upper shales are impersistent as an unconformity separates the *Murchisoni* Zone from the overlying Llandeilian. Actually the sequence between the underlying *Bifidus* Zone and the overlying *Teretiusculus* Zone is interrupted by three minor unconformities, all of which involve the *D. Murchisoni* beds.

The real fascination of this area lies in the discovery of shoreline features, including sea-cliffs with off-shore stacks and boulder beaches with boulders up to 6 feet in diameter. The rocks forming the cliffs are volcanic belonging to the Builth Volcanic Series, partly basic, partly acid lavas. The former, as a result of subaerial denudation in mid-*Murchisoni* times, developed a characteristic 'stepped' topography, contrasting with rounded hills formed by the acid igneous rocks. There are well-known analogies. The reader is warned, however, that he must not expect to see these features to-day as they were then: their reality has been proved only by meticulously accurate mapping of the contacts on a large scale (25 inches to the mile).

All these coastal features were buried, as a result of subsidence of the area, by an accumulation of feldspar-sand followed, as the water deepened, by mudstone and ultimately by graptolitic shales still yielding the fauna characteristic of the *Murchisoni* Zone.

The details of these variations serve to underline the general statement made on an earlier page to the effect that the immensity of time covered by even one graptolite zone is most readily appreciated in a 'sensitive area': it would be difficult to find one more sensitive to slight change than a coastal area subjected to volcanic activity.

The *Bifidus* Beds occur immediately underneath the great Borrowdale Volcanic Series in the Lake District, and doubtless, as in parts of North Wales, the *Murchisoni* Zone is represented by the lower part of the volcanic series, though, naturally, as there are no normal sediments at this level, there are no graptolites to prove the fact.

In southern Scotland there is no trace of either zone (nor indeed of the overlying Llandeilian), and there is no proof that these beds were ever deposited in this area. If they were, they had been completely removed during the pre-Caradocian erosion interval.

The **Llandeilo Series** succeeds the Llanvirnian and occurs in its typical development at Llandeilo,[1] a South Welsh town: the succession here, as described originally by Murchison, must serve as our standard of reference. In the neighbourhood of Llandeilo the series consists of limestones, rapidly alternating with thin sandstones and flags (Fig. 15). These alternations persist throughout a vertical thickness of nearly half a mile. Shelly fossils, including numerous typical trilobites such as *Ogygiocarella debuchi*, are locally abundant, but graptolites are typically absent. These rocks pass westwards into others of deep-water formation, the flags and limestones being progressively replaced by shales, while the shelly fossils give place to graptolites. At Carmarthen the whole of the Llandeilo Flags and Limestones are condensed into a few hundred feet of graptolitic shale. It is now known that these rocks in both areas fall within one graptolite zone (the *Teretiusculus* Zone).

The exact level at which to draw the boundary between the Llandeilian and the Caradocian is still a matter of dispute, though Fig. 15 makes the solution look easy—easier than it is in fact. In the Builth-Llandrindod area a flaggy and locally rather calcareous facies persists through the zones of *D. bifidus*, *D. murchisoni*, *G. teretiusculus* and the greater part even of *N. gracilis*. Towards the top of the *Gracilis* Zone the lithology changes, and graptolitic shales replace flags. This is exactly what happens at Llandeilo, and localities farther south, but there the change occurred much earlier. Therefore if the Llandeilo-Caradoc boundary had been fixed at the level of the change from flags into graptolitic shales at Builth instead of at Llandeilo, at least the greater part of the *Gracilis* Zone would have to be included in the Llandeilian. The substitution of shales for flags, and of graptolites for the mixed trilobite and graptolite fauna of Builth was the natural consequence of a change from shallower to deeper water. Obviously the change took place earlier in the south than in the north: in a word, the lithological boundary is diachronous, and certainly must not be used to divide two periods of geological time. This must be done by choosing an appropriate palaeontological horizon. Neither brachiopods nor trilobites are suitable for this purpose, for their distribution was controlled by the depth of water; but the graptolites, living in surface waters, were independent of changing depths. Rather unfortunately the boundary between the two critical zones (the *Teretiusculus* and the *Gracilis* Zones) is not a sharp one: the two faunas grade into one another. Nevertheless, the zonal boundary that most nearly coincides with

[1] 'Llandilo' on recent maps.

the top of the characteristic flags at Llandeilo is the base of the *Gracilis* Zone. Though other species of this genus appear in the underlying zone, *N. gracilis* itself appears to be restricted to the zone that bears its name. By a very lucky chance *N. gracilis* occurs in the basal member of the Caradocian of 'Caradoc', the type area where the Series was first described, and from which it takes its name (Fig. 15).

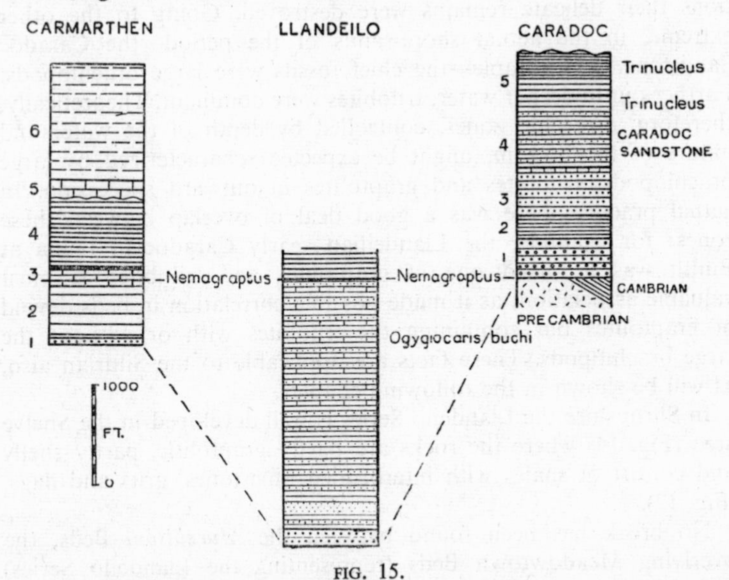


FIG. 15.

Vertical sections showing the lateral change of facies of the Llandeilo Series in South Wales and the Caradoc Series of Caradoc, Shropshire.

In the *Carmarthen Section*: 1=basal grit; 2=Hendre Shales; 3=Mydrim Limestone; 4=Mydrim Shales; 5=Bala Limestones; 6=Bala Mudstones (Slade and Redhill Beds).

In the *Caradoc Section*: 1=Hoar Edge Grit; 2=Harnage Shale; 3=Chatwall Sandstone; 4=Longville Flags and Lower Trinucleus Shales; 5=Acton Scott Mudstones with Onny Shales ('Onnian') at the top.

In the *Llandeilo Section* the strata between the basal bed (an ash passing laterally into a grit) and the shales containing *Nemagraptus* are the Llandeilo Flags and Limestones.

Certain facts relating to the relationship between the shelly and graptolitic faunas need emphasis. From the facts of distribution referred to above, one naturally associates graptolites with conditions favouring the deposition of sediments of the finest grain. They are normally absent from the coarser grained sediments; but this merely means that the conditions were unfavourable for their preservation. There would have been just as many graptolites in the surface waters near shore as over the oceanic deeps. This is proved by the occurrence of thin shaly bands or even mere films of argillaceous material interbedded with the coarser rocks, and containing graptolites. Such bands do not represent periods when these creatures invaded an area from which they had been absent previously, and from which they retired when coarser sediment was again deposited. The conditions were quiet enough for their preservation only when mud was accumulating; under other conditions their delicate remains were destroyed. Going to the other extreme, in the actual shore-sands of the period—the Caradoc Sandstone, for example—the chief fossils were large brachiopods. Farther out in deeper water, trilobites were dominant. Theoretically, therefore, three life zones, controlled by depth of the water and nature of the bottom, might be expected: characterized by large brachiopods, trilobites and graptolites in outward succession. In actual practice there was a good deal of overlap between these zones: for example, the Llandeilian—early Caradocian fauna at Builth was a mixed one of graptolites and trilobites—a most valuable association, as it made possible correlation in beds devoid of graptolites but containing the trilobites with or without the large brachiopods. These facts are applicable to the Silurian also, as will be shown in the following chapter.

In Shropshire the Llandeilo Series is well developed in the Shelve area (Fig. 14) where the rocks are partly graptolitic, partly shelly and consist of shales with interbedded limestones, grits and flags, (Fig. 12).

No break has been found between the *Murchisoni* Beds, the overlying Meadowtown Beds (representing the Llandeilo Series) and the Rorrington Flags, of Caradocian age: sedimentation must have been continuous, therefore, over this period of time in this part of Shropshire.

No beds of Llandeilo age occur in the Southern Uplands of Scotland, neither have they been proved to occur in the Lake District; but they may be represented in the higher part of the Borrowdale Volcanic Group. Time has to be found, however, for considerable folding and a period of active erosion following the volcanic episode, but preceding the renewal of sedimentation in Caradocian times in this area. These events, indeed, may have occupied more than Llandeilo times.

Even more striking variation than in the Llandeilian is exhibited by the **Bala Series**, particularly by the lower division, the Caradocian.

East of the Longmynd, as already noted, a great hiatus separates the **Caradocian** from underlying rocks. The youngest pre-Caradocian rocks are the Shineton Shales of Upper Cambrian age; but these are rapidly overstepped and the Caradocian strata come to rest directly on the Precambrian. The basal Caradocian is strongly conglomeratic and at one locality (Hope Bowdler) forms a natural cobbled pavement, below which basic Precambrian lavas occur.

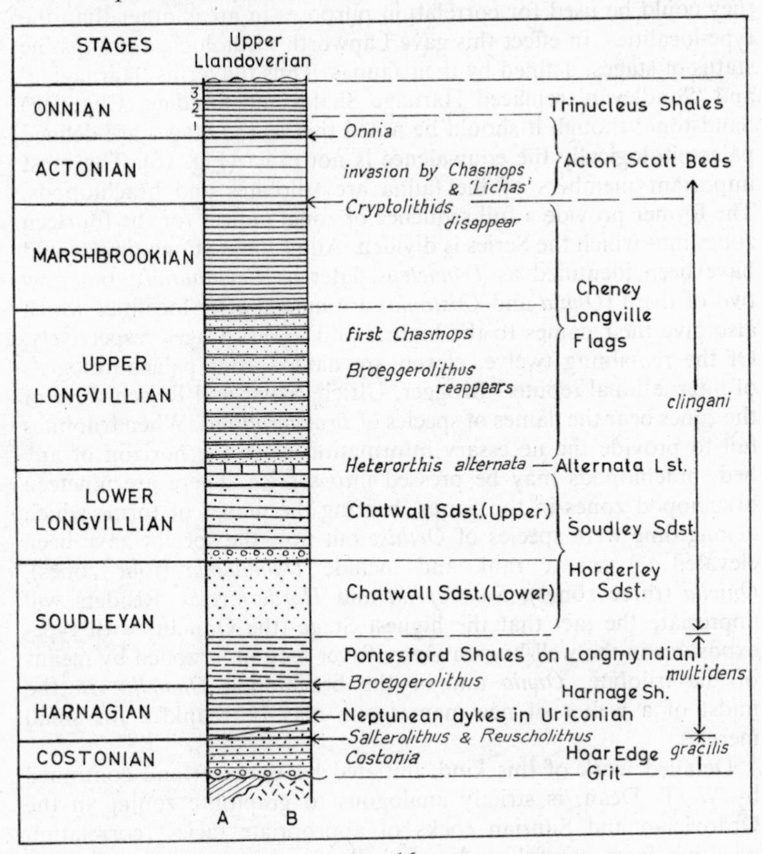


FIG. 16.

The Caradocian succession in the type area A—Tremadocian; B—**Uriconian.** Based on the work of B. B. Bancroft and W. T. Dean, *Bull. Brit. Mus.* (Natural History), 3 (1958), 193.

This undoubtedly represents a point on the shoreline of the Caradocian Sea. Further, in this neighbourhood a quarry opened for road-metal in Uriconian basic igneous rock exposed a sandstone 'dyke' containing early Harnagian fossils. The fact that these coastal features are of different ages establishes the diachronous nature of the basal Caradocian.

Murchison's Caradoc Sandstone has become the **Caradoc Series** which was divided by C. Lapworth (1916) into Groups named after localities broadly in the Church Stretton district. Later B. B. Bancroft made an important advance when he attempted to use the 'group' names in a wider sense, with time-significance, so that they could be used for correlation purposes in areas other than the type-localities. In effect this gave Lapworth's lithological groups the status of stages, defined by their faunas. Thus the terms 'Harnagian' and 'Soudleyan' replaced Harnage Shales and Soudley (Chatwall) Sandstone; though it should be noted that as the Stages are defined palaeontologically the equivalence is not exact (Fig. 16). The most important members of the fauna are trilobites and brachiopods. The former provide a full sequence of zonal indices for the fourteen zones into which the Series is divided. All of these at one time would have been identified as *Trinucleus*, later as *Cryptolithus*; but now two of them (*Onnia* and *Costonia*) are named after localities which also give their names to the highest and lowest Stages respectively. Of the remaining twelve, eleven are named after palaeontologists of international repute—Brögger, Ulrich, Salter and Reisch. Five of the zones bear the names of species of *Broggerolithus*. When trilobites fail to provide the necessary information as to the horizon of any bed, brachiopods may be pressed into service. There are nineteen brachiopod zones in the Series, bearing the names of forms which at one time were species of *Orthis*; but now the species have been elevated to generic rank and include *Dalmanella* (four zones), *Oniella* (three zones), *Soudleyella* and *Horderleyella*. Readers will appreciate the fact that the highest Stage (the Onnian) with type-exposures in the well-known Onny River section, is zoned by means of the trilobite, *Onnia* and/or the brachiopod *Onniella*: in the midst of a welter of new names one may be thankful for small mercies.

Detailed work of this kind, initiated by Bancroft and continued by W. T. Dean, is strictly analogous to graptolite zoning in the Ordovician and Silurian rocks of appropriate facies: correlation resulting from careful study of shelly faunas, especially trilobites and brachiopods, in expert hands can give just as accurate results. We would stress 'in expert hands' for work of this kind demands specialist knowledge: it is not for the general geological practitioner.

The Caradocian should, of course, be succeeded by the Ashgillian; but rocks of this age were removed (supposing that they were originally present in Shropshire) during a period of uplift and erosion that continued until well into Silurian times. The Silurian strata succeed the Onnian unconformably.

Passing now to the Shelve area west of the Longmynd, Caradocian rocks exhibit marked differences when compared with the type area: the typical Caradoc Sandstone development has gone, and volcanics

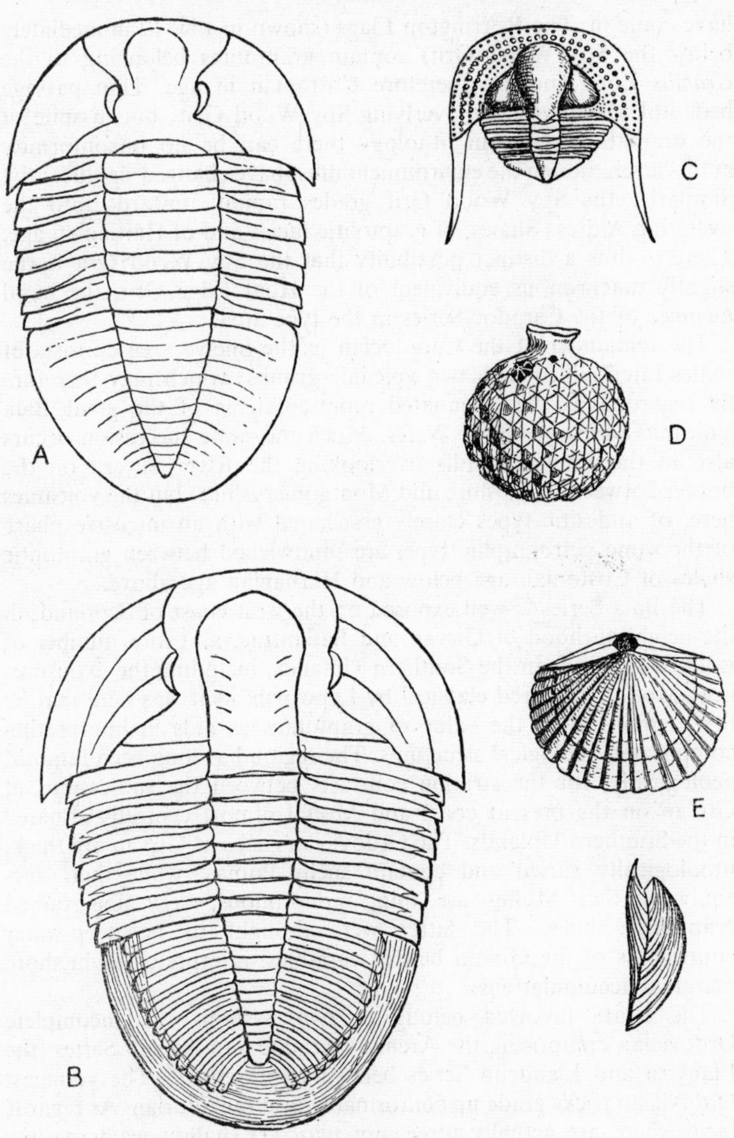


FIG. 17.

Fossils characteristic of the shelly facies of the Ordovician.

A. *Basilicus* (*Asaphus*), *tyrannus* Llandeilo Series.
B. *Ogygiocarella debuchi* (*Ogygia buchi*), Llandeilo Series.
C. *Onnia superba* (*Trinucleus concentricus*), Caradoc Series.
D. *Echinosphaera*, a cystid, Bala Series.
E. *Dinorthis* (*Orthis*) *flabellulum*, front and side views, Caradocian.

have come in. The Rorrington Flags (shown in Fig. 12 immediately below the Spy Wood Grit) contain graptolites belonging to the *Gracilis* Zone and are therefore Costonian in age. Thin passage beds link them with the overlying Spy Wood Grit; but in spite of the dramatic change in lithology there can be no unconformity at this level, though the environment must have changed significantly. Similarly, the Spy Wood Grit grades rapidly upwards into the overlying Aldress Shales, of graptolitic facies and of Harnagian age. There is thus a distinct possibility that the Spy Wood Grit is the slightly diachronous equivalent of the Hoar Edge Grit, the basal member of the Caradoc Series in the type area.

The remainder of the Caradocian in the Shelve area consists of shales interbedded with two volcanic groups[1] which may therefore be regarded as the attenuated representatives of the great Bala Volcanic Series of North Wales. Much the same succession occurs also in the Breidden Hills overlooking the River Severn on the border between Shropshire and Montgomeryshire; but the volcanics here, of andesitic types closely associated with an intrusive phase of the same petrographic type, are sandwiched between graptolitic shales of Costonian age below and Harnagian age above.

The Bala Series is well exposed on the west coast of Scotland, in the neighbourhood of Girvan and Ballantrae, and in a number of isolated outcrops in the Southern Uplands, including the exposures near Moffat, rendered classical by Lapworth, as it was here that he first demonstrated the value of graptolites as aids in interpreting complicated geological structures. The region has long been famous, geologically, for the striking contrasts between the successions at Girvan on the present coast and Moffat almost centrally situated in the Southern Uplands. The Ordovician rocks at Girvan are thick, lithologically varied and contain shelly faunas, while their age-equivalents at Moffat are thin, monotonous, very fine-grained graptolitic shales. The latter were thought to be deep-water equivalents of the Girvan belt of variables, interpreted as in-shore marginal accumulations.

The strata involved belong to two Systems: an incomplete Ordovician comprising the Arenig, Caradoc and Ashgill Series (the Llanvirn and Llandeilo Series being unrepresented). The youngest Ordovician rocks grade up conformably into the Silurian. As regards facies there are actually three, not two: (1) shallow-water neritic, (2) the axially situated graptolitic shales and (3) a very thick grey-

[1] These local divisions are shown, but not named, in Fig. 12. From top to bottom the beds shown are Whittery Shales immediately beneath the unconformity; Whittery Volcanic Group (oblique dashes); Hagley Volcanic Group (oblique dashes); Aldress Shales (ruled); Spy Wood Grit; *N. gracilis* Shales.

wacke suite, reaching 10,000 feet in thickness and situated between the other two.

Opinion is divided concerning the form of the Moffat geosyncline: one authority is impressed by its lack of symmetry, which may be more apparent than real as its southern margins are probably to be found in the Lake District, thirty miles southwards. Another

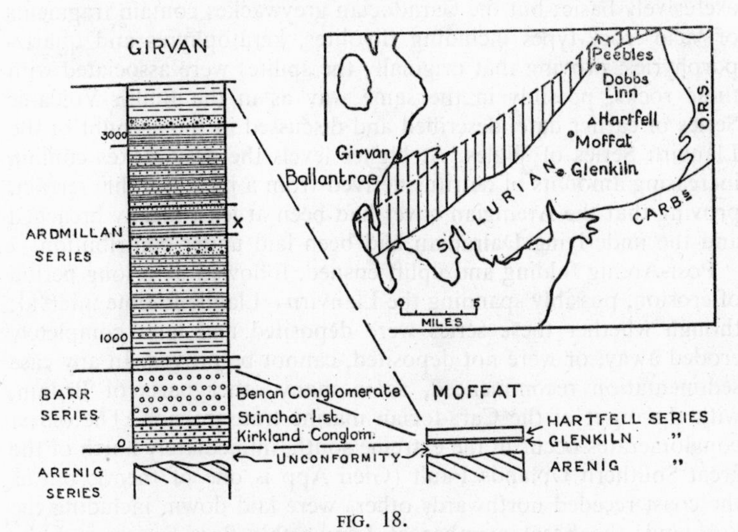


FIG. 18.

Sketch-map of the Southern Uplands of Scotland. Ordovician outcrop ruled vertically.

Vertical sections of the Bala Series at Girvan and Moffat, showing contrast in thickness and lithology.

Glenkiln *plus* Lower Hartfell = Caradocian; Upper Hartfell = Ashgillian. The X on right of Girvan column marks junction of Ashgillian with Caradocian.

The heavy projecting lines mark boundaries of the five groups into which Lapworth divided the Ardmillan Series.

Note the absence of Llanvirn and Llandeilo Series.

visualizes the geosyncline as comprising twin troughs along which currents flowed, carrying the sediment deposited as greywacke, and separated by an 'axial rise' on which only fine mud was deposited, entombing the abundant graptolites which crowd some of the bedding planes, testifying to the small amount of sediment available and to its slow rate of deposition.[1]

The Arenig Series consists largely of basic submarine lavas of spilitic type, termed the **Ballantrae Volcanic Series** and magnificently displayed in coastal sections. Nowhere else in Britain are spilitic

[1] Cf. George, T. N. and Walton, E. K. in *The British Caledonides*, 1963, pp. 9 and 89.

pillow lavas better displayed. They are associated with chert which has contributed generously to younger sedimentary rocks. Only rarely graptolitic mudstone is associated with the lavas, allowing their age to be proved. The Arenigian show little variation wherever they are exposed and give no hint of the contrasting facies exhibited by the overlying Caradocian. In the present outcrops the lavas are exclusively basic; but the Caradocian greywackes contain fragments of 'acid' rock-types including rhyolites, keratophyres and quartz-porphyries, proving that originally the spilites were associated with these rocks, possibly in the same way as in the Builth Volcanic Series of earlier date, described and discussed in the account of the Llanvirn Series of Wales. At higher levels the greywackes contain increasing amounts of detritus derived from a metamorphic terrain, proving that the Arenigian cover had been at least locally breached and the underlying Dalradian had been laid under contribution.

Post-Arenig folding and uplift ensued, followed by a long period of erosion, possibly spanning the Llanvirn—Llandeilo time interval; though whether these series were deposited and later completely eroded away, or were not deposited, cannot be proved. In any case sedimentation recommenced, as in many other parts of Britain, with the onset of the Caradocian marine transgression. The oldest conglomerates occur in the extreme south, immediately north of the great Southern Uplands Fault (Glen App is one of them); but as the coast receded northwards others were laid down, including the Kirkland, the basal member of Lapworth's Barr Series, and the Benan Conglomerate, well displayed in coastal sections. The Glen App Group is older than the Barr Series as defined by Lapworth; but that does not necessarily prove that they are of pre-Caradocian age, of course. Conglomerates occur at several levels in the Ardmillan Series also. All of these coarse-grained rocks are lenticular, interbedded with sandstone and greywackes into which they pass laterally. Some are wedge-shaped and are believed to have accumulated against submarine fault-scarps, which would account for the abnormally large boulders (up to 6 feet in diameter) which they contain.

Limestones are uncommon in this succession, but two occur in the Barr Series, the better known being the Stinchar Limestone, noteworthy for its varied fauna, which includes reef-builders—tabulate corals and algae, a notable contributor being the appropriately named *Girvanella*, together with foraminifera, large brachiopods, trilobites, gasteropods, cephalopods and lamellibranchs. Volcanic rocks of Caradocian age occur in a number of localities including the Tweed Valley and Bail Hill near Sanquhar, where the facies is andesitic. Elsewhere spilitic lavas occur which complicate the issue as formerly all lavas of this type were automatically regarded as belonging to the Arenig volcanic series. Consequently the various outcrops were thought to occur as inliers occupying the cores of anticlines. Now those which are Caradocian form synclinal outliers.

The Bala succession in the Girvan area was divided by Lapworth into two series, named Barr and Ardmillan, which unfortunately do not correspond with Caradocian and Ashgillian (see Fig. 18). Further, the graptolite-shale succession at Moffat was likewise divided into two—the Glenkiln and Hartfell Series; so that we have a wide choice of names for two intervals of geological time. At this stage nothing further need be said about the 'axial' facies nor about the greywackes; but both range up into the Silurian, and their interrelationship will be discussed in the next chapter.

The most impressive development of the Ordovician System occurs around **Murrisk in Co. Mayo, Ireland,** where the thickness of the combined Ordovician (36,000 feet) and incomplete Silurian (5600 feet) is over 41,000 feet, of which 17,000 belongs to the Arenig Series. This is much in excess of thicknesses of this Series recorded elsewhere and presents a picture of the Arenigian elsewhere in southern Scotland *before* the vast pre-Caradocian erosion. The lower part of the Arenig Series includes boulder slides (reminiscent of the well-known examples in the Rush Conglomerates of Carboniferous age near Balbriggan), turbidites and the inevitable black shales; while higher in the succession volcanic rocks become important, some of them flinty rhyolitic tuffs recalling those of the same age in the Dolgellau district in North Wales. Some of the tuffs are welded and are believed to have originated as *nuées ardentes* which flowed into the sea. The spilite—chert association, characteristic of the Arenig Series in other parts of Britain persisted into this part of Ireland, but in this locality is represented only by boulders in the local basal conglomerates.

In the English Lake District also the deposition of the Bala Series followed an episode of folding and deep erosion, so that the base of the series is unconformable to the volcanic rocks beneath. The equivalents of the Caradoc Series are the Coniston Limestone Series, the greater part of which, incidentally, is not limestone, but calcareous shales. Conglomerates, limestone, calcareous pyroclasts and, in the eastern part of the area, even a rhyolitic lava are also included, giving a maximum thickness of about 1000 feet. The **Ashgill Series** in the type area consists of poorly fossiliferous ashy shales with some limestones, some of which contain exceptionally large specimens of the straight-shelled nautiloid, *Orthoceras*. The highest Ashgillian limestone is followed conformably by a foot-thick Llandoverian limestone, succeeded by richly fossiliferous

Lower Silurian graptolitic shales. An extension of the area of sedimentation is proved by the fact that the Ashgillian oversteps the Caradocian on to older rocks, notably in inliers lying immediately north of the Craven Fault and in parts of Wales.

The general character of the Bala Series in South Wales is indicated in Fig. 15. After the deposition of the Llandeilo Flags the sea deepened and black graptolitic shales were laid down over a wide area in the south, and reach 500 feet in thickness. At the base and near the top impure limestones occur and indicate temporary clearing of the muddy water. The Ashgillian of South Wales consists chiefly of mudstones yielding an abundant shelly fauna in the more southerly parts of the country. The lowest portion is calcareous and varies from mudstone with calcareous nodules to a highly crinoidal limestone, the Bala Limestone of Fig. 15, the wavy line at the base of which is meant to indicate that locally some uplift along the Towy anticline took place, with erosion of the highest Caradocian rocks. Northwards the limestone gives place to mudstone.

The Bala of the main outcrops in South Wales pass under the Silurian rocks that occupy the greater part of Mid-Wales; but they are brought to the surface again in the cores of folds forming inliers at Plynlimon and near Llanidloes (Fig. 20). Here the beds assigned to the Bala are very thick and include massive grits. The lowest of the three divisions recognized contains *Dicellograptus anceps*, the index graptolite of the highest Ashgillian zone. The two higher divisions contain no graptolites; but as they are succeeded conformably by the lowest zone of the Silurian, they also must be Ashgillian.

Our final contrast is afforded by North Wales, where perhaps it is most appropriate to speak of the rocks as the Bala Series. In the hilly region of Snowdonia the series is largely volcanic: lava is piled on volcanic 'ash' to a total vertical thickness of more than a mile. Under the lavas and 'ashes' of Snowdon, lying in the midst of the grandest mountain scenery in the country, comes a group of unfossiliferous (and therefore undated) coarse-grained grits; and below these again, graptolitic shales belonging to the lowest zone of the Caradocian and the highest of the Llandeilian. Southward quieter conditions prevailed, and normal sedimentation resulted in the accumulation of thick marine clays, now the Bala Mudstones, which may reach as much as 8000 feet in thickness in the slate country south of Cader Idris. In this neighbourhood, about Corris, the beds have developed a strong cleavage, and quarrying for roofing slates is much in evidence. To the west, in the Dovey Valley, the mudstones and shales are graptolitic and thick. When traced eastwards through Bala and ultimately to the Berwyn Hills, changes take place: the thickness steadily decreases, graptolites give place to shelly fossils, and the grain becomes coarser, particularly towards the top of the succession where sandstones and even conglomerates come in. This foreshadows actual emergence of eastern North Wales in Ashgillian times. In North Wales, as in the south of the country, the water became sufficiently clear for limestone temporarily to replace the muddy sediments, thus providing an analogy with the Stinchar Limestone of Scotland and the Coniston Limestone of the Lake District. These widely distributed Bala Limestones have many faunal characters in common, though of course there are differences; but these are matters of detail which concern the palaeontologist. The importance of the rocks lies in the fact that they are really the first limestones of significant thickness and wide geographical extent that we have had occasion to describe, other than the Cambro-Ordovician dolomitic limestones of the North-West Highlands of Scotland. As a consequence, the shelly fossils of the arenaceous and argillaceous types are now joined by limestone-building creatures, including some corals whose names look more familiar in Silurian fossil lists, crinoids ('stone-lilies'), and the distantly related cystids.

Ordovician fossils were discovered many years ago in masses of quartzite which form conspicuous features of the coastal scenery of **South Cornwall,** especially in Veryan Bay and Gorran Haven near Mevagissey. They are termed the Veryan Series and were originally thought to include a volcanic series consisting of spilitic pillow lavas, tuffs and agglomerates comparable with the Ordovician pillow lavas so well exposed on the Girvan coast. It has been shown, however, that although the quartzites are Ordovician, the associated volcanic suite is of Upper Devonian age and correlated with the pillow lavas of the same age exposed at Pentire Point near Padstow in North Cornwall.

The quartzites were dated in 1906 by the discovery in them of Caradocian fossils including trilobites and brachiopods. Among the latter is a form identified as *Orthis altera* Barrande which others would name *Orthis budleighensis* Davidson. The admittedly meagre fauna suggests a closer comparison with the Grès de May in 'Armorica' (Normandy and Brittany) rather than with other British rocks of the same age.

### THE VOLCANIC FACIES

One aspect of the Ordovician remains for consideration. An outstanding feature of the period was widespread volcanic activity, of which there is abundant evidence on several different levels. In some cases the lavas and pyroclasts are closely associated with graptolitic shale, so that there can be no doubt that the eruptions were submarine. This conclusion is confirmed by the frequency with which the spilitic lavas show well-developed *pillow structure* as on the Girvan coast at Ballantrae, on Cader Idris in North Wales and in the Kilbride Peninsula in Ireland. In other localities there is reason for believing that volcanic cones, built up from the sea-floor, eventually rose as volcanic islands above the Ordovician seas. Volcanic activity commenced in the Arenig Period, in North and South Wales, in

DOLGELLEY-ARENIG
SNOWDON
SHROPSHIRE
LAKES
ASHGILLIAN
CARADOCIAN
LLANDEILIAN
LLANVIRNIAN
ARENIGIAN
A
B
C

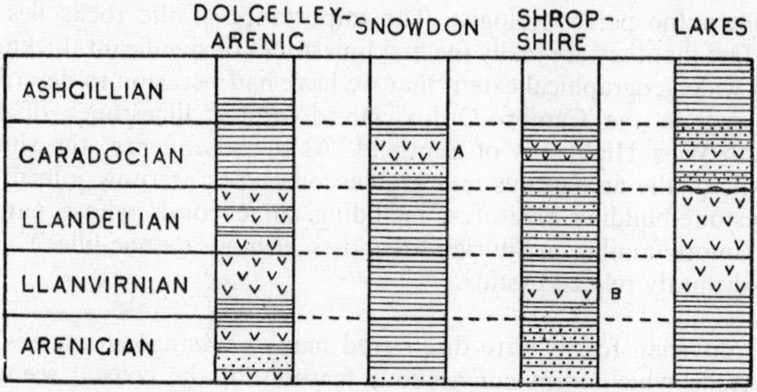

FIG. 19.
Diagram showing the volcanic horizons in the Ordovician of parts of North Wales, Shropshire and the Lake District.
Volcanic facies, – – – v v v; graptolitic, ruled; shelly, dotted.
A. Main Snowdonian Volcanic Series.
B. Stapeley Volcanic Series.
C. Borrowdale Volcanic Series.

South Scotland and Western Ireland and appears to have become most general in the time of the tuning-fork graptolites (Fig. 19): the Llanvirn Series is largely volcanic in North and South Wales, in Shropshire and in the Lake District, and these regions owe their scenic beauty to the resistance offered to denudation by the volcanic rocks and by the associated intrusions. These volcanoes maintained a more or less active existence throughout the Llanvirn and Llandeilo Periods before becoming finally extinct. By contrast in Ireland volcanic rocks of this age are feebly represented.

To the south of the Harlech Dome, Ordovician igneous rocks form the rugged hilly country, culminating in the Cader Idris range stretching from the sea to Dolgellau. To the east the escarpments continue through the Aran Mountains, the highest in Merionethshire, which link up through lesser hills with the Arenig mountain block.

The highest volcanic rocks plunge steeply under the overlying Bala Mudstones, and there is no more striking topographical contrast in the country than that between the bare, rocky and often precipitous volcanic mountains, and the much lower, smooth, grass-covered and cultivated hills occupied by the mudstones. The lowest mudstones contain the same graptolite fauna as the shales immediately *above* the Llandeilo Flags and Limestones in the type locality, proving that the volcanoes here became extinct at the close of Llandeilo time.

We have already noted that volcanic activity was renewed in some localities in Caradocian times. In the main Ordovician outcrop in the Shelve country west of the Longmynd, volcanic rocks of this age are feebly represented; they appear on a more extensive scale in the Breidden Hills on the Shropshire-Montgomery border, probably in the Southern Uplands; but they are nowhere so well developed as in Snowdonia. The main Snowdonian Volcanic Series, which builds Snowdon itself, lies well above graptolitic Bala Mudstones, yielding the same fauna (the N. *gracilis* fauna) as that obtained from the mudstones *above* the volcanics of Merionethshire.

In general, volcanic activity was more widespread and on a more impressive scale in Ireland than elsewhere in the British Isles during Caradocian and Ashgillian times. This is particularly true of the several inliers in Central Ireland and in the Leinster massif: from Pomeroy in the north to about the latitude of Dublin Ordovician volcanic rocks form important features, for example around Balbriggan, where 5000 feet of andesitic lavas and tuffs occur. In the main these volcanics are Caradocian; but locally eruptions occurred as early as the Llanvirnian and persisted into the Ashgillian. Although the details are imperfectly known, what is evidently an outstanding display of rhyolites including spherulitic, fluxional and massive types showing well-developed columnar structure occurs in South-East Ireland, reaching the coast in Waterford and attaining a thickness of 8000 feet in Co. Wexford. The rhyolites are associated with an extraordinary variety of intrusive igneous rocks ranging from ultrabasic picrites to acid microgranites and quartz-porphyries.

Attention has been directed in this chapter to many contrasts in the Ordovician rocks of different localities, and in their topographical expression. There is yet one more: from the summits of the mountains of Snowdonia, Anglesey can be seen spread out like a map. The island is largely a plateau at about 200 feet above sea-level. Ordovician rocks cross the island; but although within sight of the most spectacular display of volcanic rocks of this age in the country, there are no Ordovician volcanic rocks in Anglesey; with the exception of the Arenigian beach deposits already referred to, the whole of the Ordovician succession here consists of graptolitic shale.

Several different styles of volcanic activity are represented among these rocks, while the materials of which they are composed also vary widely. Commonly 'acid' and 'basic' lavas and tuffs are closely associated; but around certain centres of activity 'intermediate' magma is represented, for example by the essentially andesitic lavas of the Lake District and Shropshire. Of rather special interest are the basic (spilitic) pillow lavas representing submarine eruptions. The 'pillows' are associated with chert or hardened mudstone, in the latter case representing the soft mud of the ocean-floor on to which the lava was erupted. Ordovician submarine pillow lavas are magnificently displayed on the Scottish coast near Ballantrae (Arenigian), and in the Cader Idris range in North Wales where they form a special phase of the widespread Llanvirnian-Llandeilian volcanic episode.

Summarily, Ordovician volcanoes were spasmodically active somewhere or other in the British Isles region through almost the whole Period; but the centres of activity shifted from time to time. In all areas but one the volcanic rocks make up a part of the succession only: the lavas and pyroclasts belonging to the several volcanic phases are interbedded with normal marine sediments representing periods of quiescence. In the Lake District, however, the Borrowdale volcanoes, which became active during the Lower Llanvirn, persisted while an unbroken succession of lavas and pyroclasts accumulated to a total thickness of 10,000 feet. This is a minimum figure as the top of the volcanic pile coincides with an erosion interval of unknown duration, but terminated by the Caradocian marine incursion. By contrast, Llanvirn-Llandeilo volcanics are virtually absent from Ireland and southern Scotland, though in both areas volcanoes were active in Arenig and Caradocian times as detailed above.

The coarser grades of pyroclasts (the products of explosive volcanic eruptions), are readily recognized in the field; but those of finer grain are more difficult to identify accurately. Some can closely resemble the corresponding type of lava. Within recent years a variety termed *welded tuff* has been shown to be of wide distribution. Some welded tuffs look very much like flow-banded rhyolites in which dark lenticles and streaks are embedded in a lighter coloured matrix. There is no doubt that many such rocks have been regarded as lava flows; but this makes no difference to the general picture so far as historical geology is concerned: the important fact is that there were volcanic eruptions of a particular kind of magma in that place, at that time. The form of the eruptions and whether the lava was quietly erupted from a vent or completely disrupted by vent explosions is a detail of concern to petrologists only. We are not concerned with the details of the processes involved in the production of welded tuffs; but some explanation of the term is necessary. It is widely believed that a welded tuff represents a *nuée ardente* produced during an eruption of the violently explosive Peléean type. The resulting individual 'fragments' of fluid lava were pressed into the form of thin, flat discs while they were still intensely hot and plastic, the whole being 'welded' into a coherent mass of rhyolite as solid as a normal rhyolitic lava flow.

It has been shown that in several British localities where rhyolitic eruptives occur, some welded tuffs are included. This is true for example, of the Snowdonian Volcanics and the Borrowdale Volcanic Series, and will probably be found to be the case wherever magma of this composition was available. It is widely believed that *nuées ardentes* are produced only by subaereal volcanoes; but nobody can know for certain what would be the equivalent of a welded tuff in the case of a submarine eruption. Welded tuffs at Murrisk in Co. Mayo are believed to have been formed during subaereal eruptions, but to have flowed into the sea: the sudden quenching did not prevent the development of the distinguishing features by which they can be identified. This suggests that the same thing might happen in the case of a submarine eruption. The lowest volcanics of the Borrowdale Series must have been erupted under submarine conditions, for they rest directly on Llanvirnian graptolitic shales; some of the tuffs are current bedded indicating deposition under water; but some of the rhyolites are welded tuffs. Do they indicate that the volcano or volcanoes had built themselves up so as to emerge as volcanic islands like Teneriffe or Hawaii?

## REFERENCES

The British Regional Geologies of North Wales; South Wales; Welsh Borderlands; Southern Uplands of Scotland; North-West Highlands.

Papers on selected subjects:

BASSETT, D. A., GEORGE, T. N. and others in the appropriate chapters in *The British Caledonides* (1963).

BULMAN, O. M. B. Presidential address on 'Lower Palaeozoic Plankton,' *Q.J.G.S.*, **120** (1964), 455.

DEAN, W. T. 'Faunal succession in the Caradoc Series of South Shropshire,' *Bull. Brit. Mus.* (Nat. Hist.), **3**, no. 6 (1958).

DEWEY, J. F. 'The Lower Palaeozoic stratigraphy of central Murrisk, Co. Mayo . . .,' *Q.J.G.S.*, **119** (1963), 313.

JONES, O. T., and PUGH, W. J. 'An early Ordovician Shoreline in Radnorshire near Builth Wells,' *Q.J.G.S.*, **105** (1949), 65.

OLIVER, R. L. 'Welded tuffs in the Borrowdale Volcanic Series . . . and in Wales,' *Geol. Mag.*, **91** (1954), 473.

MITCHELL, G. H. 'Ordovician volcanoes,' *Adv. of Sci.*, **14** (1957), 34.

RAST, N., BEAVON, R. V., and FITCH, F. J. 'Subaerial volcanicity in Snowdonia,' *Nature*, **181** (1958), 508.

WELLS, A. K., and M. K. *Petrology of the Igneous Rocks* (Geo. Allen & Unwin), for account of Ordovician igneous activity.

WHITTARD, W. F. 'A geology of South Shropshire,' *Proc. Geol. Assoc.*, **63** (1952).

WILLIAMS, A. 'The Barr and Ardmillan Series (Caradoc) in the Girvan district,' *Mem. Geol. Soc. London*, **3** (1962).

WILLIAMS, H. 'Snowdon district,' *Q.J.G.S.*, **83** (1927), 346.

## CHAPTER IV

# THE SILURIAN PERIOD

IN certain broad aspects the Silurian resembles the Ordovician System, but there are strong contrasts also: both Systems are entirely marine, both exhibit marked lateral variations in lithology and fauna. But whereas vulcanicity, extensive both in time and space, provided the keynote to Ordovician geological history, the volcanic forces had spent themselves before the close of Bala times, and except for very local sporadic outbursts, for example in the Mendip Hills area, in early Silurian times, this Period was free from volcanic phenomena.

More than half the surface of Wales, two-thirds of the Southern Uplands and a considerable belt of country in the southern part of the English Lake District are occupied by the existing outcrops of Silurian rocks, as well as numerous small inliers brought to the surface by folding and faulting. Silurian rocks originally covered much of Ireland except the extreme north-west and south-east. Existing outcrops include part of the Dingle Peninsula, various inliers rising through the Carboniferous cover in the Central Plain and significant areas structurally corresponding with the Southern Uplands and Midland Valley of Scotland.

The type-area, Siluria, where Murchison first worked out the succession and the broad structural plan, is the Welsh Borderland country where the ancient tribe, the Silures, under the leadership of Caradoc, withstand the Roman invasion. It includes the part of Shropshire that contains the picturesque towns of Wenlock and Ludlow, which give their names to important divisions of the System. Originally there were three series; subsequently additions to, and modifications of, Murchison's scheme of classification were deemed necessary; but there is much to be said for returning to the simple tripartite division into:

3. Ludlow Series, or Ludlovian.
2. Wenlock Series, or Wenlockian.
1. Llandovery Series, or Llandoverian.

To rocks of Llandoverian age, but of graptolitic facies, Lapworth applied the term Valentian, at a time when it was thought that the typical rocks at Llandovery included only part of the series. It has been demonstrated, however, that all three divisions are, in fact, represented in the type-area. The terms Llandoverian and Valentian are therefore completely synonymous, and one is superfluous. On the grounds of priority, the series should be called Llandoverian: there is little justification for retaining Valentian, though it is still widely used.

Again, the terms Wenlockian and Ludlovian were first applied in a region where the strata are of shelly facies. Elsewhere they are of graptolitic facies, and on lithological grounds there is no need to separate the two. Further, although a full succession of graptolite zones has been established in this argillaceous development, the exact equivalence of the original Wenlock and Ludlow Series in terms of these zones is still somewhat uncertain. Therefore it is reasonable to use the name Salopian (from Salop, the postal contraction for Shropshire) for the combined Wenlockian-Ludlovian.

In the account which follows, the Llandoverian rocks are described first in the type-area, then they are traced into other parts of the country, the purpose being to build up a picture of the geographical conditions obtaining during their formation. In a later part of the chapter the Wenlockian and Ludlovian are described together as a matter of convenience.

The **Llandovery Series.**—The type-area lies in Carmarthenshire, South Wales (Fig. 20), where the succession was worked out by O. T. Jones. Approximately 4000 feet of beds are included. A basal group follows the Bala Series quite conformably, and includes dark shales with sandstones and some conglomerate bands. The main part of the succession consists of grey mudstones which include more and more sand in the higher beds. The fauna consists chiefly of brachiopods and trilobites, but there are also numerous graptolites which have made accurate correlation possible. Sedimentation was not continuous, for the series is broken by unconformities at two levels, and these automatically split the succession into three Stages, Lower, Middle and Upper. The break between the Middle and Upper is the more important, and is recognizable in several other parts of the Borderlands, Wales and Ireland.

To the west and north of the type-area the greater part of Mid-Wales is occupied by Llandoverian strata; but the thickness is much greater than at Llandovery. Over most of this large area the Llandoverian is a vast mudstone formation, with increasing quantities of sand and pebbles, brought in from the west, in higher beds which are greywackes. In some places, however, the highest part of the series consists of maroon and green shales of distinctive appearance. The country about Plynlimon is specially significant in the study of the Silurian, as the contrasts with the the type-succession are so striking. The thickness of the Llandoverian at Llanidloes is

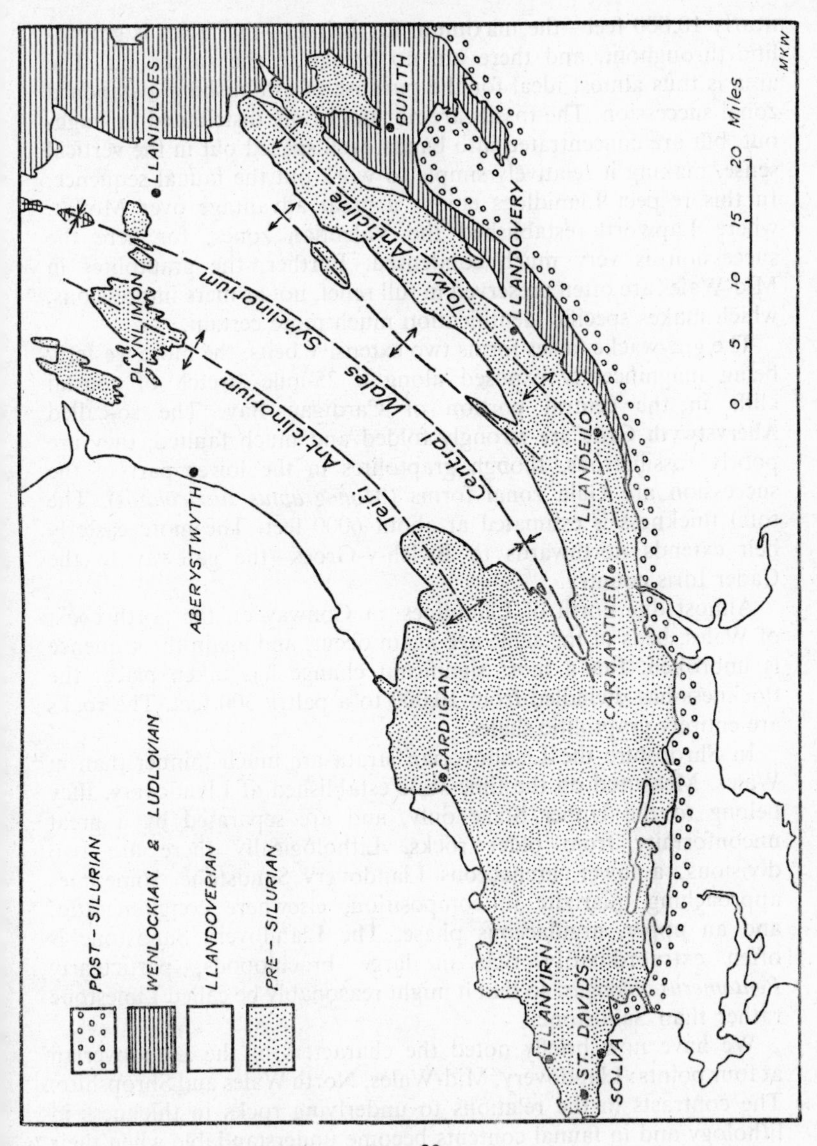


FIG. 20.

Map showing the main Caledonian folding in South Wales. Note the unconformable overstep of the Llandoverian and Ordovician by the Wenlockian, and of all these rocks by the Old Red Sandstone.

nearly 10,000 feet—the maximum for Britain—the facies is graptolitic throughout, and there are no breaks in the succession. The area is thus almost ideal for the purpose of establishing a standard zonal succession. The fossils are not uniformly distributed throughout, but are concentrated into bands, well spaced out in the vertical sense, making it relatively simple to work out the faunal sequence. In this respect Llanidloes enjoys a great advantage over Moffat, where Lapworth established the Valentian zones, for here the succession is very much condensed. Further, the graptolites in Mid-Wales are often preserved in full relief, not as mere impressions, which makes specific identification much more certain.

The greywacke facies forms two extensive belts, the more westerly being magnificently exposed along a 25-mile stretch of coastal cliffs in the central portion of Cardigan Bay. The so-called **Aberystwyth Grits** are strongly folded and much faulted, they are poorly fossiliferous, though graptolites in the lower part of the succession are Gala zonal forms (*Monograptus turriculatus*). The total thickness is estimated at about 6000 feet. The more easterly belt extends northwards to Bwlch-y-Groes—the gateway to the Cader Idris country.

Almost due north of Llanidloes, at Conway on the north coast of Wales, beds of the same age again occur, and again the sequence is unbroken. But a most significant change has taken place: the thickness has dwindled from 10,000 to a paltry 300 feet. The rocks are entirely graptolitic shales.

In Shropshire the Llandoverian strata are much thinner than in Wales. Measured on the time-scale established at Llandovery, they belong to the Upper Stage only, and are separated by a great unconformity from older rocks. Lithologically there are two divisions: a lower, arenaceous Llandovery Sandstone, sometimes approaching quartzite in composition, elsewhere conglomeratic; and an upper, argillaceous phase. The Llandovery Sandstone is often extraordinarily rich in large brachiopods, particularly *Pentamerus oblongus*, so that it might reasonably be called Limestone rather than Sandstone.

We have now briefly noted the characters of the Llandoverian at four points: Llandovery, Mid-Wales, North Wales and Shropshire. The contrasts in the relations to underlying rocks in thickness in lithology and in faunal contents become understandable when their geographical positions in relation to the Silurian Sea are realized. Mid-Wales was then remote from the coast, and out of reach of the influence of slight changes in the relative levels of sea and land. As a natural consequence, sedimentation went on without interruption over a very long period of time—through the Bala and Llandovery periods. The area must have been steadily sinking to accommodate such a vast amount of sediment; but that silting-up was gaining on sinking of the trough is proved by the incoming of coarser material, including small pebbles, even at Llanidloes, in the higher beds. In the same period of time Conway received a meagre supply of sediment that was spread out thinly over the sea-floor in these parts. Criccieth, on the south coast of peninsular Carnarvonshire, where the Lower Llandoverian is again very thin (a matter of 60 feet or so), and graptolitic, lay also in the zone of minimum thickness, which is inferred to have coincided with the axial zone of the geosyncline.

The conditions were very different at Llandovery, where shallow-water, in-shore conditions prevailed. In such areas there is a delicate balance between sedimentation and erosion: a slight change of sea-level would be sufficient to raise some portions of the sea floor

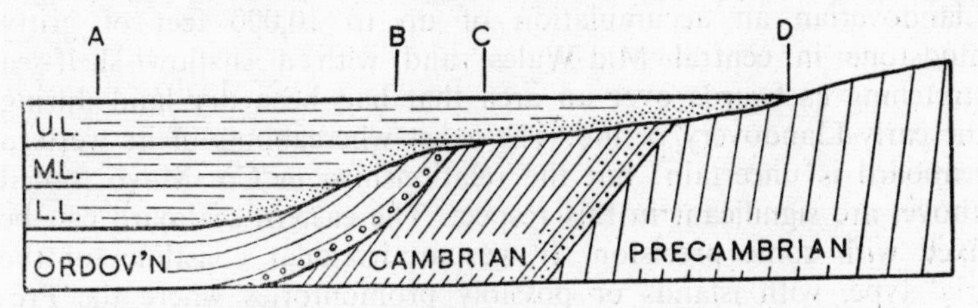


FIG. 21.

Diagram showing the general relations between the Llandoverian and pre-Silurian rocks in the Welsh Borderlands.

At 'A' the Silurian rest *conformably* on the Ordovician rocks; at 'B' the former succeed the latter *unconformably*. Between 'C' and 'D' the Upper Llandovery beds only are present. 'D' marks the 'featheredge' of the Llandoverian.

to within reach of wave-action, or even to elevate it above sea-level. In either case, erosion and redistribution of the recently deposited sediment would take place, and a break in the succession would occur. Such breaks, as we have seen, separate the Lower from the Middle, and the latter from the Upper Llandoverian; they prove emergence at two periods, followed in each case by readvance of the sea, and renewal of sedimentation. The second, and by far the more important, readvance carried the sea far to the eastward over a coastal area of low relief, that had been dry land since the emergence towards the close of the Ordovician Period. The area thus submerged by the Upper Llandoverian Sea included parts, but by no means all, of Shropshire, where the shallow-water arenaceous phase was followed, as the sea deepened, by the argillaceous phase. This is the relationship of overlap, of course, and its general characters are shown in diagram form in Fig. 21. The overstep of older rocks by the Llandoverian in Shropshire is indicated on the map, Fig. 14. Actually in this relationship far more than mere marginal overlap is involved (see p. 151). The mirror-image relationship to that seen in Shropshire is encountered in western Pembrokeshire, South Wales, where near Haverfordwest the second readvance carried Upper Llandoverian sediment on to Precambrian igneous rock. Further evidence of the wide extent of the submergence beneath the Upper Llandovery sea is forthcoming in western Ireland where in Co. Mayo the basal member of the Silurian succession is an attenuated Upper Llandoverian, resting unconformably on folded Ordovician strata and overstepping on to Dalradian.

Thus far we have established the existence of a deep gulf or geosyncline occupying the site of Wales and the Welsh Borderlands, with Conway a point on its axis, with already at the close of the Llandoverian an accumulation of up to 10,000 feet of gritty mudstone in central Mid-Wales, and with a shallow shelf-sea stretching eastwards over an area that had been dry land during the early-Llandovery period. The exact whereabouts of its western seaboard is uncertain: but the relationships in Co. Mayo, noted above, are significant in this respect. The eastern seaboard can be fixed with some precision. It was an irregular coastline, of the 'ria' type, with islands or possibly promontories where the Precambrian uplands now occur—the Longmynd, the Caradoc Hills, the Wrekin and farther south, the Malvern Hills. Careful mapping of the boundary of the Llandoverian against the Longmynd has brought to light long-shore features of the Silurian coastline, including the bases of sea-stacks (the latter have themselves long since disappeared), shingle beaches and sand-spits, which give a fascinating glimpse of the local geographical details of this 'island'. Upper Llandovery beach deposits containing large wave-worn boulders are banked against a cliff-like feature of Malvernian (Precambrian) gneiss exposed in a quarry in the Malvern Hills. This fixes another point on the coastline of the Llandoverian Sea.

The Upper Llandoverian shelf-sea spread far beyond Shropshire, however, for inliers protrude through the cover of newer rocks at a number of points in the English Midlands, notably round the margins of the South Staffs. coalfield. For example, at Rubery, beyond the southern outskirts of Birmingham, Upper Llandovery rocks of arenaceous facies, the Rubery Sandstone, with a characteristic fauna of large brachiopods, is succeeded by an argillaceous facies, the Rubery Shale, as in Shropshire. Indirect evidence of the former wide extent of this Midland sheet is afforded by the occurrence at many points of blocks of these Llandoverian rocks in the red breccias of Carboniferous and New Red Sandstone age. But the sea did not extend much farther eastward: for at Nuneaton the Coal Measures rest directly on Cambrian rocks. A similar relationship has been proved in other places in the East Midlands, and here we have evidently passed over the coast on to the Midland land-mass. Although the evidence is necessarily scanty, some idea of the extent of this landmass may be obtained from the fact that Silurian rocks have been proved by borings to underlie parts of Hertfordshire and Kent, where Llandoverian of graptolitic facies occurs.

To complete the picture it is now necessary to pass north to Scotland and the English Lake District. The nature of the evidence in the **Southern Uplands** can best be appreciated by comparing the successions at Girvan and Moffat. As in Upper Ordovician times, Moffat must have been situated in the axial zone of the geosyncline; the beds are graptolitic throughout, of very fine grain and of minimum thickness. The Lower Llandovery beds form a continuation of the Ordovician graptolitic shales and mudstones (the Glenkiln-Hartfell succession), and form the Gala Group of Lapworth. The three formations together constitute the Moffat Shales which form a single lithological unit, spanning the important Ordovician-Silurian boundary. The Silurian part of the Moffat Shales was laid down under the same conditions as the Ordovician part; there is no trace of discordance between the two, though there are striking differences between the graptolite faunas of the two parts. At the type-locality of Dobb's Linn the Silurian Moffat Shales are about 100 feet in thickness. They do not contain a single biserial graptolite of the types which characterize the Ordovician shales below; but *Monograptus* and *Rastrites* swarm in all but the lowest layers. These graptolitic shales pass laterally into rocks of the thick shelly facies towards Girvan, exactly as in the Ordovician rocks below; but what is far more significant, they are succeeded by rocks of the same type—flags, grits, greywackes, conglomerates—indeed the rocks of the Moffat district at this level become even coarser than their equivalents to the north-west. The inference is obvious, particularly when it is taken into account that the whole of the Llandoverian is graptolitic shale in the Lake District and south-westwards in Denbighshire where the evidence fails: the geosyncline, as such, had ceased to exist at Moffat: it was in the process of being silted up by a great influx of coarse sediment from the north-east.

Silurian rocks form the southern belt in the Lower Palaeozoic inlier of the **Lake District,** where they follow the Ashgillian conformably. The Llandoverian consists of some 250 feet of beds, the greater part of which belongs to the Upper Llandoverian. The lower division, the Skelgill Beds, are black graptolitic shales with some interbedded nodular mudstones; while the higher division, the Browgill Beds, are greenish, sometimes maroon, shales, with black graptolitic layers and, in the higher parts, some bands of grit—the forerunners of the vast flood of coarse detritus that spread into the area later. To the fossil-collector these Skelgill and Browgill beds are particularly satisfying on account of the richness of their graptolite fauna, and large collections of species of *Monograptus*,

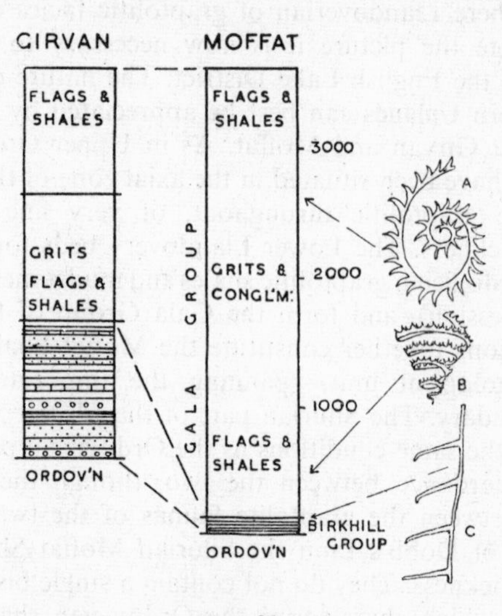


FIG. 22.

Comparative sections of the Llandovery Series at Girvin and Moffat. The graptolites illustrated are:

A. *Monograptus convolutus.*
B. *Monograptus turriculatus.*
C. *Rastrites maximus.*

*Rastrites*, and such biserial forms as *Dimorphograptus* and *Climacograptus* may readily be obtained. Some of the graptolites are of special interest as they are preserved in full relief.

Brief reference may be made to the occurrence of early-Silurian rocks well to the east of the Lake District, on the western flank of the Mid-Pennines, particularly at Austwick. Here in the neighbourhood of the Craven Faults (Fig. 47) an inlier of Lower Palaeozoic rocks has been formed by the denudation of the cover of nearly horizontal Lower Carboniferous rocks. The Upper Llandoverian is thick and incomplete through nonsequences in the succession. It occupies a position relative to the Lake District analogous to that of Shropshire and Mid-Wales and there is little doubt that the parallelism can be carried the logical step farther, and the presence of a land-mass, probably of Precambrian rocks (like the Ingletonian on which the Caradocian here rest), lay at no great distance to the east.

There is no doubt whatever that the Lake District, Wales and the Welsh Borderlands were parts of one basin: the fact is proved by

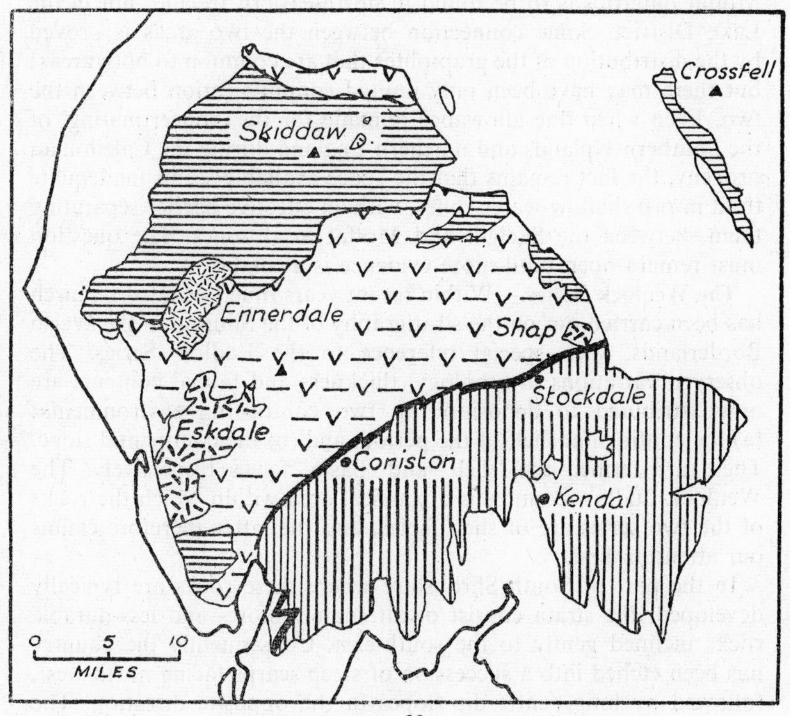


FIG. 23.

Sketch-map of the Lower Palaeozoic Inlier of the English Lake District. (For clarity the lakes themselves are omitted.)

Silurian, vertical ruling; Coniston Limestone Group, black; Borrowdale Volcanic Group, -v-; Skiddaw Slate Group, horizontal ruling. The granites at Skiddaw, Eskdale and Shap, and the Ennerdale granophyre, short oblique dashes.

the successive graptolite faunas common to all three areas (within the limits imposed by differences in lithology), and by one striking piece of lithological evidence. In the Lake District a quarter-inch green layer—the famous 'green streak'—occurs in an eight-inch band of graptolitic shales. Similarly in Mid-Wales a one-inch green layer occurs in a twelve-inch graptolitic black-shale band. Both layers contain the same fauna, and constitute the *Monograptus argenteus* Band.

There is an element of doubt, however, as to whether or not the Southern Uplands were directly connected with the Lake District. It is tempting to argue that the axis of the trough must lie on the line connecting the places of minimum thickness of Llandoverian rocks—Conway, Skelgill and Moffat. But the continuation of the Moffat outcrops is to be found in north-eastern Ireland, not in the Lake District. Some connection between the two areas is proved by the distribution of the graptolites that are common to both areas; but there may have been only limited communication between the two. Even when due allowance is made for the 'concertina-ing' of the Southern Uplands and northern England during the Caledonian orogeny, the fact remains that the space available seems inadequate to fit in *two* shallow-water zones, with an effective barrier separating them, between the Skelgill and Moffat axial zones. The question must remain open until more evidence is available.

**The Wenlock Series.**—Within recent years much detailed research has been carried out on the stratigraphy of the Silurian in the Welsh Borderlands, with special reference to the Ludlow Series. The observed variations in lithology, thickness and faunal contents are now attributed to deposition in two contrasting environments: (a) the continental shelf of the period, and (b) the continental slope. These are termed the 'shelf' and 'basin' facies respectively. The Wenlock-Ludlow country is a classical area within which the rocks of the two series are of shelf facies, and the latter therefore claims our attention first.

In the part of South Shropshire where these rocks are typically developed, the strata consist of alternately more- and less-durable rocks inclined gently to the south-east. Consequently the country has been etched into a succession of steep scarps facing north-west, followed by long gentle dip-slopes in the opposite direction. The scarps are the local 'edges' such as Wenlock Edge, Benthal Edge and View Edge. The softer rocks occupy strike-vales between. The first and most westerly of the scarps is determined by the arenaceous facies of the Llandoverian, while the first strike-valley is occupied by the argillaceous Llandoverian and the lowest member of the Wenlockian, the **Wenlock Shales.** The latter are indifferently exposed except on the banks of the Severn near Buildwas, where they contain a rich fauna of small brachiopods, *Dicoelosia* (*Bilobites*) *biloba* (Fig. 25) being a characteristic form. This is regarded as a stunted 'facies-fauna'—that is, one which, for no immediately obvious reason, was so influenced by local adverse conditions that all its members were dwarfed. The shales, which may be 1000 feet thick, become more calcareous upwards, and there is a passage into the overlying **Wenlock Limestone,** probably the best-known of all the

Silurian rocks. It forms the prominent scarp-feature of Wenlock Edge which maintains its character for some twenty miles along the strike. It has been most extensively quarried for use as a flux in the iron industry and has been burned locally for lime—most of the quarries have their lime-kilns. The Wenlock Limestone is also well known to geologists as a repository of well-preserved fossils in amazing variety. Many of the slabs are veritable fossil graveyards, crowded with the remains of many different types of organisms, among which brachiopods, corals, stromatoporoids and trilobites are noteworthy, though lamellibranchs, bryozoans and crinoids are

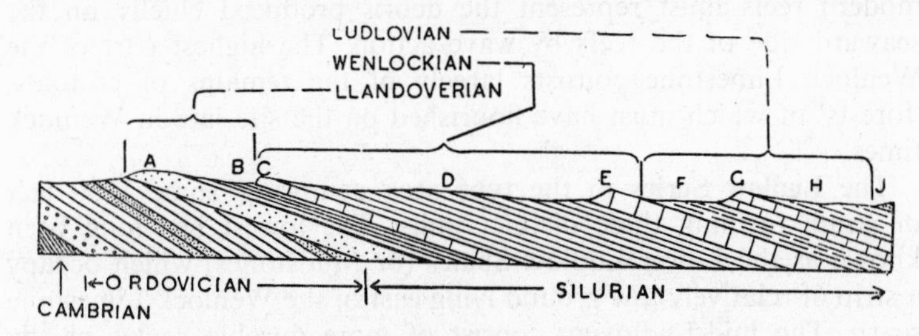


FIG. 24.

Diagram-section showing the complete Silurian succession in the Welsh Borderlands.

Note the unconformities at the base of the Silurian and base of the Ordovician.

A. Arenaceous phase of the Llandovery Series.
B. Argillaceous phase of the Llandovery Series.
C. Woolhope Limestone (in the Woolhope Dome-Malvern country only—not in Shropshire).
D. Wenlock Shale.
E. Wenlock Limestone—forming Wenlock Edge.
F. Lower Ludlow Beds.
G. Aymestry Limestone, forming View (or Weo) Edge.
H. Upper Ludlow Beds.
J. Downtonian Series of Devonian.

also abundant. Brachiopods in particular are represented by hosts of individuals belonging to many genera and species, and this branch of the animal kingdom reached the acme of its development at this time. Probably the most common type is *Atrypa reticularis*, though *Leptaena rhomboidalis* is also characteristic. By contrast, trilobites are less varied and less numerous than in the Ordovician, though in the Wenlock Limestone specimens of beautifully preserved trilobites with shining black carapaces are not uncommon. The most typical of the Wenlockian species, and probably the best known of all trilobites, is *Calymene blumenbachi* (Fig. 25). The most significant fossils, however, are the corals. Many of these occur in the position of growth, embedded in massive unstratified lenticular limestones ('ballstones'), which from their form, structure and fauna are regarded as patch reefs. The corals include rugose types,[1] such as '*Omphyma*' (Fig. 25) and tabulate such as *Favosites* and *Halysites*. If, as seems probable, these Silurian corals lived under the same conditions as their modern representatives, it is reasonable to conclude that the Silurian Sea was here less than 30 fathoms in depth, and the water-temperature was above 20° C. or about 70° F. Further, muddy sediment was excluded from the area where the reefs were forming. The reef-limestones pass laterally into thin-bedded limestones containing overturned, fragmental corals and many other types of fossils, and by comparison with modern reefs must represent the debris produced chiefly on the seaward side of the reefs by wave action. The highest part of the Wenlock Limestone consists largely of the remains of crinoids, 'forests' of which must have flourished on the site late in Wenlock times.

The **Ludlow Series** in the type area comprises some 1350 feet of strata forming three distinct units. The lowest has long been known as the Lower Ludlow Shales (or Mudstones) which occupy a strip of relatively low ground lying east of the Wenlock Limestone scarp. The mid-Ludlovian consist of more durable rocks, chiefly massive limestones termed Aymestry Limestone by Murchison well over a century ago. It forms a prominent scarp, extending for twenty-five miles along the strike, and at its best over-topping the Wenlock feature. The Upper Ludlow beds are lithologically similar to the Lower, but tend to be more flaggy and constitute the Whitcliffe Flags.

Superimposed on this broad classification based on lithology and topographic expression is another, much newer, into Stages. There are four of them, bearing locality-names. The lowest stage, the Eltonian, is subdivided into Lower, Middle and Upper. The other three are each divided into Lower and Upper, giving a total of nine sub-stages of equal status, defined in terms of their brachiopod faunas as developed in the 'shelf area'. So far this detailed classification has not extended to actual zoning, so there are no brachiopod zonal indices; but although the rocks are of shelf facies, dominantly shelly, graptolites occur in sufficient numbers to enable correlation with the sequence of graptolite zones established many years ago in the Welsh Borderlands, and which are applicable, of course, to the basin facies also. The boundaries between the stages do not correspond with those between the graptolite zones.

[1] Palaeozoic corals belong either to the *Rugosa*—single or compound corals with wrinkled (rugose) walls and well-developed radially arranged vertical plates named *septa*; or to the *Tabulata*—compound corals in the tube-like skeletons of which are numerous closely-spaced horizontal plates called *tabulae*.

The Eltonian, synonymous with Lower Ludlovian, is by far the thickest of the four Stages and consists of a monotonous series of

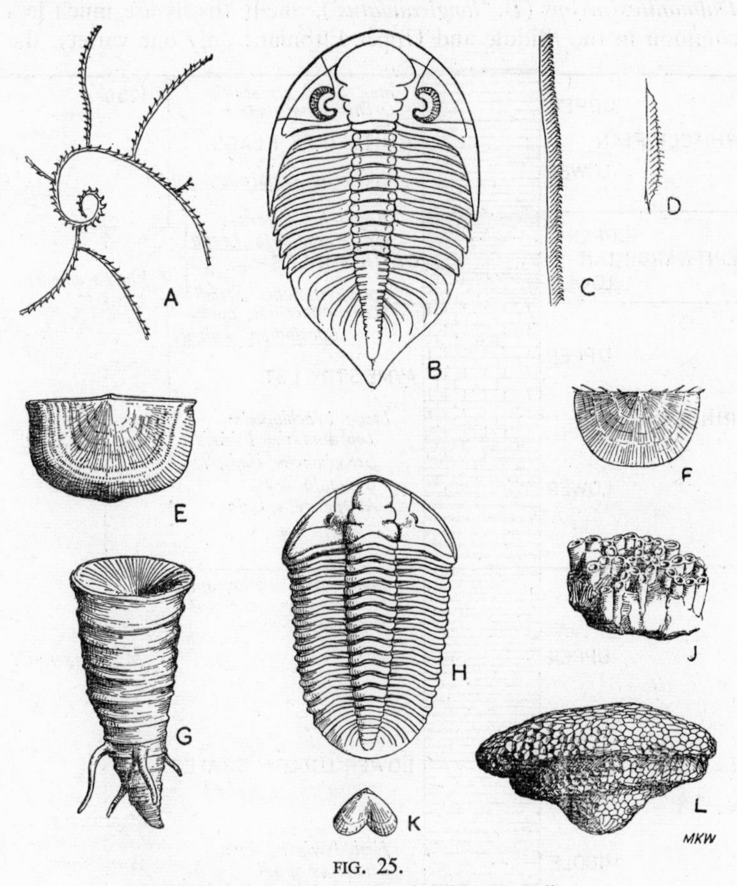


FIG. 25.

A. *Cyrtograptus murchisoni*, a Wenlockian graptolite.
B. *Dalmanites myops*, Wenlockian-Ludlovian.
C. *Monograptus* of *priodon* type, Wenlockian.
D. *Monograptus leintwardinensis*, Leintwardinian-Ludlovian.
E. *Leptaena rhomboidalis*, Wenlockian.
F. *Protochonetes ludloviensis*, Upper Ludlovian.
G. *Ketophyllum* (*Omphyma*) *turbinata*, Wenlockian.
H. *Calymene blumenbachi*, Wenlockian.
J. *Halysites catenularus*, the 'chain coral,' Wenlockian.
K. *Dicoelosia* (*Bilobites*) *biloba*, Wenlock Shale.
L. *Favosites gothlandicus*, Wenlock and Aymestry Limestones.

muddy siltstones, those in the Lower and Upper divisions being calcareous, while nodules of limestone occur in the lowest beds immediately above the Wenlock Limestone. As might be expected, the fauna of the Lower Eltonian consists of hardy, long-range survivors of Wenlockian species of brachiopods and the trilobite *Dalmanites myops* (*D. 'longicaudatus'*). Shelly fossils are much less common in the Middle and Upper Eltonian: only one variety, the

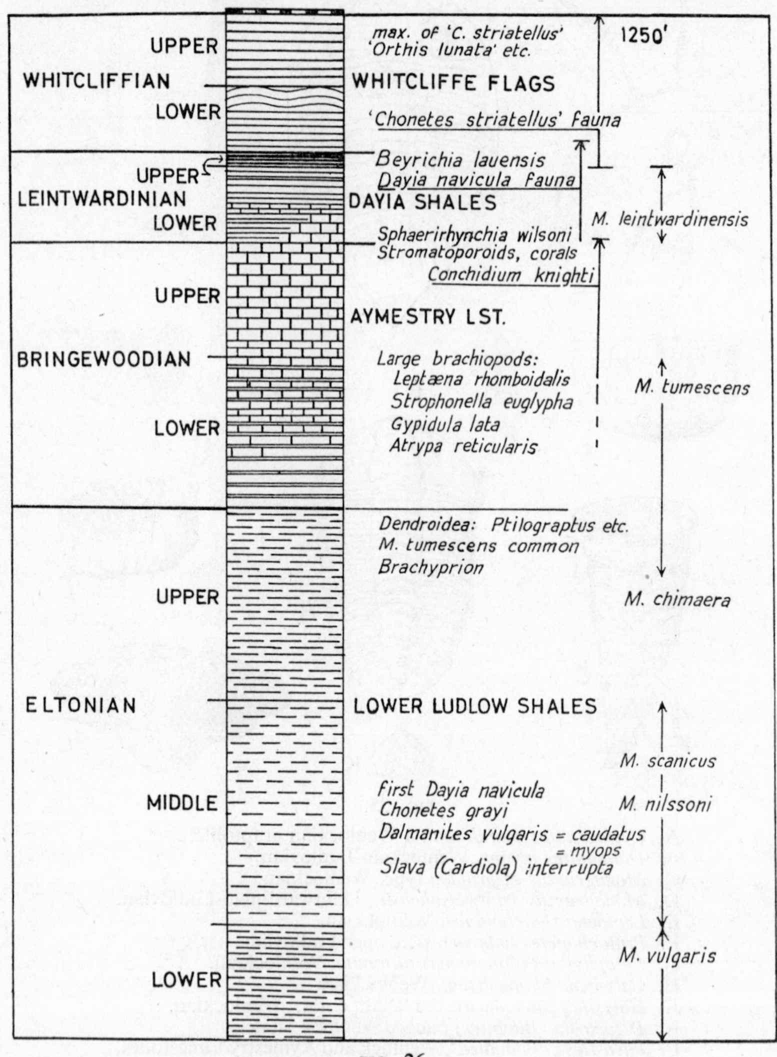


FIG. 26.

The Ludlow Series, of shelf facies, in the type area in Shropshire. *Based on the work of the Ludlow Research Group: R. Allender, C. H. Holland, J. D. Lawson, V. G. Walmsley and J. H. Mc.D. Whitaker*. See references at end of chapter. For *Chonetes grayi* read *Chonetoidea grayi*.

long-ranged *Chonetoidea grayi* is listed as 'fairly common' in the Middle division; but *Dayia navicula* makes its first appearance, while an abundance of the zonal graptolite, *M. tumescens*, is typical of the Upper Eltonian.

The Bringewoodian witnesses a striking change in lithology—from the ubiquitous calcareous siltstones to limestones—linked with a great influx of Wenlockian brachiopods and, later, corals. In effect, this was re-colonization of the area by the Wenlock Limestone fauna when environmental conditions again became favourable. It would be interesting to know where they had been lurking in the interim. The Lower Bringewood Limestones are impure, silty and interstratified with calcareous siltstones; but the Upper Bringewood limestones are pure crystalline massive limestones containing stromotoporoid and tabulate coral colonies in the position of growth, as well as large numbers of brachiopods, among which *Conchidium knighti* has the status of a zone fossil, and locally is so abundant as to form veritable shell-banks. As stated above, this mid-Ludlovian limestone is well known to many generations of geologists as the **Aymestry Limestone**; but 'Aymestry' and 'Upper Bringewood' are neither synonymous nor co-extensive. The latter is a division of Silurian time and independent of lithology; but the former is a lithological unit in the Silurian succession, limited to a special environment, and not everywhere of precisely the same age. In places the top of the Aymestry Limestone corresponds with the boundary between the Upper Bringewood and Lower Leintwardine sub-stages; but elsewhere the massive limestone (Aymestry) lithology extends well above the base of the Leintwardine Stage. The latter consists typically of the inevitable calcareous flaggy siltstones. Many of its fossils are common to the underlying stage also, but *Conchidium knighti* and the reef-builders have been eliminated. On the other hand the small brachiopod, *Dayia navicula*, a member of the fauna since early Eltonian times, increases notably in importance, to such an extent that the term *Dayia* Shales was applied to these beds. Westwards in the basin facies they pass into graptolitic shales—the *Leintwardinensis* Shales—bearing the name of Britain's last graptolite and the highest graptolite zone.

The Upper Leintwardine Stage is only a few feet thick but is considered to be faunally important, largely on account of the incoming of the '*Chonetes striatella*' fauna, overlapping the decline of the *Dayia navicula* fauna. Important indicator fossils are the ostracod, *Neobeyrichia lauensis* and the trilobite, *Calymene neo-intermedia*. These have Zonal Index status. In the basin facies strata of this age are termed the *Lauensis* Beds.

The Whitcliffe Stage comprises a poorly fossiliferous Lower, and an exceptionally prolific Upper division. The base of the stage is defined rather by the elimination of 'old' forms than the introduction of 'new' ones: the last of the Wenlockian survivals were eliminated, while the '*Chonetes striatella*' fauna gains in strength upwards. The type section through the Stage occurs in the gorge of the River Teme immediately south of the old town of Ludlow and dominated by its ancient castle. The fauna of these beds is one of the best-known assemblages in the Palaeozoic. Three species in particular have become familiar to thousands of students under their original names: *Chonetes striatella*, *Orthis lunata* and *Rhynchonella nucula*. In the course of revision these names have been changed: the first is completely unrecognizable as *Protochonetes salopiensis*, the orthid has become *Salopina lunata*, while the rhynchonellid has been rechristened *Camarotoechia nucula*. These brachiopods are accompanied by a large variety of other kinds of fossils including straight-shelled nautiloids (orthocones), annelid worms (*Serpulites longissimus*), lamellibranchs including *Fuchsella* (formerly *Orthonota*) *amygdalina* and gasteropods including *Pleurotomaria* and *Holopella*. On account of the abundance of the last-named, the highest part of the Stage in the basin facies at Builth is termed *Holopella conica* Beds.

Thus far we have studied the vertical variation of the Wenlock-Ludlow rocks in Murchison's type-area. It remains to note the lateral variations as they are traced into other districts.

To the east of the main outcrop, beds of Wenlockian-Ludlovian age occur in the inliers in Staffordshire, already referred to. The Wenlock Limestone in particular is well developed in the neighbourhood of Dudley, near Birmingham, where it has been much quarried in the past and has yielded finely preserved specimens of the characteristic trilobite, *Calymene blumenbachi*, which are known in good geological collections the world over.

Several inliers of Silurian rocks occur also south-east of the main outcrop. They are well exposed in an area lying south of Ledbury in Herefordshire and immediately west of the Malvern Hills. They form the almost perfect dome at Woolhope with its southerly continuation at May Hill, notable for a thick development of the arenaceous facies of the Llandoverian—the May Hill Sandstone. Farther south they are brought to the surface again in another small dome-like structure at Usk in Monmouthshire, while another small outcrop occurs near Cardiff, Glamorganshire. The Silurian strata in these several inliers do not differ markedly from those of the type-area, except for the incoming, at the base of the Wenlockian, of the **Woolhope Limestone**—the type-locality being, of course, the Woolhope Dome. Although not a coral limestone, it is composed in part of calcareous algae, reef-formers of lowly organization but important to this day. A very characteristic fossil is the trilobite, *Illaenus* (*Bumastus*) *barriensis*. The trivial name of this fossil refers to its occurrence at Great Barr near Birmingham, where the Woolhope Limestone, under the guise of 'Barr Limestone' again occurs.

The Woolhope Limestone acts as a corrective to the erroneous idea that all limestones are deposited in deep water, beyond the mudline. At Old Radnor it rests, with a thin basal conglomerate, directly on a platform of Longmyndian (Precambrian) rocks that must have formed a submerged shelf on which the limestone was deposited under very shallow water. Both in these southern localities and in the neighbourhood of Birmingham the water was shallow and clear; but in the intervening tract, including the Wenlock-Ludlow belt, the sea was charged with muddy sediment brought down by a large river draining the eastern land. 

Apart from the local development of the Woolhope Limestone, however, the Wenlock-Ludlow succession maintains much the same general character as far as the most easterly and most southerly inliers except that the succession is often broken by non-sequences indicated by conglomeratic layers or phosphatic fragment beds; while larger breaks may account for the absence of certain beds, notably the Aymestry Limestone which is absent from the southern part of the Woolhope Dome, although the Ludlovian is complete in the northern part of the area. In general the thicknesses are much reduced in the inliers. At a point approximately halfway between the May Hill and Woolhope inliers, at Gorsley in Herefordshire this attenuation becomes extreme: the total thickness of the Ludlovian is only $11\frac{1}{2}$ feet. A nonsequence separates the Downtonian from $4\frac{1}{2}$ feet of Whitcliffian with a thin basal phosphatized pebble-bed, resting on strata referred to the Leintwardinian and only 7 feet in thickness. A considerable unconformity cuts out the Aymestry Limestone, the *Davia* Shales (Leintwardinian) resting directly on Wenlockian. This last break, incidentally, is bridged by several thousand feet of strata in the Welsh geosynclinal area; and it is worth remembering that the maximum thickness of the Ludlovian is more than 6000 feet in the Clun Forest-Builth area. The contrast with the Gorsley succession is impressive. The significance of these features is considered later.

Brief reference may be made to a puzzling feature which is not yet completely understood. At Tites Point on the banks of the River Severn a Leintwardinian-Whitcliffian succession appears to pass up conformably into red shaly siltstone containing bands of mud-pellets and yielding *Lingula* (the species not specified, unfortunately) together with plant remains. Unless the apparently conformable relationship is illusory this looks like a 'Downtonian phase' high in the Silurian. This would be not without precedent as shallow-water and possibly terrestrial deposits, the so-called Trichrug Beds of Bringewoodian age occur locally on the eastern flank of the Towy Anticline.

When the Wenlock-Ludlow beds are traced westwards important changes take place, just as striking as in the Llandoverian strata. First there is a great expansion in thickness; and next the beds change from a calcareous to a non-calcareous facies. The distinctive shelf-sea deposits, including clear-water limestones, of the Wenlock-Ludlow belt pass westwards into a greywacke, graptolitic-shale facies, characteristic of the Welsh type of Salopian. Concurrently with the change in lithology the character of the fauna is altered: naturally the reef-building organisms disappear, and although shelly fossils are locally abundant, graptolites, often in a fragmental condition, provide the only means of accurate correlation.

These Salopian strata form a continuous outcrop from the coast at Conway to Builth; thence farther to the south-west the outcrop narrows and becomes discontinuous owing to overstep by the Old Red Sandstone. From Welshpool southwards the Wenlockian itself rests transgressively on older Silurian beds and at Llandovery oversteps on to Ordovician strata (Fig. 20). In a belt of country which includes Builth, Welshpool and Llangollen, the shale-mudstone type of sediment is dominant; and a succession of graptolite zones has been established, using *Cyrtograptus* and *Monograptus* in the equivalents of the Wenlockian, and *Monograptus* alone in the Ludlovian beds. To the north and west of this belt again, sediments of much coarser grain, including massive grits and conglomerate-bands, become important. Even at Conway, which we have agreed must have lain in the axial zone of the geosyncline during the Llandoverian Period, the Salopian bears the impress of accumulation under shallow-water conditions: even the finer-grained beds are current bedded, much of the formation is coarsely arenaceous and conglomerates occur frequently. A drastic change in the conditions of accumulation is indicated, and the coastline cannot have been far distant. To the south and east these strata increase greatly in thickness to form the **Denbighshire Grits and Flags** that occupy the Denbigh Moors and the Clwydian range (Fig. 27). The part of the succession in which the grits are best developed is approximately equivalent to the Wenlockian, and totals about 3000 feet in thickness. The overlying Ludlovian, though somewhat finer in grain and flaggy rather than gritty, is thicker still—about 5000 feet. Farther south a Ludlovian 'basin facies', consisting chiefly of grey siltstones, more than 6000 feet thick, occurs in the Clun Forest area and the Builth district. The youngest rocks of the Series occur in these areas where the overlying Downtonian strata are well developed; but in the Llangollen district the succession is incomplete: the flags, tightly folded along east-to-west lines, pass underneath the unconformable cover of Carboniferous Limestone. No Silurian beds younger than the Leintwardine Stage occur in North Wales (*Monograptus leintwardinensis* and *Davia navicula* occur together in the flags near Llangollen); but it is significant that the basal conglomerates of Carboniferous age in the same area include blocks of shelly Silurian rocks closely similar, both in lithology and fauna, to the highest Silurian beds of the Lake District. From their condition it is inferred that they have not travelled far and were derived locally.

The boundary between the two facies of the Salopian described above coincides approximately at least with the belt of faulting associated with the Church Stretton Hills and the Wrekin in Shropshire. The best known of the faults is the Church Stretton fault which passed between the Caradoc Hills and the Longmynd and is thence traceable for many miles both to the north-east and the south-west. This line in Silurian times marked the western boundary of the extensive shelf, probably at no time deeply submerged, on which the corals and other reef-building organisms flourished, and which extended eastwards to a little beyond Birmingham. Westwards of the Church Stretton line, however, the sea was in the nature of a sagging trough, which at the end of the Period had accommodated a thickness of sediment several times greater than that which the shelf bore on its surface. It is noteworthy that in late Ordovician times the 'hinge' between shelf and basin lay *west* of the Longmynd horst and coincided with the western boundary (Pontesford) fault.

The most important aspect of the Salopian of Wales—the Denbigh Moors, also the western parts of the Clun Forest area and around Builth—is the fact that the beds yield evidence of having slipped extensively down submarine slopes into the deeper parts of the geosyncline. The slipping occurred at different times in different places; but although the Wenlockian beds were sometimes affected locally, the movements took place chiefly in Lower Ludlow times. The prime cause seems to have been a very simple one. Through sinking of parts of the sea-floor the submarine slope became too steep for the great load of sediment to remain stable, so slipping under the control of gravity took place. There are slight differences of opinion in interpreting the evidence—as to whether the movement was a sudden **slumping** to lower levels or a slow, more or less continuous creep. In either case the general effects must have been much the same. Higher layers would tend to override lower ones, retarded by friction; the front, especially, of the moving mass would be folded by pressure, and many of the folds would be of the recumbent type. The wholesale slipping of one part of the mass over another would produce a surface of discontinuity, looking

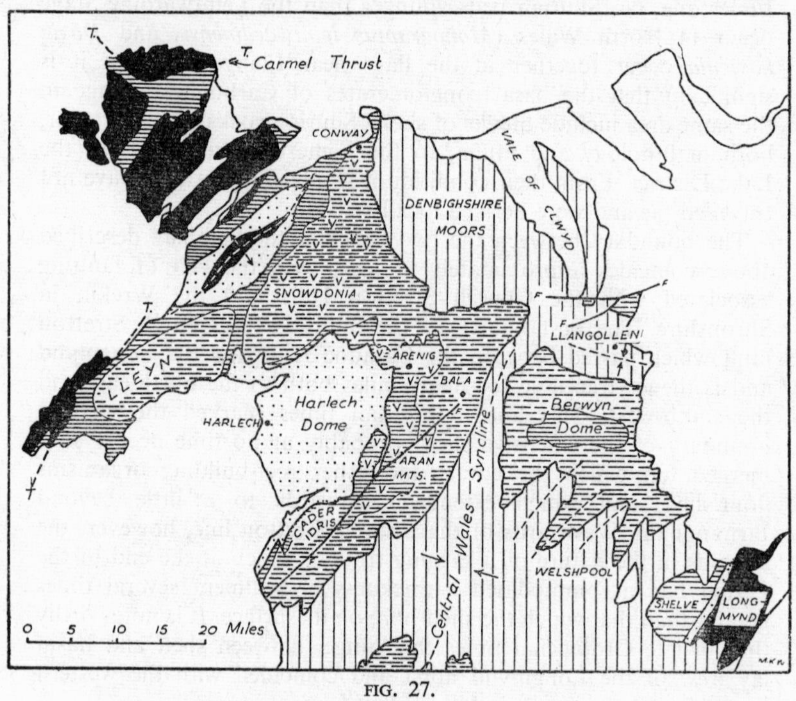


FIG. 27.

Geological sketch-map of North Wales, showing structural units and some important fold-axes and faults.

Precambrian, black; Cambrian, stippled; Ordovician, horizontal ruling; (V. volcanic rocks; continuous ruling, Arenig to Llandeilo Series; broken lines, Bala Series); vertical ruling, Silurian; post-Silurian, blank.

superficially like an overthrust fault. Some bands would become crumpled internally, some would be torn from their moorings, rolled over and over, producing 'balling-up' or snowball-like structures, all of these perhaps embedded in relatively undisturbed strata. An alternation of structurally complex disturbed beds with undisturbed ones, normal in all respects, is characteristic of these 'slumped beds'; while strong evidence of the contemporaneity of the folding and faulting is proved by the fact that the higher undisturbed layers are firmly cemented to the contorted beds below. In the case of the 'pseudo-faults', there are no signs of movement—grooving or slickensiding—on the surfaces concerned.

Many other interesting facts have been brought to light during the detailed study of the Ludlovian particularly regarding the palaeogeography of the period. The small borderland town of Leintwardine in Herefordshire occupied a unique position between shelf and basin, right on the continental edge of the Silurian Sea: the succession is therefore intermediate in character. Careful mapping has demonstrated that half a dozen deep channels occur within an area of ten square miles. They trend at right angles to the then-existing coastline and were ripped to a depth of up to 700 feet in the older, but still unconsolidated formations, by actively eroding currents. The walls of the channels are steep, and are sometimes fault-bounded. Thus the conditions were favourable for slumping (submarine sliding of loose sediment), at some levels and in some places marginal, but elsewhere down-channel. The directions of the currents themselves have been inferred from the study of various orientation features such as aligned stipes of monograptids and of elongated shells like those of orthoconic nautiloids, while isolated valves of brachiopods tend to lie in parallel positions, with their umbones (beaks) pointing up-stream. Various kinds of markings on the bedding-planes—such as skid-marks, prod-marks and ripple marks are also informative.

Among the materials filling the channels are fragments, up to boulder size, of the sediments cut through. These are identifiable in some cases from their lithology, in others from the fossils they contain, and are significant in dating the cutting and filling of the channels. Those at Leintwardine are Leintwardinian in age, post-Lower but pre-Upper, though some were not completely filled until Whitcliffe times.

From the faunal aspect the channels are interesting as they contain a specialized fauna including eurypterids (much more common in the Old Red Sandstone) and other small crustaceans, starfish and brittle stars, echinoids and annelid worms.

It is suggested that these channels were cut during a period of relatively low sea-level, when the strand-line more or less coincided with the continental edge, and the rivers of the period discharged directly on to the continental slope. If this were so, emergence of some parts of the shelf would be inevitable, with the development of a non-sequence or an actual unconformity in the succession.

It remains to glance briefly at the **Salopian of the Lake District** and southern Scotland. As compared with the type-area in Shropshire the expansion in thickness in the Lake District is greater even than in Wales. The Wenlockian consists of 1000 feet of flags, remarkably uniform in their lithology; but the Lower Ludlovian reaches 10,000 feet of much the same rock-types as in North and Mid-Wales—sandy mudstones, flags, with some grits. The succession is completed by 1500 feet of Upper Ludlovian micaceous flags containing some calcareous layers full of shelly fossils. This great expansion in thickness is all the more striking when it is remembered that this area was one of *minimum* thickness in the Llandoverian Period. We have witnessed the same transformation at Conway on the one hand, and at Moffat, rather earlier in time, on the other. It appears that the belt of maximum thickness had moved inwards towards the centre of the geosyncline, and that the types of sediment characteristic of the belt of maximum thickness were now being poured into those parts which, only a relatively short time before, had been most remote from the coastlines.

In the **Southern Uplands of Scotland** the Llandovery Series (Valentian) is succeeded by the Wenlockian which occupies most of the southern belt and dips beneath the unconformable cover of Upper Palaeozoic strata to the south. Recently the Wenlockian has been studied in considerable detail, especially in the extreme south-west—the Rhinns of Galloway—and south-east near the towns of Hawick and Riccarton. The major stratigraphical problem in the latter area concerns the age-relations of two important formations bearing the names of these towns. The *Riccarton Group* comprises 13,000 feet of rocks of greywacke facies within which a complete succession of Wenlockian graptolite zones has been established. The *Hawick Rocks*, 12,000 feet thick and completely without fossils, are seen to dip under the basal member of the Riccarton Group; but the succession is inverted and therefore the latter must be the older. It follows that the Hawick Rocks are younger than basal Wenlockian, though how much younger it is impossible to say. Both formations are closely similar in lithology: except for the presence of graptolitic shales in the former they would be identical, one point of detail being particularly significant. Both contain *red mudstones* which grade up and down into mudstones of normal grey-green colour: they therefore form part of the succession and are not tectonic slices. From these facts it is reasonable to argue that these two great formations form two facies of the Wenlock Series, laid down in slightly different environments. What these were is a problem; but it has been suggested that the Hawick Rocks accumulated in front of a delta, while the Riccarton Beds were deposited in rather deeper water as fan accumulations at the mouths of submarine canyons.

Within the Riccarton Beds cyclic repetitions of graded greywackes occur. They grade from conglomerates through the whole gamut of grain-size variation into siltstones and mudstones. The graptolitic shales are closely associated with the mudstones: they are therefore restricted to the finest sediment at the top of graded units which normally range from 30 to 50 feet in thickness, though some are 100 feet. The coarser greywackes occasionally contain shelly fossils including solitary corals, brachiopods and crinoid ossicles, while some of the finest beds contain fragmental plant remains. Towards the top the Riccarton Beds contain large mud-flakes, up to 8 inches in diameter embedded in a greywacke matrix. They are often saucer-shaped, suggesting desiccation; some had been rolled into cigar-shaped 'pebbles'.

A feature of great interest is the interstratification of the two facies—greywacke and graptolitic shale—in the Riccarton Beds. The two facies had occupied different belts within the Moffat geosyncline in Ordovician times (p. 72) and had accumulated in different environments, the greywackes in troughs, but the graptolitic shales on a submarine rise. This explanation cannot apply to the Riccarton area. The grading of the greywackes and the alternation of the two facies clearly indicate seasonal differences, presumably of climatic significance. A season, of unknown duration, but of heavy precipitation, would be accompanied by active erosion and the transporting of coarse detritus. Weakening currents are reflected by decreasing grain-size of the sediment until they became so weak, or possibly non-existent, so that only mud was deposited, quietly and without disturbance. In these circumstances graptolites would be entombed and preserved. This explanation needs one qualification: it is extremely unlikely that plankton, including graptolites, was uniformly distributed over all the Ordovician and Silurian seas: trade winds and antitrades as well as 'gulf streams' must have influenced their distribution, one would have thought, profoundly. The essential condition was a temporarily quiet environment, sheltered from current action.

In the Irish continuation of the Southern Uplands of Scotland, Silurian rocks form the greater part of the roughly triangular **Longford-Down massif** and compare closely with the Birkhill-Gala succession; but although the strata are well exposed in coastal sections in Co. Down, detailed information is scanty and it would be premature at this stage to attempt a detailed comparison with Scotland.

The continuation of the Lower Palaeozoics northwards into what is now the Midland Valley of Scotland is proved by the occurrence of a number of inliers which rise through the Upper Palaeozoic cover, at Lesmahagow in Lanarkshire and in the Pentland Hills. Wenlockian greywackes in the former and shales in the latter are succeeded by higher Silurian strata of rather doubtful age. The Wenlock shales in the Pentlands are noteworthy as containing zonal graptolites associated with mud-loving eurypterids which we have already encountered in the Leintwardine channels and which are important members of the Lower Old Red Sandstone fauna. Many of the fossils occurring in higher beds of possible Ludlovian age occur in the 'Grey Downtonian' of the Welsh Borderlands, which suggests that the change of conditions occurred rather earlier in Scotland than in England and Wales.

To the westward this major Scottish structure crosses into Ireland where the sub-Devonian floor is exposed in spectacular fashion in the **Mayo Trough** around Murrisk. Exceptionally thick Arenigian and younger Ordovician strata are succeeded unconformably by an incomplete Silurian succession. Upper Llandovery beds are attenuated and impersistent, and are succeeded, again unconformably, by Wenlockian displaying features of special interest and importance. They commence with a succession of turbidites, succeeded by a sub-littoral and tidal-flats facies, and this in turn gives place to red rocks—arkoses, conglomerates and shales, formerly thought to be O.R.S., but now known to contain a Wenlock fauna. We are of the opinion that these rocks *are* O.R.S., though of Silurian and not Devonian age. We would emphasize that the O.R.S. is a facies of the Devonian and has a diachronous base.

Lenticles of fossiliferous black and grey limestones occur in a zone of overthrusting which traverses **Cornwall** just north of the Lizard Complex. The Silurian limestone lenticles together with masses of Ordovician quartzites are embedded in a disturbed matrix of calcareous shales of Upper Devonian age. These are, of course, the most southerly outcrops of Silurian rocks in Britain. They are of special interest as they are completely dissimilar from rocks of the same age in other parts of the country. They are essentially cephalopod-limestones and have yielded specimens of *Orthoceras* spp., *Cyrtoceras* and other forms, together with species of *Slava* (*Cardiola*), including the well-known *S.* (*C.*) *interrupta*, a member of the Ludlovian fauna in the Welsh Borderlands. Otherwise the faunal affinities are strongly with the Silurian of Central Brittany and, farther afield, of Bohemia. These cephalopod-limestone lenticles were derived from the Cornubian massif which bordered the Carboniferous geosyncline on the south, and were translated to their present position along thrust-planes operative during the Armorican orogeny.

The final paragraphs in the chapter on the Ordovician Period were concerned with widespread and varied volcanic phenomena which characterized the Period. By contrast, the Silurian was virtually free from volcanic activity, being restricted to four areas: (1) the Mendip Hills, (2) Tortworth, north of Bristol, (3) Marloes in western Pembrokeshire and (4) Clogher Head at the tip of the Dingle Peninsula in south-west Ireland. In the last-named locality the eruptions commenced in the Llandoverian; but the lavas and pyroclasts are more important in the Wenlockian. They are rhyolitic and include nodular, flow-banded and spherulitic varieties, while some are columnar.

## REFERENCES

The Regional Geologies of North and South Wales, Welsh Borderlands, Southern Scotland, Northern England and English Midlands:

BUTLER, A. J. 'The stratigraphy of the Wenlock Limestone of Dudley,' *Q.J.G.S.*, **95** (1939), 37. The paper describes the lithology of the limestone, with special reference to the conditions of formation.

HOLLAND, C. H. J., LAWSON, J. D., and WALMSLEY, V. G. 'The Silurian rocks of the Ludlow district,' *Bull. Brit. Mus.* (Nat. Hist.), **8,** no. 3.

JONES, W. D. V. 'The Valentian succession around Llanidloes, Montgomeryshire,' *Q.J.G.S.*, **100** (1944), 309. Contains a full description of the complete Llandoverian of graptolitic facies.

LAWSON, J. D. 'The Silurian Succession at Gorsley (Herefordshire),' *Geol. Mag.*, **91** (1954), 227.

WALMSLEY, V. G. 'Geology of the Usk inlier,' *Q.J.G.S.*, **144** (1959), 482.

SQUIRREL, H. C., and TUCKER, E. V. 'Geology of the Woolhope inlier,' *Q.J.G.S.*, **116** (1960), 139.

WARREN, P. T. 'Stratigraphy and structure of the Silurian (Wenlock) rocks south-east of Hawick . . .,' *Q.J.G.S.*, **120** (1964), 193.

WHITTAKER, J. H. MCD. 'Geology of the area around Leintwardine,' *Q.J.G.S.*, **118** (1962), 319.

WHITTARD, W. F. 'Stratigraphy of the Valentian rocks of Shropshire,' *Q.J.G.S.*, **88** (1932), 859. A description of the longshore features on the S.E. flank of the Longmynd.

CHAPTER V

# INTRODUCTION TO GEOCHRONOLOGY

THE student of Geology is bound to be impressed at an early stage in his training by the immensity of geological time. The palaeontologist thinks in terms of the evolution of new races of creatures which appeared on the scene, multiplied and expanded until in some cases they dominated the world, then slowly declined and, like the trilobites or dinosaurs, were finally eliminated. The geologist accepts without question the principle that in past time great mountain chains arose where previously there had been none, and then, by ordinary slow processes of disintegration and decay, were levelled to the plains. In the complementary sense, in the mind's eye he can witness the accumulation of sediment building up stratigraphical units of enormous thicknesses. All of these processes demand much time for their accomplishment. The enquiring mind would like to know more precisely how much time was involved, and exactly when certain geological events took place.

Attempts to measure time on purely geological evidence are quite unreliable—there are too many unknown factors. One such method was based on the rate of accumulation of sediments. Their thickness is the only term which can be accurately measured; but even that is impossible in regions of tectonic complexity. Estimates of the average rate of accumulation of sediments have varied from one foot in a hundred years to one foot in 6,000 years. Furthermore, even in conformable strata one cannot be sure that sedimentation was really continuous. Recognizable nonsequences may represent only a fraction of the actual breaks or pauses in deposition: an unknown proportion of geological time is unrepresented in the sedimentary column.

Entirely new methods of attacking problems of geological time followed the discovery of radioactivity at the close of the last century. Radioactive elements are not stable but undergo spontaneous decomposition into 'daughter' elements. After a series of transformations a stable end-product is produced. In 1903 the physicist Sir Ernest Rutherford suggested that the radiogenic elements preserved in radioactive minerals should provide a measure of the time that had elapsed since the formation of the minerals concerned. Shortly afterwards Boltwood noted that lead was nearly always present in uranium-bearing rocks and minerals, and further, that the older the rock on geological evidence the greater was the lead/uranium ratio. These observations laid the foundations of the so-called uranium/lead and thorium/lead methods of 'absolute', isotopic or radiometric age determinations.

Radiometric decomposition proceeds steadily and not in sudden complete transformations from one stage to another in the chain of reactions. The term 'half life' is used for the period of time during which one half of a given quantity of radioactive element is converted into the radiogenic end-product. During the succeeding half life period, which may have a duration of several millions of years, half of the remainder—that is, a quarter of the original quantity will be converted, and so on. Hence the proportion of mother to daughter element changes progressively with the passage of time. For this ratio to be used for dating purposes, however, it is essential that the system should have remained a 'closed' one, with nothing added and nothing lost. In other words, the changes were entirely *internal*. Normally the radioactive elements are present in extremely minute amounts so that the analytical techniques involved in their measurement are very refined. It is claimed that under favourable conditions a few parts per million can be measured with an accuracy of 2 to 3 per cent.

The original methods, based on the uranium/lead and thorium/lead ratios, have now been largely superseded by others in which the analytical procedure is not only less involved but of more general application, in that a much wider range of rocks and minerals can be used. The U/Pb and Th/Pb methods are restricted to mineral veins containing such rare minerals as uraninite and pitchblende, or to granitic rocks in which zircon (uranium-bearing) or monazite (thorium-bearing) are present as accessory minerals. Zircon and monazite occur also as derived 'heavy mineral' grains in many sediments; but the 'ages' derived from such grains are those of the rocks in which they originally crystallized and not those of the sediments in which they ultimately came to rest.

During the past two decades new methods of radiometric dating have been developed: the potassium/argon (K/Ar), rubidium/strontium (Rb/Sr) and 'radio-carbon' methods. The first of these, the K/Ar method, can be applied to a wide range of igneous and metamorphic minerals which are relatively rich in potassium. Of these, the micas are the most valuable; but some pyroxenes and amphiboles as well as certain alkali-feldspars, notably sanidine, may also be used. The value of this method is limited by the possibility of the escape of radiogenic argon. In this respect micas have excellent argon-retaining properties; but this is less true of the pyroxenes, amphiboles and K-feldspars. Some sedimentary rocks contain, all too rarely, the potassium-bearing mineral, glauconite, and very rarely such evaporite minerals as sylvite (KCl). However, glauconite is very prone to loss of argon; while the evaporite minerals are prone to diagenetic and post-diagenetic changes (p. 309).

The rubidium/strontium method may be used successfully with micas and all the common alkali-feldspars, but not pyroxenes and amphiboles, as their content of rubidium is too small. Up to this point we have considered age determinations based on individual mineral grains laboriously separated from the parent rock. An extension of both techniques has involved radiometric analysis of complete rock-specimens—the so-called 'whole-rock' analyses, which include radioactive changes that have moved beyond the confines of individual crystal grains. Radiogenic argon lost by one mineral may be gained by another, for example apatite, and is therefore retained in the rock as a whole.

Both $K^{40}$ and $Rb^{87}$ have extremely long half-lives and therefore provide reliable means of dating ancient rocks; but they cannot be used for dating rocks younger than 10 m.y. (million years) in the case of Rb/Sr and 100,000 years using K/Ar.

The radio-carbon method is based on the ratio of radiogenic carbon, $C^{14}$, to ordinary carbon, $C^{12}$. The half-life of the isotope $C^{14}$ is a mere 5600 years, and therefore the maximum age determinable by this method, with any approach to accuracy, is less than 60,000 years. It follows, of course, that radio-carbon dating is of value to the archaeologist and the geologist concerned with events in the later stages of the Pleistocene Period.

The general reader, used to thinking in terms of the allotted span of 'three score years and ten' finds it difficult to change to a time scale in which ages measurable in tens, hundreds and even thousands of *millions* of years are commonplace. He may therefore be excused some scepticism concerning the validity of radiometric dating. Probably he is impressed by the very minute quantities which have to be measured with a quite exceptional degree of accuracy; and by the fact that the 'ages' are *calculated* from the results of such analyses. The calculations are both complicated and ingenious, but certain assumptions have to be made. The value selected for the decay ratio is a case in point: the initial ratio of radiogenic to ordinary Sr cannot be measured—it has to be assumed and a small difference in this 'constant' alters the age considerably.

When all the very real technical difficulties have been overcome there remains the problem of interpreting the results in geological terms. In the present state of knowledge this often seems to be the major problem. The criterion for the accuracy of radiogenic 'dates' and 'ages' seems to be consistency: if a 'new' date is consistent with others previously determined, and with the geological evidence, it is regarded as reliable and accurate; but if not, the anomalies have to be explained away. Normally this does not appear to present much difficulty; but it does mean that results are selected and some are discarded in the final analysis. Normally igneous rocks such as granites can be relied upon to provide material suitable for radiometric analysis, provided they have not been metamorphosed subsequently. Radiometric analyses by both the K/Ar and Rb/Sr methods carried out on the same, as well as different mineral species separated from unmetamorphosed material give consistent results within a narrow margin; but the ages of different mineral species from a granite which has been involved in metamorphism may vary widely. Interesting examples of this are provided by zircons which, in many granitic rocks are found to have 'ages' that are very much greater than those of accompanying minerals, notably biotite. This inconsistency results from the fact that zircon is highly refractory and survives many of the geological events that cause other minerals to re-crystallize. In some cases it may be that the granite was of metasomatic origin and that the zircons are relics of the 'heavy minerals' in the original sediments from which the granite was formed. Alternatively, the granite may have been involved in 'regional' metamorphism during which all the measurable minerals except zircon recrystallized. The 'Alpine' metamorphism of the originally Hercynian granite massif of St Gotthard provides an example of the latter phenomenon, giving zircon 'ages' of about 300 m.y.; but biotite 'ages' of only about 10 m.y.

Whatever the precise cause of this particular kind of anomaly, it provides an interesting petrological corollary: the discovery of anomalously old zircons in any granite, however 'igneous' it may otherwise appear, throws serious doubt on its magmatic origin. Speaking generally, however, normal igneous rocks provide the geochronologist with the most satisfactory material for his investigations. Since all the component minerals will have been formed during the relatively short period of time occupied by crystallization from the original magma, the radiometric clock will have been started (set) at one and the same instant of geological time, and they will all be of the same age.

Theoretically the most useful kinds of igneous rocks for geochronological treatment should be lavas, for they are interbedded with sedimentary rocks, and other things being equal, should provide invaluable information concerning the date of accumulation (i.e. the true 'age') of the latter. Of the various kinds of lavas, those containing phenocrysts of sanidine (K-bearing) are ideal for age-determinations. Unfortunately they are not common and rarely occur where they would be of maximum value.

Before the age of an intrusive igneous rock such as granite could be determined by radiometric methods, it could only be *inferred* from observable stratigraphical relationships. Only in very rare instances were these relationships of such a nature as to fix the time of emplacement accurately on the stratigraphical time-scale. Thus the well-known Shap granite is demonstrably post-Ludlovian, pre-Dinantian; the great Irish Leinster granite is post-Ordovician, pre-Upper O.R.S.; the small Creetown granite—one of the Galloway granites—is post-Wenlockian, but no upper time limit can be fixed. The radiometric ages of all three granites are the same: $386 \pm 6$ m.y. (*Nature*, **185** (1960), 495). This date can be accurately placed on a continuous time-scale, of course; but what this means in terms of the time spans of the various geological Systems (Periods) is another matter to which we shall return later.

The purpose behind such age measurements is two-fold: firstly to show to which of the three great periods of intrusive igneous activity a particular granite belongs: and secondly, in favourable cases, to provide information which may help in fixing geological boundaries between Systems. Any granite is, of course, younger than the rocks into which it is intrusive; but how much younger is often problematical. Thus granites in Jersey, Channel Islands, cut unfossiliferous, and therefore undated, shales which are thought to be pre-Cambrian. They might themselves be pre-Cambrian, Caledonian, Armorican or even Tertiary for all the evidence to the contrary. Only a radiometric age determination will solve this problem, as was the case with the granite which builds the small Lundy Isle, off the Somerset coast. Stratigraphical evidence of its age is non-existent; its petrographic affinities are strongly with the Tertiary granites of Scotland and Northern Ireland; but it lies within the terrain of the West of England granites, though it is far removed from the Brito-Icelandic igneous province. The problem was solved recently (1962) when its radiometric age was proved to be about 50 m.y., which is much the same as the Tertiary Arran granite; but is remote from the 280 m.y. of the nearest Armorican granite—Dartmoor.

The Weardale granite is of special interest as it is not exposed at the surface. Its presence had been inferred from the occurrence of an extensive area of lead-zinc lodes in the Alston Block of the Pennines. As the lodes cut Carboniferous rocks of Yoredale facies and therefore cannot be younger than Lower Carboniferous, it was naturally concluded that the granite must be Armorican. During boring operations specimens of the granite were obtained and the radiometric 'age' of the rock was determined. It was found to be 362 ± 6 m.y., which is a Caledonian, not Armorican date. The case is considered more fully below (p. 290).

The largest of the British Armorican granites builds Dartmoor in Devonshire. Its age has been determined several times on account of its apparent value in fixing the Carboniferous/Permian boundary. It cuts and metamorphoses the local Carboniferous (the so-called 'Culm') while boulders which may well have been derived from an offshoot of the main granite are plentiful in the Permian breccio-conglomerates. On this evidence the age of the granite is post-Carboniferous, pre-Permian, and therefore should be close to the 'date' of the boundary between these two Systems. Actually the evidence is not so conclusive as one would wish. Strictly, the Dartmoor granite is post-Viséan: because these are the youngest Carboniferous rocks which actually make contact with it. To be post-Carboniferous it would have to be post-Stephanian, and there is no evidence that this is the case. An additional uncertainty is the age of the 'Permian' in Devonshire. Palaeontological evidence is wanting. The rocks are only *believed* to be Permian on lithological grounds and because of the inferred environment in which they accumulated.

Special problems arise in the case of *sedimentary rocks*. Excluding those which were chemically precipitated, they consist of detritus resulting from the disintegration and decay of pre-existing rocks, a large variety of which may have contributed to the formation of a given sediment. These materials are, of course, of different ages; and a radiometric analysis of such a 'mixed bag' will give a resultant age which is quite unrelated to the date of accumulation. It is only possible to measure the true age of a sediment if it contains a suitable authigenic mineral—one which formed during the process of accumulation. Unfortunately such minerals are very rare. Glauconite—a K-bearing silicate—looks promising from this angle, but suffers from various disabilities which reduce its practical value. It crystallizes in rather narrowly localized and specialized conditions, and is prone to decomposition involving loss of argon.

*Metamorphism*, especially multiple metamorphism, is certainly the bugbear of geochronologists. Most of the difficulties and inconsistencies encountered in radiometric age determinations are directly the consequence of metamorphism, and/or metasomatism. These processes may alter the 'age' of a given rock just as drastically as they affect mineral composition and texture. The latter changes are visible under the microscope and are capable of interpretation by the petrologist. By direct observation and logical inference it is possible to work out a sequence of metamorphic phases to which a given rock has been subjected; but it is a very different matter to attempt to *date* the phases. If a condition of stable equilibrium has been achieved, the 'age' of the rock indicated by the radiometric clock is the 'date' of the *last* metamorphism, it may be the last of several such phases. It might happen that in some structural back-water this last metamorphic episode was without effect. The 'age' of a rock-specimen from this locality would be the 'date' of the *previous* metamorphism—not necessarily the first, of course. Normally a specimen selected by chance from this terrain would yield a resultant age depending on a degree of 'over-printing' of the older date by the younger one.

Within the last few years in attempting to discover the age of the *Moine Schists* which cover an extensive area in the Northern Highlands of Scotland, the outcrops have been systematically sampled and the 'ages' of the many samples have been determined.

The results show a wide scatter or 'pattern'; but many are consistent, indicating an 'age' of about 420 m.y. From general considerations this is known to be far too recent a date, and is, in fact the date of the last metamorphism to which these rocks were subjected. Slightly older 'ages' have been obtained for specimens occurring near the Moine/Dalradian boundary, and much more remote dates apply to Moine Schists occurring in the extreme western outcrops, on the mainland opposite Skye. These rocks are seen to be of lower metamorphic grade than those occurring farther east: they have retained recognizable sedimentary structures, though elsewhere the latter have been completely obliterated by recrystallization. In these parts of Scotland ages of 560 m.y. have been obtained. Further, a granite-pegmatite cutting Moine Schists at Knoydart near the western coast contains abnormally large muscovite 'books' up to a foot in diameter and three inches thick. The radiometric 'age' of these muscovites is 740 m.y. (in 1961, but reduced to 720 m.y. in 1963 through a change in one of the 'constants'). The folding and metamorphism of the Moines at this point must be older than this, though how much older nobody can say. We will return to the problem of the age of the Moine Schists in the next chapter. At this point we can only add that the problem remains unsolved, and that it is extremely doubtful if a solution will ever be found.

Admittedly the special problems referred to above are interesting in themselves, but they make little contribution to what, in our opinion, should be the major pre-occupation of geochronologists at the present time: to establish an accurate *Time-Scale* with the more important boundaries, between Systems, and as far as practicable, Series, reliably dated. Time-Scales do exist, notably those of Holmes and Kulp; but few, if any, of the systematic boundaries are more than mere approximations. Boundaries, accurate enough for the requirements of stratigraphers—particularly of those dealing with historical aspects—can be fixed only in localities where sedimentation was continuous over the critical interval of time. For example, in Britain, it is impossible to fix the date of the beginning of the Cambrian Period, or of the Ordovician Period. The commencement of Silurian time could be accurately dated only at Moffat in the Southern Uplands, in the English Lake District or at a few localities in Mid-Wales. Similarly the beginning of Carboniferous time is recorded in North Devon but not over most of Britain. Even in these favoured localities the basal member of the higher System (or Series) must contain material suitable for measurement. By 'suitable' is meant a mineral of the right composition which crystallized while the sediment was in process of accumulation. As already noted, glauconite, containing potassium and therefore measurable by the K/Ar method is one of the very few such minerals. *Derived* grains of glauconite occur on a number of stratigraphical horizons; but measurements of these would indicate the age of the source rock, not of the sediment which now contains them. *Authigenic* glauconite occurs in Britain low down in the Cambrian System; but it is not encountered again until the highest Jurassic, Cretaceous and Tertiary strata are reached. Age determinations have been made on the glauconite-bearing Comley Sandstone in Shropshire, but the results have proved unreliable on account of weathering which had resulted in loss of argon. Even if reliable results had been obtained, the age would have been that of the Comley Sandstone which lies an unknown distance above the base of the Cambrian System, which is what the investigators were hoping to date. Glauconite-bearing strata occur elsewhere in the world on horizons other than those referred to above; but few, if any of these occurrences approximate to the horizons selected on other evidence—usually palaeontological—as marking systematic boundaries.

The true significance of radiometric 'ages' and 'dates' remains obscure. The state of cooling represented by the 'age' of a granite is not known to correspond with any specific stage in the crystallization sequence. Indeed, it is thought possible that it 'corresponds with some phase of internal adjustment within the minerals after active crystallization had ceased'. (J. Watson, 1963.) This is equally true of granite 'ages' and of 'dates' of metamorphic phases. Yet in spite of the difference in meaning of these very ordinary words when applied to geological events as distinct from persons, the 'ages' and 'dates' serve a very useful purpose: they are *fixed points* in the continuous time-scale, and it is the relative positions of such points which is significant.

It has become the custom to refer radiometric dates to specified geological Periods: one would like to be able to do so in the interest of brevity; but there are grave difficulties. Which division of stratigraphical time a dated event falls into depends upon where the systematic boundaries are drawn. At present the positions of several are uncertain; they are liable to be changed as new, more reliable information becomes available. Thus, does the base of the Ordovician System correspond with that of the Tremadoc or of the Arenig Series? The date 505 m.y. is represented by a fixed point on the time-scale; but it may be regarded as late-Cambrian by some, though early Ordovician by others, according to where the boundary is drawn. Similarly the systematic position of the Rhaetic is debateable, while the position of the boundary between the Jurassic and the Cretaceous is still a matter of dispute. It is imperative that we speak with one voice in these matters.

In the circumstances it would appear to be less equivocal and more scientific to concentrate on the 'dates' and 'ages' rather than on their inferred positions in an inexact stratigraphical time-scale. The fact that the Dartmoor granite has a radiometric age of 280 m.y. is far more significant than the uncertainty whether this figure represents a Stephanian, Autunian or Saxonian date.

## REFERENCES

HOLMES, A. 'A revised geological time-scale,' *Trans. Edin. Geol. Soc.*, **17** (1960), 183–216.

LONG, L. E., and LAMBERT, R. ST. J. 'Rb-Sr isotope ages from the Moine Series,' in *The British Caledonides* (1963), 217.

SUTTON, J. 'Time relations within the Caledonian crystallines,' *ibid.*, 264.

ZEUNER, F. A. *Dating the Past* (Methuen: London. 1962), Chapter X.

An important work on geochronology, entitled *The Phanerozoic Time Scale*, was published by the Geological Society of London after our mss. had been sent to the printers.

See also discussion on 'Radiometric age-determinations of British rocks,' in *Proc. Geol. Soc.*, No. 1626 (Oct. 1965), 154.

## CHAPTER VI

# THE PRECAMBRIAN: (1) OF SCOTLAND

On an earlier page we explained why we do not recount the events of geological history in their strict chronological order, more particularly the reasons for omitting the ancient, pre-Palaeozoic formations. Logically after dealing with the Silurian Period we should review the Caledonian Earth Movements which, in Scotland at least, effectively separate the Silurian from the Devonian. However, it seems preferable to introduce the pre-Palaeozoic at this point: some knowledge of the rocks underlying the Palaeozoic Systems is a necessary prelude to understanding the problems connected with the building of the Caledonides.

The pre-Palaeozoic rocks provide the subject matter for two chapters, and for reasons which will emerge we give pride of place to Scotland.

In certain parts of the world in every continent Precambrian rocks occur at the surface, covering great areas in North America (the so-called Canadian Shield), in Russia, Finland and Scandinavia (together constituting the similar Baltic Shield), in South Africa and Australia. In most of these areas the Precambrian rocks fall into two contrasted groups: some of them are of ordinary rock-types, not notably different in appearance from sandstones, quartzites and other kinds of sedimentary rocks; but others are totally different, resembling igneous rocks in being crystalline, often of coarse grain, though in some cases showing a striking banding of the component minerals. These are crystalline schists and gneisses which owe their existing mineral composition and distinctive textures to deep-seated recrystallization under conditions involving very high (in extreme cases near-magmatic) temperatures and enormous pressures. As a result of these drastic changes many gneisses take on the aspect of igneous rocks of widely varying composition as they were formed from a wide range of sedimentary rock-types. As a consequence of their environment the more intensely metamorphosed rocks have been penetrated by material of magmatic origin forming injection gneisses, which are typically strongly banded.

We may remind our readers that pre-Palaeozoic time may have covered a period of 2,500,000,000 years; but the record in the rocks themselves is exceedingly scrappy and incomplete. Small areas may be studied and interpreted; but it is absolutely impracticable to combine these into anything like a history of the period. There is, however, one dominant theme which holds throughout: the pre-Palaeozoic rocks fall into two great contrasted groups as regards their nature, composition and textures. One group comprises crystalline schists and gneisses which show clear evidence of deep-seated recrystallization as indicated above. The other consists of normal sedimentary rock-types comparing closely with those occurring in the Palaeozoic Systems. The former are often termed Archaeozoic (Azoic might be even nearer the truth), or Basement Complex ('Basement' for short); while the latter are Proterozoic.

Scotland is cut up into fault-blocks by great faults which traverse the country from coast to coast. They converge upon a point lying to the south-west and splay out towards the north-east (Fig. 28).

The most northerly on the mainland is a complex zone of overthrusting which forms the boundary of the topographically distinctive North-West Highlands. Within the disturbed zone three major thrusts occur, together with many minor faults. The most easterly and the most recent is the **Moine Thrust**; but it is customary to speak of the whole zone as 'the Moine Thrust'.

The **Great Glen Fault** approximately bisects the Scottish Highlands and extend from Loch Linnhe to the Moray Firth. W. Q. Kennedy has stated the evidence for believing the horizontal displacement to be more than sixty miles along this dislocation, the movement being north-eastwards on the northern side of the fault.

Farther to the south-east the great **Highland Boundary Fault** separates two vastly different regions. As the name suggests the mountainous country of the Highlands lies to the north; while southward lies the much flatter Midland Valley or Central Lowlands, occupied by Upper Palaeozoic rocks—the Carboniferous and Devonian of O.R.S. facies.

We have already dealt with the Lower Palaeozoic rocks which occur within the Southern Uplands which lie south-east of the **Southern Uplands Boundary Fault.**

In addition to these great faults there is evidence for another which cannot actually be mapped for it is believed to run through the Minch—the deep channel separating the Outer Hebrides from the Scottish mainland. By matching homologous structures on both sides of the Minch, Dearnley believes that he can demonstrate a relative horizontal displacement of over seventy miles along the **Minch Fault.**

Apart from the areas occupied by the Orcadian Old Red Sandstone and certain narrow strips of Mesozoic rocks, almost the whole of Scotland north of the Highland Boundary Fault is occupied by pre-Palaeozoic rocks which are grouped into four 'series' of uncertain status but vast thickness. From north-west

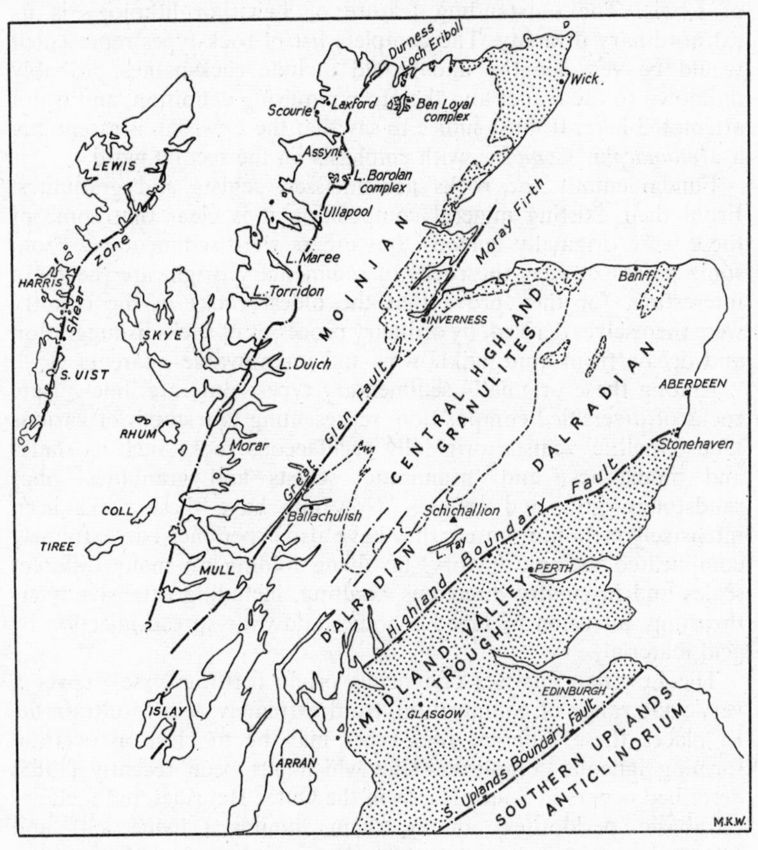


FIG. 28.

Sketch-map of Scotland showing distribution of main stratigraphical divisions. Devonian (O.R.S.)—Carboniferous stippled; Mesozoic and Tertiary omitted.

to south-east these are: (1) the Lewisian, (2) the Torridonian, (3) the Moinian and (4) the Dalradian. Of these, only the Lewisian and Torridonian are demonstrably Precambrian; the formations originally termed Dalradian include at least one limestone containing a Cambrian fauna; but there are valid reasons for believing that the greater part of the Dalradian is Precambrian. The age of the Moine 'Series' is a major problem to be discussed in due course.

1. **The Lewisian** is a true Basement Complex forming a very distinctive topographical region, the North-West Highlands, as well as the Outer Hebrides, including of course, the northerly isle of Lewis. The outstanding feature of Lewisian lithology is its extraordinary diversity. The complete list of rock-types represented would be very lengthy and would include rock-names probably unknown to the reader and therefore requiring definition, and is not attempted here. It must suffice to say that the Lewisian is essentially a *Metamorphic Complex*, with emphasis on the second word.

Fundamentally the rocks are gneisses, schists and granulites. From their existing mineral composition it is clear that some of these were originally igneous, but others were sedimentary. From some points of view the rocks of sedimentary origin are the more interesting, for they prove that the oldest rocks in the country were themselves derived, by ordinary processes of rock-disintegration and decay, from quite unknown—and unknowable—parents.

Among these originally sedimentary types some are lime-silicate rocks of diversified composition, representing limestones of various kinds; 'pelitic' schists, originally argillaceous rocks such as shales and mudstones; and 'psammitic' schists and granulites—once sandstones, grits and arkoses. Not only have these rocks been intensively metamorphosed, they have also experienced an extremely complicated tectonic history, involving folding on many different scales and in sundry directions, faulting, including extensive overthrusting, intrusion by igneous bodies and wide-spread injection by acid material.

The Lewisian gneisses of igneous origin (orthogneisses) cover a very wide range of composition, from extremely acid to ultrabasic. In places these different rock-types may be in close association forming igneous complexes. One which has been recently (1963) described occurs in South Harris in the Outer Hebrides and includes ultrabasic peridotites, among them dunites (olivine-rich) and pyroxenic varieties together with basic rocks of gabbroic type, more acid tonalites, rare anorthosites and pegmatites. These complexes resemble well-known layered complexes such as the Bushveld and Stillwater in all but size; but their small size may be deceptive. In Harris and probably elsewhere on the mainland, too, the complex is believed to be magmatically related to wide-spread basic sills and the regional dyke-suite referred to below.

Only very rarely have the original minerals survived the high-grade regional metamorphism(s) to which they were later subjected. A glance at a geological map of the North-West Highlands shows that the Lewisian outcrops are traversed by one of the best examples of a dyke-swarm available in Britain. The majority of the dykes are basaltic, and they maintain a singularly constant north-west to south-east strike, except for an earlier group which are ultrabasic in composition and strike more nearly east-west. Recent study has proved that in parts of the Lewisian tract basic dykes belonging to this suite are little altered although the country-rock into which they were injected consists of high grade, strongly foliated gneisses which obviously had been involved in regional metamorphism. This first orogenic period involving isoclinal folding, complete recrystallization and well-defined foliation is termed **Scourian** (Sutton and Watson, 1951) and is believed to have occurred some 2460 m.y. ago.

Elsewhere the dykes themselves have been converted into rocks of the same metamorphic grade as the gneisses into which they were intruded. This clearly indicates a second orogeny, later than the dyke phase and termed **Laxfordian** (Sutton and Watson, 1951). It occurred 1500 to 1600 m.y. ago. Recently (1963) the Laxfordian metamorphism has been shown to include two phases, Early and Late, both later than the dyke phase. During the Scourian and Early Laxfordian phases rocks of very high metamorphic grade were produced; but the Late-Laxfordian metamorphism was less intense. Contrary to what might be expected the effects of successive metamorphisms are not additive; but given time for equilibrium to be fully established, new mineral assemblages, exhibiting new textures appropriate to the conditions existing at the time, will be produced. In the present instance rocks of the high-grade, 'dry' pyroxene-granulite facies were converted into lower grade, 'wet' rocks belonging to the amphibolite facies, and containing hornblende and biotite. Metamorphism which down-grades the mineral assemblages is said to be retrogressive or retrograde: the Late-Laxfordian was of this type. Folding again took place, the axes being approximately at right angles to those dating from the Scourian orogeny. The most significant feature was extensive migmatization when the folded and metamorphosed rocks were 'soaked' in, and invaded by, the material of which granites are made. Ultimately more or less homogeneous granite was intruded in several areas, followed by a pegmatite phase. Some of the pegmatites, which contain minerals with measurable amounts of thorium and uranium, are important in age-determination analysis. It will be realized that in view of the time involved—nearly 1500 m.y.—the events so far recognized are remarkably few in number: but the simplest interpretation has been read into the observed facts, and the full story will certainly prove to be much more complicated. Research into the ancient rock-groups of Caledonia is proceeding apace, and it is clear that wide differences of opinion exist, even on fundamentals. The belief that the Lewisian rocks were subjected to three metamorphisms, one older, and two younger than a regional suite of basic dykes rests on the assumption that we are dealing with members of one and the same dyke phase. It is believed in some quarters that the dykes are *not* all of the same age. The time available was twice the length of the Phanerozoic; and the geological record shows that several basic dyke-swarms were injected in Britain during the latter period, so there was ample time. Unfortunately the obvious way of deciding the issue—by determining the 'absolute' ages of several dykes in different areas does not work out that way, as we shall see in the account of the Moinian.

Unfortunately these dykes are often called 'the Scourie dykes'. This term means 'the dykes at Scourie'; but this regional dyke-swarm is not restricted to this one small part of the North-West Highlands. It is preferable to refer to them by their *age*, which, incidentally is not Scourian: they are post-Scourian, pre-Laxfordian. When the dykes were injected the crustal conditions must have been drastically different from those obtaining during the Scourian orogeny. Much is made of the fact that they are a non-orogenic suite: a regional dyke-swarm cannot be injected into rocks undergoing plastic deformation. So the period of dyke injection was later than Scourian but earlier than Laxfordian. At present it is an unnamed interval of Lewisian time: it really deserves a name.

All three metamorphisms clearly indicate deep-seated environments: the rocks affected by them must have been deeply buried beneath a thick cover. Thinking in terms of the Late-Laxfordian metamorphism, the rocks exposed at the surface to-day were buried in the roots of a mountain chain when the existing mineral assemblages and textures were impressed upon them. Of these mountains no trace has survived.

Before leaving the Lewisian we wish to make it quite clear that 'Scourian' and 'Laxfordian' are not systematic stratigraphical terms like Cambrian, Silurian or Caradocian: they are the names of significant events in Lewisian geological history. 'Scourian' means the regional (dynamothermal) metamorphism which affected Lewisian rocks 2460 m.y. ago. Similarly 'Laxfordian' is the term covering the post-dyke-phase metamorphisms, the more recent episode of which dates from 1500 to 1600 m.y. ago. The rocks affected by all three metamorphisms belong to the Lewisian.

The main current problem of the Lewisian concerns the reality or otherwise of certain 'Lewisian inliers' occurring far to the eastward of the eastern boundary of the main outcrop. They look convincing enough on geological maps; but opinion is widely divided as to their real nature. For the moment, however, we will postpone further consideration of the problem until the other rock-groups have been discussed.

2. **The Torridonian.** The undulating belt of country occupied by the Lewisian ends abruptly eastwards against a discontinuous line of steep-sided mountains including Quinag, Canisp, Suilven, 'Stack Polly', Cul Mor and Slioch, which are built of different material—different in lithology, composition, attitude and in being unmetamorphosed in the main outcrop. By tracing the base of these Torridonian rocks—in the field or on the map—it is seen that the boundary is an unconformity, the surface of separation taking the form of a dissected land surface (Fig. 29). In spite of their relatively young appearance, their Precambrian age is beyond question, for the basal quartzites of the Cambrian lie unconformably upon the

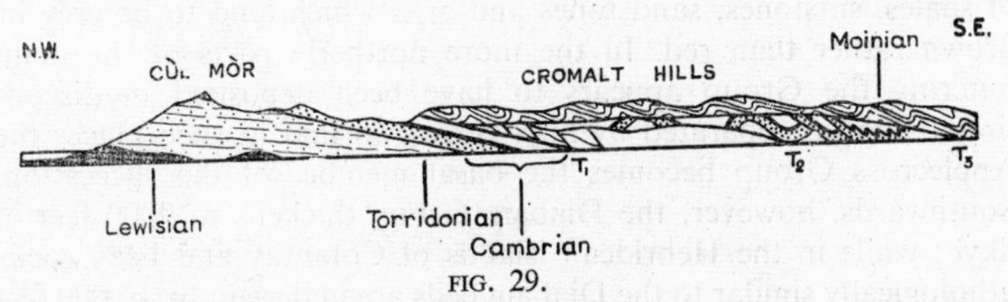


FIG. 29.

Section across the North-West Highlands of Scotland showing the disposition of the Lewisian, Torridonian, Cambrian and Moinian rocks, and the structures in the overthrust zone.

Length of section: about 4 miles, from north-west to south-east.
(*After B. N. Peach, J. Horne and others.*)

Torridonian: some of these Torridonian mountains therefore display a striking double unconformity. It is immediately evident that a vast period of time separates the Torridonian from the Lewisian—time enough for the Lewisian rocks to have emerged from the deep-seated environment of their last metamorphism, and for the veritable roots of a pre-Torridonian mountain-chain to have been exposed by denudation.

The Torridonian Series includes quite a variety of rock-types; but they are dominantly arenaceous, with arkose as the central type, grading into conglomerates and breccias on the one hand and into shales on the other. Plenty of fresh microcline accompanies the quartz grains in the arkoses, which are typically reddish or chocolate-coloured.

Among the pebbles in the conglomerates are some reminiscent of the Uriconian volcanic rocks of England; but the variation in grain-size and in thickness of the Torridonian rocks indicates derivation from the north-west; and the real interest of these pebbles lies in the fact that they are the only surviving records of an early outpouring of rhyolitic lava.

The complete Torridonian comprises four members, three of which were originally described in the Survey Memoir on the North-West Highlands—a monumental work. They are named after localities where each is typically developed: (3) Aultbea Group, (2) Applecross Group, named from the picturesque Applecross Mountains, (1) Diabaig Group bearing the name of a tiny village on the shores of Loch Torridon itself. The Upper and Middle Torridonian together reach a thickness of 10,000 feet in the main outcrop and include the typical reddish arkoses which were in mind when the formation was dubbed the 'Oldest Red Sandstone': it is very like the O.R.S. in many respects. The Applecross and Aultbea Groups are not recognizable in the most southerly outcrops.

The Diabaig Group is much more variable in lithology, consisting of shales, siltstones, sandstones and grits which tend to be grey or brown rather than red. In the more northerly parts of the main outcrop, the Group appears to have been deposited in discontinuous basins separated by high ridges, so that in such places the Applecross Group becomes the basal member of the succession. Southwards, however, the Diabaig Group thickens to 9000 feet in Skye; while in the Hebridean islands of Colonsay and Islay rocks lithologically similar to the Diabaig beds are underlain by 10,000 feet of graded greywackes, transported by turbidity currents.

The extent to which these groups succeed one another in vertical sequence or replace one another laterally is not yet known; but in recent papers on the Torridonian, the Aultbea, Applecross and Diabaig Groups are spoken of as facies, suggesting the latter alternative. With regard to conditions of deposition, the Torridonian was laid down under shallow water: much of the Diabaig Group is fluviatile in the broad sense—braided channels traversing extensive flood-plains played a major part in Torridonian palaeogeography as in the O.R.S. of the Anglo-Welsh cuvette, as described in due course. The details of lithology and sedimentary structures are often very well displayed, notably in certain coastal sections, for example Garvie Bay in Wester Ross. Here low cliffs of sensibly horizontal Torridonian with strong vertical jointing give wonderful opportunities for studying part of the succession inch by inch.

3. **The Moine Series or Moinian** is so called from its occurrence in a M'hoine, a tract of peaty moorland in the extreme north of Scotland and just east of the Moine Thrust. Actually the Moinian extends well beyond the Great Glen, and in the Grampian Highlands makes contact with the fourth and last rock-group—the Dalradian.

As regards lithology the Moinian rocks are as monotonous as the Lewisian is diversified: a highly siliceous, flaggy granulite is the most widely distributed type; but finer-grained, more pelitic rocks, as well as bands with distorted pebbles and representing original conglomerates, also occur. Over wide areas not only are the Moinian rocks lithologically monotonous, but their apparent dip and strike are uniform too. This has led to a widely held belief that the formation must be of immense thickness. Others hold that this appearance of vast thickness is deceptive; and that the original thickness of the Moinian has been enormously increased by isoclinal folding. The only way of solving this problem is by detailed mapping, which is difficult and often unrewarding. Over wide areas distinctive marker horizons which would enable the structure to be deciphered, are usually absent; and the mapper has to rely upon the discovery of sedimentary structures, particularly current-bedding, which have survived the metamorphism (Fig. 30). In isoclinally folded strata, of course, one limb of each fold is inverted, so the problem resolves itself into proving the presence or absence of inversion. But even evidence of this kind may not be entirely satisfactory. The more intense the folding of this type becomes, the more likely it is that the middle limb of each fold may be systematically eliminated, as B. C. King has pointed out. However, these difficulties are being overcome; and it has been demonstrated that areas of supposedly simple structure and uniform dip are, in fact, extremely complex as a result, not only of isoclinal folding, but also of repeated folding at different dates. The over-printing of two or three sets of folds, varying in intensity, amplitude, style and direction makes the problem of deciphering the structure of the Moine Series one of extreme difficulty.

With regard to the boundary between the Lewisian and the Moinian, Lapworth proved that the latter had been thrust over the former and that the boundary coincides with the outcrop of the Moine Thrust. Subsequent detailed mapping by Peach and Horne with their colleagues showed that several isolated outcrops, some of considerable size, occur to the east of the main boundary, well within the Moine territory. These were interpreted as inliers, which look convincing on existing geological maps; but subsequently it has been shown that certain of the Lewisian 'inliers' are *underlain* as well as overlain by Moinian rocks. In some instances detailed mapping has shown that the Lewisian gneisses in these anomalous positions are tectonic slices thrust into the positions they now occupy. Elsewhere however, thrusting could not be proved and it was claimed that these 'rocks of Lewisian aspect' formed integral parts of the Moine succession. It is not impossible that all three relationships may be true of particular areas of Lewisian gneisses; but in order to establish the time-relationship between the Moines and the Lewisian, the minimum requirement is that unconformity should be proved *in a single case*. The interpretation of the others then becomes merely of academic interest.

Proving an unconformable relationship in the highly metamorphosed environment of the Moine Schists is well-nigh impossible. The intense deformation that has affected the Moines must also have affected the Lewisian. Consequently both Moinian and Lewisian rocks have developed parallel structures—tectonic parallelism—despite any original discordance that may have existed between them. Likewise conglomerates have been reduced to a shredded and wholly unrecognizable condition. Nevertheless at two localities studied recently, where Moinian *appears* to rest unconformably on a Lewisian Basement, the evidence seems to be as conclusive as may reasonably be expected. At Loch Duich on the Scottish mainland opposite the southern end of Skye the lowest Moine Schists rest successively on several different members of the Lewisian Complex; while at Glenelg a still-recognizable conglomerate separates the two formations.

More has been written concerning the age of the Moines, and far more age measurements have been, and are being, made than for any other stratigraphical unit; but in spite of this, the matter is still obscure. Unmetamorphosed Moine sediments are nowhere available for measurement: all the dates calculated refer to metamorphic episodes in the history of the Moines, and nobody can say how many millions of years elapsed between the period of accumulation of the Moine sediments and the earliest metamorphism to which they were subjected. The *latest* metamorphism is well documented and occurred 420–390 m.y. ago. The calculated age of muscovite crystals in pegmatite injected into least-altered Moines at Knoydart in Western Scotland is 740 m.y. The method by which the pegmatite originated is immaterial; but the adjacent Moine rocks must be older than the pegmatite—there is no direct evidence to show how much older. It may be argued that as the Moinian sediments rested unconformably on Lewisian gneisses in a condition of high grade metamorphism dated at 1500–1600 m.y. ago, the former must be younger than 1500 m.y. The maximum and minimum ages are, therefore, less (probably much less) than 1500 and more (probably much more) than 740 m.y. A reasonable compromise, though it is little more than a guess, would be 1000 m.y., which is a very long way back in the pre-Palaeozoic.

One of the most intriguing current problems of the British pre-Palaeozoic is the possible equivalence of the Moinian and the Torridonian. On first acquaintance they appear to have experienced very different geological histories: the Moinian has passed through a phase of regional metamorphism, the Torridonian has not. The striking difference between them in metamorphic grade may be explained as due to different positions in the tectogen: the unmetamorphosed Torridonian, occurring west of the Moine Thrust Zone, formed part of the unmoved foreland; but the strongly folded and intensely metamorphosed Moines were translated from a deep-seated region within the tectogen to their present position along thrust-planes. Further, the Torridonian and the Moinian in suitable places display metamorphic convergence: in the near neighbourhood of the Moine Thrust both were affected by dislocation metamorphism of relatively low grade which lowered the metamorphic grade of the Moines but had the opposite effect on the Torridonian rocks. This certainly strengthens the belief that if both 'series' were in the same metamorphic grade they would be indistinguishable. Further, the sedimentary structures observed in the Lower Torridonian in Skye are like those described from the mainland areas of Glenelg and Morar, proving similar conditions of deposition, in the same kind of environment. The case for equating the Moinian and Torridonian grows stronger as time goes on; but it is extremely doubtful if this can ever be *proved.* Granted the possibility, it is reasonable to argue that the problem of the age of the Moines could be solved by determining that of the Torridonians; but unfortunately it appears that the latter do not contain suitable material for measurement, and there, for the moment, the matter must rest.

*If* the Moinian rocks are metamorphosed equivalents of the Torridonian, and *if* the age of the former is approximately 1000 m.y., the latter must date from 400 m.y. before the opening of the Palaeozoic epoch. Nobody who has studied the North-West Highlands can fail to be impressed by the immensity of time which must separate the Torridonian from the Lewisian; but it is difficult to believe that a great time-gap separates the Cambrian from the Torridonian. It may be significant that in Scandinavia the Red Sparagmite, lithologically like the Torridonian, appears to underlie the Cambrian *Holmia* Shales without visible unconformity, and is classed as 'Eocambrian'.

4. **The Dalradian.** To the south-eastward of the tract occupied by the Moinian, the Scottish Highlands have been carved in a diverse series of rock-groups collectively termed the Dalradian. These include thick, lithologically distinctive units which outcrop conveniently in a magnificent section along the Banffshire coast, where the details of the succession and the style of folding and faulting are seen to advantage. Happily metamorphism, though locally intense, has not obliterated the original sedimentary structures.

The Dalradian is now divided into three 'Series' (of uncertain status) instead of two as formerly. The rocks have been studied in great detail in several areas where local (usually Gaelic) names have been given to the stratigraphical units. Facies variations, intense metamorphism and complex structures make correlation difficult. Nevertheless over the greater part of the Dalradian outcrop the same general succession can be recognized throughout a belt of country extending south-westwards from Banffshire through the Central (Grampian) Highlands, thence by way of the Hebridean Islands of Islay and Jura into Donegal and Connemara in Northern Ireland.

The succession established in the Central Highlands is regarded as 'standard'; that occurring in the Argyllshire region (including Ballachulish and Appin) is different both as regards lithology and conditions of deposition. The Dalradian of the latter region forms the structural unit known as the *Ballapel Foundation*, while the Central Highlands succession builds the *Iltay Nappe*. The Ballapel Foundation consists largely of rhythmic alternations of limestone, pelite and quartzite and this facies extends through Kintyre into Donegal. Important formations include the Ballachulish Limestone and black slates, and the Appin Quartzite and Limestones. As a tectonic boundary separates the Ballapel Foundation from the rest of the Dalradian, correlation by the only possible way—tracing a formation from one area to another—is impracticable.

In general the *Lower Dalradian* is restricted in distribution and apparently this is due in part to accumulation in separate basins. The rocks are of 'shelf' facies and perhaps average 5000 feet in thickness. They are well exposed on the Banffshire coast where the lowest member, the Cullen Quartzite (orthoquartzite) might 'equally well be taken as the top of the Moine Series' (Sutton and Watson) and is now regarded as a connecting link between Moinian and Dalradian. Above comes a great variety of rock-types including schists which contain garnet, mica, graphite or staurolite on different horizons.

The *Middle Dalradian* is largely composed of quartzites, but schists also figure in the succession. The lowest member is one of the most significant: it is the Schichallion[1] Boulder Bed at the base of the Schichallion Quartzite which builds the well-known Perthshire peak of that name. The Boulder Bed contains boulders so large that moving ice is the only reasonable means of transport; but whether an actual ice-sheet or floating icebergs were responsible is uncertain. Among the boulders are granite, gneiss, quartzite and, of special interest, nordmarkite, an uncommon quartz-syenite bearing a

[1] Pronounced (very approximately) 'She-hally-on'.

Norwegian name, but occurring also in the Loch Borolan Complex in the North-West Highlands.[1]

The Boulder Bed occurs also in Islay (Portaskaig) and a glacial tillite has been recognized in a corresponding position in the Irish Dalradian.

The Schichallion Quartzite and its lateral equivalents (the Islay and Jura Quartzites) can be traced for fifty miles and may be up to 15,000 feet in maximum thickness. Frequent worm-casts and large-scale current-bedding indicate rapid deposition under shallow-water conditions as a delta extended itself away from a north-western landmass. Locally algal (stromatolitic) limestone reefs were established on the Boulder Beds and were later buried beneath the deltaic sands. Deepening water is indicated by the succeeding argillaceous sediments, including some dark-coloured pyritous beds laid down under possibly euxenic conditions, discussed in connection with the Dolgelley Beds in the Upper Cambrian. No correlation is implied, of course, except as regards environment.

The *Upper Dalradian* is fundamentally different from the two underlying divisions in that it is primarily a thick greywacke series consisting of mixed unsorted sediment laid down by density currents flowing axially along a trough of typical Caledonoid trend which was firmly established at this time. The Series commences, however, with a group of limestones largely converted into 'marbles' containing an interesting variety of so-called lime-silicates, and bearing several local names—the Tayvallich, Loch Tay, Boyne, etc. Limestone. It is in part at least a shelf limestone, locally with traces of oolitic structure. The limestones are massive in the more westerly outcrops, but give place to limestone-breccias eastwards, representing slipped debris. A most significant feature is the occurrence of a volcanic episode comprising an extrusive as well as an intrusive phase, the magma being basic. In places the igneous rocks are covered by the non-committal term 'Green Beds', applicable where they have been streaked out into schists or phyllites; but at their best, basic sills can be distinguished from basic lava-flows, some of which display pillow-structure and were erupted under water. In the field it has proved possible to distinguish between bases and tops of individual lava-flows, which enables the way-up of the local succession to be established. These Tayvallich Lavas are petrographically and structurally very similarly to the Arenigian lavas so well displayed on the Girvan coast: but again no correlation is implied—it is merely a close analogy. The Volcanics are succeeded by normal, coarse-grained grits.

[1] It is not implied that the boulders came from this source: the Complex cuts the Cambro-Ordovician Durness Limestone.

A feature of special interest in the Banffshire Upper Dalradian succession is the occurrence of boulder beds in the Macduff Group, and these, like the Schichallion Boulder Bed, are regarded as of glacial origin, almost certainly deposited by melting icebergs.

In attempting to date the Dalradian it is important to realize that 30,000 feet of strata are involved. They were deposited in widely varying environments; they were subjected to regional metamorphism at least twice and were folded repeatedly. All this indicates the passage of a very long period of time; but at present it is impossible to suggest how long. The evidence bearing on this age problem is, in part palaeontological. In addition age-measurements are available though they do not seem to help much.

In the belt of country immediately north of the Highland Boundary Fault rock-groups occur which are notably less metamorphosed than the Dalradian of the region farther north. Argillaceous strata are still in the condition of slates—the Aberfoyle Slates for example; while these are associated with grits, at the top the Ben Ledi Grits, underlain by the Leny Grits, and certain rocks non-commitally termed the Green Beds. The Leny Grits contain a limestone from which J. Pringle in 1938 obtained a Middle Cambrian trilobite fauna including the genus *Pagetia* and eodiscids. This was a momentous discovery as these were the first fossils to be obtained from the Dalradian. Obviously it is highly important to know precisely the stratigraphical relationship between these rocks of proved Cambrian age and the associated Dalradian; but this is much more easily said than done.

The strata which include the Middle Cambrian Leny Limestone occur within the 'sphere of influence' of the Highland Boundary Fault and it is not absolutely certain that the observed sequence is the true one; but unless there are unsuspected complications, the immediately underlying beds must also be Middle Cambrian, and it is at least possible that the Lower Cambrian is also represented lower in the Dalradian. This is the problem of the age of the Harlech Series over again. The Leny Limestone is Middle Cambrian and the associated strata must also belong to this System: room must be found for part of the Middle and the whole of the Lower Cambrian, at the expense of the Dalradian. Unfortunately through tectonic complexity and the metamorphic state of most of the rocks the position of the top of the genuine Dalradian and the base of the Cambrian is unknown. Two points seem to be significant: (1) the occurrence of the Tayvallich Volcanics; and (2) the presence of glacial boulder beds. Volcanic rocks are virtually absent from Cambrian successions in other parts of Britain; but the Tayvallich Volcanics closely match the spilitic pillow lavas of the Ballantrae

Volcanic Series near Girvan, and also the Gwna Spilites in the Mona Complex in Anglesey. Unless the structural relationships have been mis-read, an Ordovician age for Tayvallich lavas is out of the question. Correlation with the Gwna Spilites is not impossible.

The occurrence of glacial boulder beds in the Dalradian is most significant: rocks of this type and origin occur in several areas bordering the North Atlantic—Spitzbergen, Greenland and Norway, where they are of late Precambrian age. Probably the Scottish examples are of the same age. Therefore the underlying members of the Dalradian succession must be pre-Palaeozoic.

With regard to the other line of evidence—direct radiometric age measurements—the Dalradians have been sampled in several different areas; but the dates determined shed no light on the period of accumulation of the Dalradian sediments, which, of course, is their age. The dates so far determined are related, in some manner which is still not understood, to stages in the evolution of their present mineral composition, especially to the most recent metamorphic episode to which they were subjected. The dates fall within the range of those of the Moinian rocks and, as was the case with the latter, bear no relation to the true age, which remains unknown.

**Addendum: 'Way up' criteria**

A digression is necessary at this point to look more closely into the problem of deciphering the structure of a tectonically complex area of unfossiliferous rocks. The key to the problem lies in the ability to recognize certain sedimentation features which indicate the direction of 'younging'[1] or becoming younger in the depositional sense, and thus establishing the order of deposition.

A common and useful feature is graded bedding. This term is self-explanatory. Graded bedding may be observed in sediments of any degree of coarseness, even under a microscope; and in the vast majority of cases the coarser part of a bed is basal, and the finer material lies above. That is the principle involved. The way in which observations of graded bedding may be used is suggested in the accompanying Fig. 30. The succession dips uniformly to the left; but only grits '1' and '2' are right way up; grits '3', '4' and '5' are inverted. Thus a fold-axis must lie between '2' and '3'; it must be inclined with the beds and is therefore isoclinal. Two possibilities arise: the fold may be synclinal or anticlinal. The lower two diagrams (B and C) show that the westerly limb of the syncline is the inverted limb, and conversely for the anticline.

In finer-grained material grading often leads to colour-banding:

[1] This is a horrible term as there is no verb 'to young'; but it is widely used in such phrases as 'the beds young to the east.'

finer-grained tops tend to be darker—grey, green or purple; while more sandy bottoms are lighter and yellower.

Even in metamorphic rocks of appropriate composition such grading may be indicated by the existing mineral composition. As

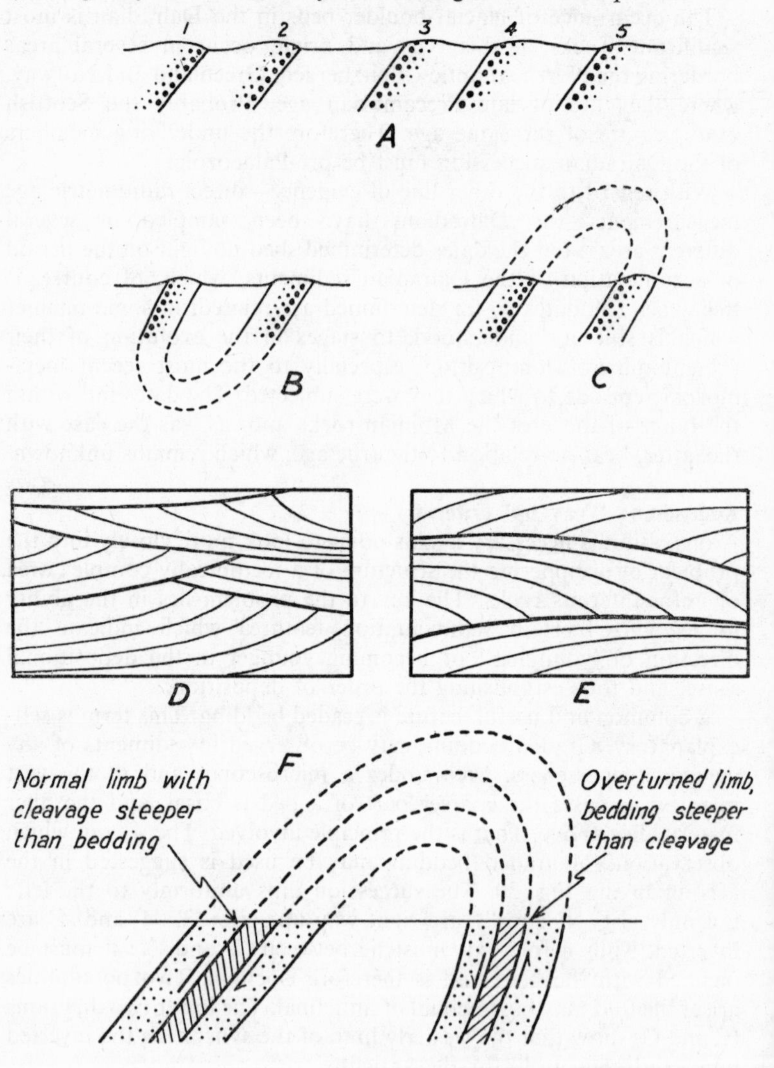


FIG. 30.

Diagram to illustrate the use of graded bedding (A, B, and C), current bedding (D and E) and fracture-cleavage (F) in determining the sequence in unfossiliferous strata in regions of intense folding.

the original grading was dependent on variation in the proportion of clay minerals to sand or silt, in the metamorphic equivalents it will be expressed by the proportion of aluminium silicates, such as andalusite or kyanite, to quartz. In other words in a schist showing such mineralogical grading, the tops will be indicated by concentrations of andalusite or kyanite.

In the coarser grades other features may be used to confirm conclusions based on the evidence of grading. Thus the upper and lower surfaces of argillaceous beds interstratified with coarse sandstones and grits are often strikingly dissimilar, the base may be quite flat, but the top highly irregular, the more mobile clayey material having been forced upwards as lobes and tongues.

Another feature commonly available is current bedding. Alterations in the direction and force of currents lead to truncation of the underlying structure and such truncation must indicate a 'top' (Fig. 30, D and E).

In regions where fine-grained silty or argillaceous rocks occur any appreciable folding is accompanied by the development of cleavage. The relationship of this to the bedding may indicate whether the succession is right way up or inverted. Fracture-cleavage is produced when an argillaceous bed is squeezed and sheared by movements parallel to the bedding planes of the two adjoining beds, provided that the latter are more competent rocks. Directions of relative movements are indicated in the accompanying diagram, Fig. 30, F.

## REFERENCES

The literature relating to the geology of the Scottish Highlands is voluminous, and includes several Survey Memoirs and Regional Geologies. In addition special aspects are dealt with in the following:

BAILEY, E. B. 'Moine Tectonics and Metamorphism in Skye,' *Trans. Edin. Geol. Soc.*, **16** (1955), 93.

CLIFFORD, T. N. 'Stratigraphy and Structure of Part of Ross-shire,' *Q.J.G.S.*, **113** (1957), 57.

DEARNLEY, R. 'Lewisian Complex of South Harris,' *Q.J.G.S.*, **119** (1963), 243.

GILETTI, B. J., MOORBATH, S., and LAMBERT, R. ST. J. 'Geochronological Study of the Metamorphic Complexes of the Scottish Highlands,' *Q.J.G.S.*, **117** (1961), 233.

KING, B. C., and RAST, N. 'Tectonic Styles in the Dalradian and Moinian of the Central Highlands of Scotland,' *Proc. Geol. Assoc.*, **66** (1956), 243.

MCINTYRE, D. B. 'The Moine Thrust . . .,' *Proc. Geol. Assoc.*, **65** (1954), 203.

RAMSAY, J., and SPRING, J. 'Moine stratigraphy in the Western Highlands of Scotland,' *Proc. Geol. Assoc.*, **73** (1962), 295.

SUTTON, J., and WATSON, J. 'Deposition of the Upper Dalradian Rocks of the Banffshire Coast,' *Proc. Geol. Assoc.*, **66** (1955), 101.

SUTTON, J., and WATSON, J. 'Some aspects of Torridonian Stratigraphy in Skye,' *Proc. Geol. Assoc.*, **75** (1964), 251.

The report on a symposium on *The British Caledonides* published by Oliver & Boyd in 1963, contains authoritative contributions by various authors dealing with the Moines and Dalradians, including full bibliographies.

## CHAPTER VII

# THE PRECAMBRIAN: (2) OF ENGLAND AND WALES

ROCKS of presumed or proved pre-Palaeozoic age in England and Wales cover a far smaller proportion of the total surface area than is the case with Scotland. However, they do occur in North and South Wales, in the Welsh Borderlands notably in Shropshire, they form the core of the Malvern Hills, and occur in a number of small inliers in the English Midlands, for example near Birmingham and at Nuneaton. They form the picturesque Charnwood 'Forest' in Leicestershire. For many years certain schists and gneisses intruded by a variety of igneous rocks in the Lizard district in Cornwall and in the extreme south of Devonshire, were thought to be Precambrian; but they are now believed to be much younger.

In England the most extensive area of Pre-Palaeozoic rocks occurs in the region of the Longmynd in **South Shropshire.** The general geological features of the region are indicated in Fig. 14, p. 58. The dissected plateau of the Longmynd is occupied by an immensely thick series of sedimentary rocks—the Longmyndian—dipping, in the south of the area, steeply and uniformly towards the west. These rocks are well displayed in deeply cut valleys which gash the sides of the plateau; but over wide areas of the latter exposures are infrequent and poor. Fundamentally the Longmyndian comprises two main members, each of the status of a geological System. The *Eastern* (*or Grey*) *Longmyndian* is essentially argillaceous, consisting of a greywacke assemblage of flags, siltstones, shales and grits, grey, greenish-grey or purple on different horizons. The monotony of the succession is broken, however, by 'marker horizons' of distinctive lithology, which are invaluable aids in mapping and interpreting the structure. Among these are various 'grits', e.g. the Cardingmill Grit, and a very distinctive volcanic horizon consisting of coarse-grained tuffs, easily recognized in the field.

The *Western* (*or Red*) *Longmyndian* is essentially different: it is dominantly arenaceous, consisting of purplish red sandstones, largely arkosic and containing conglomerates at certain levels. These typical Red Longmyndian rocks occupy two broad belts of country symmetrically disposed in relation to a central argillaceous member—the Bridges Group, consisting of purplish-red slates. This symmetrical disposition obviously suggests repetition by folding; and recently, through a careful study of the sedimentary structures of these rocks, inversion of the Red Longmyndian lying westward of the middle of the Bridges Group, has been proved. As it is the *westward* limb of the fold which is inverted, it must be synclinal (Fig. 31); and as the dips in the two limbs are essentially the same, the major structure of the Longmynd must be a compressed syncline, with its axial plane running through the middle of the Bridges Group and inclined steeply westwards (Fig. 31).

The third member of the Precambrian succession in this part of England forms a range of steep-sided, hog-backed hills separated from the Longmynd by the Church Stretton Valley, through which runs the important fault-system, known as the Church Stretton Fault. These hills, including Caer Caradoc, the Lawley and, farther north along the same line, the Wrekin which rises commandingly a thousand feet above the Midland Plain, are built of volcanic rocks—lavas, dominantly acid (rhyolitic), but basaltic in part, pyroclasts, including agglomerates, knit together by acid and basic intrusives. They constitute the Uriconian Volcanic Series, named from the Roman centre of Uriconium, near Shrewsbury. To the north-west of the Longmynd, too, similar hills occur built of identical material, and likewise separated from the Longmyndian by profound faults. The main outcrops occur on Pontesford Hill, hence the name Pontesfordian is often applied to them; but there is little doubt that the Pontesfordian and the Uriconian are one and the same. There is no absolute proof of this: the only available evidence is the complete and detailed lithological similarity between the two; but the correlation is widely accepted.

As regards the relationship between the Uriconian and the Eastern and Western Longmyndian, faulting, as we have seen, complicates the issue, but the significant facts are these. Both divisions of the Longmyndian contain material indistinguishable from the Uriconian; and if this is accepted as such, the former must be younger than, and lie above, the latter. In other words, the Uriconian rocks were laid under contribution in Longmyndian times. Secondly—and conclusively—on the outskirts of Church Stretton certain grits—the Helmeth Grits—are interposed between the Uriconian on the one hand and the basal member of the Eastern Longmyndian on the other. By interstratification these grits grade downwards into the volcanics, and upwards into Grey Longmyndian. Therefore it appears that, at the close of the volcanic episode, normal sedimentation commenced over the Longmynd area and continued until the Uriconian lavas and tuffs were buried beneath some 12,000 feet of Grey Longmyndian sediments (Fig. 31).

The evidence of included fragments is even stronger and certainly

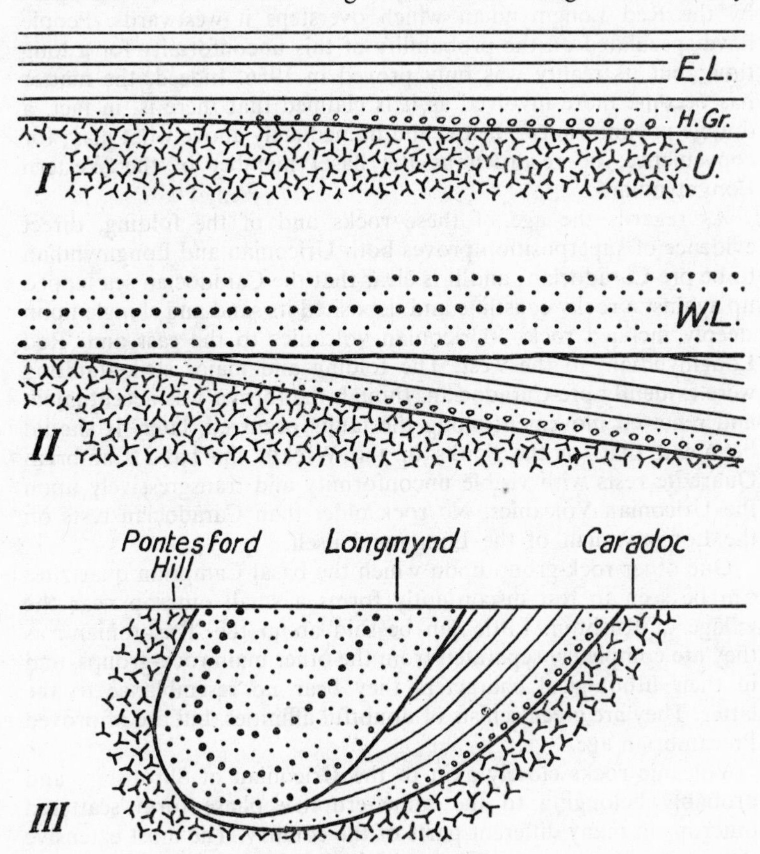


FIG. 31.

Sketch sections showing stages in the evolution of the Longmynd in Shropshire.

I—at the end of deposition of the Eastern Longmyndian.

II—after deposition of the Western Longmyndian, showing unconformable overstep.

III—interpretation of present structure—*see* text.

H.Gr.—Helmeth Grit; Faults omitted. U—Uriconian.

more obvious in the case of the Western Longmyndian: the distinctive conglomerates, referred to above, contain an abundance of Uriconian material in the form of easily recognized pebbles. Further, it appears that this material was derived from the west, i.e. from outcrops now represented by the 'Pontesfordian'. Now if, as we believe, there is only one Uriconian Series, it forms the common floor to *both* divisions of the Longmyndian; and this is possible only if the Grey Longmyndian is succeeded unconformably by the Red Longmyndian which oversteps it westwards. People have speculated on the probability of this unconformity for a long time; but its reality was only proved in 1956. Indeed, the matter has become more involved as it is claimed that there is, in fact, a double unconformity—below and immediately above what may, for convenience, be regarded as the basal member of the Western Longmyndian.

As regards the age of these rocks and of the folding, direct evidence of superposition proves both Uriconian and Longmyndian to be pre-Caradocian; and it is clear that the Caradocian sea lapped up against a rocky coastline and deposited its sand and shingle upon steeply inclined rocks—Uriconian volcanics to the east and 'Red Longmyndian' to the west. The folding and major strike-faulting were evidently pre-Caradocian, though the former was accentuated, and renewed movement along the faults occurred, later. It should be noted that on the flanks of the Wrekin the basal Cambrian Quartzite rests with visible unconformity and transgressively upon the Uriconian Volcanics. No rock older than Caradocian rests on the Longmyndian of the Longmynd itself.

One other rock-group upon which the basal Cambrian quartzites can be seen to rest discordantly forms a small outcrop near the village of Rushton. Little can be said about the 'Rushtonian', as they are completely separated from the other main rock-groups, and in their lithological characters they bear no resemblance to the latter. They are green schists of doubtful affinities, but are of proved Precambrian age.

Volcanic rocks closely akin to the Uriconian of Shropshire and probably belonging to the same eruptive phase form scattered outcrops in many different parts of the country. The most extensive outcrops occur in Jersey (Channel Islands), North and South Wales, while there are smaller patches in the Nuneaton ridge in Warwickshire, and in the Lickey Hills south of Birmingham. But in addition to these actual outcrops, evidence of the wide distribution of Uriconian rocks hidden under the Triassic cover is afforded by the many blocks and smaller fragments occurring in the red breccias of the Enville Beds in the Midlands.

**Charnwood 'Forest',** in Leicestershire, is a picturesque area rising abruptly from the Trias-covered Midland plain. It is a fragment of an ancient mountain-chain, the greater part of which is deeply buried under Cambrian, Carboniferous and Triassic rocks; but the summits here and there project through this cover and afford a striking contrast in surface-relief and land-utilization. The Precambrian outcrops form rugged uplands crowned by tor-like outcrops of volcanic tuffs, agglomerates or slates; while the adjacent Triassic lowlands afford typical pastoral scenery of the English Midlands. The Precambrian of the stratified series is divided into three groups. The Lower Charnian is made up of very fine-grained tuffs, derived from some distant source, laid down under water and converted into 'hornstones' by silicification. In the Middle Charnian violently explosive eruptions from some near-by volcano gave rise to spectacularly coarse volcanic breccias (agglomerates)—the Felsitic and Slaty Agglomerates. Finer-grained rocks supervene, and the highest in this group are again hornstones. The Upper Charnian, while containing much volcanic material, consists of slates, grits, quartzite and conglomerate. Structurally the 'Forest' is important as the Precambrian rocks have been thrown into a great elongated dome, trending north-west to south-east. This is the so-called Charnoid trend, and is important in other Precambrian terrains. Much of the northern half of the Charnwood dome is concealed beneath the Trias, it is much faulted, the slaty rocks are strongly cleaved, and in the area many intrusive igneous rocks occur. They are of the same petrographic types as the fragments in the agglomerates and tuffs, and evidently belong to the same volcanic cycle. Some, indeed, may be the fillings of the volcanic vents themselves. The coarser-grained intrusives are of syenitic composition—the so-called 'markfieldites', the Precambrian age of which is proved by the occurrence of boulders of this rock-type in the basal conglomerate of the Cambrian in the Nuneaton ridge. The volcanic and intrusive rocks of Charnwood Forest are not of Uriconian type; they belong to a different petrographic province, and were probably of a different age. A distinctive alga, appropriately named *Charnia*, was discovered a few years ago in the Charnian Volcanic Series, in tuffaceous siltstone. A tentative isotopic age is 1000 m.y.—the same as the date suggested for the Moines and Torridonian sediments.

The rocks termed **Ingletonian** and believed to be Precambrian occur in two inliers on the southern flank of the Askrigg Block of Carboniferous rocks in the northern Pennines, immediately north of the Craven Fault zone. They form the floor to the Lower Palaeozoic rocks, chiefly Silurian, on which the Carboniferous (Viséan) rest with strong unconformity. They consist of unfossiliferous greywackes graded from coarse sandstones into siltstones, isoclinally folded, in contrast with the more open folds in the Silurian.

The Uriconian of the **Malvern Hills** are not well exposed and the real interest of this area lies in the occurrence of a wide variety of crystalline gneisses, reminiscent, in their general characters, of the Lewisian of the North-West Highlands. Their genetic relationships are still under investigation. These ancient rocks form the core of the Malvern Hills, against which the Cambrian and Silurian strata have been pressed into large folds on the west; while the Triassic rocks have been banked against it on the east, and form the low-lying ground stretching away towards the Cotswold Hills.

From western **Pembrokeshire** comes further evidence of volcanic activity. Several small outcrops occur in the cores of anticlinal folds, notably in the neighbourhood of St Davids, where more than 5000 feet of tuffs occur ranging from coarse agglomerates to the finest hornstones. Locally rhyolitic and trachytic lava-flows showing fluxion and spherulitic structures are interbedded with the tuffs. The plutonic phase of this igneous cycle is represented by intrusions of granite and diorite.

About two-thirds of the island of **Anglesey** is occupied by Pre-cambrian rocks, which have been exhaustively studied by E. Greenly. Most of the island has been reduced by denudation to the condition of a peneplain, much of the surface is under cultivation; but in spite of these drawbacks, Greenly worked out the details of a very long and varied geological history. He believed that a stratified succession—the 'Bedded Succession'—rests upon a more ancient 'Gneissic Floor' of prior formation. Recently R. M. Shackleton has modified this interpretation and believes that the gneisses were formed from certain members of the Bedded Succession. The latter may be 20,000 feet in thickness and includes a very wide range of rock-types, laid down under geosynclinal conditions. Among the sedimentary rock-types are quartzites, finely displayed at Holyhead, and graded greywackes. Associated with the geosynclinal sediments are those types of volcanic rocks which elsewhere are characteristic of this environment: these are submarine spilitic pillow-lavas, one group of which may be a thousand feet in thickness, and form spectacular exposures in the Newborough dunes. These are the Gwna Spilites.

The rocks of the 'Gneissic Floor' of Greenly are coarsely crystalline and range in composition from basic to acid. Some of them may be igneous gneisses; but some are 'paragneisses' of sedimentary origin, formed by deep-seated recrystallization accompanied by permeation and injection by igneous material, in the manner considered above. Indeed, there is a strong resemblance to the more intensely metamorphosed Scottish gneisses occurring in the Lewisian. Among the high-grade metamorphics the very rare glaucophane-schist occurs and represents some of the soda-rich pillow lavas (spilites).

Later than the intense regional metamorphism and impregnation came the uprise into the tectogen of potassic granite, represented at the surface by the Sarn Granite in peninsular Carnarvonshire, and the Coedana Granite in Anglesey. This sequence of events conforms to the general pattern of an orogenic cycle, and may conveniently be termed the Monian Orogeny, comparable with, but much earlier than the Caledonian Orogeny. Actually the Mona Complex rocks form part of the floor of the Caledonian geosyncline in which the Cambrian, Ordovician and Silurian were deposited.

With regard to the structure of the Mona Complex, there is apparently a wide difference of opinion concerning the interpretation of the minor structures which are very finely exposed in coastal sections. Greenly envisaged the structure as involving great recumbent folds, like the nappes of the Scottish Highlands, piled one upon another. These are not visible but are inferred. Visible folds vary in amplitude from those measured in hundreds of feet to micro-folds affecting the argillaceous rocks and visible only under a microscope. Of the many faults visible, the most important are overthrusts; but the best known of these are Caledonian (post-Lower Palaeozoic) in age, and are considered in the next chapter.

On the mainland of North Wales Precambrian rocks occur in Lleyn and in two parallel ridges, one near the coast extending from Bangor to Carnarvon; the other farther inland, near Llanberis, and known as the **Padarn Ridge.** The latter consists almost entirely of lavas, chiefly rhyolite of Uriconian aspect, which has contributed largely to the basal conglomerates of the Cambrian which is banked against the volcanic ridge (p. 38). The Bangor-Carnarvon ridge includes a greater variety of rock-types, among them a granite occurring in Carnarvon town, tuffs, agglomerates, breccias and grits, as well as rhyolitic lava flows. These 'Arvonian' rocks are overlain unconformably by the basal Arenigian grits, so they are certainly pre-Ordovician, and there is little doubt that they are actually Precambrian.

The Kennach Gneiss, part of the **Lizard Complex,** was for long thought to be pre-Palaeozoic on lithological grounds; but its isotopic age is 366±20 m.y., which lies in the same age group as the Caledonian intrusives. Bearing in mind the main lesson of the Moines this may mean only that the Lizard gneisses, of unknown age were metamorphosed (? again) during the Caledonian orogeny. It is anomalous that the Complex lies within the Armorican front: one might have expected it to bear an Armorican imprint.

## REFERENCES

The British Regional Geologies of the appropriate areas, particularly the Welsh Borderlands for Shropshire and the Malverns; Central England for Charnwood Forest; South Wales for St Davids.

GEORGE, T. NEVILLE. *The North Wales Regional Guide* contains an excellent discussion of the differences in interpretation of the structure of Anglesey by E. Greenly and R. M. Shackleton.

JAMES, J. H. 'The structure and stratigraphy of part of the Precambrian outcrop between Church Stretton and Linley, Shropshire,' *Q.J.G.S.*, **112,** (1956), 315.

# CHAPTER VIII

# THE BUILDING OF THE CALEDONIDES

It will have been appreciated that the rocks so far studied occur in regions of often intense folding and faulting—that is, in regions of former mountain-building movements. Each such area is, indeed, part of the basal wreck of a former great mountain chain. The one with which we are concerned at the moment was named the **Caledonides** by Suess, as Scotland (Caledonia) is the largest British remnant available for study.

An initial difficulty encountered in attempting a general account of the building of the Caledonides is in explaining precisely what is meant by the term 'Caledonian'. It has an age significance, of course: it implies the period of time during which the great mountain chain whose roots are visible in the Scottish Highlands, came into being. Each such mountain-building period involves two distinct phases: (1) the period of accumulation of the sediments ultimately concerned—this is the geosynclinal phase; and (2) the orogenic phase involving the buckling of the geosyncline, accompanied by folding, faulting, the deep-seated metamorphism of the mountain-root areas (the so-called tectogen), magmatic permeation and intrusion, and, of course, the actual emergence of the mountain chain.

### The Geosynclinal Phase

The belt of country affected by the Caledonian movements is some three hundred miles wide, extending from Bloody Foreland in the extreme north-west of Ireland to the English Midlands. Similar structures and of the same age are as wide-spread as the Lower Palaeozoic rocks themselves. There is a very close link in this respect with Scandinavia: Norway and Scotland in particular have much in common.

From the very fragmentary evidence available, we have concluded that the early-Cambrian Sea advanced over a low-lying land area and initiated a long-continued period of marine sedimentation, the duration of which, according to modern estimates, is of the order of 200 million years. It is not implied that the accumulation of sediment was continuous over the whole area throughout this vast period of time: the local breaks and unconformities already referred to prove the instability of some parts of the floor of the geosyncline. Nevertheless, in parts of the latter, the Ordovician sediments had been piled upon the Cambrian and the Silurian added later, until the original pre-Palaeozoic surface supported a huge load of sediment. In North Wales the total thickness of the three Systems is some 36,000 feet, though the top of the Silurian is missing; in the Lake District the Ordovician and the Silurian together total 28,000 feet; while in Shropshire, although breaks separate the three Systems from one another, their total thickness is nearly 20,000 feet. Thus it is clear that the original floor on which these sediments were deposited must have been warped downwards to a maximum possible depth of several miles.

An obvious result of the down-warping would be a stretching of the crust beneath the geosyncline, with consequent weakening. Some geologists believe that the crust would be depressed so far into the hotter parts of the earth that the weakening would be accelerated by actual melting of the crust at the centre of the trough. Whether this is so or not does not affect the main conclusion that, as a consequence of the weakening, the crust would ultimately give way under the strain, with two important results: first, the uprise of magma, and second, the crumpling and fracturing of the materials supported by the crust. In the ideal case the major fractures are found in the marginal belts, and are low-angle thrusts, directed inwards towards the centre of the geosyncline. Movement along the thrust-planes of whole blocks of country, the essential geological structures of which are great overfolds, has been proved by observation in the field, and is a natural consequence of the shortening of the distance between the two sides of the geosyncline, known as the 'backland' (or hinterland) and 'foreland' respectively. Further, the weak sediments become intensely folded, due to the same cause, the folds near the thrust-belt being packed so closely that both limbs of the fold are inclined in the same direction, that is, they are isoclines. The latter, we may suppose, come into existence before the overthrusts: the fracturing takes place when the elastic limit is passed, and any further compression results in the bodily transportation of the compressed and indurated sedimentary rocks along the thrust-planes. Finally, the whole corrugated and fractured geosynclinal 'prism' is elevated, partly as a consequence of the expansion through heating of the down-warped material, partly due to the lessening of the compressional forces exerted by the backland and foreland.

The above brief statement outlines what was believed to happen during a mountain-building episode. It is based upon studies of Alpine tectonics chiefly. One important change of opinion that has taken place within recent years needs emphasis.

Formerly it was widely believed that throughout geological time quiet sedimentation continued through long periods of time punctuated at infrequent intervals by brief periods of drastic change involving the appearance of new mountain chains as a result of intense earth-movements. The three main events of this kind are known as the Caledonian, Armorican (or Hercynian) and Alpine orogenies. At this point we are concerned with the first only—with the earth movements which brought into existence a great mountain chain crossing North-West Europe and named the **Caledonides** by Suess. In Britain the largest area where the resulting structures may be studied is the Highlands of Scotland (Caledonia).

First we must agree what is to be included within our terms of reference: what, in the time sense, is meant by Caledonian? It is generally agreed that the strata involved comprise those belonging to the three Lower Palaeozoic Periods: the Devonian including the 'continental' facies, the O.R.S., are later (younger) than the Caledonian orogeny, which in a manner of speaking is post-Silurian, pre-Devonian (pre-O.R.S.) in age. No folding or faulting earlier than the beginning of Cambrian time should be included as Caledonian. The Scourian and Laxfordian orogenies, which profoundly affected the Lewisian in the North-West Highlands, belong to a much earlier chapter of geological history. The end of the Caledonian chapter is much more difficult to define. Folding and faulting of the Lower Palaeozoic strata continued long after the end of the Silurian Period: in fact in Scotland the most active phases of earth movement were post-Silurian, pre-Devonian and post-Lower, pre-Upper O.R.S. Actually the Devonian (including O.R.S.) and Carboniferous strata bear exactly the same relationship to the Armorican orogeny as do the Cambrian, Ordovician and Silurian to the Caledonian. Thus in a sense it is equally reasonable to regard the two Devonian phases as late-Caledonian or early Armorican: they belong to both orogenies.

Dating earth movements—episodes of folding and faulting—involves sandwiching the event between two named units as close together in the stratigraphical column as possible, the earlier (lower) of which was affected, but the younger (higher) was not. This method is simple; but the reader has probably realized that it lacks precision. If it were true that the Caledonides were post-Silurian, pre-Devonian they must have appeared 'in the twinkling of an eye'. This phrase fixes a *point* in time: it does not define an interval sufficiently long to cover the building of a great new mountain range. Nevertheless such phrases are widely used: they are concise and convenient. Similarly it is common practice to use such terms as 'pre-Arenig' and 'pre-Caradocian'; but the Scourian and Laxfordian orogenies are pre-Arenig and these are certainly not meant to be included. The term refers to structures which originated *just* prior to the local Arenig beds, which may well lie considerably above the true base of the Series in the continuous time-scale. In other words the structures referred to were developed during an unrecorded interval of time usually indicated in the field by an unconformity. Actually, to date a structure as 'pre-B' is more accurate in some cases than 'post-A, pre-B' as it may have been developing *during*, not *after* A-times: but it was completed before 'B' was deposited.

The contrasts between the marine Silurian and the continental Old Red Sandstone were the direct consequence of the building of the Caledonides. With this simple picture in mind it was easy to slip into the error of thinking that the structures shown by Lower Palaeozoic rocks at any point were the result of post-Silurian, pre-Devonian mountain-building movements. It is much nearer to the truth to view them as having been built up or evolved, in a succession of phases, spread over a very long period of time.

Another important factor has been the recognition of the fact that folding and faulting on quite important scales may take place superficially in unconsolidated sediments; and sliding under the influence of gravity has often been the cause of the visible structures rather than compression resulting from folding movements at some later period. The repeated 'slumping' of the geosynclinal sediments during the Wenlock-Ludlow period is a case in point.

The record of long-continued sedimentation in the British geosyncline throughout the Cambrian, Ordovician and Silurian Periods is punctuated by unconformities—several of them really important breaks, to which reference has been made on previous pages. Each of them involved some uplift of the area affected, tilting or folding, denudation and finally sinking once more to allow renewed sedimentation. The effects of these, even though not spectacular in individual cases, would be *cumulative*. Ignoring minor breaks within the Systems, we may refer to the pre-Arenigian unconformity in Wales, southern Scotland and North-West Ireland; the pre-Caradocian in the Lake District and Scotland; pre-Llandoverian in the Welsh Borderlands, the English Midlands and Ireland; all prior to the culmination at the close of the Silurian, and all contributory to the final structure.

Viewed from this angle we may list the more important phases of the Caledonian earth-movements as comprising the following:

(1) the post-Tremadoc, pre-Arenig folding, uplift and erosion;
(2) the intra-Llanvirn emergence and re-submergence;
(3) the pre-Bala (pre-Caradocian) folding and erosion;

(4) the pre-Middle Llandovery movements;
(5) the pre-Upper Llandovery folding; the Upper Llandovery transgression;
(6) pre-Lower Old Red Sandstone folding;
(7) pre-Upper Old Red Sandstone folding; the Upper O.R.S. transgression.

It is necessary to divide the subject matter of this chapter into two parts covering the two contrasted regions within which the Caledonian orogeny produced very different effects. Two different structural levels are represented: (1) *deep-seated*, where folding, faulting and metamorphism affected the rocks; and (2) *relatively superficial*, where folding and faulting occurred, but unaccompanied by metamorphic effects. The first includes the Highlands of Scotland together with the Outer Hebrides and the continuation of this structural unit into northern Ireland. The second includes the Southern Uplands of Scotland with their continuation into Ireland, the English Lake District, Wales and the Welsh Borderlands. The facts speak most clearly for themselves in the *non-metamorphic areas*. We therefore deal with these first.

The **Southern Uplands** lie between the S. U. Boundary Fault to the north-west and the overstepping Upper Palaeozoic strata to the south-east. Although the Girvan area lies outside the Southern Uplands proper it is important as providing a structural sample of the pre-Devonian floor underlying the O.R.S. and Carboniferous rocks in the Midland Valley to the north. The stratigraphy of the Girvan area has already been outlined. The oldest rocks exposed are graptolitic shales containing an Arenig fauna, associated with a volcanic suite of spilitic pillow lavas. In parts of western Ireland, however, the record is more complete: an abnormally thick Arenig Series rests on Dalradian metamorphic rocks. In the Girvan area (and probably in Ireland too) these Arenig rocks were uplifted, folded, faulted and eroded before the commencement of the invasion of the region by the Caradoc Sea. Whether the complete absence of the Llanvirn and Llandeilo Series in Scotland is due to non-deposition or to subsequent erosion remains uncertain; but the pre-Caradocian gap becomes less great in Ireland and progressively so southwards.

The evidence for the next step is to be found in the Southern Uplands proper; but it is difficult to write convincingly about the structure, as it is under review. Since 1899 the structure described in Peach and Horne's memoir on the region proved acceptable until recently when it has been adversely criticized. The alternative interpretation of the structure has so far only been outlined. Critics of the old interpretation maintain that Peach and Horne, following Lapworth's demonstration of isoclinal folding in the Moffat area, extrapolated this structural pattern over the whole of the Southern Uplands, including belts of country within which the monotonous greywacke lithology and the absence of graptolites made it impossible to apply Lapworth's technique. To-day the position is different. By studying sedimentary structures of 'which-way-up' significance, it has been shown that the region consists of narrow belts within which intense folding, often isoclinal, alternate with wider belts, up to three miles wide, where there is no evidence of inversion and therefore no isoclinal folding. On the other hand the strata become progressively younger in a constant direction, forming 'through-successions'. The interpretation of these facts involves the recognition of large overfolds, striking approximately NE. to SW., overturned towards the north-west, with long, gently dipping southerly limbs and short, steep northerly ones resulting from a drive from the south-east. The fold-axes occur in pairs and it is suggested that there may be five or six such units in a complete traverse of the area. These structures appear to have been produced by a single fold-phase in the Wenlock Series; but two episodes involving folding can be distinguished in the Ordovician. The earlier, as shown in the Girvan area, was pre-Caradocian; the later is demonstrably post-Wenlockian, and, taking into account the structural relationships observable in the Midland Valley inliers, is presumably Phase 6—the pre-O.R.S. which was the acme of the Caledonian movements in Scotland.

Southwards, the Lower Palaeozoic outcrops nearest to the Southern Uplands form the inlier of the **English Lake District,** only some thirty miles distant, but strikingly different in some respects. In particular the great hiatus between the Arenig and Caradoc Series around Girvan is partly bridged by graptolitic Llanvirnian in the Skiddaw Slate Series succeeded with apparent conformity by the thick Borrowdale Volcanic Series, presumably in large part Llandeilian, though actually undated. In the interval between the cessation of volcanic activity and the marine invasion by the Caradoc Sea the Skiddavian and Borrowdale volcanics were folded along NNE. to SSW. axes. The amplitude of the pre-Caradoc folds in the Lake District proper was apparently gentle; but during the ensuing erosion interval not only was the volcanic sheet completely destroyed in places; but the underlying Skiddavian as well. In places the Caradocian Coniston Limestone Group rests directly on Skiddavian; but farther afield, on the flanks of the Pennines, in the Horton inliers, on Ingletonian, of Precambrian age. Where fully developed the combined thickness of the Borrowdale-Skiddaw series is 24,000 feet. This would be a measure of both the amplitude of the pre-Caradoc folds and the denudation, provided that the thickness mentioned was maintained over the whole area under consideration.

A small-scale map of the Lake District (Fig. 23) suggests a much simpler structure than that brought out by detailed mapping on a large scale. The essentially anticlinal structure of the inlier is obvious, with the main axis trending ENE. through the Skiddaw Slate Series, near Skiddaw itself. Within the main belts, which become progressively younger southwards, many other folds, some of considerable amplitude occur, particularly in the Borrowdale Volcanic Series—folding is more difficult to demonstrate in the Skiddaw Slates on account of cleavage. These folds involve thick Ludlovian in the south. As the overlying Lower Carboniferous rocks are not affected, the folding was post-Silurian, pre-Dinantian; and although the O.R.S. is feebly represented, this means that the second fold-phase in this region was pre-Devonian, the Erian Phase of Stille. The final doming of the Lake District occurred during the Armorican orogeny.

In **Wales** Caledonian structures are magnificently displayed. The general 'grain' of Mid-Wales runs parallel to the Caledonian fold-axes shown in Fig. 20. Of these major folds, the Central Wales Synclinorium is the most persistent. When the Mid-Wales structures are traced southwards they gradually change their direction as the zone is approached within which the Armorican structures reach their maximum intensity. The latter trend east-to-west in the south of Wales, and hereabouts it becomes impossible to differentiate between the effects of the Caledonian and Armorican movements, except in so far, of course, as Carboniferous and later rocks are involved.

The main structural units produced during the Caledonian orogeny in North Wales are the Harlech Dome, with minor folds of nearly north-south trend, and the Berwyn Dome lying to the eastward. Between them passes the Central Wales syncline, which, swinging round the nose of the Berwyn Dome splays out into the Llangollen synclinorium, consisting of several minor folds of nearly east-west trend (Fig. 74).

The run of the hill-ranges of Ordovician igneous rocks in Snowdonia and the Harlech Dome brings out the nature of the folding in western North Wales. The outcrops have the shape of a slightly misshapen letter 'S', with Conway and Cader Idris at the northern and southern ends respectively. The top part of the 'S' is the Snowdonian syncline; the bottom part, the Harlech Dome. The relative position of these two major structures is the same as that of the Llangollen Synclinorium and the Berwyn Dome. The narrow belt of country lying north of the Harlech Dome and south of Snowdonia suffered severely, faulting of the overthrust type being developed along north-easterly lines. The thrust-planes rise towards the south-east, and locally hundred of feet of the higher Cambrian beds have been squeezed out of the succession. The continuation of this belt of intense compression passes the neighbourhood of Blaenau Ffestiniog, set in the hills, but notorious for the vast unsightly dumps of slate-debris thrown out in the exploitation of the Lower Ordovician Slates in the local quarries. The Cambrian Slate Belt, already noted, occupies a comparable position to the north of the Snowdonian volcanic massif, and south of the Precambrian Padarn ridge, named from Llyn Padarn, in the lower parts of the Llanberis Pass. Here again the cleavage is intense, but the strata affected are of Cambrian age (Fig. 10).

In **Wales** the geological evidence carries us farther back in time, and the record of earth movements is more comprehensive than in Scotland and the Lake District, by the inclusion of a post-Tremadoc, pre-Arenig phase. A problematic feature is the non-occurrence of rocks of Cambrian age in Anglesey. Cambrian rocks reach a maximum thickness of 22,000 feet in the Dolgellau district; they diminish to 3000 feet north of the Harlech Dome and disappear before the Menai Strait (separating Anglesey from the mainland) is reached. At one time it was believed that originally the Cambrian extended right across Anglesey: but as Arenigian beach deposits rest directly on the Precambrian in the island, uplift followed by denudation commensurate with the thickness of the missing strata would have to be invoked. It is now known, however, that in a northward traverse higher Cambrian formations overlap lower ones; it is thought probable that, at the Bangor ridge, the basal member would have been the *Lingulella* Group, and at most only part of the Upper Cambrian crossed into Anglesey. The amount of post-Cambrian uplift and denudation would be correspondingly reduced. It may well be that the gentle folding along north-south axes within the Harlech Dome and shown by the swing of the outcrops of the Harlech Grits, is an expression of the pre-Arenig phase. Between Dolgellau and the Lleyn Peninsula the basal Arenigian changes its horizon from high up in the Tremadoc Series to the level of the Rhinog Grit, 6000 feet lower in the succession. Discordance of dip and strike as well as rapid overstep are prominent features of the pre-Arenig disturbance in the Lleyn Peninsula.

Successive members of the Ordovician overlap one another northwards across Anglesey until ultimately the Caradoc Series rests directly on Mona Complex, thus duplicating the relationship seen in other parts of Britain, notably in South Shropshire (see below), and the Lake District. This great extension of the area of late-Ordovician sedimentation could be explained by a eustatic rise of sea-level; but that there was pre-Caradocian folding in Wales is proved by the fact that at a locality (with a tongue-twisting name) near Tremadoc in Carnarvonshire an anticline, 2000 feet in amplitude affects Upper Cambrian rocks, but is overstepped by the Caradocian.

The several Lower Palaeozoic inliers strung out along the Welsh Borderlands clearly display a full succession of episodes involving folding and faulting. In **South Shropshire** the Longmynd occupies a key position between the Shelve inlier to the west and the Church Stretton Valley with the Uriconian hills to the east. The presumably pre-Cambrian Longmyndian sedimentary rocks are strongly folded: the run of the outcrops and the grain of the country is Caledonoid. Northwards these folds plunge beneath an unconformable cover of Upper Carboniferous rocks; and this suggests a date for the folding. Actually the folding is very much older, for gently dipping Upper Llandovery beach deposits wrap round the Longmyndian in the south, establishing the fact that the present attitude of the Longmyndian has been little changed since Upper Llandovery times. But that is not all. A relatively small outcrop of Caradocian rocks in the neighbourhood of Pontesford rests with violent angular discordance on very steeply dipping Longmyndian. This pushes the date of the folding back to pre-Caradocian, and there the matter must rest, for no older rocks occur in the Longmynd area itself: but indirect evidence suggests that both the Longmyndian rocks and their folding are Precambrian.

In the **Shelve inlier** Tremadocian shales lie immediately west of the western faulted boundary of the Longmynd and are followed without appreciable discordance by the dramatically different basal Arenig quartzites. Therefore there is no evidence here of post-Tremadoc, pre-Arenig folding, though the lithological contrasts are significant and the concordance of attitude may be deceptive. However, the pre-Upper Llandovery phase is well displayed especially by the strike-ridges of the Llanvirnian igneous rocks which are duplicated by folding along Caledonoid lines. The NE. to SW. folds are abruptly truncated by Upper Llandovery strata showing precisely the same relationship to the Ordovician as to the Longmyndian. Several small outliers of basal Upper Llandovery beds occur right in the heart of the Shelve, resting unconformably on different members of the Ordovician succession: on the Stapeley Volcanics, the *Bifidus* Beds and parts of the Arenig Series. This indicates that the amplitude of the folds was of the order of at least 6000 feet. The wastage during the pre-Upper Llandovery erosion

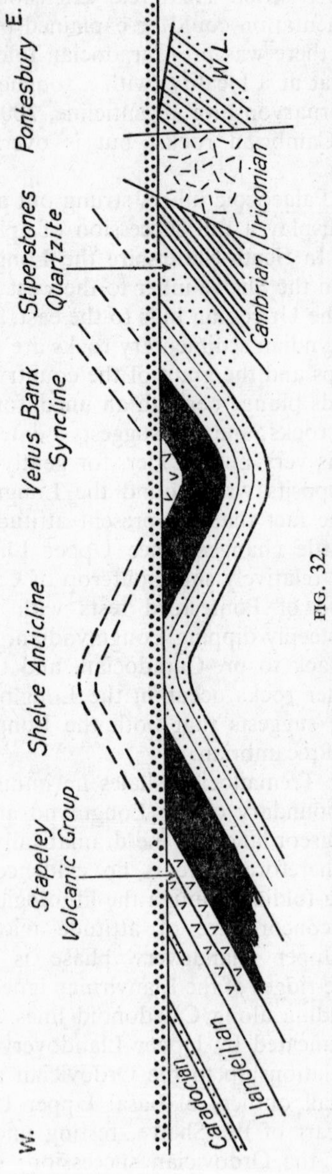


FIG. 32.

Pre-Llandoverian folding in the Shelve area, Shropshire: diagram-section to western margin of the Longmynd. W.L.—Western Longmyndian; overlying Llandoverian indicated by heavy stipple. Wedge of graptolitic Caradocian overlying Western Longmyndian on extreme right of section.

interval must represent a considerable contribution of sediment to the deeper parts of the geosyncline: sedimentation was continuous over this time-interval in mid-Wales, as we have seen.

It may be noted that in other parts of the world folding of this date was important: in North America it is termed Taconic. The Shelve area provides a sample of the structural pattern of the sub-Silurian floor over much, if not all, of the Welsh Borderlands. The **Builth inlier** lies between the border towns of Llandrindod Wells and Builth and forms a 'window' of Lower and Middle Ordovician largely wrapped round by Silurian and O.R.S. The folding in the inlier is of the same style and age as in the Shelve. Thin Upper Llandovery beds of shelly facies extended across the folds and, as a thin 'skin' of sediment, for many miles to the east and north. This 'skin' was removed from the inlier itself during a phase of pre-Wenlock warping and erosion. The Wenlockian rapidly oversteps the several members of the Ordovician succession ultimately resting directly on the Llanvirnian, which, a few miles to the west, in the Gwesyn Syncline, lies more than 15,000 feet below the base of the Wenlockian.

Farther to the south-west, between Llandovery and **Llandeilo,** Ordovician strata belonging to the Llanvirnian and Llandeilian are strongly over-folded and faulted beneath a cover of unaffected Llandovery Sandstone. Later, post-Llandovery, pre-Lower Wenlock warping and denudation caused the base of the Wenlockian to overstep the Llandoverian completely and to rest directly on mid-Llanvirn shales. In view of this great gap in the succession it would be all too easy to over-estimate the importance of the pre-Wenlock folding, which actually was quite gentle. The effects were inherited, as it were, from the much more important pre-Llandovery phase. That is not quite the whole of the story, as in due course the Lower Wenlock (together, of course, with underlying strata) were gently warped before the deposition of the Upper Wenlockian. This area lies on the eastern flank of the great Towy Anticline, and the folds here referred to may be regarded as stages in the evolution of that major structure.

Much the same applies to other well-known folds including the Malvern axis, growth stages of which occurred at intervals between early Palaeozoic and post-Triassic. Once again we find that the Upper Llandovery rocks overstep older strata—the May Hill Sandstone transgresses across Malvernian gneisses onto 'Long-myndian' and Cambrian.

It would be out of context to write in detail at this point concerning the pre-O.R.S. (Erian) phase—the stratigraphical relationships involving the O.R.S. are discussed in the *next* chapter. It is important to note, however, that Erian movements were gentle and unimportant over most of southern Britain. Nevertheless in many parts of Britain the O.R.S. rests with violent unconformity on older strata, down to and including the Precambrian. The size of the gap between the O.R.S. and the floor on which it rests is not a measure of the amplitude of the pre-O.R.S. (Erian) folding; neither is it a trustworthy indication of the extent of the pre-O.R.S. denudation. The overstep is composite, and the final effect was built up in stages spread over a very long interval of time. The missing strata had been removed in part during erosion intervals of much older date, as we have attempted to show in the preceding account. The Caledonian earth-movements were not concentrated into one brief violent interlude, but resulted from movement-phases spread over much of Lower Palaeozoic time, and varying widely in intensity and location. Similarly, the individual phases were themselves spread over a longer time-interval than is suggested by the phrases we use to date them. The movements were at least in part contemporaneous with sedimentation. This may be inferred from the observed influence of folding and faulting on (a) thicknesses of sediments and (b) their facies. The Church Stretton Fault is a case in point (p. 101), the Towy Line is another. Both of these structures were hinge-zones separating shelf from basin facies, the first-named during Salopian times, while the second operated during the late-Ordovician. It has been shown by palaeo-current data that in mid-North Wales during the Salopian there were two main current directions: (1) north–south in the Llanfyllin–Corwen area; and (2) west to east in the region of the Denbigh Moors. Thus a 'Montgomery Trough' and a 'Denbigh Trough' are recognized as important Silurian palaeogeographic features, and it is certainly no coincidence that they correspond with important structures—the Mid-Wales Synclinorium and the Snowdon Syncline respectively.

So far, Caledonian faulting has been mentioned only incidentally but some of the faults which were initiated at this time are comparable with the better-known ones in Scotland (p. 118). Overthrusting on an important scale occurs in northernmost Wales: in Anglesey the Carmel Thrust is not extensively exposed, but the displacement along it is estimated as several miles. Another major thrust of Caledonoid trend cuts off the tip of the Lleyn Peninsula and there are other smaller ones in Arvon. Large faults approximately parallel to the strike cross Wales. The Bala Fault is easily traceable on the ground from Cader Idris south-westwards to the sea; and in the opposite direction through the town of Bala and apparently links up with the Bryn Eglwys Fault which breaches the Carboniferous Limestone scarp near Llangollen. As is the case with the major Scottish faults, although of Caledonian initiation, renewed movement took place along them during the Armorican orogeny.

The major faults which bound the Longmynd horst are of rather special interest. The Church Stretton fault system to the south-east has attracted most attention by reason of its influence on sedimentation during Wenlock-Ludlow times; but the western boundary fault—the Pontesford Fault, is probably even more significant. It separates two blocks of country with fundamentally different relationships. To the westward in the Shelve area and beyond, the sub-Palaeozoic floor was down-warped at the onset of the Cambrian marine transgression. In due course, after the post-Tremadoc, pre-Arenig interval, further down-warping preceded or accompanied Ordovician sedimentation until the widespread submergence at the beginning of the Caradoc period. All this time the Longmynd horst had stood as an island or at least a promontory above sea-level; but it was submerged, one would imagine rather suddenly, and inundated by the Caradoc Sea. Therefore to the east of the boundary fault, on the Longmynd itself, Caradocian strata rest directly on Precambrian; to the west, in the Shelve inlier they are separated from that same floor by 10,000 feet of lower Palaeozoic rocks, in unbroken sequence. One is reminded of a Carboniferous analogue—the Northern Pennines block which stood as an island above the waters of the Dinantian Sea for three-quarters of Lower Carboniferous time, though sedimentation was going on continuously in the nearby basin, as described in due course.

The structures within the Midland Valley of Scotland are Armorican, as Carboniferous strata are involved; but the trough itself, like the Montgomery and Denbigh Troughs in Wales was developed during the Caledonian orogeny. Glimpses of sub-Carboniferous and even sub-Devonian structures are afforded in the Lower Palaeozoic inliers for example in the Pentland Hills and at Lesmahagow. The Highland Boundary Fault, probably descended from an earlier monoclinal fold, is dated by its relationship to the O.R.S. The Lower O.R.S. is profoundly affected by the fault, the downthrow being of the order of 10,000 feet. The Upper O.R.S. crosses it, however, and on the upthrow side oversteps a residual relic of the Lower division and comes to rest directly on the Dalradians. The fault is evidently a mid-O.R.S. (or at latest a pre-Upper O.R.S.) structure. Similarly the Southern Uplands Fault appears to have been active during the Erian Phase: the Lower O.R.S. rests on Silurian in the several inliers in the Midland Valley; but south of the South Uplands Fault it lies on Ordovician, 15,000 feet lower in the succession, and this must be a measure of the displacement.

At this point we may look at the continuation of the Midland Valley of Scotland into Ireland where the structure is continued as the Connemara Syncline. This is a largely pre-Upper Llandovery structure involving early (Arenigian) to mid-Ordovician rocks vastly thicker than elsewhere in Britain. The Arenig Series rests on a floor of strongly folded Dalradians. A very thin and impersistent Upper Llandovery Series oversteps the various divisions of the Ordovician onto the Dalradians, and is itself overstepped by the Wenlockian. The relationships therefore duplicate those of the Welsh Borderland especially those seen in the Llandeilo inlier, though the overstep is less drastic. No beds of Bala age occur, and it may well be that the folding and subsequent erosion were, in part, pre-Caradocian, especially in view of the relationships at Girvan.

**The metamorphic terrain.** The stratigraphy and age problems connected with the Moines and Dalradians were considered in Chapter VI but little was said concerning their structures. The run of the outcrops in many areas is relatively straightforward and the preparation of a geological map presents no special difficulties; but the interpretation of the structure is quite another matter. The difficulties arise from several causes. The rocks are barren of fossils, and the interpretation of structures depends upon the preservation of reliable 'way-up' criteria. Over large areas occupied by these rocks the latter have been very effectively obliterated by regional metamorphism.

The Highlands are occupied by Moinian and Dalradian formations, the fold- and fault-pattern of which are, in general, well known, if not well understood. Dealing with things actually seen—with mappable phenomena—the run of the outcrops of the distinctive rock-groups swings across country in a way dependent upon the development of major folds of great amplitude. An idea of the amplitude is conveyed by the fact that that part of the Banff coast occupied by the Dalradian coincides with one great asymmetric fold, the Boyndie Syncline. The western limb is steep, the eastern, flat-lying, while the central part is an area of great complexity—a tectonic mélange. Within the major folds minor folding on an impressive scale can be studied in the coast section, where hundreds of folds, usually recumbent, are visible even to the casual visitor. Locally dozens of such folds are piled one upon the other in such a manner that quite a thin bed may form a high cliff-section. This is a particularly well-exposed sample of Highland structures, which become more intense towards the west.

We had occasion to mention on an earlier page that correlation of the Dalradian was made difficult through structural complications.

The overfolding and complicated faulting are difficult enough to deal with in mountainous country like the Scottish Highlands; but an added difficulty has been introduced by differential movement during the folding, along the boundaries of more competent and less competent rocks: a more competent rock such as quartzite has tended to slide over an underlying less competent rock such as shale, or even its metamorphosed equivalent, mica-schist. Such differential movement has caused extraordinary variations in thickness along the strike. Some beds, particularly quartzites, have thickened considerably in the anticlinal arches and synclinal troughs. In the course of such movements some members of the succession may be thinned almost to nothing, or actually 'smeared out' of existence, so that two members, seen to be in juxtaposition at one point, may be widely separated, in the stratigraphical sense, at another. This is one of the special problems of the Highlands.

To account for some of the anomalies that he encountered when surveying parts of the South-West Highlands, E. B. Bailey found it necessary to introduce concepts appropriate to Alpine tectonics into Highland geology. Thus he visualized the Moinian and Dalradian as having been thrown into gigantic recumbent folds or nappes separated from their roots by planes or narrow zones of dislocation, which Bailey termed 'slides'. Several of these have been mapped and named—the Ballachulish Slide is perhaps the best known. It is important to realize that these nappe-structures are on too big a scale to be actually seen: they are *inferred* from detailed mapping carried out over a wide area.

In the areas occupied by the Moinian, folds of comparable amplitude to those occurring in the Dalradian have been described. Such are the Fannich Synclinorium in Ross-shire, and the Morar Anticline far to the south, described by Ritchie and Kennedy. The former, when originally surveyed, was interpreted as anticlinal; but detailed observations of the current bedding at many points has enabled a local Moinian succession some 13,000 feet thick to be established, and the structure inverted into its rightful situation.

The visible, relatively small-scale folding of the Moinian rocks becomes more intense westwards: the folds become tighter, closely packed, and on approaching the Moine Thrust, are isoclinal.

Detailed studies have shown that fold-axes trend in more than one direction: some are approximately parallel to the Moine Thrust, though actually slightly oblique to it; but others trend northwesterly. This suggests that the rocks have been folded on more than one occasion, so that an original fold-pattern has been overprinted by later ones.

**The Moines** were folded, refolded, then folded again, the folds differing in kind (intensity), orientation, wave-length and amplitude. Little imagination is needed to appreciate the difficulty of deciphering such complicated structures. When the three-dimensional forms are reduced to two on a map, the result 'looks much like structural chaos'. It appears to be generally agreed that the Moines were folded on three major occasions, and the three sets may for convenience be designated F(M)1, F(M)2 and F(M)3. The first folds are large recumbent isoclines piled one upon another; the second folds are also 'tight' but not isoclinal. In places they have caused inversion of the original structure, so that folds which appear anticlinal have cores of Moine schists but Lewisian gneisses occur higher in the structure. To distinguish such folds from true anticlines the term 'antiform' is used. Naturally synforms occur as well. It is believed that the maximum metamorphic effects were produced at the time of the F(M)2 folding when pronounced schistosity was developed and intense migmatization occurred. The F(M)3 folding occurred after the regional recrystallization: microfolds affected the newly-formed mica, and for the second time the rocks were extensively migmatized. In the extreme north-west the final Caledonian event appears to have involved the formation of the overthrusts (the Moine Thrust and others) along which great slices of metamorphosed Moines were carried across the foreland to the positions they now occupy. None of these folds is accurately dated: the normal stratigraphical evidence is wanting; and it is impossible to date folds by normal geochronological techniques. However, the Moine Thrust cuts and displaces the Cambro-Ordovician Durness Limestone, and must therefore be post-Arenig. Indirect considerations suggest that the overthrusting may have been connected with the pre-Middle O.R.S. movements in other parts of Scotland. But whatever the date, the Moine thrusting occurred during a phase of *brittle dislocation* as distinct from the *plastic deformation* which had characterized all the earlier movements. The metamorphic effects accompanying the Moine thrusting were retrogressive: biotite and garnet of earlier origin were recrystallized as chlorite, the index mineral of the lowest grade of regional metamorphism.

**The Dalradian** succession also participated in several phases of folding, faulting and metamorphism. The three most important may be designated F(D)1, F(D)2 and F(D)3, though whether these may be correlated with the corresponding folds in the Moines remains to be seen. The F(D)1 structures are huge recumbent folds, exemplified by the Tay Nappe, trending NE. to SW. The F(D)2 structures include cross folds with NW. to SE. axes and were associated with the maximum metamorphic effects. The Islay Boundary Slide extending from Schichallion to Loch Linnhe, and probably continued as the Loch Skerrol Thrust in Islay, cuts out the Lower Dalradian all along the Moine-Dalradian boundary. It truncates F(D)1 isoclines, but is extensively folded by major F(D)2 cross-folds, thus establishing the time relationship between the two phases. The F(D)3 structures are large open folds, for example the Cowal and Buchan antiforms, associated with widespread metamorphic effects of retrogressive type. This appears to have been the last major metamorphism of the Highlands and is widely believed to be dated as 420/390 m.y. ago.

As suggested in the chapter on the principles of geochronology some experts have no hesitation in placing these significant dates on the stratigraphical time-scale and in stating, baldly, that the 420 m.y. metamorphic event was mid-Silurian. For reasons already explained we hesitate to follow their lead. The time to do so will come when the Silurian-Devonian boundary is fixed with a reasonable degree of accuracy. The Moines and Dalradians, with their multi-metamorphism and complicated structures offer an almost limitless field of research; but at present positive results are overwhelmed by a host of possibilities and fewer probabilities: there appear to be few certainties upon which general agreement has been reached.

One point arises in connection with the dating, however. Although its systematic position on the Time Scale is uncertain, the 420/390 m.y. event was definitely Palaeozoic, and from general considerations must coincide with *one* of the fold-phases of the Caledonian orogeny —one would imagine, with the Erian Phase. Some people believe that the F(M)1 folds were early Ordovician: i.e. rather less than 500 m.y. ago (J. Sutton, 1963). As the estimated age of the Moine Schists is 1000 m.y., that implies that for a period of time approaching that of the whole Phanerozoic Time-Scale the Moine rocks remained unfolded; but then, in a relatively brief period suffered three fold-phases and three metamorphisms of varying degrees of intensity. The final event was the Moine overthrusting which *may* be as late as O.R.S.—it was demonstrably post-Arenig.

We conclude this difficult subject with two quotations, the first from one with unrivalled knowledge of the stratigraphical relationships between the rocks involved in the building of the Caledonides, the other from a group of people who specialize in geochronological problems:

(1) 'The British Caledonides were not the product of late-Silurian orogenesis: they are the remnants of Ordovician mountains piled on Cambrian, Silurian on Ordovician, Devonian on Silurian, mountains

degraded as they rose to provide for overlying sediment at each phasal cycle. . . .'[1]

(2) '. . . these major Caledonian structures were produced . . . in uppermost Ludlovian—earliest Downtonian times between 420 and 410 m.y. ago.'[2]

The regions where the Caledonian structures are best exposed to-day are mountainous; but it must be realized that the existing peaks are not merely the degraded remnants of the Caledonides, for the latter were completely destroyed, so far as Britain is concerned, in the ensuing geological Period. The north-east to south-west grain of these tracts of country and the pattern of their river systems is due to weathering having etched out the Caledonian structures (originally deeply buried in the roots of the mountains) on a flat, pre-Carboniferous land surface. In the Lake District, for example, at the beginning of the Mesozoic epoch, there could have been no sign of the Caledonian Mountains, as their denuded roots were covered by the Carboniferous rocks; and it is to much later uplift, followed by profound denudation, that the reappearance of the Lower Palaeozoic rocks, as we now see them, is due.

We have seen that the uprise of magma into the roots of mountain chains is a natural corollary to the buckling of the geosyncline and the collapse of its floor. Many of the granites of Scotland, Ireland and the Lake District were intruded during the building of the Caledonides. For example, the Galloway granites, the Kincardineshire granite, the Skiddaw granite, the Ennerdale granophyre, the Eskdale granite and the Shap granite belong to this period. The first and last named of these cut Silurian rocks, and are therefore post-Silurian in age; while boulders and pebbles of the Kincardineshire granite occur in the basal conglomerates of the Old Red Sandstone of early Devonian age, thus proving that the magma had consolidated into granite, and had been exposed to denudation in pre-Devonian times.

On the other hand, certain of the Scottish granites occur in close association with Lower O.R.S. lavas to which they must be genetically related. The inter-relationship is most clearly shown in the small self-contained igneous province of the **Cheviot Hills** on the borders between Scotland and England. The Cheviot granite occupies a central position, and was intruded into the surrounding andesitic lavas. At Glencoe and Ben Nevis also granites are intrusive into Lower O.R.S. lavas which are dated by the fossil plants contained in interbedded sediments. In these (and other) localities the

[1] George, T. Neville in *British Caledonides*, 1963, p. 31.

[2] Fitch, F. J., Miller, J. A., and Brown, P. E. 'Age of Caledonian orogeny and metamorphism in Britain,' *Nature*, 203 (1964), 275.

granites are younger than the dated lavas; but in spite of their Devonian age, they clearly belong to a late stage of the building of the Caledonides.

Several of the Caledonian granites in England, Scotland and Ireland have been dated by radiometric means. The 'ages' show a considerable spread; but several, including Shap granite in the Lake District, the great Leinster granite in Eire and the small Creetown granite in Galloway are approximately 390 m.y. old. The Galway granite in North-West Ireland and the Weardale granite in the Pennines are rather more than 360 m.y. These figures may indicate that Caledonian plutonic activity occurred at two periods. It may be merely a coincidence that the earlier date is approximately the same as that assigned to the latest metamorphic phase which affected the Moines, or the two events may be causally related. Unfortunately the relationship between any one of these 'ages' and the 'date' of the act of intrusion is quite unknown.

Here then, in brief, is the survey of the Caledonian structures in Britain. It remains to note how far the structural pattern conforms to the ideal case outlined above. There is a reasonable degree of agreement so far as the western half of the geanticline is concerned: Scotland, the Lake District, Wales and the Welsh Borderlands fall into place satisfactorily, except for certain anomalies concerning the attitude of, and direction of displacement along certain of the thrusts. It is difficult, however, to recognize anything in these islands in the nature of a mirror-image of the western half of the geanticline. According to current belief, it is to be found in Scandinavia, where a belt of overthrusting separates a westerly zone of structural complexity from an easterly one which has been significantly described as a 'structural backwater'—a region of low dips, and a complete absence of 'regional metamorphism.'

It is not unreasonable to look to the English Midlands for the missing evidence. For the most part the Lower Palaeozoic rocks are hidden beneath a cover of younger Palaeozoic and Mesozoic strata; but here and there folding, faulting and deep denudation have combined to bring them into view. However, when they do appear, their fold-axes trend north-west and south-east—at right angles to the typical Caledonoid grain. This is so, for instance, in the inliers such as Horton in Ribblesdale under the western flank of the Pennines (Fig. 47) and the Nuneaton ridge farther south. It is also the direction of structural trend in the Precambrian rocks themselves in a number of different parts of the country, notably in Charnwood Forest; further, the Precambrian lavas building the Caradoc Hills and the Wrekin strike almost at right angles to the trend of the hog-backed ridges themselves, and give the impression of being representative slices of the Precambrian floor thrown up by Caledonian faulting.

It appears as if the Lower Palaeozoic rocks under the Pennines and Midlands owe their structural pattern to crushing against a massif trending north-west to south-east, built of Precambrian rocks already strongly folded and with a well-developed grain in the same direction, which has been inherited by the overlying younger rocks.

## REFERENCES

The Regional Geologies of the appropriate areas, for example 'Northern England' for the structure of the Lake District.

A symposium held in Edinburgh University in 1961, with the title *The British Caledonides*, was followed by the publication in 1963 of a volume bearing the same name and containing contributions from several experts in different aspects. Some of the contributions are too specialised for the general reader; but those by T. N. George, D. A. Bassett and J. Sutton's summary are recommended.

GILETTI, B. J., *et al.* 'A geochronological study of the . . . Scottish Highlands,' *Q.J.G.S.*, **117** (1961), 233.

HOLTEDAHL, O. 'History of Norway and its relation to Great Britain,' *Q.J.G.S.*, **108** (1952), 65.

KENNEDY, W. Q. 'On the Significance of Thermal Structure in the Scottish Highlands,' *Geol. Mag.*, **85** (1949), 229.

KENNEDY, W. Q. 'The Great Glen Fault,' *Q.J.G.S.*, **102** (1946), 41.

SHACKLETON, R. M. 'The Structural Evolution of North Wales,' *Liv. & Manch. Geol. Journ.*, **1** (1954), 261.

## CHAPTER IX

# THE DEVONIAN PERIOD

BOTH the Ordovician and Silurian Systems exhibit important variations in lithology, consequent upon differences in the conditions of accumulation, the essential governing factors being depth of the sea and distance from the shore-line. In the succeeding Devonian System we again find such contrasts, but of a different order of magnitude, because for the first time we have to deal not only with several different types of marine sedimentary rocks, but also with others which accumulated in a non-marine environment. This is the direct consequence of the geographical changes brought about by the building of the Caledonides upon the site of the Lower Palaeozoic. Much of North Britain emerged as dry land for the first time since late Precambrian times, and on its surface rocks of 'continental' types were formed; while at the same time normal marine sediments were being deposited on the floor of the Devonian Sea which lay far to the south of the position it had occupied during the earlier Palaeozoic periods. Thus rocks of Devonian age exhibit two facies, strikingly different as regards both lithology and faunal characters. The **marine Devonian** must be regarded as the more typical of the two, and serves as the standard of reference. The continental facies is still known by the familiar name of **Old Red Sandstone,** though much of it is not sandstone. It is 'Old', however, compared with the 'New Red Sandstone', the name given to the combined Permian and Triassic Systems, which resemble it in many ways, both as regards rock-types and conditions of formation. Note that 'Devonian' is the name of the *Period* and of the marine facies of the System. 'Old Red Sandstone' is the name of the continental (non-marine) *facies* of the Devonian System and should not be used in a time sense.

A bird's-eye view of North-West Europe at the opening of this period would have shown the region of the British Isles as occupying a marginal position on a great continent stretching far away to the north-west. On the sky-line would be seen the peaks of the Caledonides, stretching across in parallel ranges aligned north-east to south-west, and flanked by lesser foothills. These in turn would be seen to merge into a broad plain, stretching southwards towards the sea and continuing beyond the coastline as a just-submerged continental shelf.

THE MARINE DEVONIAN

### *A.*—South Devon and Cornwall

The typical marine rocks of the period occur only in the counties of Devon and Cornwall; it is the former, of course, that gives its name to the System, and is regarded as the type locality. It must be admitted, however, that the region is far from ideal judged as a type-locality, for the geological structures are complicated, the softer rocks have been strongly cleaved, while they have been intruded by great granite bosses and basic sills that effectively disguise the rocks by the effects of contact metamorphism. The succession and structure are decipherable in terms of the fine exposures of these rocks in the Ardennes and the Rhine provinces, which provide the real standards of reference. As a fact, Murchison and Sedgwick, working in Devon and Cornwall, just anticipated their American contemporaries who were examining rocks of the same age in New York State. Had the tables been turned, the System would have borne the name 'Erian', and the type-sections would have been those in the eastern United States.

In the systematic subdivision of the Devonian System, different groups of fossils have been used. The most valuable are ammonoids and goniatites, free-swimming creatures which therefore fill the role of time-indices ideally; but they do not invariably occur, and in their absence ostracods and conodonts may be used. Many ostracods are restricted to a narrow vertical range of strata, but are widely distributed geographically: they may therefore be used for long-range correlation. It happens that they tend to be abundant in types of rocks which are otherwise unfossiliferous; they have usually escaped the distortion which makes specific identification of other types of fossils uncertain; and identification by the field geologist aided by a hand-lens is practicable. In rocks of the appropriate facies corals may be pressed into service, and even some brachiopods are useful age indicators. On the Continent Stages have been defined as shown in Fig. 33, and for convenience these are grouped into three Series—the inevitable Lower, Middle and Upper Devonian. The Middle and Upper Series are divided into ammonoid zones, each bearing the name of a distinctive species which reached its acme in that particular zone. As knowledge has grown it has become apparent that the Continental and British Devonian are closely similar.

*Lower Devonian*

The lowest beds seen are the **Dartmouth Slates**; but they cannot be even near the true base of the System, for they contain fossils characteristic of a relatively high level in the Lower Devonian. Thus the base of the System is not seen, and its relation to older rocks is quite unknown in the type-locality. The slates themselves

| STAGES | GENUS ZONES | SPECIES ZONES | |
|---|---|---|---|
| FAMENNIAN | 6. WOCKLUMERIA | 2. sphaeroides | Ostracods: Richterina spp. |
| | | 1. | Purple & green slates basin facies = Cypridinenschiefer (Eifel) |
| | 5. CLYMENIA | 2. | |
| | | 1. | |
| | 4. PLATYCLYMENIA | 3. annulata | |
| | | 2. | |
| | 3. | 1. | |
| | 2. CHEILOCERAS | 2. | |
| | | 1. curvispina | Ostracod shale facies |
| FRASNIAN | 1. MANTICOCERAS | 3. holzapfeli | Saltern Cove goniatites |
| | | 2. cordatum | Büdesheim fauna |
| | | 1. lunulicosta | Ransleigh Q'y lsts |
| | | | Lummaton Shell Bed |
| GIVETIAN | MAENIOCERAS | 3. terebratum | Hypothyridina (Rh.) cuboides |
| | | 2. molarium | Phillipsastraea<br>Wolborough Q'y lsts |
| | | 1. | |
| EIFELIAN | ANARCESTES | 2. | |
| | | 1. lateseptatus | Couvinian Shales |
| | | | Calceola sandalina |
| EMSIAN | MIMOSPHINCTES | 2. | Staddon Grits |
| | | 1. | Meadfoot Beds |
| SIEGENIAN | | 1. | Dartmouth Slates |
| GEDINNIAN | NO AMMONOIDS | | |

FIG. 33.

The marine Devonian succession in the type region. *Based on the work of M. R. House*, 'Q.J.G.S.,' **119** (1963), *and others.*

are well exposed in eastern Devonshire: they are purple and green in colour and are very sparsely fossiliferous, having yielded practically nothing but very rare and obscure 'fish' remains. As a consequence even their marine origin is suspect. It has been suggested that they are the cleaved equivalents of the Red Marls of South Wales. They contain *Pteraspis sp.*, an ostracoderm of zonal significance in the Dittonian, of Lower Devonian age, and therefore cannot be older than that series. From the coast near Dartmouth they extend in an east-west outcrop, reaching the Atlantic coast west of Bideford (Fig. 72).

Meadfoot beach on the Devonshire coast north of Torquay, gives its name to the neritic middle division of the Series. The **Meadfoot Beds** include dark slates, interbedded with thin sandstones and limestones yielding fossils in relative abundance, though they are usually difficult to extract from their matrix. Among the fossils are brachiopods, gasteropods, corals and trilobites, as well as one fossil 'fish'. One of the most interesting fossils from this division is *Pleurodictyum problematicum* (Fig. 34). The problem suggested by its trivial name is the classification of the creature; for although its shape suggests that it is a coral, its structure is unlike that of other types, and the function of 'the worm in its little inside' is problematical. On the very inadequate evidence of the discovery of one goniatite the Looe Grits, exposed on the South Cornish coast, have been correlated with the Meadfoot Beds and both are considered to belong to the Lower Emsian Stage.

The **Staddon Grits** succeed the Meadfoot Beds, and are more arenaceous than the underlying beds. Some of the rocks are true quartzites, and as a consequence of their durability the outcrop is marked by relatively high ground, for example, Staddon Heights near Plymouth, while on the coast they give rise to most picturesque scenery in North Cornwall.

The exact relationship between the three Lower Devonian formations is uncertain. It has been customary to regard them as successive members of the Lower Devonian; but to an unknown extent the lithological variations may reflect differences in facies rather than age.

*Middle and Upper Devonian*

It will be convenient at the moment to consider the Middle and Upper Series together, though the two will be referred to individually where necessary.

The general succession and lithology are indicated in Fig. 33. The massive limestones are, for a variety of reasons, the most important members. They rest upon and are succeeded by thin-bedded limestones which in turn grade into thick argillaceous formations both above and below. The massive limestones belong mainly to the Givetian Stage, but extend upwards into the Frasnian and downwards into the Eifelian: therefore the important Middle-Upper Devonian boundary occurs *within* the massive limestones at Torquay; but a few miles to the west shales interbedded with thin limestones have yielded Lower Frasnian goniatites proving

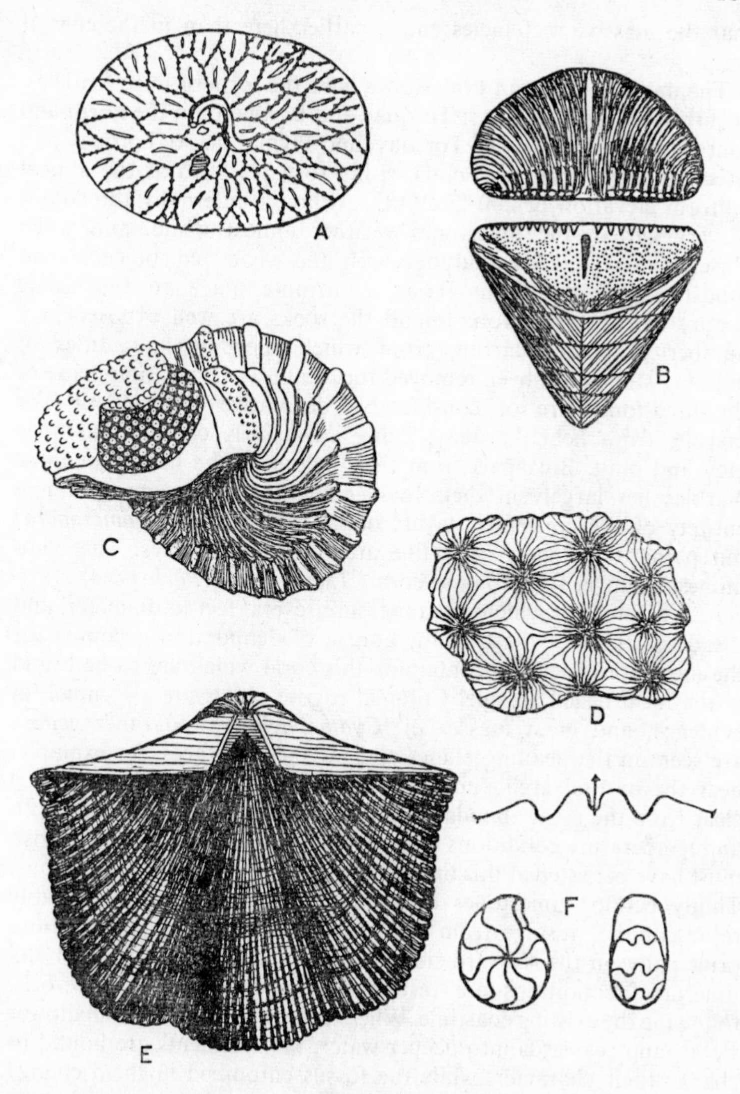


FIG. 34.

Fossils from the Marine Devonian.

A. *Pleurodictyum problematicum*, Emsian.
B. *Calceola sandalina* (the 'slipper' coral) with operculum, Couvinian.
C. *Phacops sternbergi* (*after* Barrande).
D. *Smithia pengellyi*, Givetian.
E. *Cyrtospirifer verneuili*, Frasnian (*after* Davidson).
F. *Tornoceras auris*, an Upper-Devonian goniatite, side view, apertural view and suture. Frasnian.

that the massive reef facies ended earlier here than in the coastal area.

The middle Devonian Limestones have the form of huge lenticles, occurring in three districts: Torquay and Brixham, on the north and south sides respectively of Tor Bay, and Plymouth. At Torquay and Brixham they form steep cliffs, rising to a platform at the almost uniform elevation of 200 feet O.D. Although internally the colour is very varied, the limestones weather almost white, and when closely associated by faulting, with the vivid red breccias and sandstones of the Permo-Trias, contribute much to the scenic beauty of eastern Devon. Inland the rocks are well exposed in a number of great quarries, from which enormous quantities of building-stone have been removed for local use. In addition many of the limestones are of considerable decorative value, Petit Tor marble, from near Torquay, being attractively coloured in dove grey and pink. But apart from their colouring the beauty of these marbles lies largely in their fossil contents. Some consist almost entirely of the concentric layers of the reef-builder *Stromatopora*; but perhaps the most attractive are the coral-marbles. The commonest form is the tabulate coral, *Thamnopora* (*Pachypora*) *cervicornis*, colonies of which often measure several feet in diameter, and the destruction of these in the course of denudation accounts for the numberless pebbles containing this coral which are to be found in the local beach shingle. Colonial rugose corals are also much in evidence, and great masses of '*Cyathophyllum*' and other genera are seen on the bedding planes and wave-cut surfaces, for example, near the natural arch known as London Bridge at Torquay. It is clear from the great abundance of these corals that the special depth and temperature conditions under which the coral polyp will flourish must have persisted at this time in Devonshire, giving reef conditions. Thinly bedded limestones containing fragmental corals probably represent the wastage from the reefs, resulting from wave action, principally on the seaward side. It must be understood that, at any time, reef conditions are restricted to a relatively narrow belt, following the existing coastline. When traced landwards into shallower water, and seawards into deeper water, the sediments are bound to change their character, while the fossils entombed in them change in sympathy. The massive limestones are not uniformly fossilferous: indeed in great quarries at Berry Head, the southern extremity of Tor Bay, 200 feet of massive unfossiliferous limestones and dolomites are exposed; and in some of the Torquay limestones also dolomitization is extensive and fossils are not common except on certain horizons, notably the Lummaton Shell Bed, well known for its fauna, especially of brachiopods, including *Hypothyridina*

(*'Rhynchonella'*) *cuboides*. This shell bed occurs right at the top of the Givetian.

One other special feature of the Middle Devonian remains for consideration. On the coast north of Torquay two thin greenish bands, easily eroded and only an inch or two in thickness, are interbedded with the massive limestones, and on examination prove to be pyroclastic, the products of explosive eruptions. This meagre evidence of contemporary volcanic activity is augmented inland, however, as in the neighbourhood of Totnes, near Newton Abbot, the limestones are largely replaced by volcanic rocks, including both lavas and 'ashes'. As the latter are interbedded with normal limestones and clay rocks, we are evidently dealing with the products of submarine volcanoes. Viewed as rock specimens these volcanics are usually disappointing: they have suffered from the subsequent earth movements to a much greater extent than the contemporary sedimentary rocks, and their original characters are so disguised that it is often impossible to distinguish lava from tuff. The period of volcanic activity that here commenced in Middle Devonian times elsewhere persisted into Upper Devonian and even Lower Carboniferous times, and at its maximum the volcanic belt extended from some unknown distance west of Cornwall eastwards to Moravia in Central Europe. The lavas and associated intrusive rocks belong to the spilitic suite, varying in acidity, but notably rich in sodium.

The *Upper Devonian* occupies a larger area than the underlying series, the main outcrop lying between the Dartmoor and Bodmin Moor granites, and extending from Plymouth northwards to Tavistock. East of Dartmoor a narrowing outcrop reaches to the sea-coast near Torquay; while west of Bodmin Moor a wider band reaches the coast between Boscastle and Trevose Head.

The Upper Devonian comprises two stages, Frasnian (below) and Famennian (above) which are divided into six 'stufen', in effect genus zones. These in turn are subdivided as necessary into species zones, there being twelve of these in the complete succession. We could speak precisely of a particular horizon as occurring in 'the *Cordatum* Zone of the *Manticoceras* Stufe in the Frasnian Stage'; but it would be more concise to refer to it as Upper Devonian I.2.

The Upper Devonian strata are strikingly different from the underlying Middle and Lower Series in lithological and faunal facies; and the differences are clearly brought out by comparing the successions in (1) the Torquay, Brixham and Chudleigh area with (2) the St Minver, Padstow area in North Cornwall. The former on account of tectonic complexity is more difficult to interpret than the latter; but is dealt with first.

In some localities the Frasnian commences with massive limestones forming a continuation of the Givetian below. These are overlain by typical Frasnian limestones which are dark in colour, thin-bedded, interstratified with shale, thus reflecting the characters of the Couvinian limestones; but they are sometimes nodular and contain ammonoids and other fossils which allow their systematic zonal position to be accurately fixed. Frasnian I.3 occurs at a particularly well-known goniatite locality in Saltern Cove, discovered well over a century ago. From the next zone below, I.2, in the Eifel, the famous Büdesheim fauna has provided large numbers of beautifully preserved goniatites found in museum and teaching collections. *Tornoceras* spp. is well represented (Fig. 34). Approximately at this horizon in Devon the facies changes from thin nodular limestones with shales and volcanics to red shales, devoid of ammonoids but containing ostracods sometimes in abundance. In the field they are usually identified as *Entomis serratostriata*, which is sometimes accompanied by a small, delicate, possibly free-swimming lamellibranch, *Posidonia venusta*. This ostracod-bearing red shale facies persists into and through the Famennian; but thin nodular limestones or shales with fossiliferous calcareous nodules contain ammonoids which have allowed exact and detailed correlation with the Continental successions to be established.

For comparison we pass now into **North Cornwall** where Devonian rocks are extensively displayed in coastal sections and give rise to spectacular cliff scenery, especially at Trevose Head. A complex syncline with east-west axis passes through St Minver and Padstow. The oldest rocks involved form a thick series of Grey Slates, shown as Upper Devonian on existing maps; but recently (1963) they have been proved to contain a succession of ammonoid faunas ranging from Lower Eifelian to Upper Givetian, and are therefore Middle Devonian. Higher grey slates, containing dark-coloured cephalopod-bearing bands, fall in the Frasnian. A short distance above the highest such band (in I.2), a significant colour change takes place, accompanied by a change in faunal facies: the slates are now purple ('red') and green and contain ostracods. It has not yet been shown how much of the Famennian is present in this area, but the whole of it must be represented in one locality or another as there is a passage up into the Carboniferous System. The details are considered in the next chapter.

It will have been realized, of course, that the St Minver Grey Slates with cephalopod-bearing bands are the lateral equivalents of the massive reef-limestones of Torquay and Brixham. Further, the 'red' ostracod-bearing shales or slates constitute another facies developed in a different environment. The real significance of the facies variations within the Devonian has been commented upon and speculated about for a very long time, not only in this country but also in Germany where the same facies differences are encountered, especially in the Schiefergebirge (Slate Mountains). Rabien (1956) adopted the terms '*becken*' for the ostracod slate (Cypridinenschiefer) deposited in relatively deep basins; and '*swellen*', translated as submarine 'rises' or ridges for the condensed, chiefly calcareous, nodular, cephalopod-bearing facies. No problems arise concerning the reef facies; and we may accept the ostracod shales as deep-water deposits; but it is difficult to say just how deep. R. Goldring makes out a strong case for regarding them as abyssal and indicating the culmination of the deepening of the Armorican geosyncline throughout Devonian and early Carboniferous times. His conclusion is based not only on the fine grain of the sediment and the nature of the fauna—pelagic, with normal benthonic creatures unrepresented—but also on the fact that sedimentation was abnormally slow, particularly in the case of the cephalopod-limestones. Clearly, with the passage of time the positions of the various depth zones would slowly change; and in any given locality a vertical succession of these facies would be built up. This is illustrated by the Chudleigh inlier, where massive Givetian reef limestones containing among other fossils, *Stringocephalus burtini*, are abruptly overlain by thin-bedded limestones containing Frasnian (I.2) ammonoids. These in turn are succeeded by red ostracod shales in places interbedded with nodular shales or limestones containing cephalopods belonging to all the Famennian zones.

Summarily, although limestones do occur in the Upper Devonian, they are definitely subordinate to argillaceous rocks, and the Upper Series consists essentially of shales, often converted by pressure into slates. Indeed in some parts of Cornwall, near Tintagel, for example, they have gone beyond the slate stage of metamorphism, and are now phyllites, with cleavage planes made glossy by white mica in minute flakes.

A well-known formation in the Upper Devonian of North Cornwall is the **Delabole Slate**, at one time extensively quarried for roofing-slates, but perhaps better known on account of the distorted valves of *Cyrtospirifer verneuili* (Fig. 34), obtained from these beds by quarrymen and sold to visitors as 'Delabole butterflies'.

The main development of volcanic rocks in North Cornwall is in the Upper Devonian Series, and they are particularly well developed in the vicinity of Padstow, where, at Pentire Point, they form a cliff approaching 300 feet in height, composed solely of basic pillow lavas of spilitic type. The lavas are associated with massive sills of similar magmatic type.

### *B.*—North Devon and Somerset

A glance at the geological map of Devonshire shows that the rocks we have considered above are followed to the north by a broad belt of Carboniferous strata, occupying the central parts of the county. Ignoring the many structural complications of faulting and minor folding, we may say that the 'sheet-dip' of the Devonian, that is, the dip of the System as a whole, is northwards under the Carboniferous. Somewhere about the middle of the county the sheet-dip must change, however, for the Devonian rocks again reach the surface in North Devon and the adjacent parts of Somerset, where they have an essentially *southerly* dip.

Without at this stage entering into details, it may be said that on emerging from beneath the cover of Carboniferous rocks, they have so completely changed in lithological character as to be almost unrecognizable when compared with the typical Devonian of the southern outcrops. They differ from the contemporaneous strata in the south in three important respects: firstly, limestones are much less important; secondly, volcanic rocks are almost completely absent; and thirdly, thick sandstones occur at three different levels. The chief interest centres round these sandstones, which are totally unlike any Devonian rocks in South Devon or Cornwall: but which, on the other hand, so closely resemble the Old Red Sandstone that most people who have studied both are convinced that they *are* Old Red Sandstone. Accepting the sandstones as continental, these rocks of the North Devon outcrop take on a new significance, for in them we can observe an interstratification of true marine Devonian with continental Old Red Sandstone, and we can read into the succession evidence of alternations of marine and continental conditions (Fig. 35). A very close parallel occurs in the Ardennes and the Eifel where the Lower and early Middle Devonian are neritic; but there are numerous intercalations of O.R.S. (thinning southwards) especially in the Lower Devonian of the Dinant Syncline.

The lowest rocks exposed build the Foreland Head near Lynmouth, and are termed the **Foreland Grits.** They consist essentially of red and grey grits and sandstones, but are accompanied by finer red slates and bands of coarser conglomerates. It is significant that the only fossils recorded are Lower Old Red Sandstone plants, including *Psilophyton*, a typical sedge.

The second of the sandstone groups forms the Hangman Point, east of Combe Martin, rising nearly 600 feet above sea-level. These **Hangman Grits** are so like the Foreland Grits in general characters that they were thought to be faulted repetitions of the latter; but typical Middle Old Red Sandstone plants and fish-scales have been obtained from the former, proving them to lie on a definitely higher horizon. A thin group of variable strata above the Grits constitutes a series of passage beds between the continental phase below and the marine phase above. They include a distinctive, tough rock, which on wave-smoothed surfaces displays numerous sections across brachiopod shells identified by J. W. Evans as *Stringocephalus burtini*, a well-known Middle Devonian age-indicator in the German

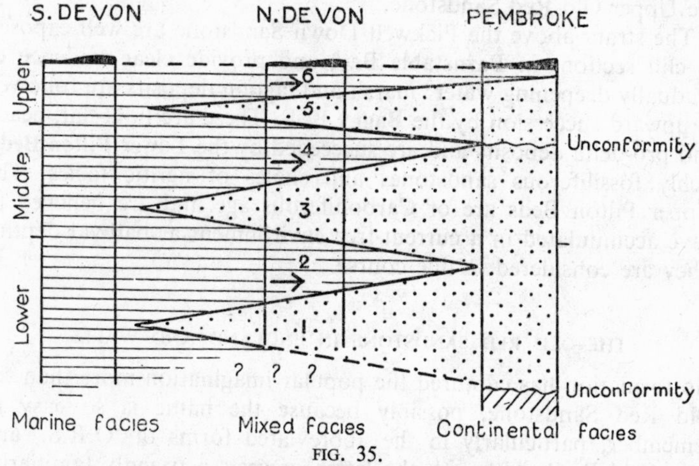


FIG. 35.

Diagram showing changes of Facies of the Devonian rocks from South to North
The North Devon-Somerset succession is as follows:
1. Foreland Grits; 2. Lynton Beds; 3. Hangman Grits; 4. Ilfracombe Beds and Morte Slates; 5. Pickwell Down Sandstone; 6. Baggy and Pilton Beds.
The black at the top of the columns represents the basal Carboniferous rocks.

Devonian. Its occurrence at this level in North Devon is of considerable stratigraphical significance.

The **Ilfracombe Beds** are finely displayed in cliff sections in the neighbourhood of the town of that name and Combe Martin. They consist dominantly of grey slates, strongly cleaved and jointed, interbedded with very subordinate limestones and thin sandstones. In the coastal section there are many limestone outcrops; but they were shown in 1962 to be faulted repetitions of two main (30 feet) limestones together with much thinner ones. Among the fossils obtained from the thicker limestones are several kinds of corals including the long-range *Alveolites* and the ubiquitous *Thamnopora* (*Pachypora*) *cervicornis*, as well as others not occurring in the limestones of South Devon, but known from the Middle Devonian in Bohemia. The faunas from these Ilfracombe limestones range from the Givetian possibly into the Lower Frasnian. It follows, therefore, that these beds are the age-equivalents of the massive reef limestones of Tor Bay, though both lithological and faunal facies differ considerably.

The third sandstone group, unlike the two lower ones, has given way to marine erosion to form the wide bay between Morte Point and Baggy Point. These **Pickwell Down Sandstones** again contain no fossils other than plants and fish remains, this time referable to the Upper Old Red Sandstone.

The strata above the Pickwell Down Sandstone are well exposed in cliff sections in Barnstable Bay, and provide clear evidence of gradually deepening water: marsh and lagoon deposits are followed in upward succession by the **Baggy Beds.** These are tidal-flat, beach and pro-delta deposits and are succeeded by the **Lower Pilton Beds,** richly fossiliferous sandstones and shales of neritic facies. The Upper Pilton Beds are of Carboniferous age and are believed to have accumulated in a current-free environment at bathyal depths. They are considered in due course.

## THE OLD RED SANDSTONE IN ENGLAND AND WALES

No formation has captured the popular imagination more than the Old Red Sandstone, possibly because the name is so easy to remember, particularly in the abbreviated forms of 'O.R.S.' and even 'Old Red'. Although the latter suggests a friendly familiarity amounting almost to levity, it is widely used even in official publications. A more legitimate reason for its popularity is that the System has been immortalized by the writings of Hugh Miller, which are among the very few geological books that can truly be claimed as literature. In beautiful language he has described the rocks together with the bizarre fossil remains they yielded to his careful search when he was plying his trade of master mason.

The special lithological characters of the Old Red Sandstone must have been recognized at a very early date; but the systematic position of the formation in the stratigraphical column could only be proved by the application of the fundamental law of superposition of strata. It is sandwiched in between the fossiliferous marine Silurian below and the fossiliferous marine Lower Carboniferous above; the marine Devonian is similarly conformably succeeded by the Carboniferous, and therefore the two formations must be of the same age, in spite of the fact that they have scarcely a feature, and certainly not a single obvious feature, in common.

O.R.S. outcrops occur in Scotland, Ireland and in the Cheviot

Hills, while the largest one in North-West Europe is a roughly triangular area embracing parts of Shropshire, Herefordshire, Monmouthshire and Brecknockshire. The widest part of the triangle is in the south, where the pitch of the beds carries them beneath the Carboniferous rocks of the South Wales coalfield, to which they form a marginal belt extending to the sea at Milford Haven and St Bride's Bay. The wide separation of the main outcrops and the relatively unfossiliferous nature of the rocks conspire to render correlation exceedingly difficult, and up to a point highly speculative. On certain fundamental aspects of O.R.S. stratigraphy there has been much difference of opinion, and on some of them agreement has not yet been reached.

The first of these problems to claim our attention concerns fixing the base of the O.R.S. So far agreement has not yet been reached because most writers on the subject have been concerned with finding a base common to the Old Red Sandstone and to the marine Devonian. The two terms cannot be synonymous, however, for the O.R.S. is merely a facies of the Devonian, depending for its distinctiveness upon a set of circumstances, environmental and climatic, which have not been exactly duplicated before or since. As the base of the O.R.S. was determined by a change in physical conditions, it must be diachronous in some degree. The exact date of the change probably coincides with the beginning of Devonian time somewhere; but elsewhere, for example in Co. Mayo, it occurred earlier, in the Wenlockian and again in other places, after the beginning of the Devonian Period.

The amateur geologist, W. Wickham King, added considerably to our knowledge of the O.R.S., particularly of the more northerly parts of the Anglo-Welsh basin of sedimentation or *cuvette*, where he established a succession that appears to extend but little changed over a wide area. The general succession, mostly described and named from the West Midlands, is as follows:

4. Farlow Series (Farlovian)—Upper O.R.S.
   Unconformity
3. Brecon Series (Breconian)[1]
2. Ditton Series (Dittonian) } Lower O.R.S.
1. Downton Series (Downtonian) } Lower O.R.S.

The **Downtonian** or Downton Series commences abruptly with a particularly well-known and lithologically unique layer, the Ludlow

[1] Brecon Series (Breconian) is a recently introduced term covering the strata between the highest Dittonian and the unconformity beneath the Farlovian. Formerly these strata were termed Brownstones and Plateau Beds, and in the Clee Hills area are known as the Clee Series.

Bone Bed, consisting of scales, spines and fragmental 'fish' remains,[1] together with occasional shelly fossils, embedded in a meagre sandy matrix cemented by calcite. Some years ago it was exposed during

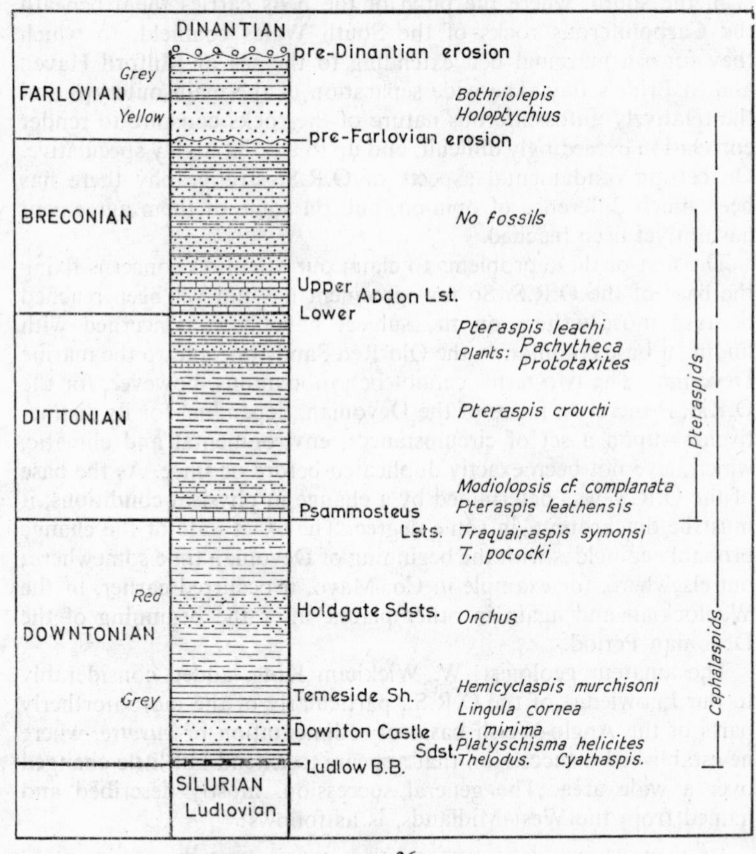


FIG. 36.

Diagram showing the Devonian (O.R.S. facies) in the Welsh Borderlands, based on work of H. W. Ball and D. L. Dineley, *Brit. Mus. Bull.* (*Nat. Hist.*), **5** (1961), 177.

road-widening operations near the old bridge which spans the River Teme immediately south of Ludlow, but it has since been collected away to chisel depth. The rock has the colour of gingerbread. It is succeeded by a few feet of grey shale containing at the top a layer

[1] Strictly the word 'fish' should be restricted to jawed aquatic vertebrates breathing through gills in the adult condition and furnished with fins for propulsion. This definition would exclude the O.R.S. ostracoderms and other families by popular usage referred to as fishes: strictly they are agnathids and *not* true fishes.

crowded to such an extent with the shells of the gasteropod, *Platyschisma helicites*, that it is called the *Platyschisma* Band. The gasteropod is accompanied by the lamellibranch, *Modiolopsis complanata*, and in places 'fish' remains including spines of *Climatius* and scales of a cephalaspid, when it is termed the Downton Bone Bed, which has been recognized at several localities in the Welsh Borderland.

The distinctive Downton Castle Sandstone follows, massive, yellow in colour, sometimes cross-bedded and some 40 feet in thickness. Perhaps its most distinctive fossil is the very small, aptly named *Lingula minima*; but the ostracod, *Beyrichia* is locally common, and 'fish' remains also occur. Of outstanding interest from the evolutionary point of view is the occurrence of the oldest known land plants, including *Pachytheca devonica*. The 'Yellow Downtonian' is succeeded abruptly by some hundred feet of greenish-grey, red or green shales or mudstones termed the Temeside Shales, famous for the abundant eurypterid remains which they contain.

By far the greater part of the Downtonian outcrop is occupied by the **Red Downtonian,** a red or purple marl formation about 1300 feet in thickness and divided into Upper and Lower divisions by the lenticular Holdgate Sandstones forming a mappable feature. Sandstones, typically red but sometimes purple or green, tend to become more important towards the top of the Red Downtonian.

The **Dittonian**, named from Ditton Priors near the Clee Hills, consists of some 1200 feet of alternating marls, sandstones and 'cornstones'. The Dittonian forms a prominent platform visible in the profile of Brown Clee Hill. A so-called '*Psammosteus*' Limestone phase occurs at the base.[1] In places one such limestone is thicker and topographically more important than others which may be associated with it. It is then mapped as the '*Psammosteus*' Limestone. Elsewhere a number of limestones of equal status occur within the phase. In spite of their name these limestones are without fossils; but associated sandstones contain 'fish' remains which have allowed their zonal position to be fixed. The lowest of the *Psammosteus* Limestones belongs to the highest zone of the Downtonian; but the major part of the phase belongs to the lowest zone of the Dittonian. Therefore the important Downtonian–Dittonian boundary, defined palaeontologically, lies within the Limestone phase, and is not a mappable line. For practical purposes the division between the two Series is drawn at the base of the '*Psammosteus*' Limestones.

[1] The name '*Psammosteus*' Limestone was in vogue when this book was written; but at the time of the last revision the generic name had been changed to *Phialaspis*; now it has been re-christened *Traquairaspis* after a famous Scottish authority on O.R.S. fishes. In view of these changes there is much to be said for retaining the original name, using single 'quotes' round the generic name.

The Dittonian marls, which are particularly important in the middle part of the succession, are virtually the same as those in the Downtonian. The more abundant sandstones are red, purple, yellow, green or variegated and tend to be calcareous. Current bedding is ubiquitous, while other features indicating accumulation in very shallow water are ripple marks, while sun-cracks and even fossil rain-prints prove exposure to the open air.

In the area of the Clee Hills the Dittonian is succeeded conformably by the **Clee Series** consisting of drab, buff or grey sandstones with subordinate shales. These rocks build the greater part of Brown Clee Hill. The base is defined by two thin Abdon Limestones which provide a useful mappable base. They are subject to rapid variation in lithology; but the horizon may be widespread as their equivalents may be recognized in parts of South Wales. No fossils of diagnostic value have been found in the Clee Series; but on general grounds they are thought to be equivalent to some part of the Breconian, and to the **Senni Beds** in particular.

The Brownstones, well developed in the Brecon Beacons, occur above the Senni Beds and are succeeded by the Plateau Beds, so named as they cap the flat, plateau-like tops of the Beacons. Their relationship to underlying beds is uncertain: formerly they were regarded as being conformable to the Brownstones and to be the uppermost member of the unbroken major cycle of sedimentation which commenced with the Ludlow Bone Bed. The cycle closed with emergence, initiating an erosion interval of unknown duration. Subsequently the Upper O.R.S. (Farlovian) was deposited unconformably on older rocks including the remnants of the Plateau Beds. Recently it has been stated that the Plateau Beds occur *above* an unconformity which separates them from the Brownstones. On the other hand it is said that they pass up, without break, into the distinctive Upper Old Red Sandstone. In North Pembrokeshire breccias, of Plateau Beds lithology, are interstratified with sandstones like those making up the underlying Cosheston Beds, so that there appears to be no break at this level. In Pembrokeshire as already noted, a temporary incursion of the sea took place giving a marine wedge in the Upper O.R.S. This apparently extended to the Brecon Beacons as *Cyrtospirifer verneuili* and marine algae are associated with *Bothriolepis*.

In the west of South Wales the O.R.S. succession differs in certain particulars from the standard succession of the Brecon Beacons and Clee Hills as shown in Fig. 37. The Cosheston Beds, a thick green sandstone formation, must be equivalent to the Senni Beds and overlying Brownstones. The succession appears to be unbroken: marl, identical with that in the **Red Marls** below, is interstratified with sandstone like that making up the major part of the Cosheston Beds. Thin inorganic limestones also occur, and there is a close lithological similarity to the Dittonian beds of more easterly parts of the cuvette. In the higher parts of the succession the dominance

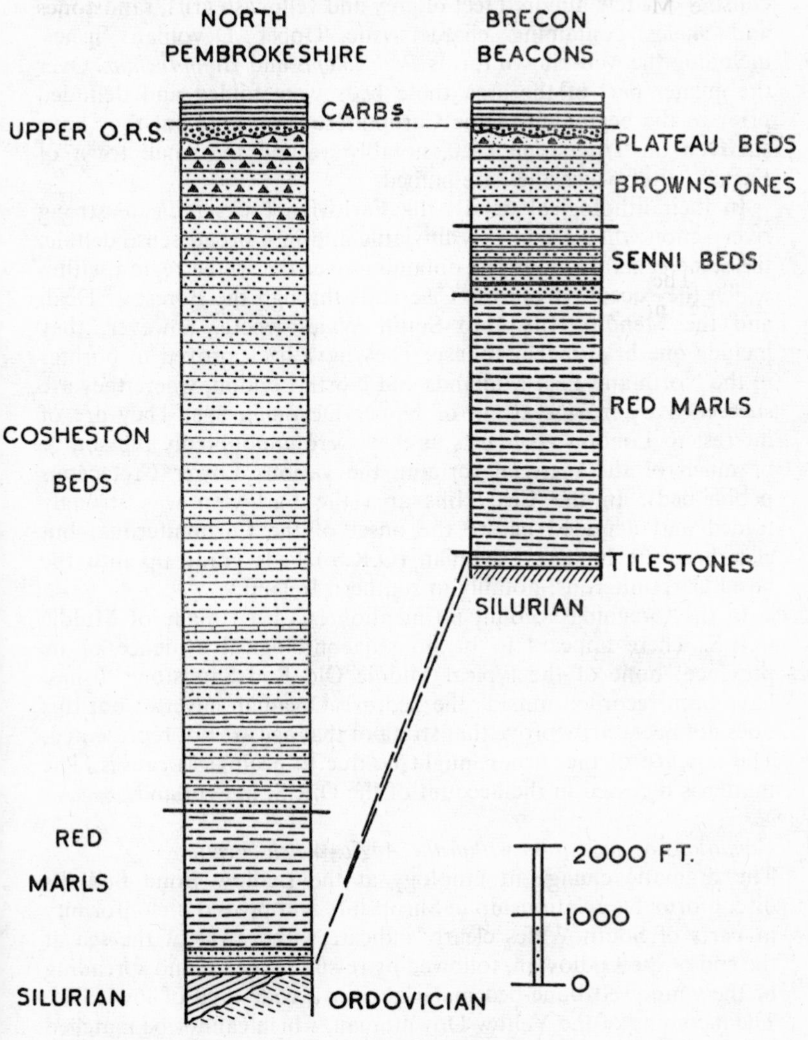


FIG. 37.
Comparative sections of the old Red Sandstone in South Wales.
(*After J. Pringle and T. N. George.*)
At the top of the O.R.S. column for the Brecon Beacons the break may be *below* the Plateau Beds (see text).

of sandstone at the expense of marl parallels the change from Dittonian to Clee Series.

In the English Midlands the O.R.S. succession is completed by the **Farlow Series** which rests unconformably on older rocks and consists of a few hundred feet of grey and yellowish grits, sandstones and shales containing characteristic Upper Devonian 'fishes' including the well-known forms *Bothriolepis* and *Holoptychius*. Over the greater part of the area these beds were folded and denuded prior to the beginning of the Carboniferous Period; but they have survived on Titterstone Clee, notably around the small town of Farlow, after which they are named.

In their lithological details the Farlovian rocks indicate strong river action: they are largely fluviatile and in a broad sense deltaic, the same general conditions obtaining over the whole region within which they occur—from the Clee Hills through the Forest of Dean and the Mendip Hills into South Wales where, however, they include one brief marine phase. They have been proved in borings in the North and East Midlands and North London, where they are succeeded by marine strata of Upper Devonian age. They are of interest to London geologists as they were undoubtedly the source of much of the material forming the various Lower Cretaceous pebble-beds. In the Clee Hills area the Farlovian was strongly folded and denuded before the onset of the Carboniferous; but elsewhere the highest Devonian (O.R.S.) beds grade up into the basal Carboniferous, notably in southern Ireland.

In the foregoing account no mention has been made of Middle O.R.S. There appears to be no palaeontological evidence of its presence: none of the typical Middle Old Red Sandstone 'fishes' have been recorded outside the Scottish Orcadian cuvette; but this does not necessarily prove that strata of that age are not represented. The absence of the 'fishes' might be due to ecological causes. The matter is dicussed in the account of the O.R.S. in Scotland.

*Conditions of deposition within the Anglo-Welsh cuvette*

The dramatic change in lithology at the Ludlow Bone Bed, its disconformable relationship in Shropshire and proved unconformity in parts of South Wales clearly indicate withdrawal of the sea at the end of the Ludlovian, followed by re-submergence and spreading of the winnowed bone-bed material over a wide area of low relief. The incoming of the Yellow Downtonian, which cannot be matched lithologically at any lower level in the Palaeozoic, marks the inauguration of a completely different regime which persisted throughout Lower Devonian time and, indeed, until the end of the Period in these latitudes. The new physiographic feature was a great delta

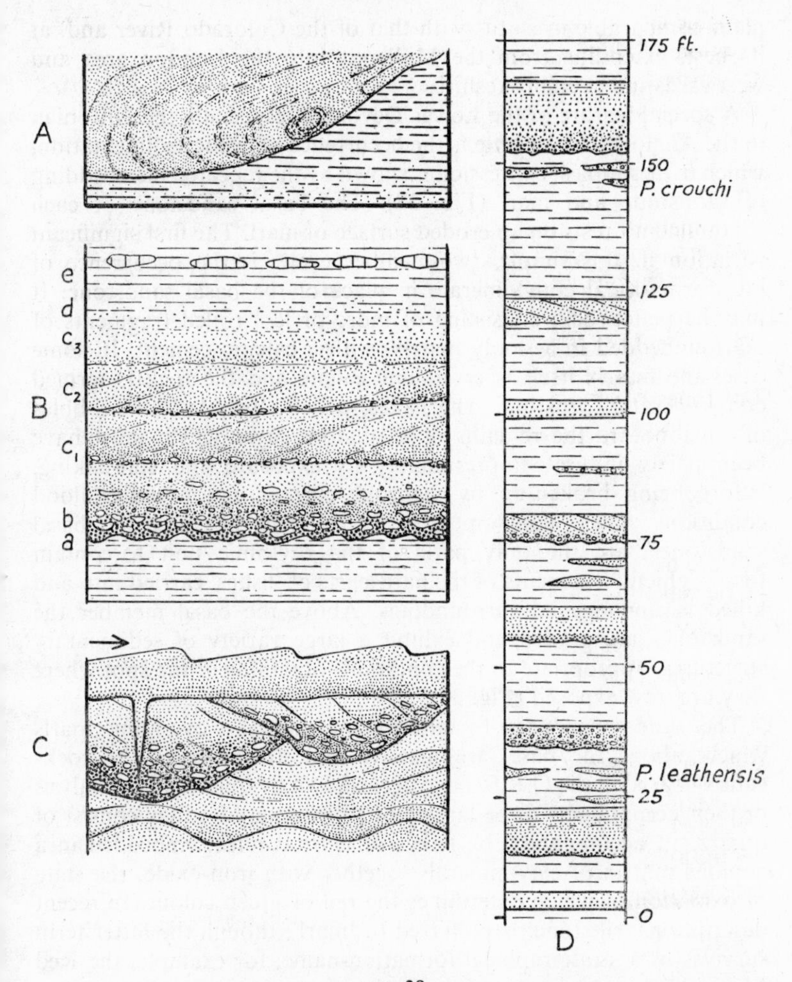


FIG. 38.

Some Dittonian sedimentation structures.

A. Slumping down the flank of channel cut in 'marl.'

B. Unit of rhythmic sedimentation: (a) eroded surface at base; (b) pellet conglomerate; (c) cross-bedded graded sandstones; (d) siltstone; (e) 'marl' with inorganic limestone nodules.

C. Multiple channel cut in curly-bedded sandstone and infilled with cornstone containing a sandstone 'dyke' on left; asymmetric (current) ripples at top and symmetrical (wave) ripples at base.

D. Diagram illustrating part of the Dittonian succession near Cleobury Mortimer, Shropshire.

A and C based on drawings by H. W. Ball and D. L. Dineley in *Bull. Brit. Mus.* (*Nat. Hist.*), **5**, no. 7 (1961).

D after D. L. Dineley and D. W. Gossage in *Proc. Geol. Assoc.*, **70** (1959), 231.

plain comparable in status with that of the Colorado River and, at its best, extending from the Midlands into the London area and westwards into Pembrokeshire.

A special feature of the Lower Devonian, especially the Dittonian in the Anglo-Welsh cuvette is the occurrence of cyclic sedimentation, which in its simplest expression is shown by the repeated interbedding of sandstone and marl (Fig. 38). The basal sandstone of each rhythmic unit rests on an eroded surface of marl. The first significant variation in this simple, two-member cycle, is the occurrence of intraformational conglomerate in place of the basal sandstone. It may be pellet-rock, consisting of more or less rolled fragments of marl embedded in a sandy matrix, with a calcitic cement. In some cases the matrix itself is crystalline calcite and the rock is termed conglomeratic cornstone. The flakes, pellets, 'pebbles' and cobbles of siltstone are the remains of a siltstone layer which must have been partly indurated, presumably by exposure and sun-baking, before being broken-up by vigorous current action under flood conditions. These conglomerates, or in their absence, the basal sandstones, are the only parts of the rhythmic unit to contain fossils, chiefly fragments of the hard parts of 'fishes' carried into and killed in uncongenial surroundings. Above the basal member the sandstones are graded and exhibit a large variety of sedimentary structures, appropriate to the conditions obtaining at the spot where they are now exposed (Fig. 38).

The sandstones pass by alternation into the overlying marls which, above the base, are massive and unstratified. The rocks called 'marls' in the O.R.S. have been shown by quantitative analysis of their components to be largely of siltstone grade: they consist of quartz silt accompanied by flakes of detrital mica, embedded in a copious matrix of clay-minerals together with iron-oxide, the state of oxidation of which determines the red or green colour. In recent descriptions 'siltstone' is preferred to 'marl', though the latter term survives as a stratigraphical formation-name, for example, the Red Marls.

The rhythmic alternation of sandstone and marl, especially characteristic of the Dittonian though not unknown in the other series, is most readily explained as the consequence of alternating wet and dry seasons, of unknown duration. Abnormally wet seasons would result in distributaries bursting their banks (levées) and causing wide-spread sheet-flooding when a layer of sediment, rich in plant debris, would be thinly spread over a large area. New distributaries would rip out new channels in the deltaic sediments. Such channelling is encountered repeatedly in all the O.R.S. series including the Farlovian, proving the deltaic environment to have been re-established after the temporary interruption represented by the hiatus below the Farlow Series.

As the sheet-floods subsided mud-flats would have emerged, strewn with playa and ox-bow cut-off lakes. On the flats the superficial layers of sediment would be sun-baked during the ensuing dry season, with the development of desiccation cracks; while in circumstances which are easy to imagine, such layers might be broken into flakes, later rolled into 'pebbles', providing the essential materials of the pellet rocks and mud-flake conglomerates. Elsewhere hard water was drawn to the surface by capillary attraction and evaporated, with the formation of surface limestones ('*calcretes*') or small nodules ('*race*'), in the surface layers. These also might be broken up and incorporated in basal conglomeratic cornstones.

In view of these conditions, at any one time several quite different local environments would have existed in different parts of the delta, varying from aeolian to fresh-water (fluviatile), lacustrine, brackish (lagoonal, 'pro-delta') and, very rarely marine (intertidal). General considerations based largely on lithology and sedimentary structures suggest this must have been the case: it is confirmed by the palaeontological evidence, considered below.

Opinion concerning the probable climatic conditions during the formation of the O.R.S. has changed considerably in the last quarter-century. Formerly it was widely believed that a hot dry desert environment best fitted the facts; but it is now realized that red rocks do not necessarily indicate such environments. Red sand certainly does occur in parts of existing deserts; but red or red-brown soil covers the surface of large parts of Africa which are certainly not deserts. Deep lateritic weathering under monsoonal climatic conditions could have provided the raw material of which the dominant marls are composed. There must have been copious seasonal precipitation: rivers were clearly the vehicles of transport and to a considerable extent the sediments themselves are fluviatile. As was shown in the account of the Devonian of North Devon and Somerset thick southward-thinning wedges of O.R.S. alternate with northward-thinning marine Devonian strata. On one occasion late in the Period the latter extended across the present Bristol Channel into the southern part of the O.R.S. cuvette; while the former must be replaced by marine strata beneath mid-Devon. In other words the delta front through much of the Period lay in the latitude of mid-Devon; but varied its position, sometimes occurring in the present South Wales.

In **South Cornwall** a very variable series of rocks, mostly of a grey slaty aspect, have for long been collectively termed 'killas'. The interpretation of the succession is rendered difficult by tectonic complexity: the rocks have been folded, faulted, thrust, cleaved and crushed during the Armorican orogeny, and in the main they are almost unfossiliferous. The discovery of Ordovician (Caradocian) fossils in a quartzite group and of Silurian (Wenlockian) fossils in limestones led to wrong conclusions concerning the ages of the rock-groups as it was not realized by the pioneer surveyors that the strata dated by these fossils were tectonic slices thrust into their present positions by Armorican earth-movements.

In early Survey Memoirs the South Cornish killas were divided into several groups bearing local names, e.g., Falmouth, Grampound and Portscatho Beds; but re-examination of the area and the discovery of fossil plants (1937) proved that most of the rocks are of Devonian age, later than the Dartmouth Slates and Meadfoot Beds. The greater part of the succession is considered, on rather slender evidence, to be of Middle Devonian age and of non-marine, i.e., O.R.S. facies. Lithologically the **Gramscatho Beds**, as they are now called, are unlike Middle Devonian rocks occurring elsewhere in Britain; but they do resemble strata of this age occurring in 'Armorica'—Brittany and Normandy—and, rather farther afield, in Bohemia.

The Gramscatho Beds fall into three divisions: Lower, consisting dominantly of grits associated with grey slates with gritty lenticles, sandstones, very thin smears of coal and fragments of the plant *Dadoxylon*. The Middle division is partly volcanic, with spilites, tuffs and agglomerates together with cherts, slates and thin limestones. Sandstones and slates make up the Upper division, which contains indeterminable plant fragments.

The Gramscatho Beds are succeeded by an argillaceous formation with a conglomeratic base in overlapping relationship to the underlying formations. The most significant member of the succession is an Upper Spilite Series consisting of pillow lavas with cherts, tuffs and agglomerates associated with black shales and presumably correlative with the pillow lavas of Pentire Point near Padstow in North Cornwall, and of Upper Devonian age.

## OLD RED SANDSTONE OF SCOTLAND

In Scotland the O.R.S. occurs in two main areas, the Midland Valley in the south, and the regions bordering the Moray Firth in the north, extending to the Orkney and Shetland Islands. The former is known as the Caledonian, and the latter as the Orcadian cuvette (Fig. 39). Although the two main outcrops are now completely isolated, it is not known to what extent they originally overlapped, if at all. It is commonly assumed that the present outcrops approximate in extent to the original basins within which the sediments accumulated. The basins were intermontane in character, lying between the major ranges of the Caledonides. It is significant, however, that *basal* Lower O.R.S. rocks occur north of the Highland

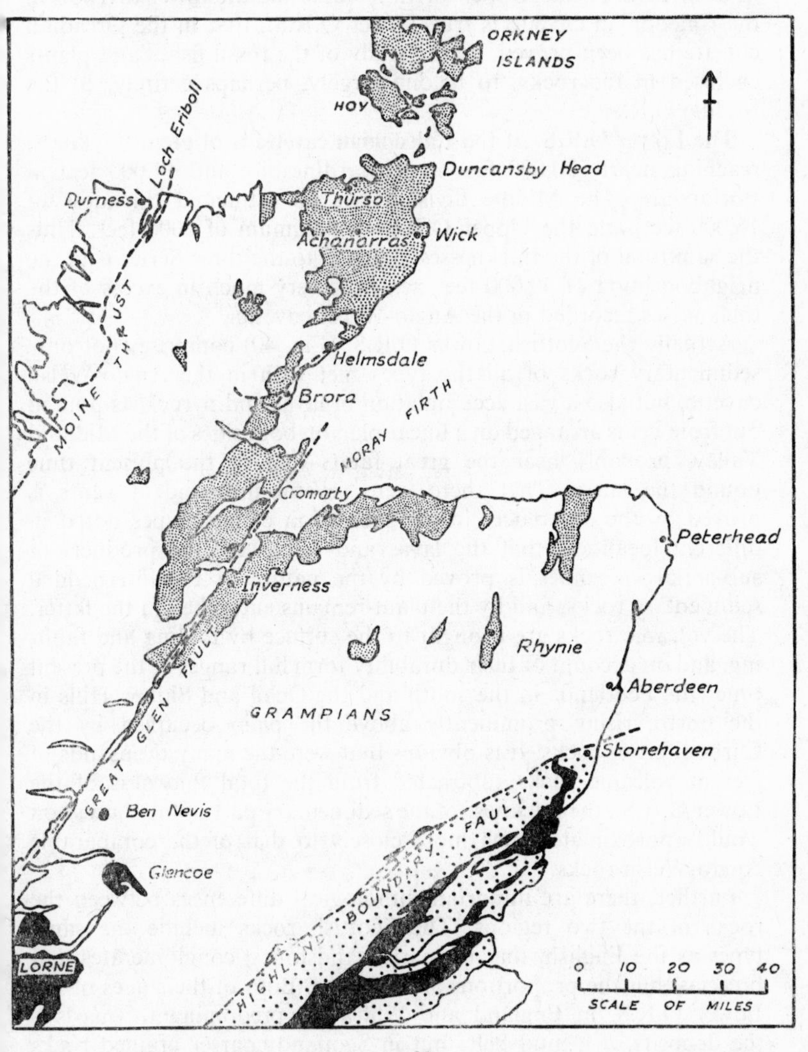


FIG. 39.

Sketch-map of part of Scotland showing the Old Red Sandstone outcrops. Orcadian, fine stipple; Caledonian coarse stipple; volcanic facies, black (in Middle O.R.S. in Hoy, in Lower O.R.S. in the south).

Boundary Fault, while outliers of Middle O.R.S. lie approximately halfway between the Caledonian and Orcadian outcrops at Rhynie.

In both main basins the O.R.S. falls naturally into two major divisions, separated by great unconformities. The higher division in both cases is true Upper O.R.S.; but while the lower division in the Caledonian cuvette is true Lower O.R.S., that in the Orcadian cuvette has been proved, by the study of the fossil fishes and plants enclosed in the rocks, to belong largely, perhaps entirely, to the Middle O.R.S.

The Lower O.R.S. of the **Caledonian cuvette** is of great thickness, reaching nearly 20,000 feet in Kincardineshire and 14,000 feet in Forfarshire. The Middle division has an estimated thickness of 16,000 feet, and the Upper O.R.S. a maximum of 3000 feet. Thus the sum total of the thicknesses assigned to the three Series is in the neighbourhood of 40,000 feet, which is very much in excess of the thicknesses recorded in the Anglo-Welsh cuvette.

Actually the Scottish Lower O.R.S. (Fig. 40) comprises not only sedimentary rocks of all the types met with in the Anglo-Welsh cuvette, but also a vast accumulation of lavas and pyroclasts poured out from vents arranged on a linear plan on both sides of the Midland Valley, probably near the great faults that at the present time bound the latter. That there were several independent vents is proved by the differences in the succession of lava types noted in different localities; that the lavas and tuffs were the products of sub-aerial volcanoes is proved by the nature of the interbedded sedimentary rocks, and by the plant-remains entombed in the latter. The volcanic rocks are brought to the surface by folding and faulting, and on account of their durability form hill ranges at the present time: the Pentlands in the south and the Ochil and Sidlaw Hills in the north, rising prominently above the plain occupied by the Carboniferous rocks. It is obvious that were the many thousands of feet of volcanic rocks subtracted from the total thickness of the Lower O.R.S., the thickness of the sedimentary part of the succession would approximate much more closely to that of the comparable Anglo-Welsh rocks.

Further, there are important lithological differences between the rocks of the two regions. The Scottish rocks include the same types as the English, that is, marls, sandstones, conglomerates and breccias, but the proportions are different. Both of the stages of the Lower O.R.S. in England and Wales are predominantly marls—the deposits of a mud belt; but in Scotland coarser grained rocks are dominant, including some massive conglomerates of great thickness, built up of boulders of spectacular dimensions. For example, the Dunnottar Conglomerate Group in Forfarshire is thicker than the whole of the O.R.S. of most parts of the Anglo-Welsh cuvette. It is, of course, in accordance with first principles that such coarse-grained sediments should have accumulated to a much greater thickness than material of the clay-grade in any given time. Finally, it should be remembered that the rocks were laid down in different environments: in the south they were spread out thinly on a sensibly

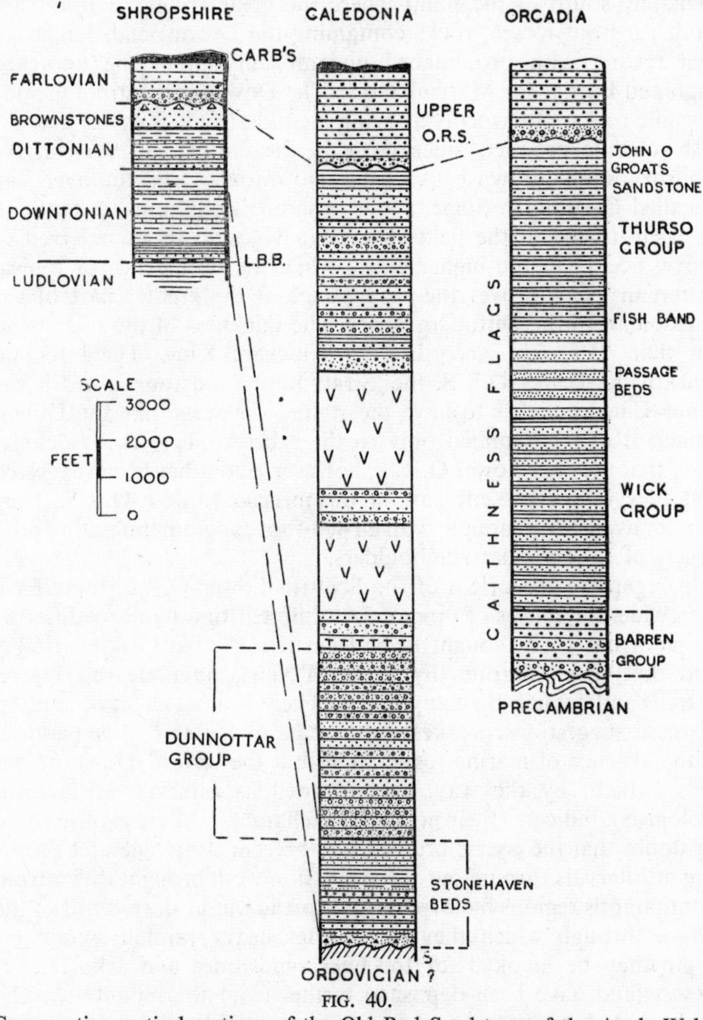


FIG. 40.

Comparative vertical sections of the Old Red Sandstone of the Anglo-Welsh, Caledonian and Orcadian cuvettes.

In the Caledonian column V = volcanic; T = tuffs.

In the Shropshire column L.B.B. = Ludlow Bone Bed.

flat coastal plain, while in the north they accumulated on a highly dissected land-surface in intermontane basins dominated by the Caledonides, which at their acme are pictured as rivalling the Himalayas in height and grandeur.

The relations between the O.R.S. and the underlying rocks are clearly exposed at a number of points. Thus at Stonehaven, immediately south of the point where the great Highland Boundary Fault runs out to sea, rocks containing the Downtonian fauna are seen resting with pronounced unconformity upon the upturned Highland Border (or Margie) Series. The Downtonian strata include volcanic rocks, noteworthy as being the oldest O.R.S. lavas, and the first volcanic products since those in the Ordovician System. An arbitrary line is drawn between the Downtonian and the overlying so-called Caledonian Stage, at the base of a conglomerate that can be easily traced in the field. The main volcanic series, referred to above, occurs in the higher stage, while the occurrence of typical Dittonian fishes proves the equivalence of the greater part of the Caledonian to the Dittonian Series. The thickness of the stage is no less than 9500 feet, according to Wickham King. There remain beneath the Upper O.R.S. the 'Strathmore Sandstones', and if the name 'Caledonian' is to have the status of a stage like the Downtonian, it can be applied only to these beds. There is no definite *proof* that they are Lower O.R.S., however, and it has been suggested that they may represent part of the missing Middle O.R.S. They start, conveniently enough, with an 800-foot conglomerate, consisting largely of 12-inch quartzite boulders.

In regard to the origin of the Scottish Lower O.R.S. there have been wide differences of opinion. At different times and by different people it has been thought to be lacustrine (Sir A. Geikie strongly held this view), marine (by Peter M'Nair), fluviatile (by Joseph Barrell) and aeolian by many others. There is an element of truth in all these suggestions, weakest in the case of the second suggestion, as the absence of marine fossils in all but the lowest (Downtonian) beds (which, by the way, are regarded as Silurian by Scottish geologists), indicates their non-marine character. There is little room for doubt that the coarse breccias and breccio-conglomerates occurring at intervals throughout the succession were brought down from mountainous regions by torrents and spread out at the mouths of the gorges through which they raged after heavy rainfall. A similar origin may be invoked for the finer sandstones and arkoses, but these would have been deposited farther from the mountains. The marls may have been wind-carried in part, like loess of existing deserts, but seem eventually to have been deposited in water, probably in playa lakes, that is, seasonal lakes persisting only for relatively short times. The picture that is called up is one of rapid erosion in a mountain-girt environment. The measure of the rock destruction wrought during this period is the vast thickness of the O.R.S. rocks; while the outstanding size of many of the boulders in the conglomerates is striking evidence of the transporting power, depending upon gradient and velocity, of the mountain torrents of the period.

FIG. 41.
Typical coastal scenery of the Caithness Flagstones, West Mainland, Orkney Islands, Scotland.
(*From photograph by H.M. Geol. Survey.*)

At this point it is convenient to refer to one of the smaller outcrops of O.R.S. that builds the **Lorne Plateau** in South-West Argyllshire and two small outlying patches in Glencoe and on the summit of Ben Nevis respectively. The O.R.S. in this area rests with violent discordance on the Dalradian strata. The rocks are almost wholly volcanic, consisting chiefly of andesitic lavas, but they are freely cut by a swarm of dykes, Caledonoid in trend, and of much the same petrographic type as the lavas themselves. Locally ordinary O.R.S. sediments are intercalated at or near the base of the volcanics and have yielded Lower O.R.S. plants. The small patches at Glencoe and

Ben Nevis owe their preservation to downfaulting of the cauldron subsidence type.

**Orcadian Basin**

In Aberdeenshire and Caithness the O.R.S. occupies wide areas, and rests with great unconformity upon an irregular land surface carved out of the crystalline Highland Schists and the Caledonian granites intruded into them. The existing outcrops occur chiefly in the coastal areas bordering the Moray and Dornoch Firths, and extend beyond the mainland to the Orkney and Shetland Islands. The area occupied by the O.R.S. consists essentially of a fertile plateau, deeply dissected by the existing rivers, and affords a striking contrast to the relatively bare upland regions occupied by the Highland Schists. The former extension of the outcrop westwards is proved by the occurrence of outliers on the mountain tops far inland.

In general the rocks of the western outliers and of the more westerly parts of the main outcrops comprise coarse-grained breccias, conglomerates, feldspathic sandstones or arkoses, and red mudstones. Traced eastwards the grain-size diminishes, the red colour is lost and the marginal deposits pass into the most typical part of the Orcadian O.R.S., the essentially grey **Caithness Flagstones.** The complete succession comprises:

Upper O.R.S. { Yellow sandstones of Hoy and Dornoch, 4000 feet (in Orkneys).

Middle O.R.S. {
*Unconformity.*
John o' Groats Sandstone Series, 2000 feet.
*Unconformity.*
Thurso Flagstone Group, 5000 feet.
Achanarras Fish Band.
Passage Beds, 2300 feet.
Wick Flagstone Group, 5000 feet.
Barren Group, 2000 feet.

*Unconformity.*
Highland Schists.

The Barren Group is a basement series, including the same rock-types as those which constitute the typical Lower O.R.S. of the Caledonian area; the breccias must represent scree deposits that accumulated at the foot of mountain slopes, and, as is to be expected, they vary in character with the nature of the underlying or adjacent rock. Thus, when they rest on Highland Quartzite, they consist of angular fragments of this rock and show all the characters of the existing screes except that they are indurated; when the underlying rock is mica-schist, the basal beds consist of fragments of this much softer rock, and it is often possible to demonstrate that the underlying land surface in these places has the form of a valley. As the name 'Barren Group' implies, these rocks are quite unfossiliferous,

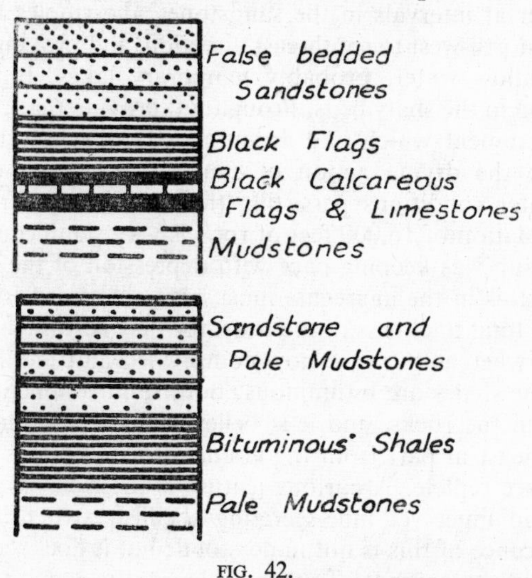


FIG. 42.
The rhythmic unit in the Caithness Flagstone Series.
*Above.*—In the Thurso Group. *Below.*—In the Wick Group.

and there is thus no definite proof of their age. The first fossils occur some thousands of feet above the base of the succession, and there is nothing inherently impossible in the suggestion that the Barren Group may belong to the Lower, not Middle O.R.S.; but whatever their age, they certainly fill the role of marginal and basal deposits to the far thicker flagstones above. The highly distinctive part of the succession is the Caithness Flagstone Series, which is unique among O.R.S. rocks; indeed it is true to claim that the flagstones cannot be exactly paralleled in the rest of the stratigraphical column. The most striking of their many interesting characters is the rapid alternation of bands of several different types of sediment, comprising dark limestones, pale sandstones, greenish-white mudstones and nearly black flags. These are repeated in much the same order, through thousands of feet of strata (Fig. 42). This *rhythmic* sedimentation clearly reflects a manifold repetition of the same set of conditions, time after time, through a lengthy period. The tendency is to regard such rhythmic sedimentation as seasonal, each group of strata constituting the rhythmic unit representing the sediment that accumulated in one season; but, as in most similar cases, it is quite impossible to suggest the duration of the season. Further, there is some doubt as to the mode of accumulation of the strata. They are definitely non-marine and consist chiefly of sediment carried into the area by rivers and deposited on a plain. Ripple-marks recur at intervals in the sandstones, the ripples maintaining a constant north-west to south-east direction, and proving accumulation in shallow water, probably temporary lakes. But suncracks are common in the shaly beds throughout, proving that from time to time the sediment which had accumulated on a lake bottom was exposed to the drying action of sun and air. Such evidence of shallow-water conditions persisting through the time required for the accumulation of 16,000 feet of rock is very significant; it proves that silting-up was keeping pace with depression of the floor of the basin, and this in the aggregate must have amounted to more than the present total thickness of the beds, for they accumulated as loose sediments, whereas they are now compressed and indurated rocks. Many of the shales are bituminous; both solid bitumen and oil are contained in the rocks, and it is believed that these materials were formed at least in part from the abundant fish remains with which the rocks are replete. A curious feature is the richness of many of the rocks in lime, yet lime-secreting shellfish are entirely absent. The significance of this is not understood; but it does seem to prove that, even in the absence of other evidence, the rocks are definitely not of marine origin. The limestones must be either detrital (i.e. derived from the disintegration of the Cambro-Ordovician Durness Limestone), or chemically precipitated like the 'cornstones' in the Anglo-Welsh O.R.S.

Well to the south of the main outcrop a small outlier of the Middle O.R.S. occurs at Rhynie in Aberdeenshire, and from these rocks a most interesting assemblage of terrestrial fossils has been obtained, including plant remains petrified in silica—the earliest of their kind. In addition, spiders, scorpions and the remains of several varieties of insects shed light on the local conditions.

One of the major stratigraphical problems is the apparent absence of the Lower O.R.S. from 'Orcadia', and of the Middle O.R.S. from 'Caledonia'. It will have been noted above that these enormous gaps in the succession may be more apparent than real; for strata at least 3000 feet thick, unfossiliferous and therefore undated, lie *above* the highest horizon from which Lower O.R.S. (Dittonian) fossils have been obtained in 'Caledonia' (Fig. 37). It may therefore be that these rocks really belong to the Middle O.R.S. Similarly a comparable thickness of unfossiliferous rocks *underlies* the lowest horizon from which Middle O.R.S. fossils have been obtained from the Caithness Flags, and although these fill the role of basement beds to the Flagstone Series, they may be part of the Lower O.R.S., for the relations between the two divisions are quite unknown. If there is any truth in these suggestions, it follows that actually all three divisions—Lower, Middle and Upper—are present in both main areas.

Otherwise North-East Scotland cannot have been an area of sedimentation during Lower O.R.S. times, but rather one supplying sediment that was being transported from the area and deposited elsewhere. Apart from a complete reversal of conditions, which is almost inexplicable, we must suppose that the Middle O.R.S., not necessarily of the same lithological type as the unique Caithness Flagstones, was deposited in the Caledonian tract, but was removed prior to the deposition of the Upper O.R.S. During this erosion interval the Lower and Middle O.R.S. were folded on a large but relatively gentle scale, and then uplifted. It is estimated that no less than 8000 feet of Lower O.R.S. were removed during this erosion interval in Caledonia. Should the whole of the Middle Series be added also? In any case it is little short of amazing that during the recent survey of Hoy in the Orkneys the officers concerned reached the conclusion that a thickness of 10,000 feet of Middle O.R.S. was denuded from that area during the same erosion interval. This period of denudation was brought to a close by a volcanic eruption in the Orkney region, of the violently explosive type, that spread a 50-foot layer of volcanic ash over the area immediately underneath the Upper O.R.S.

The **Upper O.R.S.** in Scotland as in England and Wales, extends beyond the boundaries of the underlying divisions, coming to rest directly upon pre-O.R.S. rocks (Fig. 43). One locality where these relations are well exposed is the world-famous Siccar Point, where James Hutton first demonstrated the unconformable relationship more than a century ago. The rocks involved are the Silurian, cleaved and highly inclined as a consequence of the Caledonian orogeny, rising like reefs into the overlying, gently inclined Upper O.R.S. Similarly in the south the latter rocks extend well to the north of the limits of the Lower O.R.S. outcrops and rest directly on Dalradian beyond the great Highland Boundary Fault. As the Lower O.R.S. is obviously affected by the fault, while the Upper O.R.S. extends across it unchanged in attitude, we have definite evidence that the fault post-dates the Lower, but ante-dates the Upper, Series.

In both cuvettes the Upper O.R.S. constitutes a sandstone-conglomerate series. In the extreme north of Scotland it is splendidly exposed in the magnificent cliffs of Duncansby Head and Cape Wrath, as well as in Orkney. The combination of distinct stratification and well-marked vertical jointing has given rise to spectacular denudation features, including the finest sea-stacks, natural arches and sea-caves to be found anywhere round our coasts. The most famous of the sea-stacks, the Old Man of Hoy, towers 450 feet above the sea.

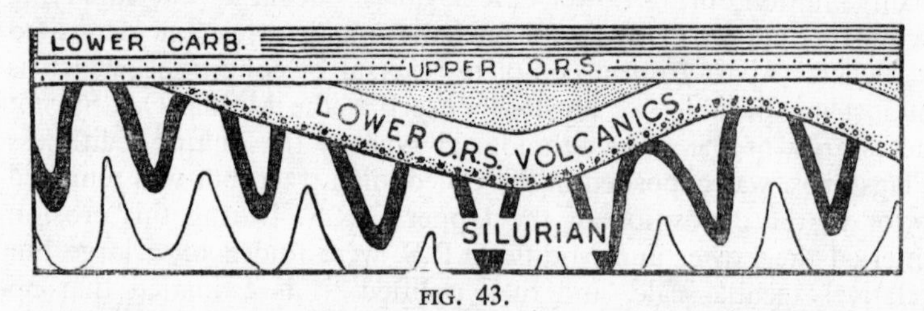


FIG. 43.
Diagram showing relations between Upper and Lower Old Red Sandstone, Silurian and Carboniferous.

In the Orcadian cuvette the Upper O.R.S., though reaching 4000 feet in Orkney, is incomplete; but in the Caledonian cuvette there may be a passage up into the overlying Carboniferous System, for example, on the outskirts of Edinburgh; but the relationship is uncertain.

A development of the Upper Old Red Sandstone which is of special importance forms the coastal strip of the southern shores of the Moray Firth between Nairn and Elgin. Local divisions have been defined, the basal member, the **Nairn Sandstones,** being the most significant. All the known specimens of the genus *Psammosteus* yet discovered in Scotland come from this region. In the Baltic province a detailed zonal classification of the Middle and Upper Devonian has been established, based on the distribution of different kinds of psammosteids. Some of these have been matched in the Nairn Sandstones and higher beds. The precise ages of the Baltic divisions are known, as in this region marine and continental facies of the Devonian are interstratified. The Nairn Sandstones contain *Asterolepis* and *Psammosteus undulata*, the latter being the zonal index of the lower Frasnian. Another significant form occurring in Scotland is *P. falcatus*, the index fossil of a higher Baltic Upper Devonian zone, which occurs also in remote Ellesmereland, Central Poland and Timan.

### THE O.R.S. IN IRELAND

Although marine Devonian rocks are unrepresented in Ireland, the O.R.S. originally covered most of the country. Wherever upfolds bring Lower Palaeozoic rocks to the surface in the Central Irish Plain, the O.R.S. is found to overlie the Silurian; but farther north the Silurian is over-stepped and the O.R.S. rests first on Ordovician and ultimately on the Dalradian, for example in the Curlew Mountains and in various outcrops in Co. Donegal. In the south-east also the O.R.S. rests directly on Ordovician rocks; but thins out so that ultimately, in Co. Wexford, basal Carboniferous conglomerates rest directly on pre-Devonian rocks.

The most important outcrops occur in the south and more particularly in the south-west, occupying an extensive Armorican belt lying south of the latitude of Kiltorcan, and including the mountainous country of Macgillycuddy's Reeks, with Carrauntoohil, nearly 3500 feet. The O.R.S. succession reaches its maximum thickness, 17,000 feet, in these outcrops, and is finely displayed in long coastal sections, notably along the shores of Dingle Bay, which gives its name to the basal member, the **Dingle Beds.** These, together with the overlying **Glengariff Grits,** some 10,000 feet thick, include wedges of boulder- and cobble-conglomerates which originated as piedmont deposits banked against the flanks of mountains rising for upwards of 2000 feet into the O.R.S. The Dingle Beds rest with strong unconformity on Silurian strata, and are themselves succeeded by higher members of the O.R.S. succession which rest unconformably on their upturned edges. On this evidence the Dingle Beds are post-Silurian and older than some (undated) part of the O.R.S. It is commonly believed that they are Downtonian in age, but there is no supporting palaeontological evidence.

In general the O.R.S. in Ireland consists of conglomerates below, succeeded by grits and sandstones, grading up into siltstones and marls. The uppermost O.R.S., largely greenish yellow siltstones, tend to be singularly uniform in lithology and thickness over all the southern outcrops. They were named **Kiltorcan Beds** (Hull, 1879) and have long been famous for the fossils they contain, especially the plants, which include a fern, *Archaeopteris hibernica*,[1] tree-ferns and club-mosses, *Bothrodendron kiltorkense* and *Lepidodendron*. In addition *Eurypterus*, *Pterygotus hibernica* and various 'fishes' including *Bothriolepsis*, *Coccosteus* and *Holoptychius*, distinctive of the Scottish Upper O.R.S., and the long-range *Pteraspis*. A significant

[1] It should be noted that *Archaeopteris* is an Upper Devonian fern; but *Archaeopteryx* is a Mesozoic fossil bird.

mollusc is *Archanodon jukesi*, the Devonian equivalent of the modern fresh-water 'mussel', *Unio*.

At a number of localities in southern Ireland a passage may be seen between the Upper O.R.S. and the basal Carboniferous: sedimentation was evidently continuous over this period, as conditions changed from continental to marine. Actually there had been a preliminary incursion of the sea during the Upper Devonian: marine fossils similar to those occurring in the Baggy Beds of North Devon occur locally as they do in Pembrokeshire in South Wales.

In northern Ireland the O.R.S. occurs within the Irish extension of the Midland Valley of Scotland, the most extensive outcrop occurring around Fintona, though the long, narrow pericline of the Curlew Mountains is also noteworthy. The **Fintona Beds** are undated; while the O.R.S. of the Curlew Mountains is believed to belong to the Lower O.R.S. on general lithological grounds, largely because of the importance of contemporary igneous rocks: more than a third of the total thickness (7500 feet) consists of andesitic lavas and pyroclasts.

Both the Highland Boundary Fault and the Southern Uplands Fault cross into Ireland and both were active during the formation of the O.R.S., and controlled sedimentation. Further, contemporary earth-movements were accompanied in these areas by volcanicity; but this was not restricted to the north of the country, for lava flows and associated pyroclasts are found locally in the south also, for example near Killarney and in Co. Waterford.

The lavas are petrographically very like those of the same age in the Midland Valley of Scotland and we are evidently dealing with isolated fragments of one great igneous province. Andesites are dominant, but in places they are accompanied by trachytes and even rhyolites.

**Faunal Aspects**

Without entering into full details it is germane to the present discussion to consider the general characters of the fossils in these rocks. The Ludlow Bone Bed, the basal member of the Downtonian consists of fragmental remains of fossil 'fishes' and crustaceans that are exceedingly rare in the beds below, but which are characteristic of the beds above. These 'fishes' and crustaceans occur at intervals right through the Downtonian, and several of the genera and even species occur also in the Dittonian, so that on these grounds the two stages are to be regarded as indivisible. Apart from a single occurrence of marine fossils in the Plateau Beds of Breconshire, fish—and other animal-remains appear to be absent above the Senni Beds. This is consistent with their being largely aeolian deposits.

The conglomerates with rounded pebbles and the shales in the higher parts of the Upper O.R.S. indicate different conditions, with great rivers spreading sheets of gravel over low-lying areas, and with at least temporary lakes in which the finer sediments were deposited. With the changed conditions the 'fishes' reappeared.

Returning now to the Downtonian, in addition to the 'fishes' and mud-loving crustaceans, a shelly fauna is found, consisting of two elements: a flourishing lamellibranch and gasteropod assemblage, and a dwindling brachiopod assemblage surviving from the Silurian. Of these latter, the more highly organized types survived for only a short time and are restricted to the lowest beds in the stage. *Lingula*, with its simpler requirements, was able to adjust itself to the changing conditions, but this long-range genus is represented by *L. cornea* and *L. minima* both, in effect, dwarfs, and at a higher level they disappear. Lamellibranchs, for example *Modiolopsis*, persist to much higher horizons, but even they are dwarfed and in turn disappear. Shelly fossils in the Dittonian are very rare and restricted to the basal zone. The shelly fauna tells a convincing story of an unsuccessful fight against adverse conditions. As to the nature of these we can only surmise; but the cuvette represents a portion of the Silurian gulf cut off from free comunication with the outer sea. In this epicontinental sea some members of the later Silurian fauna were able to exist for a time, long or short, according to their ability to adapt themselves to uncongenial conditions. Their extinction one by one may have been due in part to the exceptionally muddy condition of the water, and in part to concentration of iron salts in the enclosed waters, which is suggested by the colours of the rocks. The gradual extinction of the relict Silurian shelly fauna in the Downtonian 'sea' is paralleled at higher levels in the stratigraphical column: the dwindling Carboniferous fauna imprisoned in a cut-off arm of the Permian Sea suffered the same fate, and an even closer analogy may be afforded by the 'lacustrine' Wealden Beds of southern England, which contain Jurassic fossils, while the beds of the same age farther north are marine and yield Lower Cretaceous forms.

### *The Old Red Sandstone Vertebrate Faunas*

In the sense that the Cambrian was the age of trilobites, and the Ordovician the age of graptolites, the Devonian has been called the 'age of fishes', though they were admittedly immeasurably fewer in numbers than at present. The Devonian System is unique in that it is the only one that is, indeed that must be, classified on its 'fish' faunas. Were there no other evidence available, the O.R.S. would be divided into three series, characterized by three successive 'fish' faunas; the first, occurring in the Lower O.R.S., differing markedly from the second in the Middle O.R.S., and this differing, though less strikingly, from the third in the Upper O.R.S.

The distribution and mode of occurrence of the fish-remains are significant. At regrettably infrequent intervals throughout the Old Red Sandstone there may be uncovered in a quarry or natural exposure a band crowded with fossil fishes, and for a time the locality is famous. In a short time, however, the fossiliferous rock

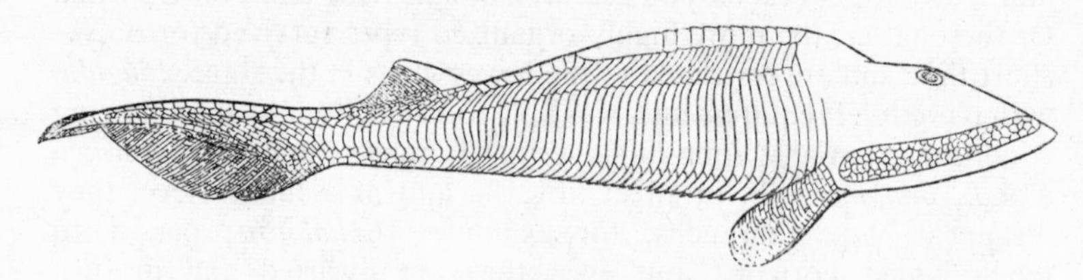

*Hemicyclaspis murchisoni* from the Ledbury Beds, Downtonian Stage. (M. K. W. *after* Stensio.)

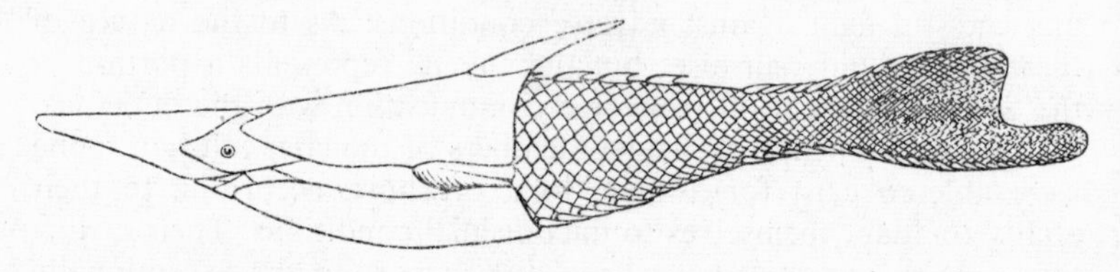

*Pteraspis rostrata*, Dittonian Series (M. K. W. *after* E. I. White).

FIG. 44.

Typical Ostracoderms from the Lower Old Red Sandstone.

is 'worked out' and evidently must have been a lens, rather than a continuous stratum. There are well-known exceptions to this general rule, the famous Achanarras Fish Band being a case in point. This extends over the greater part of the Orcadian Basin, including Orkney (where, however, it is known under another name), and at certain points is literally crowded with fossil fishes, which unlike most of those from the O.R.S. in England and Wales, are in a beautiful state of preservation. One can only speculate on the causes of such a wholesale slaughter of fishes; but either a change in salinity or extensive desiccation is indicated. It is thought that these fishes lived in fresh water—those occasionally found elsewhere in the marine Devonian were undoubtedly washed out to sea and entombed in an environment different from that in which they had lived—and a relatively slight change in salinity will kill-off fresh-water fishes. A small-scale illustration may be observed in Norfolk, when a simple cause—a strong wind from the right direction coinciding with a particularly high spring tide will cause salt water to invade some of the 'Broads' and in a short time there may be thousands of dead coarse fish floating at the surface, and many are left stranded on the fields as the floods subside. Alternatively, the same effect may have been produced by desiccation. In this connection it is highly significant that the fossils are most prolific in calcareous bands, and there is little doubt that this indicates evaporation of hard water to the point where calcium carbonate was deposited. The secret of the preservation of large numbers of complete fishes is probably to be found in the habits of existing lung-fishes, which live in places subject to periodic desiccation. At the end of the wet season they bury themselves in mud and hibernate throughout the drought. Failure of the 'rains' in the Orcadian Basin would ensure many potential fossils, already entombed in fine-grained sediment, and therefore with the first and most hazardous stage of fossilization safely accomplished.

At the present time the evidence of the fossil fishes has proved to be of limited value in correlation as they are exceedingly rare and, when found, are often not sufficiently well preserved to allow specific identification. Unfortunately much material of this kind had been 'identified' and conclusions (necessarily erroneous) have been based upon these 'identifications'. E. I. White states that 'a fair proportion of recorded identifications are now (1945) known to be erroneous, and still more are suspect'.

Two other rather puzzling features may be noted. Firstly, compared with the number of specimens correctly identified, the number of species and varieties seems extraordinarily large. Secondly, several disquieting instances of discrepancy between the palaeontological and the stratigraphical evidence have been noted. Fishes that from their structure might reasonably be judged to be early members of their race occur higher in the stratigraphical succession than might have been anticipated; and conversely, forms that are high in the evolutionary sequence occur in beds placed low in the succession on stratigraphical evidence.

A representative collection of Devonian fishes would look strangely unfamiliar, for not a single one closely resembling the dominant bony fishes of the present time would be among them; a few would bear some resemblance to that anachronism among modern fishes, the sturgeon, but the majority would have no living counterparts.

In the Lower O.R.S. the dominant forms were the jawless *Ostracodermi* in which the head and fore part of the body were heavily protected with bony plates—a feature shared by many 'fishes' of the period. These extraordinary creatures are divided into three, or possibly four groups, two of which are represented by the important genera, *Pteraspis* and *Cephalaspis*. The *Pteraspids* range from the higher Downtonian (as defined by King) through the Dittonian (where they reach the acme of their development), to the Coblenzian (Emsian) in Germany. A typical Dittonian species, *P. rostrata*, is illustrated in Fig. 44. With regard to *Cephalaspis*, specimens from the Downtonian are rare, and usually poorly preserved; but fine examples of the related *Hemicyclaspis murchisoni* and other genera belonging to the same group have been found. Specimens of *H. murchisoni* from Ledbury are among the most complete examples of *Cephalaspids* known, and a reconstruction is illustrated in Fig. 44. Only one species of *Cephalaspis* (*C. magnifica*), and only one specimen at that, is known from the Middle O.R.S. of Britain, and none from the Upper O.R.S.

Obviously from their shape the ostracoderms were specially adapted for living on the bottom, where they found their food in the mud and sand. The *Ostracodermi* were accompanied by another important group, the *Acanthodi*, which also reached their acme in the Lower O.R.S.; but they persisted through the Middle O.R.S., and Carboniferous and even Permian forms are known. Usually small in size, they are distinctive on account of their covering of very small scales, nearly square in shape, highly polished, and about a millimetre in size. Even the fins were so covered. Restorations of forms from the Middle O.R.S. resemble small sharks, though whether or not they are related to the latter group is still a matter of dispute. Another group of highly specialized, heavily armoured 'fishes', the *Arthrodira*, also made its appearance in the Lower O.R.S., though the Middle O.R.S. species, *Coccosteus decipiens*, is the best known.

Probably the most grotesque of these creatures were the *Antiarchi*, characterized by inadequately small heads well protected by a helmet of bony plates hinged on to a suit of body armour. Although furnished with fins on the back and tail, the Antiarchs were provided with armoured paddles in place of the normal pectoral fins. This explains the derivation of the name *Pterichthyodes*, formerly *Pterichthys*, 'the winged fish'—one of the characteristic members of the group, though *Bothriolepis* is even better known. One must invoke the incompleteness of the geological record to account for the sudden appearance, fully organized, in the Middle O.R.S., of this group. Their ancestors are quite unknown and they themselves did not survive the Devonian Period.

The most primitive members of three other great groups appear for the first time in the Middle O.R.S. of Northern Scotland. Of these the lung-fishes, or *Dipnoi*, are certainly among the most interesting of all fishes. In the Middle O.R.S., although apparently represented by two genera only, *Dipterus* and *Pentlandia*, they were in places extremely common. It is well known that lung-fishes, structurally like their Devonian ancestors though far larger, exist to-day and arouse interest for two chief reasons: firstly, they only flourish in foul, muddy water—if kept in fresh water they quickly develop cancerous growths; secondly, they are able to hibernate for several months sealed up in 'cocoons' of mud and slime. This is an adaptation admirably fitting them for life in arid regions in which the waters they inhabit undergo a seasonal desiccation. The bearing of this upon the problem of the conditions of accumulation of the O.R.S. is obvious. The name *Dipnoi*, meaning double-breathers, has reference to a primitive lung-sac additional to gills possessed by these fishes, which enables them to obtain an adequate supply of oxygen from the air when the water is rendered foul by decaying vegetation or depleted of oxygen by overcrowding. From the nature of their jaws and teeth it is inferred that the lung-fishes fed on plants; they in turn served as natural live food for their carnivorous contemporaries, notably the related *Osteolepids*. These latter are of importance in the course of evolution for they represent the stock from which, in the Carboniferous Period, the amphibians were developed, and are therefore in the line of descent of the reptiles and ultimately of the mammals. This group is represented by *Holoptychius*, which characterizes the Upper O.R.S. in many parts of the world where these rocks occur.

The Middle O.R.S. contains also the remains of the first-known Palaeoniscid fishes (*Cheirolepis*), from which sturgeons and all the other bony fishes of the present time (except of course the lung-fishes) are descended.

Not the least interesting of the Devonian fishes, though the smallest in size and the simplest in structure, is the problematical *Palaeospondylus gunni* from the Middle O.R.S. Much controversy has raged round the status and classification of this little fish with the long name, and its relationship is still unsettled.

It is difficult to assess the value of the O.R.S. 'fishes' as indicating the environments in which they lived, as distinct from those in which their remains are discovered. As noted above, the remains, usually disarticulated and fragmental, are concentrated in the basal members of the cyclothems which clearly indicate flood conditions, sometimes 'catastrophic' (Allen). Clearly these creatures cannot have been marine: they were either fluviatile, lagoonal or both. In circumstances involving catastrophic flooding some of their remains must have been carried into the seas and entombed in marine sediments. As shown above in the case of *Psammosteus*, some genera are of very wide (inter-continental) distribution and this must mean that at least part of their lives were spent in the sea. On the other hand it is not impossible that some kinds, like the salmon and eels of our own times, spent much of their lives in marine waters, but periodically visited the rivers for spawning purposes. In such cases casualties and entombment would occur in *both* environments.

## REFERENCES

*Marine Devonian:*

Regional Geology, South-West England.

HENDRICKS, E. M. L. 'Rock succession and structure in South Cornwall,' *Q.J.G.S.*, **93** (1937), 322.

HOUSE, M. R. 'Devonian ammonoid successions and facies in Devon and Cornwall,' *Q.J.G.S.*, **119** (1963), 1.

*Old Red Sandstone:*

Regional Geology, South Wales, Midland Valley and Northern Highlands of Scotland.

ALLEN, J. R. L. 'Depositional features of Dittonian rocks: Pembrokeshire compared with the Welsh Borderlands.' *Geol. Mag.*, **100** (1963), 385.

BALL, H. W., and DINELEY, D. L. 'Notes on the Old Red Sandstone of the Clee Hills,' *Proc. Geol. Assoc.*, **63** (1952), 207.

BALL, H. W., and DINELEY, D. L. 'Old Red Sandstone of Brown Clee Hill and adjacent area,' with WHITE, E. I., on the Palaeontology, *Bull. Brit. Mus.* (*Nat. Hist.*), **5,** no. 7 (1961).

DINELEY, D. L., and GOSSAGE, D. W. 'Old Red Sandstone of the Cleobury Mortimer area, Shropshire,' *Proc. Geol. Assoc.*, **70** (1959), 221.

GEORGE, T. N. *Proc. Geol. Soc.*, **103** (1947), 11.

KING, W. W. 'The Downtonian and Dittonian strata of Great Britain and North-West Europe,' *Q.J.G.S.*, **90** (1934), 526.

Caithness Memoir for description of conditions of accumulation of the Middle O.R.S.

WHITE, E. I. *Q.J.G.S.*, **94** (1938), 85, and *Quart. Journ. Geol. Soc.*, **101** (1945), 215, for conditions of entombment of O.R.S. fossils and discussion of the environment in which they lived.[1]

WHITE, E. I. 'Vertebrate Faunas of the Lower Old Red Sandstone of the Welsh Borders,' *Bull. Brit. Mus.* (*Nat. Hist.*), **1** (1950), 51.

*The Volcanic Facies:*

HATCH and WELLS. *Petrology of the Igneous Rocks.*

Glencoe and Ben Nevis Memoir for discussion of cauldron subsidence.

[1] We are indebted to Dr White for the loan of the originals from which Fig. 43 was drawn.

CHAPTER X

# THE CARBONIFEROUS (1): THE DINANTIAN (AVONIAN)

## INTRODUCTION

FROM the point of view of its economic importance, the Carboniferous System in Britain stands supreme, and there is thus some justification for studying it in greater detail than the other Systems. The geological history of the period is long and complicated, and for convenience can be made the subject-matter of three successive chapters. Although the System is divided into two major divisions only it is customary to recognize three lithological units:

3. Coal Measures } Upper Carboniferous.
2. Millstone Grit }
1. Carboniferous Limestone—Lower Carboniferous.

Of these three divisions, the Lower Carboniferous in Britain is essentially of marine origin, the Millstone Grit is essentially deltaic, while the Coal Measures were formed in low-lying, swampy, lagoonal areas. This general sequence of rocks and of conditions is widespread in North-West Europe, for example in Belgium, France and Westphalia in Germany. Indeed, although there are notable exceptions, it is the general Carboniferous succession the world over. It may be noted that American stratigraphers urge the division of the Carboniferous into two Systems (Periods) of equal status, the Mississippian and Pennsylvanian respectively, approximating to our Lower and Upper Carboniferous. If it were not for this it would be logical to divide the System into Lower, Middle and Upper Carboniferous. As it is, there is an increasing tendency to speak of 'mid-Carboniferous' as an alternative to 'Namurian'.

The lithological units noted above are by no means constant in their lithology: the Lower Carboniferous in particular exhibits a wide variation in facies. Largely on this account it is necessary to employ stratal terms, independent of lithological, faunal and thickness variations, and in theory bounded by time-planes. These major time divisions of the Carboniferous are capable of definition in palaeontological terms and are listed overleaf:

| Series | Subdivision | |
|---|---|---|
| Coal Measures | Stephanian | |
| | Morganian | often grouped together as Westphalian |
| | Ammanian | |
| Namurian | | |
| Dinantian | Viséan = Upper Avonian | |
| | Tournaisian = Lower Avonian | |

## THE LOWER CARBONIFEROUS: THE DINANTIAN (= AVONIAN) SERIES

*Palaeogeographic setting*

The Dinantian Sea, like its Devonian precursor, in the present British Isles region lay south of a largely hypothetical northern Atlantean Continent, fragments of which survive in the mountains of Co. Mayo and Donegal in Ireland and in the Scottish Highlands. Its southern margin lay off-shore beyond the present Irish coast, but just impinges on the southernmost parts of Devon and Cornwall. This landmass, of unknown dimensions, is the Cornubian Massif.

The palaeogeography of Lower Carboniferous England, and to a less extent Ireland, is complicated by a number of positive areas (ridges) of Caledonian aspect and ancestry, between which negative areas (troughs) repeatedly subsided, allowing great thicknesses of sediment to accumulate (Fig. 45). The southernmost ridge is named St George's Land, which includes the uplands of Mid- and North Wales and of the English Midlands (the Mercian Highlands) which linked up with the Brabant Massif. Westwards this barrier extended across into Ireland where its western termination was the Leinster Massif of Lower Palaeozoic rocks with a Caledonian granite core. Inland from the Leinster massif the greater part of Ireland—the present Mid-Irish Plain—was covered by a shallow, clear shelf sea which was continuous with that which occupied the so-called South-Western Province in southern England and South Wales.

Beyond the edge of the shelf sea deeper water conditions prevailed, reaching perhaps abyssal depths over parts of Devon, Cornwall and southernmost Ireland. Within this area Carboniferous rocks quite different from the normal Carboniferous Limestone occur and are covered by the term Culm facies.

North of the St George's Land–Mercian Highlands barrier lay the extensive Central Province or Central Pennine Trough, which extended northwards to the (Isle of) Man–Cumbrian ridge to the west and the Northern Pennines (Askrigg and Alston Blocks) to the east. Beyond these positive areas again lay the Mid-Northumbrian trough which stretched westwards to link up with the Solway area

FIG. 45.

Sketch-map showing the main palaeogeographical features in early Dinantian times. *Based chiefly on the work of T. N. George and W. D. Gill.*

and northwards to terminate against the great Southern Uplands massif which is aligned and was presumably continuous with the Lower Palaeozoic Longford–Co. Down massif in Ireland. The complex trough of the existing Midland Valley of Scotland lay to the north and its waters lapped against the shores of the Atlantean Continent.

The study of British Lower Carboniferous rocks must start with the region known as the South-West Province, where the pioneer work of Vaughan, started in 1903, has been followed by much detailed research, in the course of which the changes in the development of the rocks and their fossil contents have been traced from point to point with great accuracy. The **South-West Province** includes the Avon section near Bristol, the Mendip Hills to the south, the marginal tracts of the coalfields of South Wales and the Forest of Dean, and the Clee Hills in the Midlands. In this area the Avonian shows a relatively simple development, consisting essentially of massive, well-bedded grey limestones of marine origin, constituting the typical Carboniferous Limestone of 'standard' type (see Fig. 49). The maximum thickness of nearly 3000 feet is recorded from the Mendip Hills, where the rocks are finely displayed in the well-known Cheddar Gorge and Burrington Coombe. In the picturesque Avon Gorge the total thickness is rather less, but the series is complete, there being an upward passage from the Old Red Sandstone exposed at one end of the section, through the whole of the Avonian to the overlying 'Millstone Grit' at the other. The fine natural cliff-like sections in the Gorge have been extended by quarrying, while cuttings made in recent road-widening operations have bridged the gaps between the natural exposures so that the conditions for studying the rocks are good. In order to provide a standard of reference the Avonian of this fine section has been zoned, and here the first difficulty is encountered. The rocks are chiefly marine limestones and the only fossils available for the purpose are brachiopods and corals. Both groups are far from ideal for the purpose, compared with the free-swimming trilobites and the floating graptolites, for example. As we have seen in studying the Devonian rocks, corals flourish under conditions limited by depth and temperature: they constitute a facies fauna, and cannot be expected to serve as reliable indices in rocks varying in lithology. It is frankly admitted that goniatites, which had appeared in the Devonian Period and are proving so valuable for zoning purposes in this and other countries, would allow correlation over wide areas, even on an international scale; but the English Avonian contains no goniatites in these type areas. In the circumstances the surveyors have had to make shift with the materials at their disposal, and, although they break down when applied to long-distance correlation, even the corals and brachiopods have proved remarkably valuable

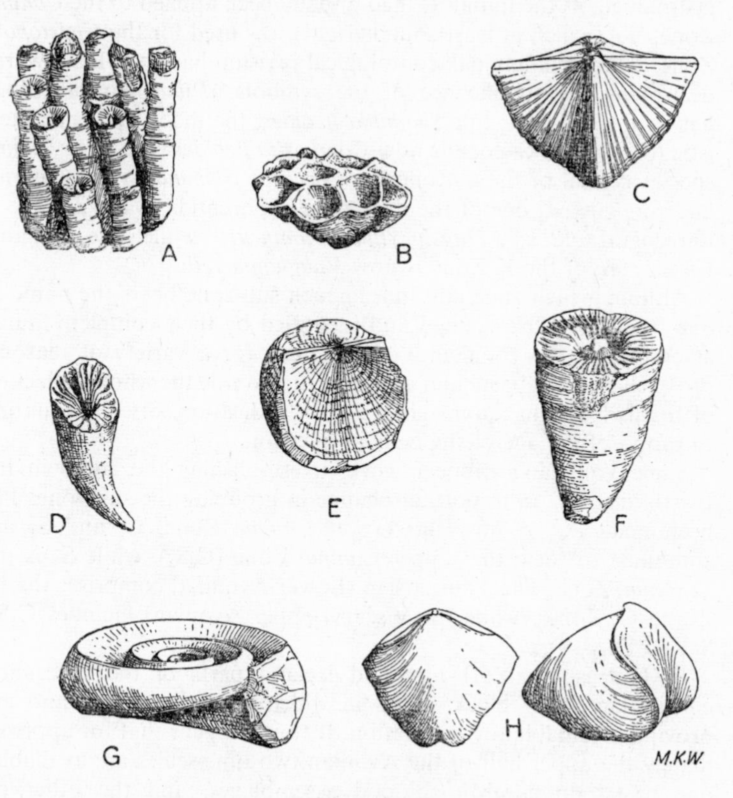


FIG. 46.

Typical fossils of the Carboniferous Limestone.

A. *Lithostrotion martini*, Viséan, a compound coral.
B. *Michelinia grandis*, Viséan, a tabulate coral.
C. *Spirifer trigonalis*.
D. '*Zaphrentis*' sp., a simple rugose coral, characteristic of the Z-zone.
E. *Dictyoclostus* (*Productus*) cf. *semireticulatus*, with the skirt of the ventral valve broken away.
F. *Dibunophyllum* sp., a rugose coral from the D-zone.
G. *Straparellus* (*Euomphalus*) *pentangulatus*, a gasteropod.
H. *Pugnax acuminatus*, a distinctive brachiopod. Dorsal and side views.

and reliable indices of horizon over relatively small areas. There are five main zones. Long familiarity with the zones has led to the use of the initials rather than the full names of the indices: thus one speaks of the D-zone, S-zone, C-zone, Z-zone and K-zone, and, in the historical sense, of 'D-times', etc.

The initials are those of the zonal indices: *Dibunophyllum*, *Seminula*, *Caninia*, *Zaphrentis* and *Cleistopora*. With regard to the last-named, as the initial 'C' had already been applied to the *Caninia* Zone, 'K' (which at least sounds right) was used for the *Cleistopora* Zone. Unfortunately palaeontological revision has gone far towards destroying the significance of the symbols: *Dibunophyllum* alone has so far survived; but *Seminula ficoides*, the index and characteristic fossil of the S-Zone is now *Composita ficoides*; the large *Canina* species typical of the C-Zone have become *Siphonophylla cylindrica* and *S. gigantea*; one of the distinctive zaphrentids of the Z-Zone is unrecognizable as *Hapsiphyllum konincki*; while the original *Cleistopora* of the K-Zone is now *Vaughania vetus*.

Although each zone and indeed each sub-zone bears the name of one fossil, they are defined and identified by their complete faunal assemblages: the zonal index itself may, for a variety of reasons, prove elusive in a particular quarry; but as a rule the whole collection of fossils from that point gives a clear indication, often amounting to proof, of the age of the beds in question.

Since Vaughan's pioneer work in establishing the zones in the Bristol district, an important change in grouping the sub-zones has been made. $C_1$ is now the Lower *Caninia* Zone, $C_2$ and $S_1$ are combined to form the Upper *Caninia* Zone ($C_2S_1$), while $S_2$ is the *Seminula* Zone. The Tournaisian (Lower Avonian) comprises the K, Z and $C_1$ Zones, while the Viséan (Upper Avonian) includes $C_2S_1$, $S_2$ and D.

In Lancashire, Yorkshire and Ireland parts of the succession consist largely of black shales in which goniatites occur and are proving invaluable for correlation. It thus happens that for approximately the upper half of the Avonian two time-scales are available: one based on coral-brachiopod assemblages, and the other on goniatite-lamellibranch faunas. On account of the absence of goniatites from the type Avon section, and owing to the fact that outside the South-West Province there are differences in the coral-brachiopod assemblages, the exact equivalence of the two sets of zones is difficult to establish. Among the cephalopods *Goniatites sensu stricto*, *Merocanites* (*Prolecanites*) and *Beyrichoceras* are important and are used as zonal indices in the $B_1$, $B_2$, $P_1$ and $P_2$ stages. *Posidonia*, an important lamellibranch, lends its name and initial to the P-stages of the Upper Avonian. Approximately $B_1 = S_2$, $B_2 = D_1$, $P_1 = D_2$ and $P_2 = D_3$.

The geological history of the Lower Carboniferous Period opens with an extensive marine transgression, in the course of which the greater part of the British Isles area was progressively submerged, and a sheet of sediment, locally reaching the thickness of 8000 or

9000 feet, was deposited upon it. The transgression rapidly flooded England south of the Midlands; but in the early stages the rest of the country seems to have stood above sea-level. The evidence for this conclusion is the local absence of the lower zones and a significant difference in the geological relations in the extreme southerly outcrops on the one hand, and the rest of the country on the other.

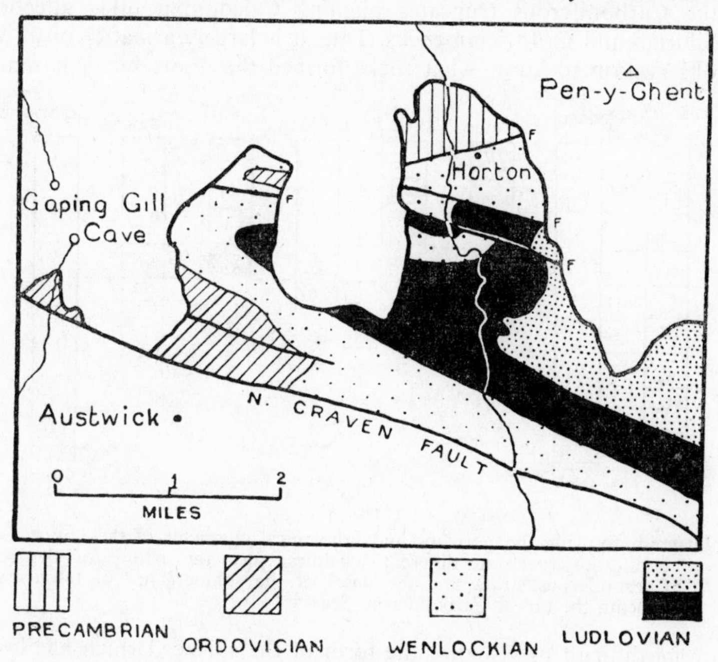


FIG. 47.
Sketch-map of a fragment of the sub-Carboniferous floor near Ingleborough, in the Pennines. Carboniferous left blank.
(*After W. B. R. King.*)

Only in the South-West Province (including North Devon), and southern Ireland is the sequence from Devonian to Carboniferous unbroken: there is apparent conformity between the two Systems. But elsewhere an unconformity, often a great one, separates the Carboniferous rocks from the floor on which they rest. At one point or another the sub-Carboniferous floor consists of every major formation between the Precambrian and the Devonian. The incomplete Dinantian rests directly on Precambrian in Anglesey, in the Pennines near Ingleborough, and in Leicestershire on the borders of Charnwood Forest; on Cambrian in South Shropshire near the Wrekin; on Ordovician and Silurian on the margins of the Lake District massif, in the Flint-Denbigh coalfield and in the Pennines; on Silurian in the Southern Uplands and on Old Red Sandstone in the Cheviots. In a few localities, notably south of Ingleborough, denudation has laid bare portions of the sub-Carboniferous floor on a sufficiently extensive scale to allow its structures to be seen (Fig. 47). In the case illustrated, the base of the Carboniferous truncates pitching Caledonian folds affecting Silurian and Ordovician rocks. Thus it is largely a matter of direct observation to know what rocks formed the floor; but it is much

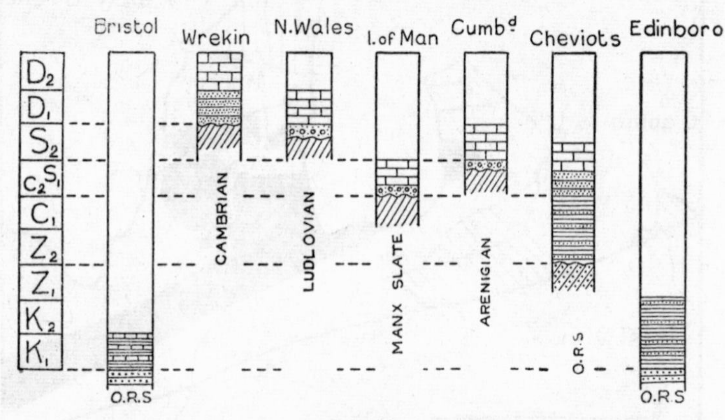


FIG. 48.

Diagram showing the horizons and lithological character of the lowest Carboniferous rocks in different localities; also the nature of the sub-Carboniferous strata and the dates of the submergence of these areas beneath the Lower Carboniferous Sea.

more difficult to visualize the form of the surface, which has been warped by subsequent earth-movements and displaced by faulting. The form of the surface can only be *inferred* from the successions at different points on the outcrops. Once again we would emphasize the fact that at the opening of the Carboniferous Period none of the present upland areas existed as we know them to-day. As a consequence of the phenomenal denudation during the Devonian, the Caledonian mountains had been planed down to their roots, while the foothills had disappeared. It must have been a gently undulating surface across which the early Carboniferous Sea transgressed; but it was not a plain. Had it been so, the basal beds would everywhere be of the same age, but this is far from being the case. The date of the inundation at any point is known if the base of the Carboniferous is visible, and if its position in the zonal succession can be determined. The relevant details for a number of places are shown in Fig. 48. Obviously the Carboniferous transgression occurred earliest in the Bristol district, while of the localities shown, the Wrekin area was the last to be submerged—in D-times. If the zones represent approximately equal periods of time, this implies that this part of England kept its head above water until Dinantian (Avonian) time was four-fifths spent.

We will look into this matter, as it affects southern England, more closely. When traced northwards from the Mendip Hills and

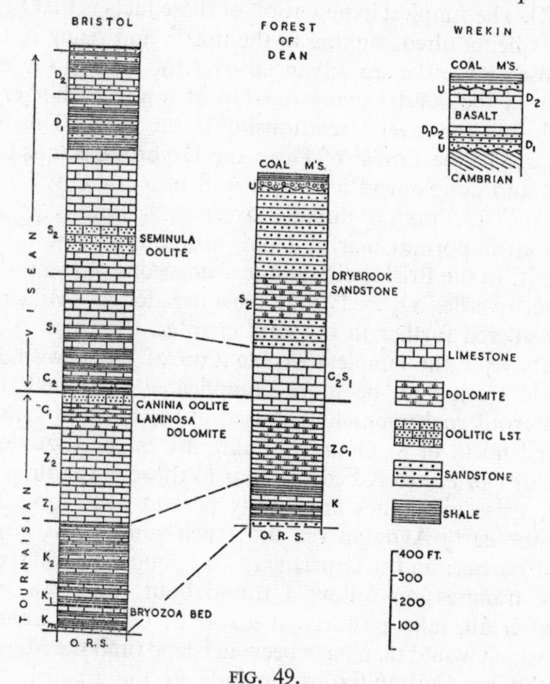


FIG. 49.
Comparative sections of the Lower Carboniferous of Bristol (Avon Gorge), Forest of Dean and the Wrekin.

the Bristol district, the Avonian progressively diminishes in thickness until, between the Titterstone and Brown Clee Hills, it disappears altogether, and in a belt of country crossing the Midlands there is no Lower Carboniferous. On the north side of this belt, however, the rocks once more appear, very thin at first, but becoming progressively thicker when traced northwards (Fig. 48). The absence of the Dinantian from parts of the Midlands is believed to be due to non-deposition: that is, the area stood as an island or promontory above the waters of the early Dinantian Sea. The name 'St George's Land' has been applied to this Carboniferous land area. Of course, a steady sinking of this land would give rise to the variations in thickness we have noted above; for in these circumstances the sea would gradually encroach, the land would be progressively submerged, and the sediment would show the normal 'overlapping' relationship. As a fact the explanation cannot be as simple as this; for while the attenuated Dinantian north of St George's Land belongs to the higher zones $S_2$ and D, as might be expected, that which occupies a comparable position to the south is Tournaisian (K and Z). The simplest explanation of these facts is that St George's Land was being tilted, sinking in the north, and rising in the south. As a consequence the sea advanced over the land in the north, but withdrew in the south, giving overlap of lower by higher zones in the north, but the reverse relationship in the south. This is referred to as *offlap*. In the Forest of Dean the Drybrook Sandstone, much of it red and conglomeratic, might well pass for O.R.S., if it were not for the fact that it directly overlies $S_1$ limestone, and itself contains an important marine band, a dolomitic limestone with $S_2$ fossils in it. In the Bristol district the arenaceous phase, if it is indeed the same, overlies $D_2$ beds and masquerades as 'Millstone Grit'. It is considered further in the next chapter. (See also p. 222.)

The above is the simplest explanation of the known facts; but the whole truth may be more complicated. Although the oldest Carboniferous rocks actually exposed in the Skipton area in Yorkshire, well north of St George's Land, are in the C-zone, a boring passed through Z into K beds, similar to those in the Bristol district. Further, these low zones are locally present near Ravenstonedale, so that the early Avonian sea did reach some areas north of the Midland barrier, and it is pertinent to enquire by what route. Did the Z-K trangression follow a roundabout route via Ireland, or did it, after all, take a short cut *across* St George's Land between Wales (which would then have been an island) and the Mercian Highlands—the pre-Carboniferous uplands in the English Midlands? This suggests the possibility that the absence of the Tournaisian (Lower Avonian) zones from the Midlands may be due not to non-deposition, but to destruction of the beds as a result of uplift and denudation. Significant evidence on this problem is forthcoming from other parts of the country and will be referred to in due course. In any case, however, in Viséan times the sea advanced again, this time definitely from the north, reaching North Wales in the late $S_2$, and the Wrekin district in early $D_1$ times.

On the northern flank of the barrier the Viséan limestones are *underlain* by an arenaceous phase, the position of limestone and sandstone being reversed as compared with the Clee Hills and Forest of Dean (Fig. 49). The Viséan of the Wrekin in South Shropshire is the nearest outcrop to the Clee Hills where the Dinantian thins out against the barrier. The succession consists of two members: (1) a basal conglomeratic sandstone followed by (2) a very thin $D_2$ limestone containing a basaltic lava flow. The beds are flagrantly unconformable to the Lower Palaeozoic rocks below, transgressing in a short distance from Lower Cambrian to Ordovician and Silurian strata. The same general relations hold for the Viséan of North Wales; but here, on the borders of the Flint-Denbigh coalfield, the basal group locally swells out to form a thick succession of red, purple and green sandstones with conglomerates and shales, closely resembling O.R.S. Indeed, the materials were formed during the Devonian, but were redistributed during the initial ($S_2$) Carboniferous transgression. As they change their horizon and vary in thickness from point to point, the old land surface was evidently here one of some relief. Above the basement beds comes a considerable thickness of typical Carboniferous Limestone, finely displayed in the Llangollen area where it forms a spectacular scarp feature. Standing on its summit and looking westwards over the deeply dissected country occupied by the Silurian and Ordovician rocks, one gets the impression that these limestones, if projected westwards would clear the hilltops, suggesting the former wide extension of these beds in the heart of North Wales. One small outlier lying ten miles to the west, near Corwen, lends credence to this view. Occupying a position relative to the Midland Barrier comparable with that of North Wales, is an extensive concealed outcrop lying beneath part of Lincolnshire and Nottinghamshire, disclosed by borings made during the development of the oilfield. The general picture is one of ridges of Precambrian (Charnian) rocks, and Cambrian quartzites with intervening valleys, some of considerable depth. The Viséan rocks are banked against and overtop the ridges. In places the succession, like that in North Wales, ranges from $S_2$ to $D_2$, while locally a basement group underlies the limestones and again shows lithological characters more appropriate to the O.R.S. than to the Dinantian. At one spot a unique group of red breccio-conglomerates and sandstones, unfortunately quite unfossiliferous, but certainly older than $C_1$, is piled up to a thickness of 1700 feet.

Undoubtedly St George's Land was the most persistent of the Carboniferous uplands, for it was not finally submerged until 'Westphalian' times were far advanced. There were, however, other elevated tracts which exercised a profound influence upon sedimentation during the period, and this is perhaps the most important aspect of the study of the Lower Carboniferous rocks.

North of St George's Land lies the **Central Province,** which embraces the Lower Carboniferous rocks lying between St George's Land and the Isle of Man–Lake District–North Pennine massif to the north. This Central Province marks the site of a trough bounded by relatively stable upland areas; but its central portion sagged repeatedly, and thus accommodated a great thickness of Lower Carboniferous sediments. In the account which follows we will concentrate on the variation in lithology and fauna, which is such a striking feature of these rocks. Part of the northern margin of the trough was the natural geographical region of the northern Pennines (Fig. 50). This region is bounded on three sides by some of the most important fault systems in the country: on the south by the Craven faults; on the west by the Dent and Pennine faults; and on the north by the Stublick faults which are followed approximately by the Tyne Gap. The North Pennine block is divided into two portions by the Stainmore 'pass', the northern part being termed the Alston Block, and the southern the Askrigg Block. Beyond the North Pennine Block lay another trough, that of north-eastern England, referred to as the Mid-Northumbrian Trough, the northern limit of which can only be guessed at. It is certain that the Cheviot massif, built of Old Red Sandstone lavas and tuffs on a floor of Silurian rocks, stood as an island above the early-Carboniferous Sea, as did the Lake District massif farther to the south-west (Fig. 48); but the outcrops sweep round the former obstruction, cross the Border and disappear against the Southern Uplands massif. It is impossible to gauge the extent to which the latter area was overridden by Lower Carboniferous sediments; but beneath the Coal Measures in the Thornhill and Sanquhar coalfields occur thin fossiliferous limestones and shales which are referred to the highest Viséan. Further, certain small volcanic necks pierce the Lower Palaeozoic rocks of the district: they are filled with volcanic breccia or agglomerate, and among the fragments are recognizable pieces of Dinantian rocks. Such fragments are of great interest, for they are samples of the rocks lying near the surface when the volcanoes were in explosive eruption: here is positive proof, therefore, of the former existence of Dinantian rocks in the Southern Uplands, although all trace of the sheet (except at Sanquhar) has now disappeared.

Once across the Southern Uplands, however, we are on surer ground, in a region where the Lower Carboniferous rocks again become of great importance, and attain to the maximum thickness for the British Isles. Carboniferous rocks occur beyond the Highland Boundary Fault at two points only: one in Argyllshire (Pass of Brander) and the other, Inninmore, on the mainland immediately north-east of Mull.

The use of the word 'trough' or 'basin' requires some explanation. One of the most striking facts of Carboniferous stratigraphy is the great disparity in thickness between the rocks in the troughs and

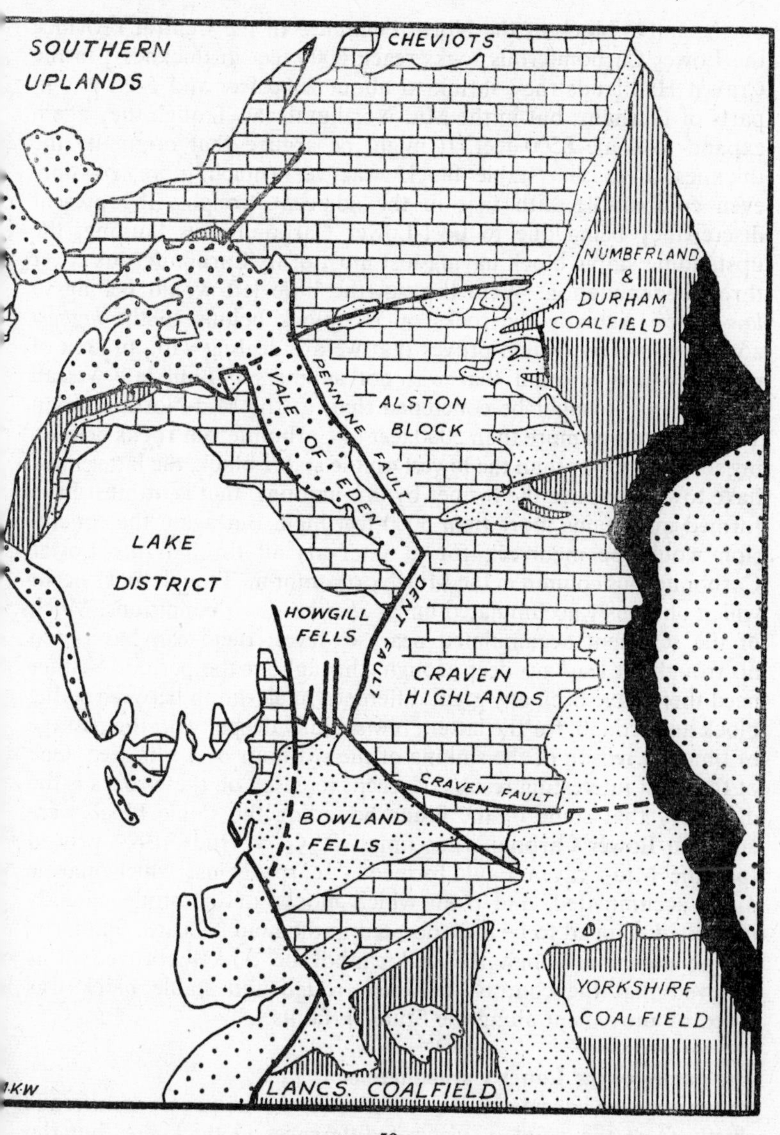


FIG. 50.

Geological sketch-map of Northern England showing main structural units.

Pre-Carboniferous, blank; Lower Carboniferous, bricks; Namurian, fine stippling; Coal Measures, vertical ruling; Magnesian Limestone, black; Permo-Trias, coarse stippling; L, Liassic outlier near Carlisle. The Craven Highlands = Askrigg Block.

on the stable block of the North Pennines. In the Central Province the Lower Carboniferous rocks reach 6000 feet in thickness; in the Craven Highlands they shrink to about 2000 feet and even less in parts of Durham; but in the Mid-Northumbrian Trough they again expand to some 8500 feet. It might be argued that originally the thickness over the 'stable block' was very much more, possibly even comparable with that in the adjacent troughs, the present discrepancy being due to post-Lower Carboniferous faulting, the upstanding stable block having lost most of its Carboniferous cover through denudation. Were this so, the little left would belong to *low* zones. Actually the rocks on the block belong to the *highest* zones exclusively, which proves that we are dealing with an area of relatively high ground that was not submerged until late Viséan times. Next, it might be concluded that, as the Mid-Northumbrian Trough contains more than 5000 feet of Carboniferous rocks belonging to zones lower than the lowest on the stable block, the latter must have towered above the former by this amount: that is, it must have formed mountains more than 5000 feet high. But again the conclusion would be incorrect, for at intervals all through the Lower Carboniferous column in the Mid-Northumbrian Trough rocks occur which obviously accumulated under *shallow-water* conditions. Much of the sediment accumulated near sea-level; there can have been no trough, at least no deep trough, throughout the period. Neither need there have been any great difference in elevation between stable block and trough, for the latter grew steadily deeper with the passage of time, by reason of the sinking of the sea-floor over this area. One of the most interesting results of recent research on these rocks is the discovery that some of the faults bounding the stable block were active in Lower Carboniferous times. R. G. S. Hudson has proved that the Mid-Craven Fault formed a scarp against which marine muds accumulated, and from which blocks of limestone, already indurated, slipped to be incorporated in the mud beneath. Similarly, in the north, although the fact cannot be directly proved, it is believed that the contrast between trough and stable block was aided by movement along the Stublick faults.

### The Facies of the Lower Carboniferous

So far we have considered the variation in the Lower Carboniferous chiefly from the point of view of differences in thickness: but the System is important also by reason of the variety of lithological and faunal facies it exhibits. Probably in this respect the Carboniferous is unique, and if this is no exaggeration, it implies an unprecedented variety of geographical environments, of which facies differences are but the reflection. It would take us outside the scope of this work to consider all the facies and phases in detail: only the more important can be studied. It must be clearly understood that each one of these different facies is dependent upon the prevailing environmental conditions. Only in so far as such conditions are constant can the boundaries of a facies correspond with time planes. Normally a facies is diachronous.

It is only in the South-West Province and southern Ireland that Tournaisian (Lower Avonian) strata are extensively developed. They fall into two units: (1) the **Lower Limestone Shales** and (2) the **Main Limestone.** As the name implies, the former consists of rapid alternations of shale and limestone. This facies is strikingly uniform in the South-West Province; but in southern Ireland the proportion of shale varies widely, and in the extreme south Lower Limestone Shales of normal lithology expand into the so-called **Carboniferous Slate,** though this formation includes sandstones, grits and mudstones, the whole reaching 8000 feet in thickness. Two rock-groups bearing local names are included—the Coomhola Beds, succeeded by the Ringabella Beds. The former rest on O.R.S. with apparent conformity, and it is uncertain how much of the group should be allocated to the Devonian and how much to the Carboniferous. The Ringabella Beds are of finer grain and more calcareous, with a distinctive quartz-conglomerate at the base. It indicates a non-sequence and coincides with the base of the Z-zone, marked by the incoming of zaphrentoid corals. In Ireland this is often regarded as a convenient, easily mappable base to the Carboniferous System.

The change from Lower Limestone Shales to **Main Limestone** in the South-West Province was one of the most significant events in Carboniferous geological history. In a very short space of time shale, originally mud, was eliminated: what had been a mud belt gave place to a clear shelf sea in which corals flourished, zaphrentoids being first on the scene, followed in due course by 'swarms' of large caninioid types, and the Carboniferous Limestone regime was firmly established.

The most typical and most wide-spread of the Dinantian rock-types is massive grey bioclastic limestone—the Carboniferous Limestone of the 'man in the street' and termed 'standard' by stratigraphers, though it is far from uniform in lithology and fauna. Such limestones are widely distributed from $C_1$ to $D_1$ in the South-West Province; they occupy much of the Central Irish Plain, and are prominent north of St George's Land around the Flint-Denbigh coalfield and in the southern Pennines. Special kinds of limestone including lagoon-phase types, and the several varieties of reef-limestone are not included as standard. Many of the standard limestones contain a mixed fauna; but in others one kind of organism is dominant—in some, brachiopods (spirifers, productids or pustulas); in others, crinoids or foraminifers. Some varieties are texturally distinctive, especially the oolitic limestones, the *Caninia* Oolite in $C_1$ and the *Seminula* Oolite in $S_2$ being well-known examples (Fig. 49).

Normally the limestones are calcitic; but locally they have been affected by diagenetic alteration and converted into dolomitic limestones. The replacement of calcite by dolomite appears to have been penecontemporaneous in the case of the *Laminosa* Dolomite, a wide-spread and distinctive horizon in $C_1$; but several other standard limestones become dolomitic as they are traced towards the then-existing coastlines.

The development of nodules or layers of chert is typical of limestone in the Z-Zone in the South-West Province: but this form of silica is common at higher levels and in other parts of the country. Thus D-limestones in Derbyshire and North Wales contain much chert, some of which may have been deposited on the sea floor as colloidal silica; but it is definitely secondary in other cases, as oolitic and other textures as well as fossils have been pseudomorphed in silica.

During the initial stages of the Dinantian transgression certain extensive flat areas were flooded to a shallow depth. Perhaps by reason of shallowness alone or possibly due to the presence of a barrier free communication with the outer sea was limited and consequently circulation and aeration were restricted. In such an environment special types of sediment were deposited and specialized faunas flourished instead of the usual corals and brachiopods. Such a set of rocks constitutes a **lagoon phase.** Lagoon phases occur at three levels in the Dinantian: in the K-Zone, at the base of $C_2S_1$ and locally at the top of $D_1$. The first of these is cryptically referred to as $K_m$, 'm' standing for *Modiolus* (originally *Modiola*),[1] a kind of lamellibranch which, judging from its numbers, found the conditions congenial. Among the special rock-types occurring in *Modiolus* phases are calcite-mudstones, algal limestones and, in $K_m$, the *Bryozoa* Bed. In the Avon section this is a dull red ferruginous limestone, rich in the remains of crinoids and polyzoans; but in the Forest of Dean and in the Cardiff district it is so charged with haematite as to be a valuable iron ore. Lagoon phase calcite-mudstones of early Viséan ($C_2S_1$) age were deposited on a sensibly flat extensive coastal plain cut in gently inclined Tournaisian strata on the southern flanks of St George's Land. They change abruptly

[1] The characteristic lamellibranch, *Modiolus* (formerly *Modiola*) which gives its name to these lagoonal phases is now named *Promytilus*, but we prefer to retain the old name, otherwise the familiar symbol, $K_m$, would be meaningless.

to standard crinoidal, brachiopod and coral limestones beyond the barrier (if any), formed under deeper water, neritic conditions. 'Mudstone' has been used extensively in previous chapters for massive, as distinct from laminated, *argillaceous* sedimentary rocks consisting chiefly of clay minerals. Calcite-mudstones resemble these rocks only in their excessively fine grain; but they contain no clay minerals, consisting solely of calcite in a state of extremely fine subdivision. This may have been chemically precipitated; but probably much of its was formed by the disintegration of algal tissue. Genuine algal limestones are typical of lagoon phases, the Whitehead Limestone containing '*Mitcheldeania*' and occurring in the Forest of Dean is a good example.

From the point of view of environment during deposition the Avonian limestones are neritic shelf deposits and some formed genuine reefs in the shelf seas of the time. Several varieties of reefs are distinguishable according to the nature of the organisms concerned. Naturally corals take pride of place, especially certain colonial rugose forms among which *Cyathophyllum*, *Lithostrotion* and *Lonsdaleia* are important.

As an illustration of the role of corals in reef-limestone formation we may look at Viséan reefs described recently (1962) from the north-western portion of the extensive Lower Carboniferous outcrop underlying the Central Irish Plain. Near the base of the 1000 feet succession of bioclastic D-limestones a reef occurs which consists of densely packed colonies of *Lithostrotion*, perhaps a dozen species being represented, but one of them, *L. pauciradiale* (formerly *L. irregulare*) is overwhelmingly dominant. They are piled one upon another through a vertical thickness of 400 feet, and continuous over many square miles of country. It does not conform to the popular conception of a coral reef; but is an extensive sheet-like organic structure. Some 300 feet above the *pauciradiale* reef a second one occurs, structurally identical, but less impressive in its dimensions. Again this is a *Lithostrotion* reef, but the dominant species is *L. martini*. Towards the top of the Viséan three other sheet-reefs occur, built chiefly of *L. junceum*.

The bioclastic limestones below, between and above the *Lithostrotion* reefs are of standard Carboniferous Limestone types, variable in lithology and faunal content. The associated fossils include algae, polyzoa, foraminifera, brachiopods and large solitary rugose corals including *Caninia* which is common near the base of the succession and *Dibunophyllum*, together with various clisiophyllids, towards the top.

These *Lithostrotion* sheet-reefs cannot be exactly matched elsewhere in Britain, though the associated limestones and the fossils are all well represented in the South-West Province, in the North Midlands, in North Wales (Flint, Denbigh and Anglesey) and in the Midland Valley of Scotland, proving the existence of a unitary depositional basin over the whole region late in the Viséan.

Although the colonial rugose corals figure most prominently in the reefs, corals of *simple* types are abundant on certain horizons. In this respect zaphrentids (*Zaphrentites*, *Hapsiphyllum*) and *Cyathaxonia* are important. The former is not restricted to the Z-Zone; but when conditions were favourable these genera were liable to occur in sufficient numbers as to constitute *Zaphrentis*- and/or *Cyathaxonia*-phases which occur locally on several horizons as high as $P_2$ in the Viséan.

Among the many and varied limestones occurring in the South-Western Province one of outstanding interest is that which forms the **Waulsortian reef** facies, so named after type occurrences in Belgium and France, and developed on the southern flank of the Dinant basin. It is believed that Waulsortian reefs originally covered half Ireland (some 3000 square miles) and may have reached a maximum thickness, in the neighbourhood of Cork, of 4000 feet. Not far south of Cork the outcrops suddenly cease against the Carboniferous Slate; but northwards the reefs thin through overlap and lateral passage into normal Viséan shelf-limestones. In the south the Waulsortian reefs rest on Tournaisian of typical Lower Limestone Shales lithology and fauna; but in the north, in Tipperary, they total 1000 feet and are overlain by thick Viséan ($C_2S_1$–? $S_2$) neritic limestones. Apart from problems of age-relationships the Waulsortian reefs have attracted much attention from the point of view of their origin, and of their composition. Until 1964 it was commonly accepted that they consisted of closely interleaving fronds of algae and 'fans' of bryozoa with much calcite-mudstone filling the interstices and with clear crystalline calcite ramifying through the mudstone. As a result of a detailed study more particularly of the mode of growth of the 'reefs', it appears that although bryozoa may be present in quantity the structures regarded as algal fronds are inorganic in origin. The chief contributors to the formation of Waulsortian reefs remain unidentified as their remains have not been preserved; but algae and sponges are mentioned as possibilities, we would add, with strong emphasis on the former. The recrystallization of some of the original calcareous mud into 'sparry' calcite would provide an inorganic skeleton to the structure.

In early stages of growth Waulsortian reefs are knoll-like in form and appear to be identical with the reef-knolls of Derbyshire and elsewhere in England; but being Irish they are termed knoll-reefs. Either term conjures up a truer picture than the recent suggestion—'calcareous mud-bank', although individual knolls later link up into ridges rising perhaps 50 feet above the sea floor, and ultimately ridges coalesce into composite sheets—the characteristic form of 'reefs' of this type. The early, reef-knoll stage of development is seen in many examples around the latitude of Dublin; but as noted above, the sheet-form is best developed in the extreme south. The stratigraphical relationships indicate that the sheet was rooted in the south and grew northwards.

In Kerry and Cork the Waulsortian sheet reef ends abruptly against the **Carboniferous Slate**—an argillaceous formation which in several respects resembles the Culm facies as developed in Devon and Cornwall and for which an alternative name is 'Irish Culm'. In the Cork Syncline typical Tournaisian strata of Lower Limestone Shales lithology and fauna pass southwards into more sandy, less calcareous beds, which in turn grade into slates, in places strongly cleaved and with intercalations of coarse grit of southerly provenance. These changes in lithology are accompanied by drastic faunal changes: the crinoids, corals, brachiopods and bryozoans disappear and although other kinds of fossils, including goniatites, occur, they are few and so distorted by cleavage as to make specific identification difficult. With regard to conditions of deposition, the 'Irish Culm' is basinal, although not necessarily abyssal. The sea must have been deeper than the shelf sea of the Mid-Irish Plain and was presumably continuous with that over the Devon-Cornwall region.

In present exposures which were situated near to the Viséan coastlines contemporary strata are completely different from the normal Carboniferous Limestone, and constitute a distinctive **marginal facies** which varies from place to place, of course, but consists of rock-types appropriate to such an environment. The marginal facies is most impressively and extensively developed in North-West Ireland where, between the coast of the Atlantean Continent and the neritic shelf limestones of the interior, two distinct lithological 'zones' may be distinguished. The inner zone of coarse grained arenites including conglomerates, wedging into coarse sandstones associated with silty shales, is fringed by an outer zone of shales with thin 'ribs' of limestone, abundantly fossiliferous, with many zaphrentoid and caninioid corals as well as brachiopods, largely spirifers and productids. The inner zone consists of boulders, cobbles and pebbles together with large quantities of quartz sand, derived from Moine and Dalradian metamorphic rocks like those exposed to-day in the uplands of Mayo and Donegal. The coastal assemblage is usually covered by that accommodating term 'deltaic': certainly the coastal flats were traversed by powerful distributaries which sometimes pushed coarse arenites through the shale belt to make direct contact with the neritic bioclastic limestones beyond. The 'deltaic' sediments are impressively thick. Thousands of feet of sands and gravels accumulated in a Caledonoid trough which deepened to accommodate them during early Viséan times (chiefly $C_2S_1$), and a corresponding elevation of the supplying areas is a reasonable inference. The contrast with the conditions in the Mid-Irish Plain is striking: standard Carboniferous Limestone of the varied lithologies noted above, although covering an area of several thousand square miles, is surprisingly uniform in thickness and it is only in the extreme south that important modifications take place.

Basal Viséan strata, whatever their precise age, are liable to display marginal features similar to those described above, in suitable environments. Thus in Anglesey thick littoral conglomerates and coarse sandstones grade upwards into sandy limestones and these in turn, into standard massive limestones. As in North-West Ireland, the littoral deposits were banked against a diversified landscape which was ultimately buried under more than two thousand feet of Viséan rocks.

A distinctive feature of the marginal Viséan in the South-West Province is the **Chepstow delta** which occupies a triangular trough-like depression with north–south axis passing near Chepstow and filled with coarse-grained, cross-bedded, pebbly sandstones deposited by a strong-flowing river. They are well represented by the Drybrook Sandstone in the Forest of Dean and by equivalent strata in the Bristol district where they attain a maximum thickness of 1200 feet of more varied deltaic sediments comprising coarse sandstones, sandy limestones, grey shales and rare fireclays. The Chepstow delta first became a recognizable feature of St George's Land palaeogeography in $S_2$-times and persisted little changed throughout the rest of Viséan time.

Probably no region is more instructive for illustrating the various facies of the Lower Carboniferous than the Craven district in the Central Province, for here within an area of but a few square miles the rocks exhibit four facies. South of the Craven faults much of the Lower Carboniferous succession consists of thin black limestones interbedded with shales (Fig. 51). This constitutes the **basin facies,** distinctive in lithology and fauna which comprises thin-shelled lamellibranchs such as *Dunbarella* ('*Pterinopecten*') and goniatites. As the succession is unbroken here, it provides an almost perfect standard of reference for all those areas in which goniatites occur. North of the Craven faults the Lower Carboniferous falls into two lithological units: a lower division consisting of massive 'standard limestone', which forms a prominent scarp along the Pennine front—

this is appropriately named the 'Great Scar Limestone'; and a higher division consisting of many alternations of thin marine limestones, often richly fossiliferous, with shales and sandstones. These constitute the **Yoredale facies** which persists right across the North Pennine block into Northumberland, and indeed the higher part of the Lower Carboniferous of the Midland Valley of Scotland is of the same general type. It must be clearly understood that the Yoredale rocks constitute an unstable-shelf facies, *not* a series or stage. The facies does not occupy a constant horizon: its boundaries

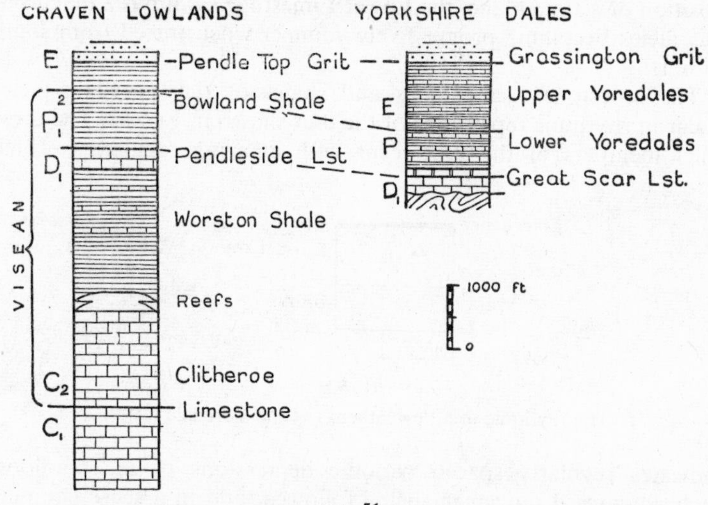


FIG. 51.

Comparative sections of the Lower Carboniferous in the Craven Lowlands and Yorkshire Dales, to the south and north respectively of the Craven faults.
Note the contrast in (1) thickness due to the late submergence of the stable block of the North Pennines, and in (2) lithological facies.

are strongly diachronous—so much so in fact that, while Yoredale beds lie above the Great Scar Limestone in the southern part of the Craven Highlands, when traced northwards the main Viséan limestone takes over the Yoredale aspect through the progressive intercalation of wedges of sandstone and shale at lower and lower levels until ultimately the whole of the standard limestone is Yoredalian in aspect. Further, the Yoredale facies transgresses the important boundary between the Lower and Upper Carboniferous: only the lower part belongs to the Viséan, the rest is Namurian, and as such is considered in due course.

One other feature of the Yoredale facies concerns the occurrence of valuable marker-horizons such as the *Girvanella*-Bed, the *Orionastraea*-Band, and the *Saccaminopsis*-Band. These are relatively thin beds easily recognized in the field by the abundance in them of a calcareous alga, *Girvanella*, a compound rugose coral, *Orionastraea*, and a foraminifer, *Saccaminopsis* respectively. By tracing the *Girvanella*-Bed across Northumberland from Brampton to Alnwick, a marked diachronism within the Lower Limestone Group has been demonstrated: the *Girvanella*-Bed lies at the base at Brampton, but gradually climbs to the top of the Group at Alnwick. Which, in point of fact, is diachronous? If one assumes that the *Girvanella*-Bed occupies a constant stratigraphical horizon and thus fixes the position of a time-plane, the Lower Limestone Group is a diachronous facies becoming progressively younger when traced from south to north.

The limestones, sandstones and shales of the Yoredale facies occur in rhythmic repetitions of the unit shown in Fig. 52. The three chief members of the unit recur with amazing regularity, which

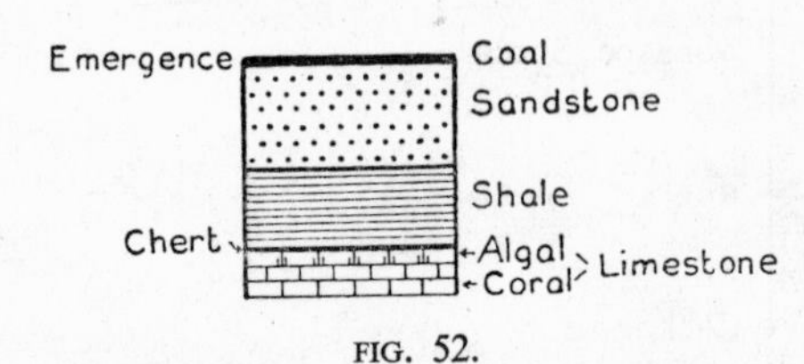


FIG. 52.
The rhythmic unit ('cyclothem') of the Yoredale facies.

indicates regularly spaced periodic depressions of the sea-floor, each downward movement being followed, and in a sense counteracted, by silting up.

In parts of Ireland (as in England and Scotland), the standard Viséan limestones are succeeded by a sandstone-shale phase which has long been identified, by the Irish Survey, with the Yoredales. Thus in Co. Fermanagh a so-called 'Yoredale Sandstone' up to 400 feet thick and of $B_2$ age is overlain by 700 feet of 'Yoredale Shales', shown by their goniatite faunas to range from $P_1$ to $E_1c$. No goniatites have been discovered in the top 200 feet, which are therefore undated. In the Omagh Syncline the term 'Yoredale Series' was applied to a thick (1500 feet) sandstone formation, quartzitic below but rather calcareous above, with intercalations of shale and thin limestones especially towards the top of the succession which contains an $S_2$ fauna. The lower part may well be early Viséan, $C_2S_1$. In neither case is the term 'Yoredales' applicable: lithologically they have nothing in common; in particular the characteristic rhythmic sedimentation is lacking. The so-called 'Yoredale Sandstones' invite comparison with the Fell Sandstone of northern

England; while the Irish 'Yoredale Shales' are analogous with the Bowland Shales and Edale Shales.

A facies of doubtful status and wholly Irish is the **Calp.** This name was applied by the Irish Survey to the middle of the three main limestones developed in the Central Plain. It is a local name of unknown origin and covers black Carboniferous limestones associated with dark-coloured ('black') shales. In the Dublin area the Calp is a monotonous series of dark, fine-grained limestones rhythmically interbedded with dark, 'earthy' shales and mudstones, the whole being about 1000 feet thick and of early Viséan ($C_2S_1$) age. Elsewhere, however, strata of Calp facies are of P-age.

One of the most interesting of the Lower Carboniferous facies, the significance of which is still being discussed, is the limestone **reef-knoll facies** which is well developed in the Craven district and also in the eastern Pennines in Derbyshire. Reef-knolls occur on different horizons in a zone marginal to the buried 'massifs'. The rocks of this facies usually form prominent rounded hills, the reef-knolls, which in their isolation contrast strongly with the continuous scarp features formed by normal 'standard limestones'. These knolls consist of white unbedded limestone, rich in brachiopods and bryozoa, rather than corals. The reef limestone is seen to pass laterally into thinly bedded, dark-coloured limestone, often crowded with small conical rugose corals, chiefly *Zaphrentis*, while it is succeeded by black goniatite-bearing shales. Reef-knolls of only a slightly different type occur in $C_1$ in Pembrokeshire. They are essentially bryozoan reefs built of massive dolomites. Evidently the topographical form of reef-knolls reflects their geological structure; but there is a sharp difference of opinion as to whether the reef-form is original, or due to penecontemporaneous earth-movement, followed by denudation, before the overlying shales were deposited. Probably both explanations are true of different cases. Thus Hudson has shown that the Cracoe reef-knolls originally formed a continuous reef-belt which was faulted and dissected before being covered unconformably by black shales. On the other hand, Parkinson suggested that other reef-knolls were original secretions on the sea-floor, and of the same age as the shales that were being deposited between and around them.

From the detailed study of the Carboniferous rocks of the Central Province an important general principle has emerged. The several lithological and faunal facies described above bear a constant spatial relationship to the stable blocks surrounding the central trough. The thick-bedded standard limestones were laid down under shallow water which just submerged the stable blocks, and constitute the so-called **'massif facies'**, As we have seen, the Craven Highlands block was fault-bounded on the south. Beyond the submarine fault-scarps, in the deeper parts of the basin, thinly bedded black limestones and shales containing goniatite-lamellibranch faunas were deposited and constitute the **'basin-facies'.** The latter occurs in Ireland also, notably in the south where they have been named *Posidonomya* Shales which form isolated outliers resting on the Carboniferous Slate. The generic fossil name reminds us that the shales contain the typical fauna of thin-shelled lamellibranchs, while goniatites prove the age to be $P_2$. A feature of special interest is the occurrence in the $P_2$-Shales of fish remains identified as *Coelacanthus.* This genus until a few years ago was thought to have been extinct since Viséan times; but a specimen was caught off the Zanzibar coast and since then others have been found in these waters. Only slightly different are certain dark grey shales and mudstones forming the lower part of a 600-foot succession near Dungannon in North Central Ireland. They contain the same $P_2$ fauna, while the lower part locally yields large numbers of small simple rugose corals, chiefly species of *Zaphrentis* and *Cyathaxonia* as in the corresponding beds in Northern England.

Between the massif limestones of the Central Province and the basinal sediments occurs a group of rock-types which constitute a **marginal facies** of a rather special type. The rocks involved are reef-knoll limestones, limestone-breccias and conglomerates, associated with *Zaphrentis*-phase limestones and dark shales. As they were deposited on steep slopes high original dips are characteristic, and the significance of the breccias and conglomerates is self-evident. These features are well displayed in the northern part of the Central Province, notably in the Craven district; but they occur, in reverse order, of course, just north of the Derbyshire Dome. The northern margin of the Central Province continues across into Ireland, and runs inland from the coast at Balbriggan, where Silurian rocks meet Carboniferous. Slightly southward a reef-facies is well developed and a special feature is a magnificent display of boulder beds up to 500 feet thick, containing boulders several feet in diameter, and evidently formed by land-slipping as the basin to the south subsided. The limestone breccias in the Central Province are analogous, but nothing in England has yet been described to compare with this *Rush Conglomerate* Group, which is of $C_2S_1$ age.

In the troughs of Mid-Northumbria and the Midland Valley of Scotland yet other facies are developed in the Lower Carboniferous. (Fig. 53). The outstanding feature is the almost complete absence of standard limestone, while by far the greater portion of the succession accumulated in a non-marine environment. The lowest division, the **Cementstone Group,** presents similar characters in both areas, and one is immediately impressed by the complete difference between these rocks and their age-equivalents elsewhere. The Group consists of many repetitions of blue-grey shale and thin argillaceous dolomitic limestones, which are the 'cementstones'. No fewer than 100 separate cementstones interbedded with shales occur in a measured thickness of 130 feet at the Scottish type-locality, the Bight of Ballagan on the southern scarp of the Campsie Fells. It is a striking example of rhythmic sedimentation. The shales represent mud washed down during wet seasons into lagoons, while the intervening cementstones represent desiccation products precipitated from the shrinking waters of the lagoons during the ensuing dry season. It is significant that the shales are striped in red and green colours, indicating a high iron concentration, while gypsum sometimes occurs. The sandstones are less constant in their vertical distribution; they are often current bedded and are highly micaceous. Of special interest is the occasional occurrence of streaks of coal associated, as in true Coal Measures, with fireclay.

The relationship between Carboniferous and O.R.S. in the Midland Valley of Scotland is still uncertain. In places there appears to be conformity between the two systems. Near the base of the Cementstone Group layers of red sandstone and marl of O.R.S. aspect occur, suggesting a transition from the one to the other; but appearances may be deceptive. Taken at its face value the evidence suggests that the lowest Cementstone rocks are of K-age; but in all other parts of the region no rocks older than Viséan occur, and locally the Cementstone Group rests with visible unconformity on older rocks. The uncertainty results from the complete absence of fossils of any zonal significance. One of the distinctive horizons in the Oil Shale Group, the Pumpherston Shale (indicated by a broken line below the Burdiehouse Limestone in Fig. 53), is the lowest Calciferous Sandstone horizon to have yielded zonal fossils—specimens of the goniatite, *Beyrichoceras* (mid-Viséan, $S_2$(B), in age).

Above the Cementstone Group in Scotland comes the **Oil Shale Group,** also very distinctive in lithological facies, and limited to a restricted area in the Midland Valley. The lateral equivalents of these beds include several marine horizons in East Fife; but in Midlothian the Group is entirely non-marine. The dominant rock-type is shale, and certain bands are richly bituminous. These yield mineral oil on destructive distillation, though the oil-distilling industry is now but a shadow of what it was, on account of the keen competition of the great oilfields overseas; but the great flat-topped dumps of spent shale remain as an unsightly monument to the industry. The oil shales themselves represent swamp-pool vegetation which accumulated under quiet conditions in shallow 'lagoons', reached only by sediment of the finest grade. Apart from the dominant shale, the Group includes some thick sandstones and lagoonal, non-marine limestones, of which the Burdiehouse Limestone, up to 50 feet in thickness, is the best known. This yields plant-remains,

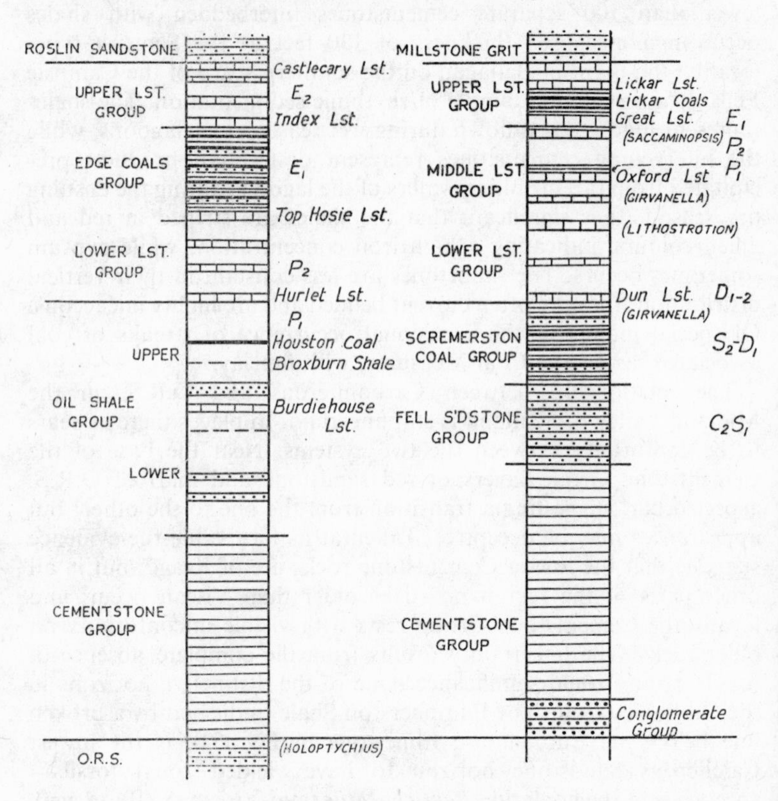


FIG. 53.

Comparative sections of the Dinantian–Namurian rocks of Edinburgh District (left) and Northumberland (Alnwick).

*Not to scale.* Lithology indicated conventionally. Zonal indices, in some cases tentative, indicated by initials.

The Cementstone and Oil Shale Groups together constitute the Calciferous Sandstone Series. Igneous rocks are omitted.

and certain levels swarm with ostracods. As to conditions of formation, the shales were evidently deposits of river-borne silt and mud, laid down on extensive mud-flats which were subject to periodic drying-up, for mud-cracking and desiccation-breccias are common. Like the O.R.S. cornstones, the non-marine limestones must have been formed in fresh-water lagoons. For the first time in this part of the country swamp forests, so typical of Coal Measure conditions, became established temporarily at about the middle of the period, yielding the lowest workable coal seam (the Houston Coal), which incidentally is separated by 1000 feet of barren strata from the next coal seam of economic importance'.

In northern England the Cementstone Group is succeeded by the **Fell Sandstone,** which from the topographical point of view is the most important rock in Northumberland; for it forms a splendid scarp feature, capped by extensive moors and dissected by deep, well-wooded valleys. Essentially the Fell Sandstone bears a striking lithological resemblance to the Millstone Grit: in so far as the term 'deltaic' is applicable to the latter, it applies to the former also; it was a precursor of the fluvio-deltaic facies of the typical Namurian. The Fell Sandstone is very thickly bedded, individual sheets of sandstone being as much as 100 feet in thickness; but other types of sediment are not completely excluded, for at intervals limestones up to 6 inches thick rest on sandstone, and are succeeded by thin shale bands. Plant-remains are the commonest fossils and the only ones found in the sandstones; but the limestones are sometimes crinoidal, and in these cases are, of course, marine. Once more 'Coal Measure conditions' are indicated by occasional streaks and at least one thin seam of coal.

It is the overlying formation, however, that is of **coal measure facies** in the northern part of Northumberland, in Scotland and Northern Ireland. In the neighbourhood of Berwick, the Scremerston Coal Group contains up to ten valuable coals.

The distinctive feature of the highest group in the Lower Carboniferous of both North England and Scotland is the occurrence of richly fossiliferous, pale-weathering limestones at several different levels, and hence in Scotland the rocks have been termed the 'Carboniferous Limestone Series', but this is a most unsatisfactory name. If the term is used at all it can have only one meaning: it must be synonymous with the strata covered by the term 'Carboniferous Limestone', i.e. the Lower Carboniferous in the type-area of south-western England. This is the sense in which the term is used by the Geological Survey in England; but it has a very different meaning in Scotland, where the 'Carboniferous Limestone Series' includes the uppermost Viséan and the lowest Namurian (Fig. 53). Further, the limestones which are present make up only a small part (actually 162 feet out of 2500 feet of the total thickness of the Series in one measured section), the remainder being shales and sandstones. The limestones themselves vary in thickness from a few inches to 50 feet. Some of them are highly crinoidal and contain in addition large numbers of delicate bryozoans, brachiopods and zaphrentid corals. Others are essentially coral limestones: it is difficult to imagine a more richly fossiliferous coral limestone than that which outcrops on the banks of the Bathgate reservoir, north of the town of that name. It literally swarms with corals, including *Clisiophyllum*, *Palaeosmilia* and *Aulophyllum*, beautifully preserved, and associated with colonies of *Lithostrotion*, *Lonsdaleia* and numbers of small brachiopods and *Gigantoproductus*.

The individual limestone of greatest stratigraphical importance is the Hurlet, which although usually only a few feet thick can be traced over a very wide area, probably beyond the Midland Valley into the Northumbrian Trough. This implies that the region flooded by the Hurlet Sea had been previously peneplanated and that uniform conditions prevailed over the whole area. In West Lothian the Hurlet Limestone rests on 6000 feet of Calciferous Sandstone sediments; but to the west it spreads onto the volcanics and the post-volcanic Upper Sedimentary Group. In spite of the implied uniformity of conditions the post-Hurlet Lower Carboniferous rocks vary considerably in thickness due to renewed unequal subsidence. On the mid-Ayrshire shelf the strata are locally unrepresented; but in the Glasgow district they total 600 feet in thickness and elsewhere even greater thicknesses have been recorded. Throughout, the facies is essentially deltaic; but each of the several limestones represents a brief period of deeper water, marine conditions.

In Northern England coals occur in the Limestone Series: seams up to a foot thick occur in the Lower Limestones; the best household coal in the North of England occurs in the Middle Limestone Group.

*The Volcanic Facies*

From the scenic point of view the most important rocks in the Scottish Carboniferous are of igneous origin. In what is now the Midland Valley volcanoes were intermittently active throughout the period; in fact some did not become finally extinct until the Permian Period. Lavas and pyroclasts erupted from these centres built up thick sheets which, by faulting and denudation, have been much reduced in extent. The beautifully terraced scarp of the Campsie Fells, built chiefly of basaltic lava-flows, is the largest existing fragment of the great Calciferous Sandstone lava field, termed by Sir A. Geikie the 'Clyde Plateau'. The Kilpatrick and Cathkin Hills in the Glasgow district and the Garleton Hills east of Edinburgh are also remnants of the same lava field.

In addition to the lavas and pyroclasts, numerous basic sills, chiefly of teschenite, form prominences rising above the general level of the plain. The fine crag on which Stirling Castle is perched and the well-known Salisbury Crags in Edinburgh are outstanding examples. The actual sites of some of the volcanoes are located by agglomerate-filled vents which are scattered plentifully over the district, many of them being conveniently dissected by marine erosion on the shores of the Firth of Forth. Others, filled with lava, form steep-sided hills, the 'green hill vents' of Ayrshire being good examples. The most famous of the Carboniferous volcanoes is, however, Arthur's Seat, which dominates Edinburgh, and provides a most picturesque setting for the capital city of Scotland.

The volcanic phase is most extensively preserved in the western parts of the Midland Valley where lavas represent the Calciferous Sandstone sediments of more easterly localities, in places almost completely. Above the volcanics sediments locally occur in hollows in the upper surface of the volcanic sheet and include richly fossiliferous calcareous shales and bioclastic limestones obviously closely related as regards lithology, fauna and conditions of deposition to the overlying Lower Limestone Group.

Further outbreaks of volcanicity resulted in the eruption of basaltic lavas on the north bank of the Firth of Forth at Burntisland where the prominent Binn represents the relics of a volcano active during Oil Shale times. With the passage of time the volcanic centres migrated progressively westwards, and in the Bathgate Hills west of Edinburgh basaltic flows are interstratified with sediments belonging to the Scottish Carboniferous Limestone Group; while in Ayrshire basalts of Namurian age are commercially valuable as, by intense alteration, they have been converted into bauxite.

In Ireland Lower Carboniferous eruptive rocks are much less extensively developed than in Scotland. In Co. Antrim basaltic lavas are interbedded with the Calciferous Sandstone Series near Ballycastle. They consist of types well known in the Edinburgh district and elsewhere in the Scottish Midland Valley, and are overlain by tuffs resulting from more distant eruptions. The massive sills and quartz-dolerite dykes which are a distinctive feature of the Scottish igneous province are absent in Antrim; but volcanic vents occur in the Central Irish Plain, associated with pyroclastic intercalations in the nearby $C_2S_1$ limestones. Eruptions occurred at this time farther south, as far as Co. Cork and Co. Limerick. In the latter case lavas of a wider range of composition, from trachytes to olivine-basalts, occur in association with pyroclasts, sills and vents. Later in time ($D_2$) but in the same area, lavas of more extreme types, including picrite-basalts were erupted.

In England, also, volcanoes were active in Lower Carboniferous times. Locally eruptions in the Severn Estuary area caused basaltic lavas to be interstratified with C-limestones at Weston-super-Mare; while in Derbyshire basaltic lavas and tuffs are interstratified with the limestones high up in the succession in the D-zone. On the margin of the Coalbrookdale coalfield in Shropshire the D-zone contains a lava-flow of olivine-basalt, underlain and succeeded by limestone. This lava (Fig. 49) is of approximately the same age as the basalts in Derbyshire. As noted above, the period of eruption which in South-West England commenced in Middle Devonian times locally persisted into the Carboniferous.

## REFERENCES

The British Regional Geologies covering the appropriate areas, particularly: Bristol and Gloucester District (1948); and South Wales (1948) for the South-Western Province. The Midland Valley of Scotland; and The Pennines and Adjacent Areas, for recent accounts of contrasting facies of the Lower Carboniferous.

For discussion of reef-knolls see:

Black, W. W. 'Diagnostic characters of the Lower Carboniferous knoll-reefs in the north of England,' *Trans. Leeds Geol. Assoc.*, **6** (1954), 262–297.

Caldwell, W. G. E., and Charlesworth, H. A. K. Viséan coral reefs in the Bricklieve Mountains of Ireland, *Proc. Geol. Assoc.*, **73** (1962), 359.

George, T. Neville. 'Lower Carboniferous Palaeogeography of the British Isles,' *Proc. Yorks. Geol. Soc.*, **31** (1958), 227.

George, T. Neville. 'Devonian and Carboniferous foundations of the Variscides in N.W. Europe' in *Some aspects of the Variscan foldbelt* (Manchester University Press, 1962).

Parkinson, D. 'Lower Carboniferous reefs of northern England,' *Bull. Amer. Assoc. Pet. Geologists*, **41** (1957), 511–537. This paper is fully illustrated by maps and sections and contains a most useful summary and discussion.

## CHAPTER XI

# THE CARBONIFEROUS (2): THE NAMURIAN

THE Millstone, or Moorstone, Grit as it was at one time named, is the second of the great lithological divisions of the Carboniferous System and corresponds, more or less, with the Namurian Series. Where best developed it comprises some 6000 feet of coarse grit, sandstone and shale. The series is best developed in eastern Lancashire and western Yorkshire, reaching its maximum thickness near Burnley, from which point it thins away in all directions. In its typical development it covers wide areas of open moorland dissected by steep-sided valleys, on the flanks of which the successive grits form prominent scarp features, with gentler grassy slopes marking the outcrops of intervening shales. From Yorkshire and Lancashire the formation extends into Derbyshire north of the Peak District and southwards into Staffs and Leicestershire. Beyond the Midland Barrier of Avonian times the Namurian occurs between the Lower Carboniferous and the Coal Measures of the South Wales and Bristol coalfields; while in the north it occupies the same position in the Midland Valley of Scotland.

*The Relation of the Namurian to Underlying Rocks*

In different localities the Namurian shows striking differences in its stratigraphical relationship to the underlying beds: in places it rests conformably upon them and the usual difficulty arises in fixing the most suitable base for the Series; elsewhere, however, the presence of an unconformity removes any doubt on that score.

The unconformable relationship claims our attention first, and is nowhere more convincingly displayed than along the north crop of the South Wales coalfield. The facts are shown diagrammatically in Fig. 54. It will be seen that in the north-east 'corner' of the coalfield the Namurian rests directly on rocks belonging to the K-zone of the Dinantian; but traced westwards, other zones appear in succession from beneath the Namurian cover, until a point is reached where all the zones are represented. Still farther west the Namurian once more oversteps the Dinantian zones on to Lower Old Red Sandstone and finally comes to rest on Lower Palaeozoics at the western end of the coalfield near Haverfordwest.

The sequence of events which has led to these relations is easily interpreted from the section: at the end of Viséan times the rocks were folded—those places where the Avonian strata are thinnest and least complete must be near anticlinal axes, while a synclinal axis must run through the central part of the outcrop where the beds are most complete. Before the deposition of the Namurian, the folded rocks were deeply denuded, the maximum loss of material being suffered, as usual, by the anticlinal areas.

A similar unconformable relationship occurs in South-West Ireland, Derbyshire and in the Dale country of Yorkshire where the grits transgress across the Yoredalian, while higher grits overlap lower ones towards the north. In the Craven Lowlands south-west

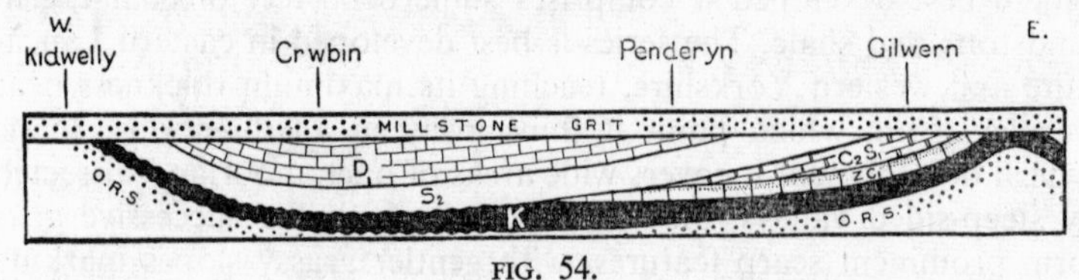


FIG. 54.

Diagram-section across part of the South Wales coalfield showing relations between Millstone Grit and Avonian rocks and the Mid-Dinantian unconformity. (*Based on the work of T. N. George.*)

of the stable block, however, there is a passage from Viséan to Namurian: the unconformity noted elsewhere is bridged, and it proves difficult to draw a line between the two series. This is also the case in Scotland, the Bristol district and North Wales. Originally the Millstone Grit included the beds between the Rough Rock at the top, and the Kinderscout Grit at the base (see Fig. 56); but later it was found that other grits of similar lithological character occur at much lower levels, in close association with black shales lying above the typical Carboniferous Limestone, as already noted. The obvious thing to do is to draw the line at the base of the lowest grit showing the Millstone Grit type of lithology, and to apply the same principle to the upper limit of the formation. It is not quite as easy as this, however, for the Millstone Grit is a diachronous formation, and in some areas is of the same age as the highest part of the Viséan, while elsewhere it is Ammanian in part. In these circumstances a base must be chosen on palaeontological evidence.

The typical Namurian fauna includes many thin-shelled lamellibranchs, such as *Posidonia* (formerly *Posidonomya*) *becheri*, and many goniatites (Fig. 55). In the hands of those who have closely studied them, these latter shells are proving of great value. Originally a sequence of goniatite zones was defined by Bisat, each bearing a generic name: these were 'genus zones', and each was divided where necessary into sub-zones, carrying the names of species and termed

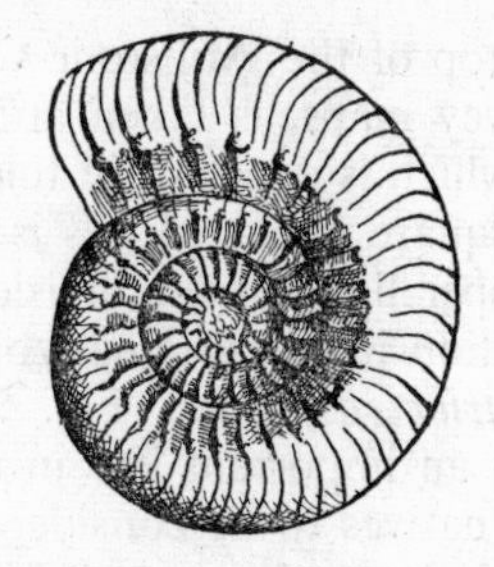


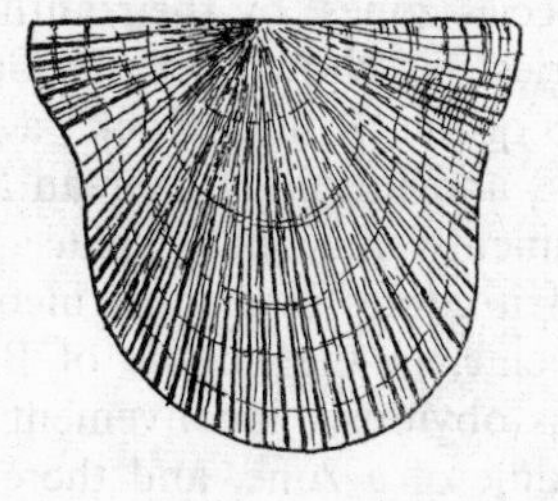

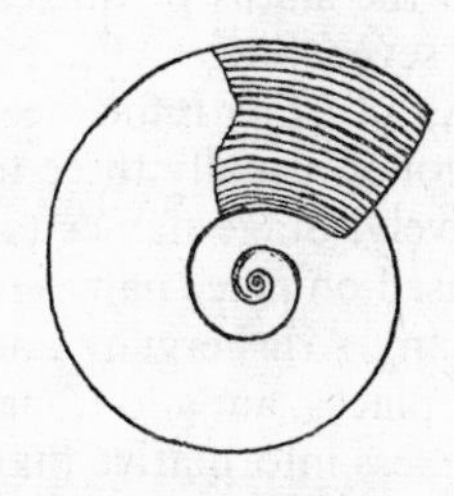


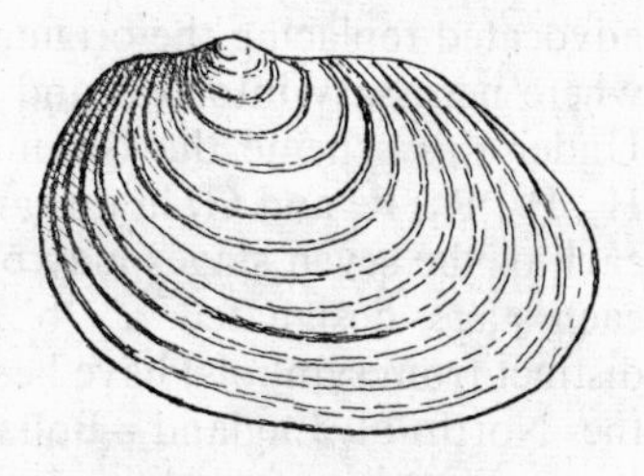

FIG. 55. Goniatites and other marine fossils from the Carboniferous. The goniatites shown are the index fossils of Bisat's genus zones, G, R, H and E and P. *Posidonia becheri* and *G. crenistria*, P-zone.
(*Reticuloceras* after D. A. Wray.)

'species zones' by their author. Now the top of the 'Millstone Grit Series', as shown on the Geological Survey maps, is taken at the top of the 'Rough Rock', a massive grit which is constant in thickness and lithology over an area of 4000 square miles, so this is an eminently reasonable place to put the upper limit of the division; but it comes in a most inconvenient position in the original zonal scheme, in the middle of Bisat's G (*Gastrioceras*) Zone (Fig. 56). It is obviously inconvenient to draw such an important line in the middle of a zone, and there are two alternatives to be considered: the upper limit of the 'Millstone Grit Series' may be moved up to the top, or down to the base of the G-zone. The former course would result in including in the 'Millstone Grit Series' a considerable thickness of typical Coal Measures; while the latter course would place in the Coal Measures Series the most typical of the Millstone Grits. It is indeed a choice of two evils. The fact is, 'Millstone Grit Series' cannot be made to fit into this zonal scheme. There is, however, a real place in stratigraphical nomenclature for 'Millstone Grit' as the name of a distinctive lithological unit; but it cannot give its name to a chapter of geological history: a second name is absolutely essential. The **Namurian Series,** is independent of lithology and bounded by time-planes. Hudson and Stubblefield (1945) advocated replacing the original genus zones of Bisat, splitting them where necessary into two and raising them to the status of Stages. Under this scheme the Namurian comprises seven Stages, $E_1$, $E_2$, $H_1$, $H_2$, $R_1$, $R_2$ and $G_1$ in upward succession. As a further refinement each of the seven stages may be divided into zones, usually three to each stage, designated 'a', 'b' and 'c' respectively. Stage names (as distinct from symbols) have been suggested, based on place names in the North of England—Bollandian, Pendleian, Arnsbergian and Kinderscoutian, for example; but their use places an additional strain on the memory, and in any case they are less informative than symbols. The reader knows precisely the position, in the Namurian time-scale, of say, $E_2$c. It is not necessary to have two parallel schemes of nomenclature, and confusion may well arise between 'Kinderscout Grit' and 'Kinderscoutian': the two do not cover the same time-interval.

Recently mid-Carboniferous goniatites have been discovered in strata formerly regarded as belonging to the Lower Carboniferous, and these rock-groups have therefore been placed in the Namurian. Certainly in lithology and conditions of formation the affinities of these beds are with the Carboniferous Limestone rather than Millstone Grit. Only the lowest of the three groups in the Scottish 'Carboniferous Limestone Series' has been retained in the Viséan: the rest have been promoted to the Namurian. Similarly the Lower

Carboniferous of Northumberland has lost its upper member (the Upper Limestone Group) to the Namurian, while the Middle and Lower Groups remain in the Lower Carboniferous. Stratigraphy and palaeontology are at variance here: it must be confessed that these recent discoveries have complicated the issue, particularly in relation to the facies of the Namurian.

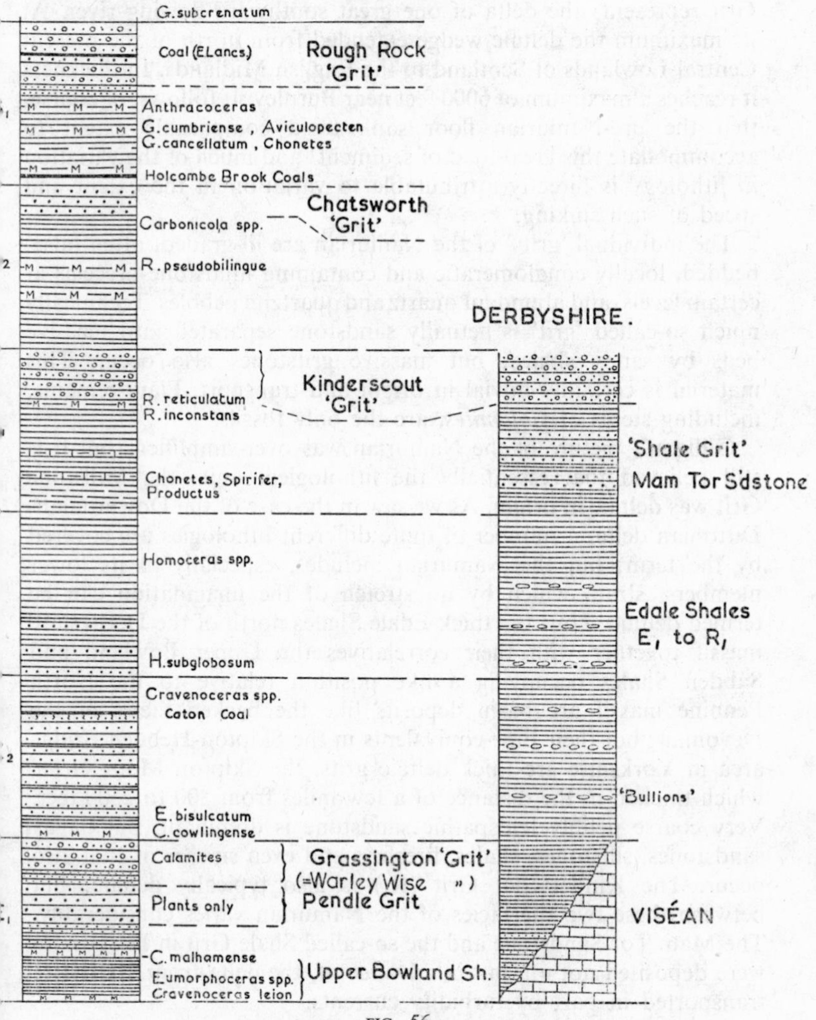


FIG. 56.

Diagram showing the Namurian succession in north-western England and in Derbyshire (Edale–Castleton area).
(*Based on data from F. W. Cope and F. M. Trotter.*)

*The Facies of the Namurian*

The leading idea that the typical Namurian is **deltaic** in facies dates from studies of its lithology, the type and direction of current bedding, and the nature and presumed sources of the materials of which it is made. Professor A. Gilligan claimed that the Millstone Grit represents the delta of one great southward-flowing river. At its maximum the deltaic wedge extended from north of the present Central Lowlands of Scotland to the English Midlands. In thickness it reaches a maximum of 6000 feet near Burnley. It follows, of course, that the pre-Namurian floor sank to a comparable extent to accommodate this great load of sediment: and much of the variation in lithology is directly attributable to variation in the extent and speed of such sinking.

The individual 'grits' of the Namurian are ill-graded, often false-bedded, locally conglomeratic and containing mudstone-breccias at certain levels, and abundant quartz and quartzite pebbles. Technically much so-called 'grit' is actually sandstone separated into massive beds by sandy shales; but massive gritstones also occur. This material is certainly fluvial in origin and transport. Plant-remains, including stems of *Calamites*, are the only fossils.

Gilligan's picture of the Namurian was over-simplified; but it is still believed that essentially the lithological unit—the Millstone Grit was deltaic in origin. As we saw in the case of the Downtonian-Dittonian delta, a number of quite different lithologies are covered by the term; but the Namurian includes, especially in its lower members, strata which by no stretch of the imagination can be termed deltaic. Thus the thick Edale Shales north of the Derbyshire massif together with their correlatives the Upper Bowland and Sabden Shales occupying a like position relative to the North Pennine massif are basin deposits like the becken facies of the Devonian; but their time-equivalents in the Skipton-Hebden Bridge area in Yorkshire are thick deltaic grits, the Skipton Moor Grits, which thicken in the distance of a few miles from 300 to 2500 feet. Very coarse pebbly feldspathic sandstone is dominant, but flaggy sandstones, siltstones, shales, fireclays and even smears of coal also occur. The Kinderscout Grit ($R_1$) is also typically deltaic; but between these two the facies of the Namurian varies considerably. The Mam Tor Sandstone and the so-called Shale Grit in Derbyshire were deposited not on, but in advance of, the delta-front, and were transported in part by turbidity currents.

The main sources of supply of the Namurian sediment lay to the north; but St George's Land must also have contributed: a southerly derivation has been proved by palaeocurrent data in the case of some of the grits, e.g. the Ashover and Belper Grits in Derbyshire. The individual Grits are separated in vertical sequence by shales, some of which are demonstrably marine, but others are described as non-marine, largely on negative evidence. The more important marine horizons are dated by the goniatites they contain and serve to delimit the several Namurian stages. They are most valuable marker horizons. Thus the *E. bisulcatum* Band near the base of $E_2$ occurs *in* the Edale Shales, but *on* the Skipton Moor Grit and Grassington Grit which spreads across the North Pennines massif. Two others delimit the H-Stages: *H. beyrichianum* below and *H. eostriolatum* above. The *R. gracile* Band separates $R_1$ from $R_2$; and the *G. cancellatum* Band separates the latter from $G_1$. Although theoretically these marine horizons must be diachronous to some extent, for practical purposes they are regarded as indicating time planes.

In addition, minor marine horizons occur of varying degrees of importance, depending on their fossil contents. In some only spines and scales of fishes occur; in others only *Lingula* is found; but often the latter is accompanied by a variety of brachiopods, thin-shelled lamellibranchs including *Posidonia* and *Dunbarella* as well as gasteropods. The association of goniatites with these other fossils raises the status and greatly increases the value of the marine horizons in which they occur.

In the shales the goniatites are usually crushed flat; but they are found uncrushed in occasional bands of argillaceous limestone or in layers of nodules termed 'bullions'. In places this **marine-shale facies** is dominant, as in the Craven Lowlands, Derbyshire, North Wales and southern Ireland. In the Craven area the Bowland Shales and the Sabden Shales at a higher stratigraphical level are important; while in the Peak District in Derbyshire the Edale Shales, up to 900 feet in thickness rest unconformably on Viséan of massif facies, and in due course are succeeded by the lowest of the local Millstone Grits—the Kinderscout ($R_1$) Grit. The Edale Shales contain goniatites characteristic of the E, H and $R_1$ Stages, and therefore include the lateral equivalents of the E, H and $R_1$ Millstone Grits of other localities (Fig. 56).

Intermediate in type between the two facies described above is the **grit-shale** facies into which the marine-shale facies grades laterally. These interbedded thinner grits or sandstones and shales occupy a zone marginal to the delta-fronts.

Unfortunately one of the grits in $R_1$ occurring near Todmorden is known as the 'Shale Grit', apparently on the grounds that it is finer grained than typical millstone grit.

Namurian facies including calcareous rocks are more variable. The

Namurian in Cumberland contains thick, shallow-water, marine limestones associated with calcite-mudstones and calcareous shales carrying a coral-brachiopod fauna. The environment was obviously a clear, shallow, warm shelf-sea, and the facies, **calcareous marine.**

Limestones are present, but less dominant, in those parts of the Namurian that are of **Yoredale facies.** This has been described above, as strata of Yoredale facies range in age from Viséan to Namurian. Two sub-facies may be recognized according to whether the calcareous or the arenaceous member of the cycle is dominant: they may be distinguished as the 'calcareous Yoredalian' and 'arenaceous Yoredalian' facies respectively. Both Lower and Upper Limestone Groups of the Viséan—Namurian succession in Southern Scotland and the Middle Limestone Group of the Northumbrian succession are of calcareous Yoredale facies; while the Upper Limestone Group of the northern Pennines and Northumberland belongs to the arenaceous Yoredale sub-facies. It is not difficult to find a reason for the difference between the two.

The final variant is that which contains coal as an important member of the succession. Thin carbonaceous films—they can scarcely be called coal-seams—occur at intervals throughout the Namurian Series, and in all the facies except the marine shale and the shelf-sea limestone facies. At rare intervals, and in the right environment, actual seams with seat-earths of fireclay or ganister were formed in $E_1$, $E_2$, $R_2$ and $G_1$ times: those in $G_1$ include the Holcombe Brook coals and a workable coal in the Rough Rock Grit in Lancs.; while $R_2$ contains several prominent coal-seams. Indeed the $R_2$ and the $G_1$ Stages are essentially coal measures in their lithology, and the latter group would undoubtedly be included in the Coal Measures were it not for the evidence of age afforded by the goniatites. North of the typical Millstone Grit country the Upper Limestone Group, essentially of arenaceous Yoredale facies includes the important Lickar Coals which have been worked over a long period.

A much more important development of coal measures occurs in the Midland Valley of Scotland and in its continuation south-westwards into Co. Antrim. In the former area the middle of the three groups into which the 'Carboniferous Limestone Series' is divided, formerly termed the Edge Coal Group, but latterly the Limestone-Coal Group, contains some of the most important coal seams in Scotland, in the East Lothian Coalfield lying east of the Pentland Anticline. In the corresponding Ballycastle Coalfield in the extreme north of Co. Antrim, the succession is closely similar. All three groups (Lower Limestone, Limestone-Coal and Upper Limestone) are exposed in coastal sections, though inland the rest of the

Carboniferous tract is occupied by the Calciferous Sandstone Series. The division between the Lower Limestone Group and the Limestone-Coal Group is conveniently drawn at the base of the Main Coal, some 4 feet thick; while a marine band 120 feet higher in the succession is correlated with the Index Limestone, of $E_2$ age, in Scotland (see Fig. 53). Coal is not the only material of economic value occurring in these strata: clay-ironstones and self-calcining ironstones—the raw material of the great iron industry which flourished in East Lothian during the eighteenth century—also occur.

Thus in the Midland Valley in Scotland and in Antrim the special environment of the delta-swamp forest that is characteristic of

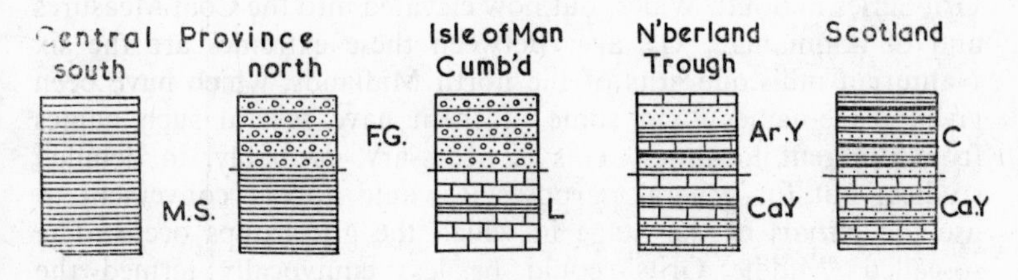


FIG. 57.

Diagram illustrating facies variations in the Namurian Stage, $E_1$.

M.S. Marine shale facies: Bowland (Lancs.), Holywell (N. Wales), Edale (Derbyshire) and Churlet (Staffs.) Shales.
F.G. Fluvial grit facies, e.g. the $R_1$ (Kinderscout) Grit and the $E_1$ (Warley Wise or Grassington) Grit.
L. Limestone facies.
Ca. Y. Calcareous Yoredalian.
Ar. Y. Arenaceous Yoredalian.
C. Coal-rich facies—the Edge (or Limestone-) Coal Group of Midland Valley of Scotland.

Westphalian times and of the typical Coal Measures were anticipated for a time, in the early Namurian. The Limestone-Coal Group is of $E_1$ age, and is therefore the age-equivalent of the Grassington ($E_1$) Grit and of part of the Edale Shales.

Thus we have proved, with the aid of the goniatites, the contemporaniety of several of the Namurian facies (Fig. 57). If the distribution of the several facies were completely known, it would be possible to make an accurate palaeogeographic reconstruction, but such is not attempted here. The general picture is, however, clear, with the central feature an extensive delta occupying the North Midlands in England and built of fluvial detritus derived from northerly or north-easterly sources. It extended westwards into a shelf-sea, deepening towards the west, on the floor of which marine shale was accumulating.

A vertical section through the Namurian displays a crudely cyclic alternation of facies reflecting differences in geographical environment, and obviously involving relative changes in the levels of sea and land; but which of them actually moved is an open question. It has been the custom to invoke movements of uplift and depression of the land areas as the ultimate cause of such cyclic variations; but it is difficult to find an adequate cause for such 'jack-in-the-box' earth-movements, and the modern tendency is to regard eustatic changes of sea level as the more likely control.

On lithological grounds the Fell Sandstone of Viséan age is the first of the 'millstone grits': it has already been dealt with. The last of them, though not identical in mode of origin, is the Farewell Rock, formerly included as the most typical part of the Millstone Grit Series in South Wales, but now elevated into the Coal Measures and of Ammanian, $G_2$, age. Between these extremes are the six Namurian millstone grits of the north Midlands, which have been given place-names—and some of them have several such names from different localities. This is necessary, probably, in detailed studies; but for general purposes it would appear convenient to use the initials of the Stage in which the grit-groups occur. The so-called 'Middle Grits' could be less equivocally termed the $R_2$-Grits: they are the fifth in a succession of six grit groups.

In the account given above we have concentrated on what may be regarded as the typical Millstone Grit country which embraces the English counties of Lancashire, Yorkshire and Derbyshire; but we have also had to go outside the boundaries of this area, into Cumberland, Northumberland and southern Scotland. The remaining areas where Namurian strata occur are North Wales, South Wales, the Bristol Coalfield and Devonshire; but before considering these in detail it is necessary to give further consideration to the Scottish Namurian.

As we have shown, this includes the Edge Coal Group overlain by the Upper Limestone Group, in which, in spite of its name, marine limestones are very subordinate to sandstones and shales. In a country in which limestones are neither common nor thick, each of the Carboniferous limestones is well known by name to Scottish geologists, and they have been very accurately mapped. Above the Upper Limestone Group occurs an essentially arenaceous formation, named from the type-section, the Roslin Glen east of the Pentland Hills. This **Roslin Sandstone** is succeeded by Ammanian Coal Measures, and is therefore stratigraphically analogous to the English Millstone Grit, from which it differs greatly, however, in certain respects. It consists of red and yellow sandstones with subordinate shales, conglomerates, fireclays and thin coals, in all some 500 feet thick. Westwards from the type-area the Roslin Sandstone thickens to a maximum of nearly a thousand feet near Falkirk; but thins away to almost nothing in the Glasgow district. Over much of the western parts of the Midland Valley of Scotland the Namurian is represented by basaltic lavas erupted under subaerial conditions. The lavas are associated with, and locally represented by bauxite clays, notably in Ayrshire.

It has long been known that plant- and fish-remains recovered from the basal beds of the formation are markedly different from those occurring at the top. The suggestion of a break thus indicated *within* the Roslin Sandstone is supported by the evidence of the goniatites, though it is very meagre, and of a negative, rather than positive, nature. Shale-bands low down in the Roslin Sandstone have yielded a goniatite fauna indicating a horizon high in the E-Zone or low in the H-Zone; but apart from this, no representatives of the H-, R- and $G_1$-Zones have yet been discovered. Definitely Ammanian forms of goniatites occur in the highest part of the Sandstone, which is thus Ammanian in age, though not in lithology. Further, in places the E-Zone has been proved closely to underlie the *Communis*-Zone in the Ammanian; this is *not* the basal zone, but the one immediately above (Fig. 61). Therefore there must be an unlocated unconformity cutting out not only the equivalents of the greater part of the English Millstone Grit, but also the lowest part of the overlying Coal Measures.

In **Northumberland** also a few hundred feet of 'Millstone Grit' lie between the Upper Limestone Group (of $E_2$ age) and the *Communis*-Zone of the Coal Measures. The precise age of the beds is unknown; but they certainly bear a much closer resemblance to the Scottish Roslin Sandstone than to the English Millstone Grit of the southern Pennines.

The Namurian originally covered much of **Ireland**; but subsequent denudation has destroyed much of it. It has survived around the margins of the coalfields and in a broad trough extending from beyond the coast of Co. Clare and roughly following the estuary of the Shannon to about the latitude of Dublin, whence it must have crossed the site of the present Irish Sea to link up with the main English outcrops north of St George's Land. As we have already seen, the so-called Carboniferous Limestone Series of Scotland, two-thirds of which is Namurian, crosses into northern Ireland and is of importance in the Ballycastle Coalfield which includes workable Namurian coals.

In the Clare trough Viséan limestones are succeeded by the black **Clare Shales,** varying in thickness from 40 to 1600 feet. The Viséan shelf limestones, of $D_2$(P) age, were folded and denuded prior to the deposition of the Clare Shales which are closely similar to the Edale Shales of Derbyshire. They are thickest in the axial portion of the trough but thin towards its margins, through basal overlap. The formation includes a full succession of goniatite zones and these have allowed it to be shown that the base climbs steadily from $E_1$a at the centre to $R_1$a at the margins. Evidently the trough deepened through much of the Namurian and indeed affected strata younger than the Clare Shales. One important result of the sinking was instability of the marginal parts of the trough, with consequent slumping on an extensive scale. In the fine coastal sections in Co. Clare it can be seen that slumping occurred on at least twenty occasions. Some of the slumps are sheets, but others are channel-like, with sheared margins. The usual slump structures are well displayed, the most impressive being overfolds 'resembling alpine structures'. The slumped material moved inwards towards the axis of the trough, which is Caledonoid in trend: i.e. the movement was to the south-east in Co. Clare but to the north-west in Co. Tipperary.

On the upper surfaces of most of the slump-sheets sand-volcanoes were developed on a scale which, for this country, is unique. The volcanoes resemble basaltic domes in form, but on a miniature scale: they vary from one to three feet in diameter, though some may measure as much as 50 feet across. The material erupted from the craters was water-charged sand, of relatively low density, imprisoned beneath a newly moved slump-sheet of denser material.

Apart from these physical phenomena the Clare Shales are noteworthy as including at the base, a few feet of commercially valuable phosphorite; and at a higher level ($E_2$b), up to 10 feet of pure sponge-spicule chert. Reference has been made above to the goniatites in these beds; but they are not the only fossils. As in analogous formations in England, the familiar thin-shelled lamellibranchs such as *Posidoniella* and occasional trilobites also occur.

Namurian strata occur in **North Wales** along the margin of the Flint-Denbighshire Coalfield, and are noteworthy on account of a striking change in lithological facies when traced from south to north. In the south the beds are of Millstone Grit type; they lie above the well-known and magnificently exposed Carboniferous Limestone forming the Eglwyseg[1] Escarpment near Llangollen, and dip under the Coal Measures in the neighbourhood of Ruabon.

Passage beds link the Avonian with the overlying Namurian in

[1] Pronounced Eggloo-us-egg.

the sense that the highest parts of the Avonian are arenaceous limestones which grade up into calcareous sandstones and gritstones of the Namurian. Similarly at the top of the latter Millstone Grit lithology grades into Coal Measure lithology. Therefore it appears that sedimentation was continuous and of much the same type from late-Avonian, through Namurian into Ammanian times. Traced northwards along the strike, however, the massive sandstones and gritstones give place gradually to a facies of black shale with thin limestones resembling the marine-shale facies of the Peak District and Bowland Forest in north-western England. These are the **Holywell Shales**—Edale Shales under another name—and they have yielded goniatites of all the Namurian stages. Now this area lay to the north of St George's Land to which reference has been made above (p. 204). Surely the changes just noted must indicate derivation from St George's Land: the Namurian must here be marginal, shallow-water, marine, and the Holywell Shale facies deeper water marine, presumably linking up with the basinal Bowland and Sabden Shales in Lancashire.

We now pass beyond the Midland Barrier, on the higher parts of which no Namurian occurs, to the South-West Province where it again becomes important.

In the **South Wales Coalfield** area, as shown above, the Namurian rests unconformably upon Lower Carboniferous, and locally on Old Red Sandstone. Before the Namurian was defined the Millstone Grit of this area was divided into three distinctive units:

3. The 'Farewell Rock', chiefly sandstones and quartzites.
2. Shale Group, chiefly shales, but associated with some sandstones and grits.
1. Basal Grit Group, a variable series, essentially arenaceous and coarse-grained below, but becoming progressively more shaly upwards and grading into the Shale Group.

By the irony of circumstances the 'Farewell Rock' group, so named as it meant farewell to valuable coals when these rocks were encountered in mining operations, has recently been transferred to the Ammanian Coal Measures, on the evidence of the discovery within the group of the *G. subcrenatum* Band, which defines the base of the Ammanian.

These lithological groups are most easily distinguished in the north-east, but towards the south-west this becomes more difficult as the arenaceous beds pass laterally into shales. At the same time the whole formation becomes much thicker and more complete, as lower zones come in towards the south-west. In other words, with the post-Viséan uplift, accompanied by folding and denudation, the sea withdrew to the southward. Sedimentation was almost continuous in the south-west, all Namurian Stages being represented; then sedimentation slowly crept north-eastwards across the outcrops of successively lower Dinantian zones, so that the gap increases until in the extreme north-east of the coalfield the highest Namurian beds rest on the oldest Dinantian. This northward advance, due to slow sinking of the Midland Barrier continued into Ammanian times. Much of the Namurian in South Wales would constitute a Coal Measures facies were the proportions of the several rock-types a little different. At intervals thin coals, usually not much more than carbonaceous laminae, occur, and are succeeded by dark shales grading upward into quartz silt, sandstone and sometimes quartz conglomerate. Another coal seam rests upon its upper surface. In essence this is the Coal Measure rhythm. In the Basal Grit Group and Shale Group at least ten marine bands occur, so that periodically the coastal flats were inundated by the sea; but each subsidence was counterbalanced by sedimentation, the material being derived from the Midland Barrier and St George's Land. Once again there was no actual connection between the Namurian of the type English area and these South Wales equivalents, though they are closely linked by lithology and conditions of accumulation.

In the not far distant **Bristol coalfield** area the relationships noted in the Namurian of the southern part of the North Wales coalfield recur. That is, a massive sandstone formation which yields one of the best-known Bristol building-stones is sandwiched between Carboniferous Limestone and Coal Measures. The lower part grades down into the highest Viséan, while Westphalian plants occur in the upper part which grades upward into the Coal Measures. Palaeontological proof of the age of most of the Namurian is meagre: goniatites are practically unknown here; but from a recent boring plant-remains and a poor fauna demonstrate the age of the fossiliferous level as E-Stage. As the beds are coarse-grained and as the succession is apparently unbroken, it is difficult to see why the thickness should be so small—some 600 feet in all. Evidently there is a matter here that well merits examination.

In the most easterly of the Southern Group of coalfields—the concealed **Kent Coalfield**—no Namurian is known to occur. Rocks of Namurian age occur also in **Devonshire.** They are usually regarded as forming part of the so-called Culm, and as a matter of convenience are described in the next chapter (p. 267).

## REFERENCES

The appropriate Regional Geologies, especially the most recent edition of *The Pennines and Adjacent Areas.*

GILL, W. D., and KEUNEN, P. H. 'Sand volcanoes on slump-sheets in the Carboniferous of Co. Clare, Ireland,' *Q.J.G.S.*, **113** (1957), 441.

HODSON, F., and LEWARNE, G. C. 'A mid-Carboniferous (Namurian) basin in . . . Limerick and Clare, Ireland,' *Q.J.G.S.*, **117** (1961), 307.

HUDSON, R. G. S. 'The Goniatite Zones of the Namurian,' *Geol. Mag.*, **82** (1945).

NEVES, R. 'Namurian plant spores from the southern Pennines, England,' *Palaeontology*, **4** (1961), 247.

READING, H. G. '. . . Factors affecting sedimentation of the Millstone Grit (Namurian) in the Central Pennines,' *Developments in Sedimentology*, **1** (1964), 340.

TROTTER, F. M. 'Sedimentation of the Namurian of North-West England and adjacent areas,' *Liv. and Manch. Geol. Journ.*, **1** (1951), 77.

CHAPTER XII

# THE CARBONIFEROUS (3): 'WESTPHALIAN'–STEPHANIAN

It is not as fully realized as it should be, that the former industrial pre-eminence of this country was based on a concatenation of circumstances dating from the 'Westphalian' Period: the simultaneous existence of vast coastal swamps, of appropriate climatic conditions to allow a luxuriant growth of vegetation, of an abundance of the right types of plants adapted for living in such environments, of the right degree of crustal instability to ensure the deep burial of the peats, after bacterial decay had proceeded just far enough to render these the most valuable potential coals in the world.

Coal as a source of power is being rapidly superseded by oil, while atomic power threatens both in the near future; but the successful exploitation of coal and its byproducts is still an important factor in the industrial development of this country. This involves the accurate interpretation of coalfield structures and a detailed knowledge of the successions within the coalfields. Coal has been wrought in some of the English coalfields since Elizabethan times, and intensively since the Industrial Revolution. In the course of mining operations, a vast amount of detailed information has been collected, and for no other part of the stratigraphical column is there such a wealth of data available for study, and in no other areas are the underground structures so fully known.

'Coal Measures', like Carboniferous Limestone' and 'Millstone Grit' is a descriptive lithological term applied to a distinctive facies of the Carboniferous. It has no time significance and must not be used in a time sense. Coal-bearing strata (which is what 'Coal Measures' means) are of different ages in different parts of the world: even in Britain it is just as appropriate to apply the term to parts of the Namurian (and even of the Dinantian) as to Upper Carboniferous rocks in the mining areas of the English Midlands. Until recently it was customary to group the latter (and their time-equivalents elsewhere) as Westphalian; but as the latter term has been used in several senses it has been thought advisable to employ two names, Ammanian and Morganian, defined originally in the South Wales Coalfield, in its place (Fig. 62). The youngest post-Morganian Carboniferous rocks form the Stephanian Stage. The strata between the top of the Namurian and the base of the Permian are thus divided into three stages of equal status: the Ammanian, Morganian and Stephanian. A single, 'omnibus' series name is badly needed to cover these strata, comparable in significance with 'Namurian' and 'Dinantian'. The best that can be done at present is to call them 'Coal Measures', which, in parts of the country and for parts of the succession, is a misnomer. Further, were it not for the archaic custom of lumping together middle and upper divisions as Upper Carboniferous, they could rightly be called 'Upper Carboniferous'.

The Coal Measures are a series of varied sedimentary rocks attaining to a local thickness of 8000 to 10,000 feet and comprising sandstones, shales, mudstones, fire-clays, ganisters and coal seams, the latter varying from a few inches to several feet in thickness. In the aggregate the total thickness of the coal seams in any coalfield is only a small fraction, generally 2 or 3 per cent., of the total thickness of the coal measures in that field. These rock-types, as shown above, all occur in the Namurian and even in the Lower Carboniferous of North England and Scotland. The only difference is that in Ammanian times coal measure conditions became very much more generally established than at any former period.

The essential condition for the formation of a coal seam is a luxurious growth of vegetation, which subsequently suffers deep burial under accumulations of sediment. The Namurian Period was the essential prelude to the Ammanian; for the great quantities of coarse river-borne detritus, spread out as deltas on the fringe of the northern continent, built up extensive sandy and muddy flats on which the swamp-forests were established. Examination of the plant-remains in these rocks has shed much light on their habitats: many of them give clear evidence of adaptation to a watery, or swamp, habitat, and it appears that they grew immersed in a few inches of water, like the mangrove of existing tropical marginal swamps. Immediately beneath each coal seam occurs a 'seat-earth', representing the soil in which the trees were rooted, a fact that is clearly established by the many fossil roots and rootlets (*Stigmaria*) found in them. Many of these 'seat-earths' are valuable fire-clays, so called because they may be made into bricks capable of withstanding very high temperatures, which makes them suitable for lining furnaces. The coal seam is normally overlain by a 'roof' of shale, in which the shells of lamellibranchs are frequently abundant: these are the 'mussel bands' of the miners. Above some coal seams marine beds occur, proving that a relative rise of sea-level submerged the swamp-forests, bringing the period of peat formation to an end. Above the marine shales, mudstones and thick sandstones normally occur, succeeded by fire-clay once more, and this in turn is followed by a second seam of coal, and the cycle has been completed. This rhythmic unit is repeated scores of times in the Coal Measures. It appears, however, that sinking of the marginal swamps was accompanied by *uplift* of the inland areas, from which considerable thicknesses of relatively coarse detritus were shot out over the former marshes as deltas, gradually extending themselves seawards. As the upland areas were denuded, sand gave place to clay—sandstone is succeeded by mudstone and finally by fire-clay—and by this time the sunken marginal areas had once more been silted up to sea-level, approximately, and the swamp-forests again became established.

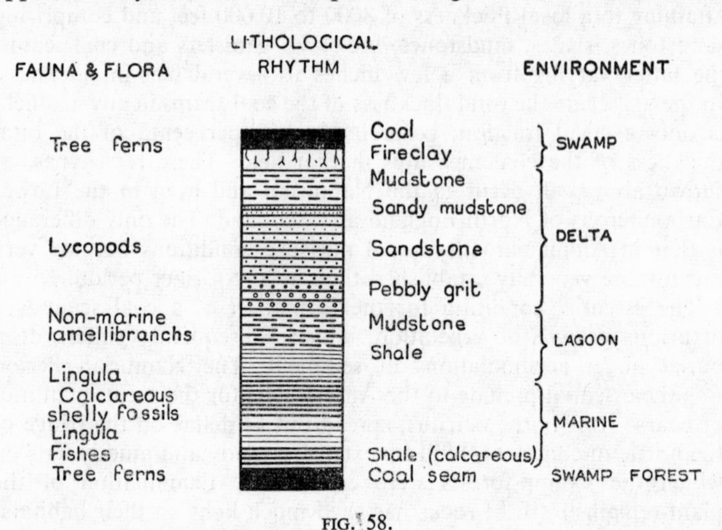


FIG. 58.

Diagram showing the rhythmic unit (cyclothem) of the Coal Measures.

Each of these episodes is thus a complete cycle of sedimentation, and the Coal Measures provide us with one of the very best illustrations of a rhythm in sedimentation. The unit of the Coal Measure rhythm is shown in diagram form in Fig. 58. The impression conveyed by this regular repetition of events is that the crust was maintained in a condition of delicate balance: depression of the sea-floor was rapidly neutralized by silting-up while the complementary movements of uplift inland were counterbalanced by rapid denudation and the transference of vast loads of sediment from the uplifted to the depressed areas. Such maintaining of the *status quo* is referred to as 'isostatic readjustment', and there is perhaps no better illustration of the manner in which **isostasy** effects a balance than this.

The cyclic repetition of events has left its impress upon the fossil contents of the rocks, and faunal and floral rhythms no less striking than the lithological one can be detected. The coals themselves, of course, consist of plant debris, and a sequence of types occurs even here, for each layer in a seam appears to consist of the remains of one genus of plant.

From the abundance of lycopods in the deltaic rocks it is obvious that these giant club mosses flourished on the delta-flats. The actual swamp forests consisted chiefly of giant club-mosses (*Lycopodiales*) including *Lepidodendron* and *Sigillaria*, horse-tails (*Equisitales*) for example, *Calamites* and *Annularia*, and tree-ferns (*Filicales*). The actual coal-seams consist largely of the remains of these plants. The marine shales which are, of course, waste in the coal industry, are locally rich in the remains of pteridosperms—plants which are strikingly like ferns in general appearance, but bear seeds, as the name implies. Well-known long-range forms are *Neuropteris* and *Alethopteris* (Fig. 59). From their occurrence in marine shales it is inferred that the pteridosperms clothed higher ground lying above the coal swamps, but were laid under contribution following the relative rise of sea-level consequent upon each marine phase.

The marine bands occurring above the coal seams in the coal measure cycle vary considerably in the fauna they contain. In some only fish scales and spines occur; in others only *Lingulae* are found; but normally these are accompanied by a variety of other fossils.

In the thicker marine bands the spines and scales of fishes occur in the basal bed; these highly mobile creatures were soon followed by horny-shelled brachiopods, the commonest being *Lingula* and *Orbiculoidea*, which in turn were followed by more highly organized calcareous shelled brachiopods including '*Productus*', accompanied by thin-shelled lamellibranchs (*Dunbarella*), goniatites (*Gastrioceras* and *Anthracoceras*), large crinoids and echinoids (sea-urchins). In the ideal case we can imagine these several groups of organisms retreating in the reverse order when the conditions began to change and the period of maximum submergence was passed. In any case it is a fact that *Lingula* was the last of the brachiopods to persist.

## CLASSIFICATION AND CORRELATION OF THE COAL MEASURES

It is ironical that in the one system in which accurate correlation is of vital importance to the community, the means of effecting it should be less satisfactory than in most other systems. This results directly from the conditions of formation of the Coal Measures. In the main they are not open-sea sediments, and they therefore do not contain the remains of free-swimming organisms, nor even the less satisfactory, but still usable brachiopods and corals which the palae-ontologist has turned to good use in the Lower Carboniferous. The coal swamps and lagoons proved congenial, however, to certain kinds of **non-marine lamellibranchs,** the shells of which are the most abundant animal remains in the rocks (Fig. 59). Frequently they are crowded together in thin shale beds, which are referred to by miners as 'mussel bands': in addition they occur more widely scattered throughout the Coal Measures, but in such numbers as to be inconspicuous. Although lamellibranchs are among the last fossils a palaeontologist would choose to use for zoning purposes, yet the vital necessity for accuracy in coalfield geology has forced him to make the best of a bad job, and use the material at his disposal. After other means had proved more or less unsatisfactory, attention has been turned to the non-marine lamellibranchs in recent years, and they have proved unexpectedly valuable. A series of lamelli-branch zones, first defined by Professor A. E. Trueman, in the South Wales coalfield has proved capable of application to the other British coalfields and, in general outline, to the Ruhr and the Donetz Basin. The identification of the zones is not easy; the lamelli-branchs belong to the genera *Carbonicola*, *Anthracosia*, *Anthra-conauta*, *Anthraconaia* (formerly named *Anthracomya*) and *Naiadites*, and many of the species range through considerable thicknesses of strata. It is the character of the complete assemblage of fossils, rather than the presence of one distinctive type, that determines the zone. Formerly, in attempting to identify horizons in the Coal Measures, the geologist had to use the accumulated local knowledge gathered in the course of mining operations in the field under investigation: correlation between one coalfield and another was practically impossible. Now, 'with the aid of a pair of callipers (for specific identification of the fossils), the geologist, from a statistical study of a few score lamellibranchs collected from a "mussel band", can fix accurately the zonal position of that band'. There is no need to stress the great importance of this development of the zonal method in the exploitation of the Coal Measures. In certain coalfields, e.g. Lancashire, sub-zones have been established which allow finer, more precise correlation. It remains to be seen how far these sub-zones may prove of more than local value.

Non-marine lamellibranchs are used (a) in the specific identi-fication of coal-seams within a restricted area, such as one coalfield; and (b) for correlating groups of strata over wider areas, i.e. in inter-coalfield correlation. In (a) attention is concentrated on the lamellibranch population occurring in the shales immediately over-lying a coal-seam. In (b) the technique is different: the complete population of the group of strata under consideration is studied with

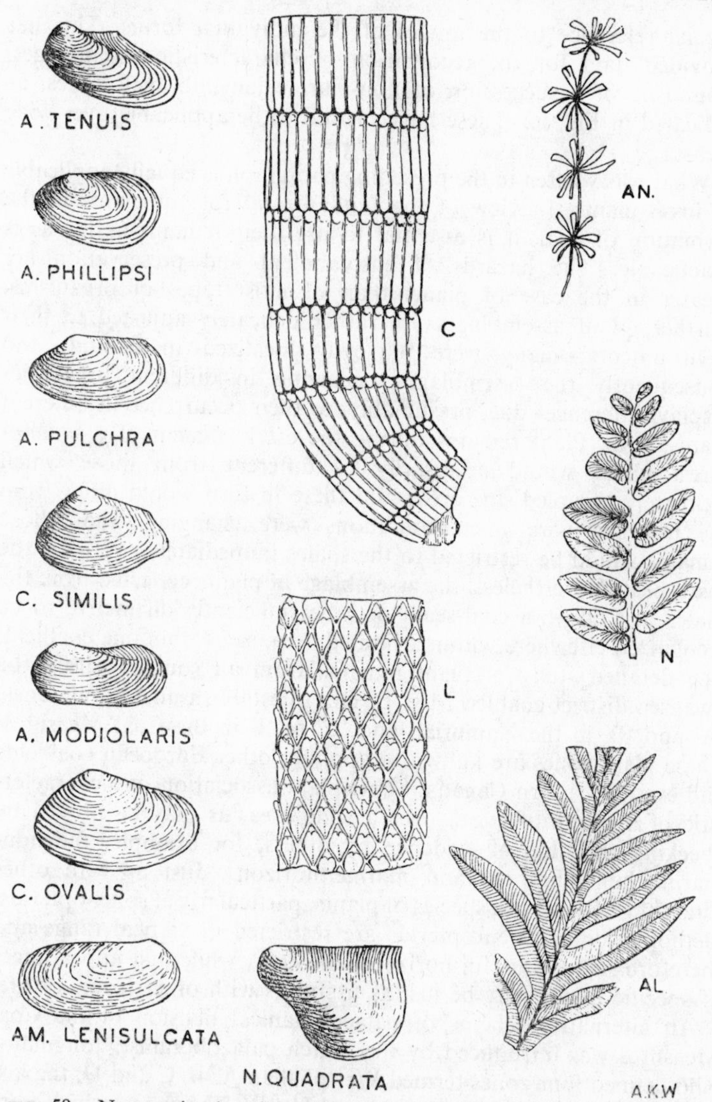


FIG. 59.—Non-marine lamellibranchs and plants from the Coal Measures.

AN. *Annularia sphenophylloides*. Radstockian, Radstock.
C. *Calamites*, a 'horse-tail'—a fragment.
L. *Lepidodendron*, a lycopod (giant club-moss).
N. *Neuropteris gigantea*, a Pteridosperm, Coalbrookdale.
AL. *Alethopteris*, a Pteridosperm, Radstock.

The lamellibranchs are the zonal forms (except *Naiadites*), in order. Recently *C. communis* has displaced *C. ovalis* as a zonal index: the *Ovalis* Zone is now the *Communis* Zone.

A. *Anthraconauta*. C. *Carbonicola*. A'm. *Anthracomya*, now renamed *Anthraconaia*.

special reference to the ranges of the individual forms. This has provided data for the recognition of characteristic assemblages, diagnostic of a succession of non-marine lamellibranch zones, as indicated in Fig. 62. These have proved to be applicable over wide areas.

What was written in the preceding paragraph is equally applicable to **fossil plants.** In view of the fundamental role of plants in the formation of coal, it is essential to use their remains as far as is practicable. The hazards of entombment and preservation are greater in the case of plants than of most types of organisms. Further, plant assemblages are rather delicately adjusted to their environments; many were narrowly localized in habitat, and consequently the assemblages occurring in different lithologies display differences due, presumably, to their occurrence in different plant zones. Plant remains during the establishment of a swamp-forest phase would necessarily be different from those which ultimately 'peopled' the area; and these in turn would differ from the last survivors when conditions were changing, and whose remains would be restricted to the shales immediately overlying the fossil peat. Nevertheless, the assemblage of plants collected from the shales just above a coal-seam may be sufficiently distinctive to be recognized elsewhere within a limited area, say within one coalfield. The detailed study of plant remains from all sources within the Swansea district enabled Miss E. Dix to establish nine floral zones. 'A' and 'B' in the Namurian and 'C' to 'I' in the Coal Measures. These plant zones are known to apply to other European coalfields and even to eastern Canada. Some plant associations are characteristic of a group of strata over a wide area, as may be proved by checking this line of evidence by others, for example, the non-marine lamellibranchs and marine horizons. Just as with other kinds of fossils certain species of plants, particularly of sphenopterids, alethopterids and neuropterids are restricted in vertical range and therefore serve as useful horizon-indicators; while first appearances of specific plants may be just as useful as with other forms of life.

An alternative scheme of palaeobotanical division of the Coal Measures was introduced by the Dutch palaeobotanist, Jongmans, who defined four zones termed Westphalian A, B, C and D, the last two being subdivided into Lower and Upper. The zones, which were based on plant distributions in the coalfields of northern France, Belgium and Germany, would appear to be rather broader than those of Dix.

As long ago as 1934 A. Raistrick studied the **microspores** separated from coal-seams in Northumberland and Durham, and since then progress has been made on lines parallel to those developed in the use of fossil plants. Spores in some ways are more suitable for correlation than many parent plants, for they are not subject to the limitations imposed on the latter by their environments. Although they possess no means of propulsion, winds, currents and insects ensured wide distribution. They are found in a wide range of coal measure lithologies, though they are not all equally well preserved. It does not seem necessary to relate specific spores to their parent plants, although this has proved possible in a number of species. Indeed, it might well happen that the relatively durable spores might be the only parts of certain plants to survive the hazards of entombment; but this does not detract from the value of the spores in zoning problems.

A scheme of subdivision of the Namurian and 'Coal Measures' of the coalfields of the English Midlands was proposed in 1954 on the basis of spore-distributions in the coals themselves. Five spore-assemblages, designated S0, S1, S2, S3 and S4, were defined, with transitional zones between them. Of these, S0 is apparently coextensive with the Namurian; but recent studies have shown that if the marine and non-marine shales, as well as the coal-seams, are included more detailed subdivision is possible. It should be realized that zones defined by spore-assemblages are less precisely delimited than is the case with graptolite zones in the Lower Palaeozoic or ammonite zones in the Jurassic. The time ranges of selected spores show a characteristic 'drift' from lower to higher horizons. Nevertheless, it is claimed that 'it is now possible for spore-assemblages from random samples of coal or shale from the Namurian succession of the Central Province to be dated in relation to the sequence of goniatite zones' (R. Neves, 1961). This is the ultimate desideratum, of course. What has been done for the Namurian can be done for the 'Coal Measures'; the material and the principles involved are the same. Thus the study by specialists of spore-assemblages in the coal measures gives promise of coming up to the expectations of L. R. Moore who anticipated that 'the study of microspores may well provide the greatest possible range of evidence in correlation' (1958).

Another important factor in the problem of correlation of the Upper Carboniferous rocks is, as we have already seen for the Namurian, the occasional occurrence of **marine bands.** These are most frequent in the Ammanian, they diminish in number upwards, and finally are absent from the highest measures. In the marine bands the fossil assemblages often lack distinctiveness, and there has therefore been much uncertainty as to the equivalence of different bands in different coalfields. The additional evidence afforded by the non-marine lamellibranchs in the rocks immediately above and below the marine bands has removed this uncertainty, and it is becoming clear that some (at least) of these bands are singularly constant over wide areas. As this fact is established, the marine bands become increasingly valuable as index-horizons. At present they bear different names in different coalfields; but it is hoped that this defect in nomenclature will be remedied in the near future—there is no reason why the same band occurring in half a dozen coalfields should be burdened with six different names. For example, one of the most constant, the Cefn Coed[1] marine band characterized by the occurrence of the goniatite *Anthracoceras hindi* in South Wales, is the Gin Mine band in North Staffordshire, the Mansfield marine band in Yorkshire and Nottingham, and Skipsey's marine band in Scotland. It is also known under different local names in Lancashire, Cumberland, South Staffordshire, Warwickshire and Derbyshire, and it appears probable that it may be correlated with marine bands in France, Belgium, Holland and Westphalia. If this be so, it proves uniform conditions over much of North-West Europe at the time of its formation; and in any case, the proved correlation over the area of the British coalfields shows that sedimentation was effected in one great coal basin, and not in a number of smaller, isolated ones. The simultaneous submergence of North-Western Europe to a shallow depth suggests that it may have been caused by a uniform rise of sea-level (eustatic movement); but whether or not, it remains an extraordinary phenomenon. The Cwm Gorse[2] marine band is stratigraphically important, for it comprises 300 feet of strata in western South Wales, not exclusively marine, but seven district marine horizons (the higher ones containing *Anthracoceras cambriense*), are interbedded with strata containing non-marine lamellibranchs and drifted plant-remains.

Within recent years the position as regards inter-coalfield correlation has improved greatly. In 1961 ten marine bands were known in the coalfields bordering the Pennines and several of these have been identified in the South Wales Coalfield.

### DISTRIBUTION OF THE COAL MEASURES

As noted above, there is conclusive evidence that at least at intervals sedimentation was continuous over the whole area within which Coal Measures occur in Britain, and indeed at the time of the Cefn-Coed-Mansfield submergence, over the whole of that part of North-West Europe where they are found. During the formation of individual coal seams uniformity of physiographical conditions held over a

[1] Pronounced *Keven Koid.*
[2] Pronounced *Koomgorze.*

proved area of 1000 square miles in South Wales, probably over a much wider one in Lancashire, Yorkshire and Nottinghamshire, while in North America named seams are worked over areas of 6000 to 8000 square miles. It is probable that, in view of the extent of some of the marine bands, these are minimum figures, limited by the inherent difficulties of long-range correlation. When we consider the distribution of these Coal Measures as a whole, we are presented with the picture of a continuous wide zone, stretching west to east from Britain, through France, Belgium, Westphalia and Silesia to the Donetz Basin in Russia. This zone constituted a physiographic entity lying south of the northern continent represented to-day by relics in the Scottish Highlands and the tip of Northern Ireland. Southwards it was bounded by the Sudetian-Variscan mountain arcs whose overthrust northern margin just impinges upon our southern coasts in Cornwall and Devon. Eastwards lay the open sea, for the 'Westphalian' is marine in Central Russia: and deeper water lay to the westward, too, judging from the evidence presented by the Cwm Gorse marine band in Wales, though here we are on less certain grounds as the boundaries of the coal measure belt pass east to west out into the Atlantic.

At the end of the period, when 10,000 feet of coal measures had accumulated in parts of the Midlands and South Wales, it is difficult to believe that any part of the country south of the Scottish Highlands could still be free from these rocks; but there is clear evidence that a land-barrier still existed on the site of St George's Land and separated the swamp-forest zone into two primary basins. The evidence is given below. To-day the Coal Measures occur in isolated outcrops. Three factors have been operative in determining their present distribution. The most important and the most obvious is folding of the sheet of Coal Measures in late Carboniferous times, and its complete destruction in the uplifted anticlinal areas. The measures were preserved only in down-warped areas which are tectonic or secondary basins. Secondly, during the following two periods, the Permian and Triassic, the potential coalfields were buried deeply beneath a cover of sand and 'marl', and in later times by other Mesozoic sediments. Only in so far as this cover has been removed by subsequent denudation have the Coal Measures once more been exposed. Thirdly, post-Triassic, and presumably Tertiary faulting, has played an important part in delimiting the coalfields.

A geological map of England shows a roughly symmetrical disposition of the coalfields on either side of the Pennine Hills. The attitude of the Coal Measures east and west of the latter is such that, if continued, their dip would carry them clear of the Pennine heights. The Pennine uplift, whenever effected, has evidently been an event of prime importance in effecting the separation of the Northumberland and Durham, and the Yorkshire, Derby and Nottingham coalfields on the east, from the Whitehaven, Lancashire, and North and South Staffordshire coalfields on the west. Further, the Coal Measures in the western part of the North Staffordshire coalfield dip westwards under the Mesozoic cover of the Cheshire Plain, on the other side of which they re-emerge in the Flint and Denbigh coalfield and here dip eastwards. There can be no doubt that the Coal Measures are continuous, though deeply buried, in the syncline of the Cheshire Plain.

In much the same kind of way the separation of the Lancashire from the North Staffordshire and the latter from the South Staffordshire coalfields has been effected by cross-folds and faults.

Although we have emphasized the unity of the Coal Measures in England and Wales, when the successions in different coalfields are compared, it is found that certain broad similarities link South Wales with the Forest of Dean, Bristol and Kent into a southern group, differing in certain aspects from the Midland Group and the Northern Group.

The coalfields situated about the southern Pennines and including the North Staffordshire, Leicestershire, Derbyshire, Warwickshire, South Staffordshire, Wyre Forest and Coalbrookdale coalfields form a **Midland Group** united by common characters. Although remote from the Pennines, the Flint-Denbighshire coalfield in North Wales shows many similarities to those of the Midland Group, and will be considered with them. The measures are divided into two series: a lower series of grey Productive Measures, and an upper series of red Unproductive Measures without workable coals. The type-coalfield of this group, which indeed serves as a standard of reference for the whole country, is that of **North Staffordshire.** In the appended sketch-map and section only the major features are represented (Figs. 60, 61): the structure is simplified by the omission of most of the faults. Essentially the structure is synclinal, the axis pitching southwards, so that the Productive Measures plunge under the Unproductive Measures, and these in turn under the Trias. On the western flank of the coalfield a minor anticline, aided by important faults, carries the Coal Measures beneath the Cheshire Plain. The succession is shown in Fig. 62. The Productive Measures follow the Namurian conformably and include several valuable seams and a number of marine bands, the best known being the Gin Mine band (=*Anthracoceras hindi* marine band) in the *Similis-Pulchra* zone. The thin Black Band Group contains coal-seams as well as valuable ironstones. It will be noted that the important Potteries towns are situated on, or very near, the outcrop of the Black Band Group. Above come the Etruria Marls, the outcrop of which is marked by great excavations from which enormous quantities of clay for the manufacture of bricks and the coarser grades of pottery

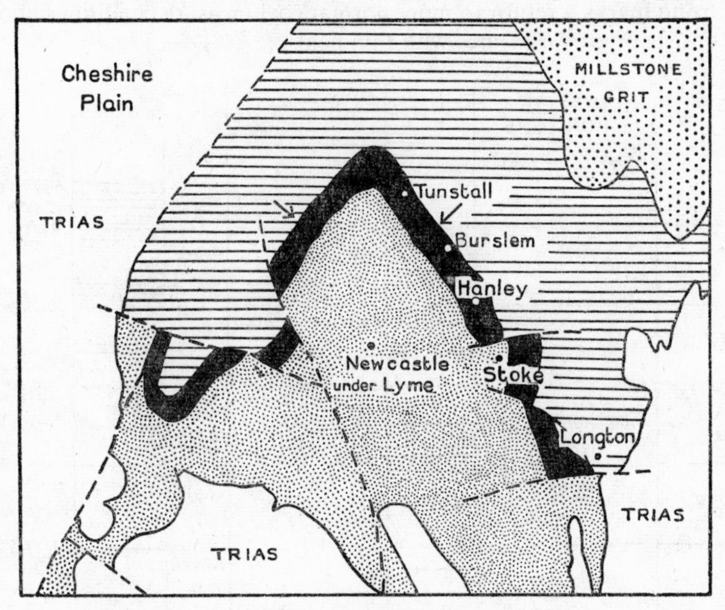


FIG. 60.
Simplified geological sketch-map of the North Staffordshire coalfield. Productive Measures, ruled; Black Band Group, black; Red and Grey Series (Unproductive Measures), stippled.

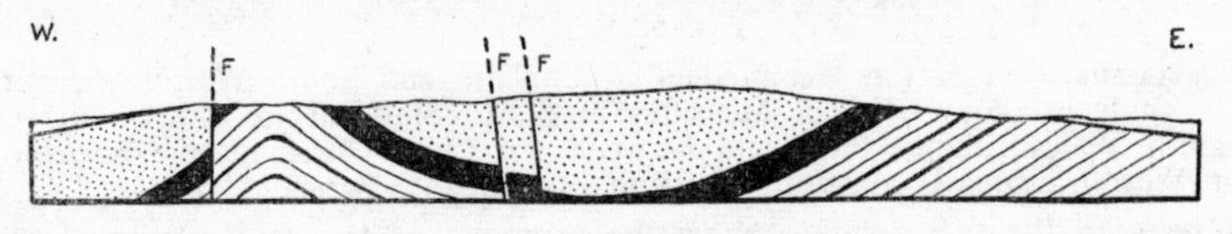


FIG. 61.
Sketch-section across the North Staffordshire coalfield in a west-to-east direction through Stoke.

have been removed. The rocks in this group are strikingly different from the underlying normal coal measures, and indicate the beginning of a fundamental change in conditions. The dominant rock-type is marl, of red, purple, or green mottled type; but especially in the lower part of the group thin bands of grit or fine conglomerate, termed 'espley rocks', occur, while the higher part contains thin *Spirorbis* limestones, sometimes with fish-remains. These rocks bear some resemblance to the Triassic marls, and may indicate a period of more arid conditions—a foretaste of those which culminated in the deserts of the Permo-Trias. Others regard these red beds as lateritic soils redistributed by movements of uplift. The Newcastle Group marks a return to more normal coal measure conditions and consists of grey measures with thin coals.

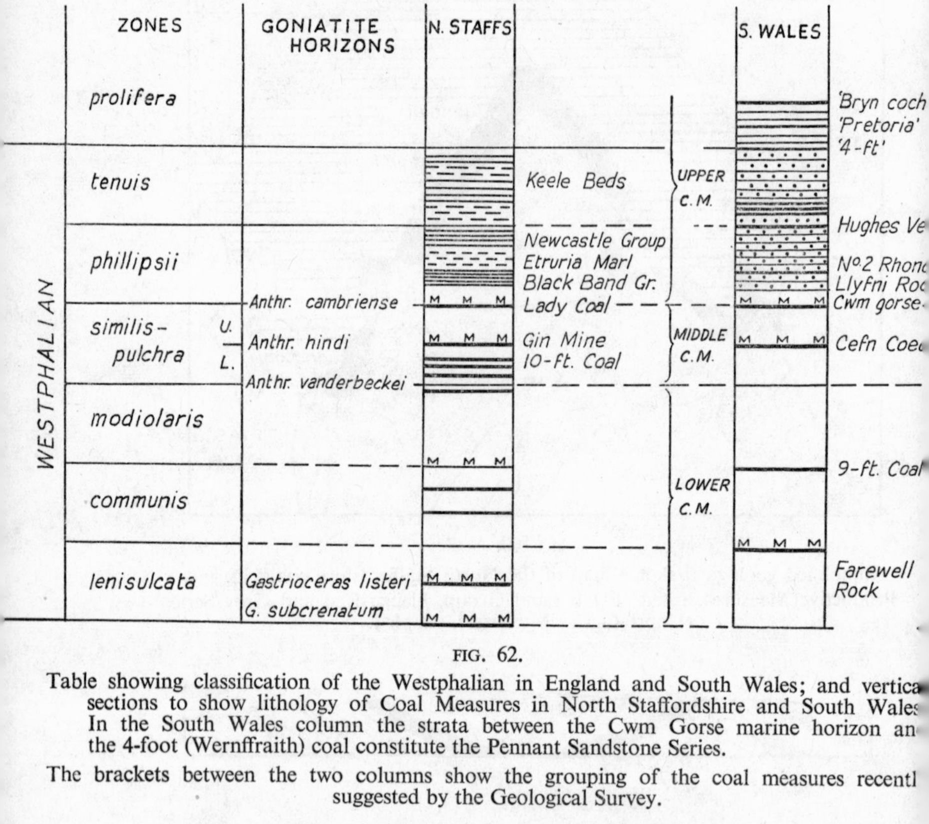

FIG. 62.

Table showing classification of the Westphalian in England and South Wales; and vertical sections to show lithology of Coal Measures in North Staffordshire and South Wales. In the South Wales column the strata between the Cwm Gorse marine horizon and the 4-foot (Wernffraith) coal constitute the Pennant Sandstone Series.

The brackets between the two columns show the grouping of the coal measures recently suggested by the Geological Survey.

The overlying Keele Group consists mainly of red and purple sandstones, together with bright red marls and clays. A link with the Etruria Group is the occurrence of *Spirorbis* limestones, closely similar to the cornstones of the O.R.S. and presumably formed under the same conditions—evaporation of hard water in shallow lagoons. Formerly these rocks were thought, on account of their lithological characters, to be Permian in age; but sufficient plant-remains have now been found to refer them definitely to the Stephanian Stage.

The strata between the main Productive Measures and the Keele Group constitute the Staffordian Series of Kidston, the natural base of which would appear to be the bottom of the Black Band Group; but Dr. Dix has shown that the floral break occurs lower, at the level of the Chalky Mine Coal. This level agrees closely with the junction between two of the lamellibranch zones, the *Similis-Pulchra* Zone below and the *Phillipsi* Zone above. Here two important genera, *Carbonicola* and *Naiadites*, disappear. This is also the level of the *Anthracoceras cambriense* marine band which defines the base of the Morganian (Trueman).

In North Staffordshire the succession from the Namurian into the Stephanian is unbroken; but when the beds are traced southwards, higher divisions overlap lower ones and come to rest directly on older rocks. Consequently the succession becomes less and less complete, owing to the progressive elimination of first the Namurian, then the Productive Coal Measures and then the Black Band Group. In the coalfields south of Shrewsbury the basal member of the Carboniferous succession is the Etruria (or Ruabon) Marl; but even this is overlapped extensively, and the equivalents of the Newcastle Group come to rest with violent unconformity on all formations between the Precambrian and the Carboniferous Limestone (Fig. 63). The Midland Barrier was still very much in evidence late in Carboniferous time. This being so, another feature that might be anticipated from first principles is the occurrence of breaks in the succession in the marginal parts of the basin. Thus, in the Coalbrookdale coalfield near Wellington, Shropshire, the Newcastle Group rests unconformably on the higher part of the Productive Measures that show evidence of having been quite strongly folded, faulted and eroded in pre-Morganian times. It may be noted that formerly the unconformity was interpreted as a fault—the 'Symon Fault'. This relationship is of considerable significance in connection with the tectonic history of Central England. This unconformity is seen also in the Flintshire coalfield, and outside the Midlands, in the Whitehaven coalfield (though here the break may occur rather lower), and in the Forest of Dean.

Still farther north of the Midland Barrier and lying on either side of the Pennine Hills are the **Lancashire coalfield,** and the **York, Derby and Notts coalfield.** Both coalfields are partially concealed by a cover of newer rocks; the Coal Measures in Lancashire plunge southwards under the Trias; while east of the Pennines the general easterly dip carries the Upper Carboniferous under the Permian, Trias and Jurassic rocks (Fig. 64). More than half the Yorkshire, Derby and Nottinghamshire coalfield is concealed, and it has recently been proved to stretch farther eastwards than was thought

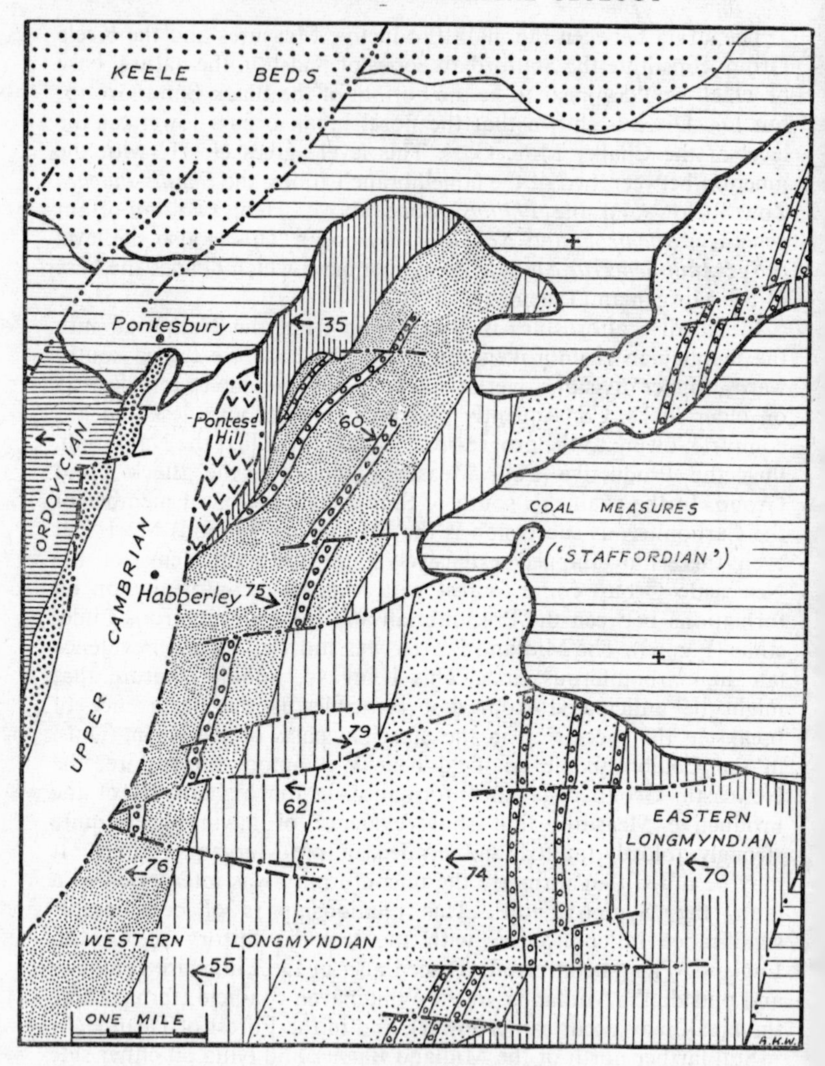


FIG. 63.

Map showing the unconformable relationship between the Coal Measures and Palaeozoic and Precambrian strata in Shropshire. (From the Shrewsbury Sheet (152) of the Geol. Survey, some details omitted.)

Three lithological divisions of the Western Longmyndian are distinguished: arenaceous groups, stippled; conglomerates, small circles; slate group, ruled. Precambrian volcanic group of Pontesford Hill, small v's. Caradocian east of Pontesbury, close vertical ruling. Pre-Carboniferous faults, –·–; post-Carboniferous, –· ·–.

to be the case, while a new concealed coalfield has been discovered south of Lincoln. As the coal seams lie about 4000 feet below surface-level, it will be some time before the need arises to exploit the new coalfield. Although it has not yet proved possible to correlate many of the individual seams across the Pennines with absolute certainty, it will be only a matter of time before this is done. Certain marine bands and groups of lithologically distinctive strata are common to both coalfields. Thus in the *Lenisulcata* Zone the Bullion Mine marine band containing *Gastrioceras listeri* lies a short distance above the well-known coal bearing the same name, famous on account of the coal-balls—concretions containing wonderfully preserved plant-remains—obtained from it. The same group of beds occupies an analogous position in the Yorkshire and Derby coalfield, though there known under different names. A distinctive group of deltaic flagstones, traceable over hundreds of square miles, marks the top of the *Lenisulcata* Zone and occurs on both sides of the Pennines. The best known of several names applied to them is Elland Flags (in Yorkshire). The marine band occurring high up in the *Similis-Pulchra* Zone, and already noted as being particularly widespread, is important not on this account alone, but because it occurs in the midst of the most valuable group of coals in these fields. Finally there is another marine band (the Top Marine Band containing *Anthracoceras cambriense*) known in both fields, and occurring at the junction of the *Similis-Pulchra* and *Phillipsi* Zones, so that it serves as a convenient base to the Morganian.

So far we have stressed the uniformity of conditions within the coal basins. For certain horizons the fact is proved by the numerous instances noted above; but closer scrutiny reveals significant minor variations. The splitting of a single coal seam into a number of thinner ones is a relatively common phenomenon, and is the chief cause of the difficulty experienced in correlation. The outstanding example is in the Midland Group of coalfields. The Great Seam or Ten Yard Coal, 30 feet in maximum thickness, is the most important seam in the South Staffordshire field. In the short distance of 5 miles it splits up into a dozen thin seams separated by an aggregate thickness of 500 feet of shale and sandstone. Similarly in Yorkshire the famous Barnsley Coal, consisting of three distinct layers, splits up northwards so that the top layer gives place to eight separate coals. The significance of the phenomenon is self-evident: it establishes the fact of differential subsidence, increasing away from the Midland Barrier.

The **South Wales Coalfield** (Fig. 68) is the most important in the **Southern Group** in which a special characteristic is the separation

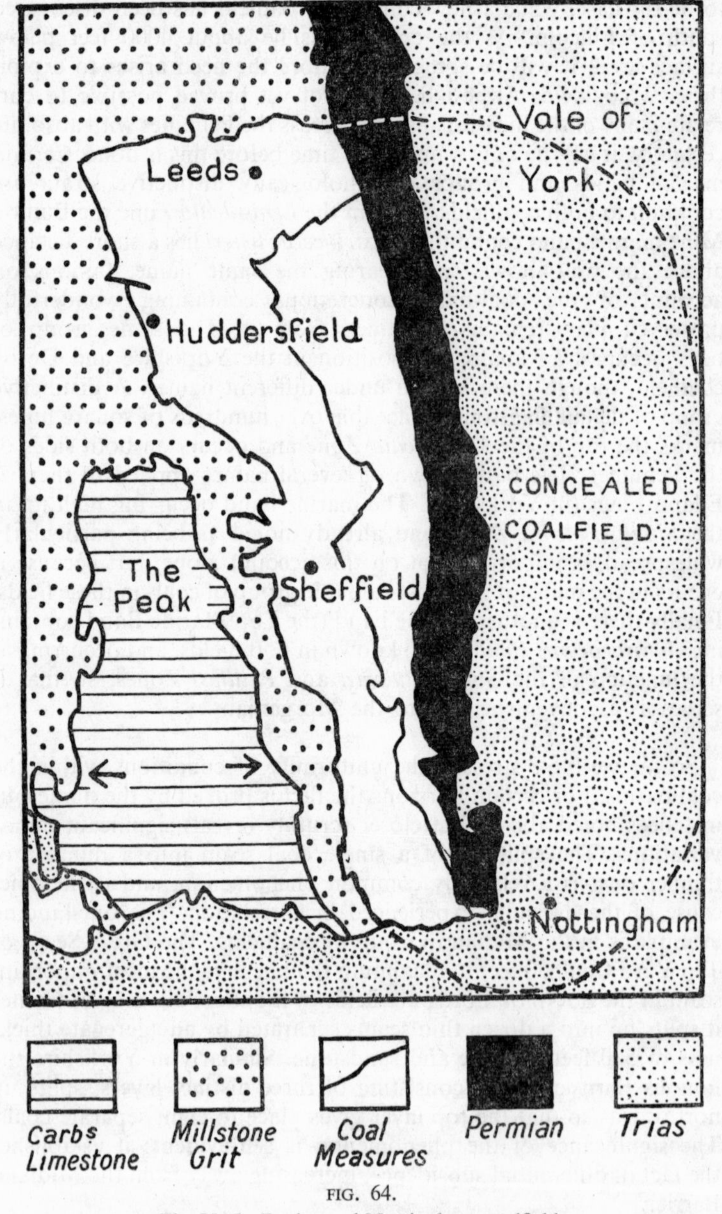


FIG. 64.

The York, Derby and Nottingham coalfield.

The limits of the concealed coalfield shown by chain-line. Distance north to south about 60 miles. (See Fig. 65 for east-to-west section across this coalfield.)

of the productive measures into two 'series' by the intercalation of a thick group of massive grits and sandstones, comprising the Pennant Sandstone Group. A difficulty of nomenclature arises here. It has been customary to refer to the measures below the Pennant Group as the Lower Coal Series (or Group); while those above the Pennant Group were the Upper Coal Series (or Group). Alternative names are 'Sub-Pennant' and 'Supra-Pennant' respectively. The new Survey classification cuts right across this scheme. The Supra-Pennant measures are grouped with the Pennant Series as Upper Coal Measures; the Sub-Pennant measures are arbitrarily divided into Middle and Lower Coal Measures (Fig. 62). The revision of

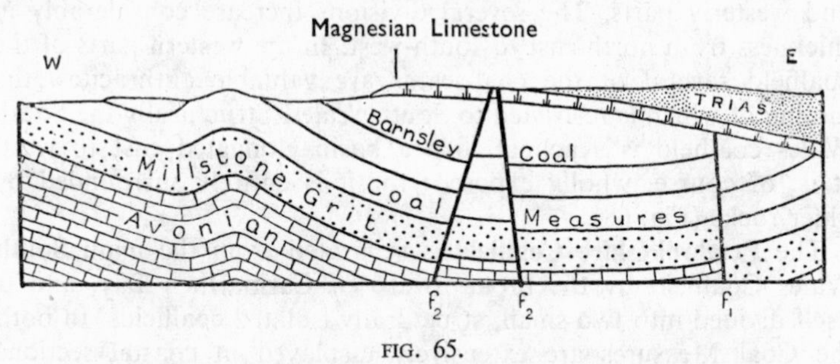


FIG. 65.

Diagram-section across the York, Derby and Nottingham coalfield. $F_1$, pre-Permian (Armorican) Fault; $F_2$, post-Triassic (Alpine) Fault.

nomenclature appears to be a mixed blessing so far as this particular coalfield is concerned. Certainly the use of the old terms enables a relatively simple, though possibly less accurate, picture to be drawn; but the chief justification for the alteration is the new fact that the Pennant Series is a diachronous formation. 'Pennant conditions' —the onset of a strongly arenaceous phase—set in earlier in the neighbourhood of Swansea than elsewhere. When traced across the coalfield this feature changes its horizon by the equivalent of 1800 feet: but the essential three-fold division into Sub-Pennant, Pennant and Supra-Pennant still stands. The Pennant Sandstone Group is divided into two, Upper and Lower, at a very constant horizon—the Hughes Vein coal. The lower measures are mined in the eastern part of the South Wales coalfield (Fig. 68) in the steep-sided vales, such as Rhondda and Taff Vales, which deeply dissect the upland plateau occupied by the Pennant Group. The Sub-Pennant Group contains the more important coal seams, and is essentially a shale facies, with sandstones much less prominent than is usually the case. Locally in the south of the coalfield the Morganian appears to be unconformable to the Ammanian: the basal beds are conglomeratic and a group of red beds lies immediately above.

The Pennant Group consists of feldspathic and micacous sandstones, often strongly false-bedded, and containing coals and shale bands in the west of the coalfield. In the Supra-Pennant Group sandstone is important; but the most striking feature is the occurrence of a series of red sandstones, red marls and purple shales at the top of the succession. These strongly recall the lithology of the Keele Group of North Staffordshire, and on the evidence of the plant-remains obtained from them were referred to the Stephanian by Dr Dix. The Supra-Pennant Group has been largely destroyed by denudation, particularly in the central part of the coalfield; but the beds are preserved in synclinal outliers in the extreme easterly and westerly parts. The several divisions increase considerably in thickness from north-east to south-west. In the western parts of the coalfield several of the coal-seams are valuable anthracites, the mining of which is restricted to South Wales. Structurally the South Wales coalfield is synclinal, like a basin elongated east to west. It is, of course, wholly exposed: for it is entirely surrounded by older rocks (Fig. 68).

The **Pembrokeshire Coalfield** is separated from the main South Wales Coalfield by the broad sweep of Carmarthen Bay, and is itself divided into two small, structurally isolated coalfields. In both the Coal Measures are extensively displayed in coastal sections which are noteworthy in two respects: firstly, the rocks were strongly folded and faulted during the Armorican orogeny; and secondly, slumping effects are displayed to great advantage on the shores of Carmarthen Bay. The strata which slumped occur in the lowest Ammanian cyclothem, between the *G. subcrenatum* and the *G. listeri* marine bands and the sliding is believed to have been triggered-off by 'seismic shuddering'. The two small coalfields are complementary in that Ammanian strata are well exposed in the more easterly, and Morganian in the more westerly coalfield. In the former, fossil plants, goniatites and other marine fossils as well as non-marine lamellibranchs combine to provide unusually complete evidence for accurate, detailed zoning.

Some little distance to the east of the South Wales coalfield lies the small **Forest of Dean** coalfield. Here the most striking feature is the transgression of a coarse conglomerate at the base of the Coal Measures across the Viséan $S_2$-Sandstone on to Breconian O.R.S. The Namurian does not occur, and the lowest Coal Measures belong to the Morganian. Sedimentation in Carboniferous-III times commenced here much later than in the nearest part of the South Wales coalfield, thus telling of the continued submergence of St George's Land, and providing a parallel to the conditions seen in the Midlands north of the barrier.

As might be expected from its geographical situation the **Bristol Coalfield** shows many points of similarity to the nearest parts of the South Wales Coalfield. The tripartite division into Lower Coal Series, Pennant Series (up to 3000 feet thick) and Upper Coal Series (including the Radstock Group), and the occurrence of a conglomeratic horizon associated with red beds near the base of the Morganian, may be noted. In the southern part of the Bristol coalfield in the **Radstock** district the Coal Measures are partly concealed by Mesozoic rocks: the hilltops are in the Jurassic, while the valley bottoms are in the Coal Measures.

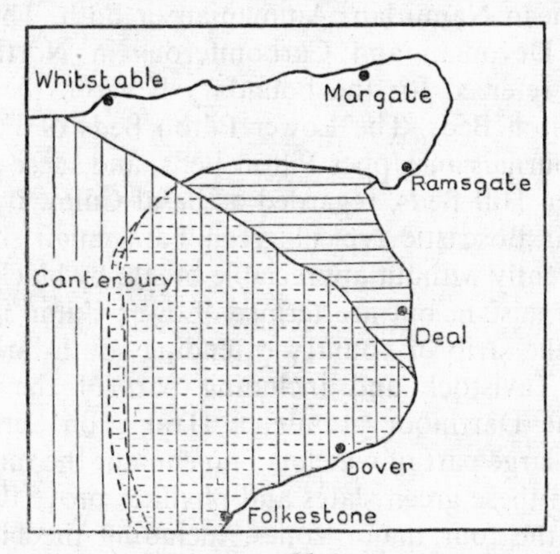


FIG. 66.

Sketch-map showing the extent of the Carboniferous (horizontal ruling), and Jurassic rocks (vertical ruling) in East Kent.

The **Kent Coalfield** is entirely concealed by a thick cover of Jurassic, Cretaceous and Tertiary rocks. The approximate extent of the coalfield, which has been explored by borings, is shown in Fig. 66. The several stages in the evolution of the existing structure are indicated in Fig. 67. The Coal Measures succeed the Dinantian unconformably; they are shaly below, and include well-developed marine beds. Above, the Pennant Series follows, with probable unconformity.

## The Culm of South-West England

In 1840 Sedgwick and Murchison jointly published an account of the 'ancient stratified deposits' of Devonshire in which they introduced the term 'Culm Measures' for a group of strata lithologically resembling coal measures, but containing layers of impure coal (culm) consisting of *drifted* plant debris. This is an eminently suitable name for a facies of the Coal Measures; but in our opinion it should not have been extended to include other lithologies. In particular what is widely termed 'Lower Culm' has nothing in common with the culm measures; and culm measures without culm is as inappropriate as coal measures without coal.

'The Culm' in the process of time has come to be synonymous with the 'Carboniferous of South-West England'—a usage which is to be deplored. The rocks covered by the term 'Culm' have yielded, all too infrequently, fossils characteristic of the Tournaisian, Viséan, Namurian and Ammanian. 'Lower Culm' appears to be synonymous with Lower Carboniferous (Dinantian); but 'Upper Culm' may mean Namurian, Ammanian or both. The relationship between the Devonian and Carboniferous in North Devon has already been referred to: the boundary between the two Systems bisects the Pilton Beds. The Lower Pilton Beds of Famennian age grade into Tournaisian Upper Pilton Beds, and these are succeeded by the Codden Hill Beds, regarded as basal Culm. By contrast, on the coast near Boscastle typical green Famennian shales are succeeded, apparently without appreciable break, by black shales which must be Tournaisian, but are termed 'Lower Culm' in recent publications. In the strip of country extending southwards from Okehampton to Tavistock and including part of the metamorphic aureole of the Dartmoor granite, a 'Transition Series' has been established, a large part of which is Famennian: the rare ammonoids obtained from these green slates and phyllites prove the presence of three out of the four major zones, including the highest (*Wocklumeria*). There is no proof of the Carboniferous age of overlying members of the Transition Series; but there is a gradation from Upper Devonian into 'Lower Culm' lithology.

Strata of Dinantian age include the Codden Hill Beds which, apart from much detrital quartz consist entirely of chert in the type area; but elsewhere the chert is associated with mudstone or rapid alternations of mudstone and thin carbonaceous limestones. Within the Dartmoor metamorphic aureole the more argillaceous rocks have been converted into chiastolite slates or into tougher hornfels containing andalusite and cordierite, while the cherts have been recrystallized into quartztite bands. North-west of Dartmoor the Lower Carboniferous ('Lower Culm') succession consists of a lower shale-with-quartzites group and an upper shale-with-limestone group. In the former some at least of the quartzite layers contain still recognizable radiolaria, and the presence of radiolarian chert may be regarded as diagnostic of 'Lower Culm'. The shale-with-quartzite group is important also for another reason: it contains a volcanic series of chiefly spilitic lavas and tuffs, best developed around Meldon, which appears to mark the approximate site of the eruptions.

Towards the top of the Viséan ('Lower Culm') a band occurs rich in the valves of *Posidonia becheri*, while just above, goniatites prove the horizon to be near the boundary between $P_1$ and $P_2$. There is no doubt that many of the lithological and faunal features displayed by these 'Lower Culm' rocks closely resemble those of the basin facies of the Viséan of parts of the Central Province. In fact at one time they were regarded as constituting a 'Pendleside phase' duplicated by the Bowland Shales, etc., in the Pendle area, in Lancashire. There is one significant variation, restricted to the north-east corner of the county. Around Westleigh the basinal facies gives place to standard Carboniferous Limestone of typical South-West Province Viséan lithology.

The base of the **Namurian** coincides with a marked change in lithology. In the northern outcrops a thin sequence of sooty black shales occurs, containing $R_1$ and $R_2$ goniatites. No diagnostic fossils have been obtained from lower levels; but that does not necessarily mean that zones E and H are unrepresented. This goniatite-bearing facies does not persist to the southern outcrops where a greywacke series occurs instead. The greywackes are possibly of H-age in the Exeter district; but they have yielded $R_{2a}$ goniatites farther north. The Okehampton–Tavistock area may provide a link between the two facies as black, lustrous shales are interbedded with dark grey, graded greywackes in rhythmic units. Unfortunately they have not been dated.

These various lithologies are duplicated in the Namurian in other parts of Britain: they are not unique. It is immaterial whether they are called 'Middle' or 'Upper' Culm. The thing that really matters is they are mid-Carboniferous–Namurian in age.

The true **Upper Carboniferous** in Devonshire consists largely of sandstones, siltstones, shales and mudstones in sequences closely similar to those displayed by the Coal Measures in other parts of England and Wales. They are of deltaic facies and represent a southward extension of the delta flats on which swamp-forests were established farther north. The two environments (Devonshire and South Wales-Bristol) differed in two important respects: in the former the plant debris *drifted* into place at times when the supply of terrigenous sediment was minimal. Seat-earths are, of course, absent. By contrast, farther north, in the South Wales–Bristol belt, the raw material of the genuine coal-seams accumulated *in situ*, as peat, in the swamp forests, and each coal-seam is underlain by a seat-earth. The coals are not 'diluted' to any appreciable extent with terrigenous sediment. In this sense each seam represents a period of non-deposition of sediment.

Directional data for the 'culm measures' indicate that the sources of supply lay to the northward, while slumping and channeling suggest deposition on a southward-sloping surface, presumably the delta-front, with deeper water to the south. The slumped beds are succeeded conformably by greywackes which are well exposed in coastal sections in North-West Devon. They were transported by turbidity currents, and are of Ammanian, $G_2$, age.

We must refer again at this point to the Carboniferous Slate of southern Ireland which is often termed **Irish Culm,** though it is difficult to understand why. If it is conceded that the term 'Culm' should apply to culm measures only, then the 'Irish Culm' is not Culm on lithological grounds. The Culm Measures in Devonshire are of Ammanian age; but the 'Irish Culm' is much older, ranging from uppermost Devonian to early Viséan. The Irish rocks are very imperfectly known, though more detailed information concerning them will be available shortly. One point of similarity is the occurrence of hard (cherty) shales of Upper Viséan age ($P_2$), which occur as outliers on either the Waulsortian reef or on Carboniferous Slate. The stratigraphical relationships are in some doubt, but it is believed that a wide non-sequence separates these $P_2$ shales from the beds on which they rest. As they contain chert and the $P_2$ fauna of thin-shelled lamellibranchs and goniatites they are obviously closely similar to the so-called 'Lower Culm' of Devonshire. An interesting point of detail is the occurrence of the uncommon phosphate-mineral, wavellite, in the Irish *Posidonomya* (*Posidonia*) $P_2$ Shales. Probably the best-known teaching and museum specimens of this mineral come from the Codden Hill cherts, where it occurs encrusting joint-planes. This mineralogical detail certainly strengthens the case for correlating the Irish $P_2$ Shales with the appropriate part of the Devonshire Lower Culm. As shown above (p. 217) the lowest part of the Carboniferous Slate is uppermost Devonian, though of O.R.S. facies, and grades up into basal Tournaisian. Similarly, in Devonshire the youngest Devonian, of marine facies, the Famennian Lower Pilton Beds, grade up into basal Carboniferous Upper Pilton Beds. Therefore it must be agreed that the time-range of the Carboniferous Slate is the same as that of the Lower Culm; but the strata in Devonshire are much condensed compared with the vastly expanded Irish succession.

In southern **Scotland** the Coal Measures have survived over parts of the Midland Valley, and occur also in the small Sanquhar coalfield in the Southern Uplands. To the east of the Pentland Hills the Coal Measures occur in a basin elongated north to south; the Central Coalfield lies east of Glasgow; while the Ayrshire coalfield lies to the south-west. The Coal Measures present certain broad features reminiscent of those in the English Midlands Group, particularly in the division of the strata into a lower Productive Group and an overlying Red Barren Group, lithologically very similar to the Keele Group. The *Lenisulcata* Zone is not recognized among the Coal Measures, but is probably represented by the upper part of the Namurian as in South Wales. It was formerly believed that the coal seams in the Productive Group occurred at lower levels than those in the English coalfields; but this has

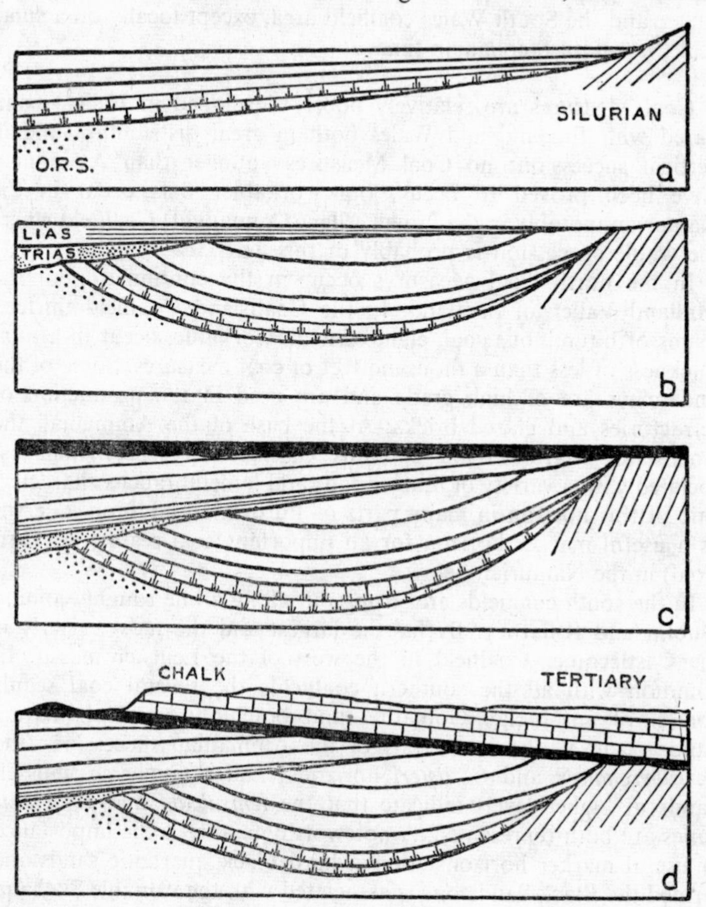


FIG. 67.

Diagram-sections illustrating the evolution of the concealed Kent coalfield.
(a) In Westphalian times.
(b) In early-Jurassic times.
(c) In early-Cretaceous times.
(d) At the present time.

been proved incorrect: the main concentration of seams in Wales, England and Scotland occurs in the Morganian, in the *Communis*, *Modiolaris* and *Similis-Pulchra* Zones. This is a fact of prime importance in Coal Measure stratigraphy. The boundary between the Productive and Barren Groups is drawn at Skipsey's marine band, so that the conditions which gave rise to the red beds in the Midlands commenced earlier in Scotland—in late Ammanian times on the English time-scale—reached the Midlands early in Morganian times, and the South Wales coalfield area, except locally on a small scale, not until Stephanian times.

Coal Measures are relatively poorly developed in **Ireland** compared with England and Wales both in areal distribution and in vertical succession: no Coal Measures younger than Ammanian have been proved to occur; but workable coals occur in the Namurian, notably in the Lough Allen (Connaught) Coalfield where the whole succession is probably of this age.

In the north Coal Measures occur in the continuation of the Midland Valley of Scotland. In the Coalisland Coalfield thirteen seams of bituminous coal, eight of them workable, occur in a total thickness of less than a thousand feet of coal measures. Some of the underclays are of high grade and are used in the production of refractories and glazed bricks. At the base of the Ammanian the Coalisland Marine Band contains *Gastrioceras subcrenatum* associated with a variety of brachiopods and lamellibranchs characteristic of this horizon in many parts of Europe. In addition it serves as a useful marker horizon for an important coal seam (the Yard Coal) in the Namurian below.

In the south coalfields are strung out along a line roughly joining Dublin and Killarney. By far the largest and the most easterly is the Castlecomer Coalfield to the west of the Leinster massif. In common with all the southern coalfields the several coal seams consist of anthracite. Goniatite- and brachiopod-bearing marine bands occur in the lower part of the Ammanian succession—the *G. subcrenatum* and *G. listeri* horizons; and non-marine 'mussel' bands at higher levels indicate that the *lenisulcata* and *communis* zones are both represented. A noteworthy feature is the importance of useful marker horizons: thus a hard black quartzitic sandstone termed the Black Sandstone is associated with the valuable Skehana Anthracite, roofed by the *G. listeri* Marine Band; while the Clay-Gall Sandstone stretches right across the coalfield and is lithologically very distinctive. It contains rolled fragments of clay (now indurated, of course) derived by contemporaneous erosion of an underlying clay band. It is deltaic and of southerly provenance.

The most southerly Irish coalfield is Kanturk, lying just north of the Armorican front. The thickness of coal measures—2000 feet is the maximum for the country; but unfortunately it has not proved possible to establish the time range, though the Namurian rocks beneath contain thin anthracite seams roofed by thick goniatite-bearing shales. As might be expected from their geographical situation, the Coal Measures are much folded, faulted and crushed, over much of the area the strata are vertical, while the anthracite seams are often completely pulverized.

## REFERENCES

As might be expected, the literature describing the Carboniferous rocks is voluminous. The individual coalfields have been described in very great detail in the Memoirs of the Geological Survey; but there are useful summary accounts—amply sufficient for normal purposes—in the Regional Geologies of the appropriate areas. In addition a very useful account on a more general basis will be found in Raistrick and Marshall's *Nature and Origin of Coal and Coal Seams*, 2nd edn., 1946, and A. E. Trueman's *The Coalfields of Great Britain*, Arnold, 1954.

The following papers are recommended for reading:

DEARMAN, W. R., and BUTCHER, N. E. 'Geology of the Devonian and Carboniferous of the North-West Border of the Dartmoor Granite,' *Proc. Geol. Assoc.*, **70** (1959), 51.

JENKINS, T. B. H. 'Sequence and correlation of the Coal Measures of Pembrokeshire,' *Q.J.G.S.*, **118** (1962), 65.

MOORE, L. R. 'Correlation problems in the Coal Measures,' in *The Upper Palaeozoic*, a symposium, University College, Swansea (1958), 29.

PRENTICE, J. E. 'The sedimentation history of the Carboniferous in Devon,' in *Some aspects of the Variscan Fold Belt* (Manchester University Press, 1962), 93.

SIMPSON, S. 'Culm stratigraphy . . . in Devon and Cornwall,' *Geol. Mag.*, **96** (1959), 201.

STUBBLEFIELD, C. J., and TROTTER, F. M. The classification of the Coal Measures is dealt with briefly in *Geol. Soc. Bulletin*, no. 13 (1957), 1.

TRUEMAN, A. E. Presidential Address to the Geological Society of London, 'Stratigraphical problems in the Coal Measures of Europe and North America,' *Q.J.G.S.*, **102** (1946), 49, and 'Stratigraphical Problems in the Coalfields of Great Britain,' *Q.J.G.S.*, **103** (1947), 65.

WILLS, L. J. 'Palaeogeography of the Birmingham Country,' with special reference to the Red Rocks of the Midlands in *Proc. Geol. Assoc.*, **46** (1935), 211.

## CHAPTER XIII

# THE ARMORICAN EARTH-MOVEMENTS

THE existing structures in the coalfields described in the preceding chapter were developed during the second great mountain-building episode, which was comparable in its effects with the Caledonian orogeny of an earlier period. It is relatively easy to assign a date to the movements, for the highest true Coal Measures are involved, while the Permian strata are unaffected (see, for example, Fig. 65). A complete account of the Armorican structures would carry us over nearly the whole of the British Isles; but there are certain regions where they are more important than in others, and in the account which follows we shall concentrate on these.

The most drastic effects were produced, as might be expected, in the Carboniferous geosynclines, where the younger strata were still unindurated. Thus we look to the broad belt of country comprising southern Ireland, South Wales, southern England and, on the Continent, a zone extending through Brittany, the Ardennes and the Rhineland to the Harz Mountains in central Germany, to study typical Variscan structures. It is inferred that this region marked the site of a great mountain chain, the Variscides, consisting of two arcs: a western one, the Armorican arc, and an eastern, Hercynian arc. The former is named from Brittany—Armorica of the Romans, and the latter from the Harz Mountains—Hercynia of the Romans. The Armorican arc includes southern Britain, Brittany and the Central Massif in France, the trend of the folds changing from east to west in Britain to north-west to south-east as we pass from Britain across France. The Hercynian arc in turn trends north-eastwards from central France, then east-north-eastwards through the southern Rhineland to the Harz Mountains. The Variscan or 'Altaid' mountains (Suess) have long since disappeared, their roots have been laid bare and their structures dissected by subsequent denudation.

In the chapter on the Caledonian orogeny we experienced difficulty in deciding where to end the mountain-building episode. Similarly, at this point we have to decide where to start the account of the building of the Variscides. The answer to the problem seems to be easier in some parts of the country than in others. Thus there is no doubt that what happened in Scotland immediately before and during the formation of the O.R.S. belongs to the Caledonian orogeny. In fact, many people equate the acme of the Caledonian movements with the pre-O.R.S. phase. By contrast, in southern England and the Welsh Borderlands the effects of these two phases were negligible or non-existent.

In peninsular South-West England, on the other hand, it is immediately apparent that the marine Devonian strata are structurally linked with the Carboniferous: both evidently participated in the earth-movements which culminated at the end of the latter Period. The Devonian and Carboniferous rocks together constitute the depositional phase of the Armorican orogeny, in exactly the same way as the Cambrian, Ordovician and Silurian are collectively related to the Caledonian orogeny. Thus although the marine Devonian and the O.R.S. are of the same age, the former is tied to the Carboniferous and their structures are Armorican; but the structures shown by the latter are late-Caledonian—Erian and Svalbardic. Even so, the lithology of the Scottish O.R.S. clearly shows that the Caledonides were already in being: the actual building of the Caledonides was in large measure completed by the opening of the Devonian Period. The vast accumulation of coarse-grained detritus bears witness to the active demolition of the Caledonides: the lesser ranges at least had been levelled to the plains by the onset of the Carboniferous Period.

In the account of the building of the Caledonides a major theme was the gradual building up of the structures in stages spread over a considerable period of time. This is equally true of the Armorican structures, but perhaps the evidence is more convincing owing to the more complete exploration of the structures carried out during mining operations. It has been clearly demonstrated that the movements concerned were of different orders of magnitude. In their varying lithology the Carboniferous rocks bear witness to the instability of the surface upon which they were accumulating. The manifold repetition of the sedimentary rhythms in the Yoredale Beds and Coal Measures tells of repeated sagging of the basins in which they were deposited, with complementary rejuvenation of the upland areas whence they were derived. Unequal local subsidences are demonstrated by the splitting of thick coal seams into a number of thin ones by the intercalation of wedges of sandstone and shale. On a bigger scale, within the limits of one coalfield, careful measurements of thicknesses of strata between known horizons clearly prove *contemporaneous* folding, for the beds thin over the anticlinal axes and thicken in the synclines—this is so, for example, in the North Staffordshire coalfield, proving that the present big folds were actually growing in Westphalian times. When the folding was more intense and the amplitude greater, the crests of the growing anticlines were denuded, and with the renewal of sedimentation an unconformity was developed which breaks the sequence. The discovery and tracing of such breaks has followed accurate zoning of the Carboniferous rocks, and it is becoming clear that some of the breaks are of much more than local significance.

The culmination of the Armorican movements may reasonably be regarded as having occurred after the accumulation of the Coal Measures but prior to the onset of Permian time. This is very convincingly shown on geological maps by the striking unconformity of the Permian of north-eastern England on older rocks (Fig. 79). But this is not the whole story: other breaks, only slightly less in importance, interrupt the sequence to a varying degree in different regions; and it is possible to recognize at least five such phases, not only in the British region, but in some cases, over a much wider area. These are:

Phase I. Intra-Dinantian (pre-$C_2S_1$).
II. Post-Viséan, pre-Namurian (Sudetic).
III. Post-Ammanian, pre-Morganian.
IV. Post-Morganian, pre-Stephanian (pre-Keele Beds).
V. Pre-Clent Beds.

Phase I, the Mid-Avonian or **Mid-Dinantian earth movement,** of pre-$C_2S_1$ date, produced a mere shallowing of the sea (with, of course, some lithological changes), in the Bristol district, but led to the formation of coarse limestone breccias and conglomerates in the Craven Lowlands and at Rush in Ireland; while traced over a wider area, the actual unconformity becomes evident, as in South Wales (Fig. 54). Actually these movements produced even more striking effects in Nassau in western Germany (hence they are sometimes termed Nassauian) and in Belgium.

Phase II, the second step in the development of the Armorican structures was of like nature, and gave rise to the unconformable relationship between the Namurian and older rocks. These movements again were widespread and are known as the **Sudetic movements,** which in Britain included three phases. In the Craven Lowlands it has been shown that some of the north-east to south-west (Lancastrian) folds into which the Carboniferous rocks have been thrown, were initiated at this time.

The effects of Sudetic movements are most obvious in the South-West Province. Thus, sedimentation was practically continuous in the southern part of the South Wales Coalfield area, but was continually interrupted in the north. In Pembrokeshire Namurian-R rapidly oversteps all the Dinantian, coming to rest on Lower Palaeozoics. Over the Usk anticline Upper O.R.S. and Dinantian are absent, probably as a result of pre-Namurian denudation. Elsewhere in Britain the Namurian varies enormously in thickness: in the Midland Valley of Scotland the Limestone Coal Group diminishes from a maximum of 1600 feet to less than 150 feet on the 'rises'. Similarly the overlying Upper Limestone Group dwindles from 1200 feet to less than 100 feet on the Ayrshire Platform. Even more striking is the southward thinning of the Namurian from nearly 6000 feet to nothing against the Mercian Highlands. It may be noted that very striking effects were produced on the Continent: In the Brabant massif Namurian rests directly on Famennian; while acute folding of the older rocks restricted later Namurian sedimentation to narrow troughs, 'pocketed in the synclines of the fold ranges'. T. N. George speaks of Upper Carboniferous sedimentation 'in a context of well-established struts and sags'. The same terms might well have been applied to parts of Britain. In this respect the Clare Trough in southern Ireland is noteworthy (p. 243).

Phase III, the last of the fore-shocks before the climax of the Armorican movements, caused the development of the 'Symon Fault' unconformity in the Coalbrookdale coalfield, and the removal by denudation of Ammanian Coal Measures in the Forest of Dean.

The evidence for Phases III/IV of the Armorican orogeny comprises firstly the drastic change in lithology at the end of the deposition of the true Coal Measures; and secondly the striking difference in attitude between the Permian breccias of the Midlands and the Magnesian Limestone of North-East England on the one hand, and the underlying Upper Carboniferous rocks on the other (Fig. 65).

From considering the time relations of the Armorican movements we pass to the structures themselves. There is no single trend that can be described as typically Armorican, for the folds 'box the compass'; but in the southern parts of Britain, an east-to-west trend is characteristic, and clearly resulted from a northward drive.

Armorican folds affecting the Old Red Sandstone and Lower Carboniferous rocks are splendidly exposed in South-West Ireland, where differential marine erosion has developed a ria type of coastline: the resistant Old Red Sandstone folded into east-to-west anticlines forms long parallel ridges which continue seawards as promontories, while the softer basal rocks of the Carboniferous System occur in the intervening synclines which have determined the positions of long, narrow inlets.

One of the most striking folds of this age is the great synclinal basin of the **South Wales coalfield,** with its prolongation westwards into Pembrokeshire (Fig. 68). The main fold is slightly overturned towards the north, the dips along the 'north crop' being much

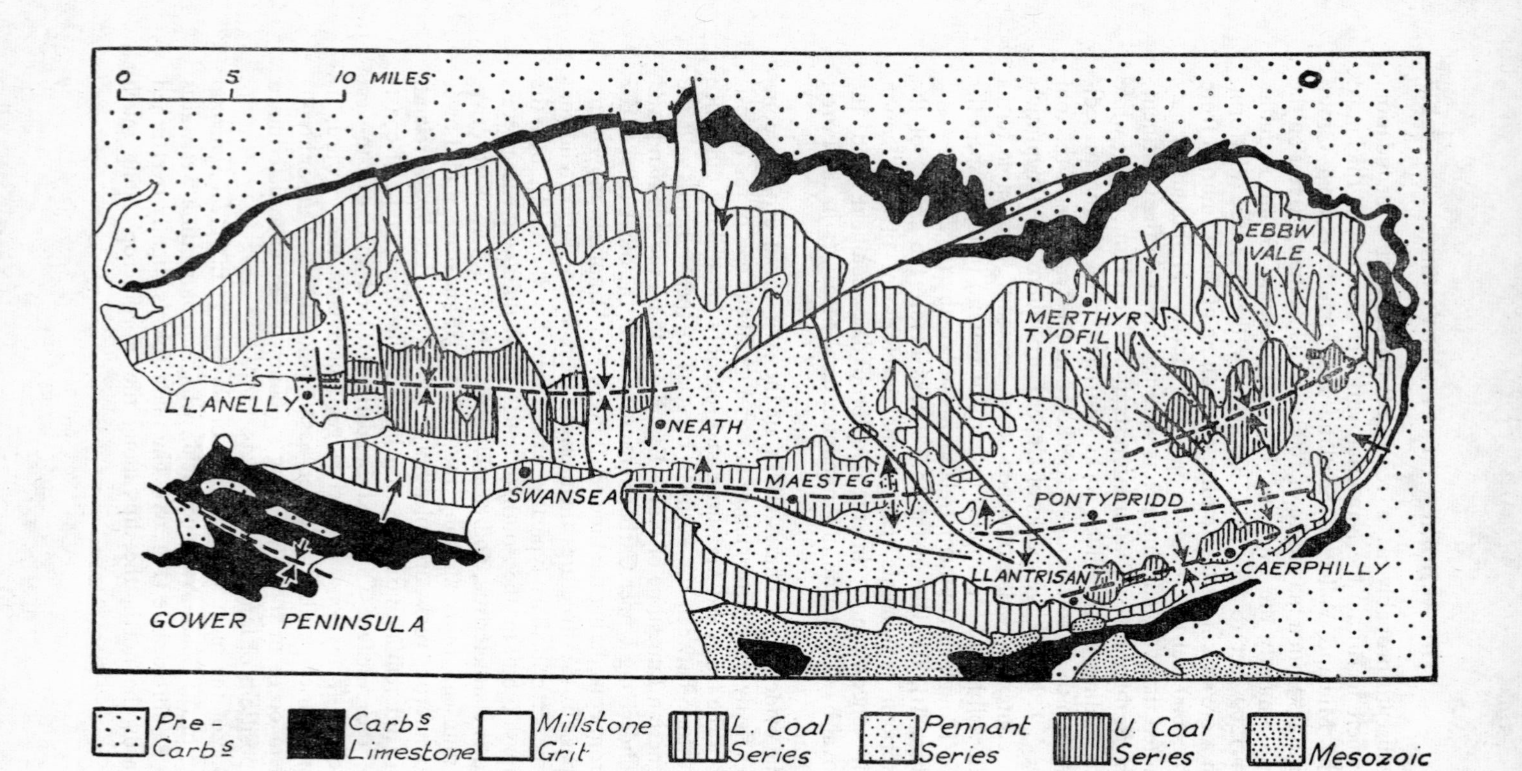


FIG. 68.

Map of the South Wales coalfield showing the minor fold-axes and some of the faults. Note the small outliers aligned along the prolongation of the Vale of Neath faults.

less than in the south. Within the main structure there are minor folds such as the Pontypridd and Maesteg Anticlines, from whose crests the Upper Coal Group has been denuded away, though it is preserved in synclines to the north and south. The minor folds trend slightly transverse to the main axis, and swing from ENE. in the eastern part of the coalfield to WNW. in the Gower Peninsula. More intense folding took place in the extreme west, where outside the actual coalfield the old Caledonian structures were intensified and swung out of their typical Caledonoid trend into the east-west alignment. Particularly to the north of the Pembrokeshire coalfield local inversions occur due to overturning of the axial planes of the folds towards the north, while many of the associated faults are overthrusts. This zone of maximum intensity extends eastwards from Pembrokeshire through Gower to the Mendip Hills (Fig. 69).

In addition to minor folds the South Wales coalfield is traversed by many faults with an unusually constant orientation—NNW. to SSE. The most striking structural feature is the **Neath Disturbance** which roughly bisects the coalfield and extends for at least 40 miles north-eastwards from Neath—it may be for a much greater distance. The Neath Disturbance is the most important of a small number of narrow belts within which structural complexities occur. These are narrowly localized and include compressional folds which may be overturned and are Caledonoid in direction though obviously Armorican in age. The most important fault within the disturbed belt is also Caledonoid in direction, and from its effects upon outcrops is interpreted as a sinistral shear fault. This Dinas Fault has been traced for many miles. It truncates and displaces NNW. to SSE. Charnoid faults, which mostly downthrow to the westward, though some occur in pairs, forming troughs. These must be older than the Dinas Fault. The general sequence of events within the Neath Disturbance appears to have been: (1) Caledonoid folding, almost contemporaneous with (2) Charnoid faults, some of which show clear evidence of horizontal movement (strike-slip) resulting from lateral shear; but in other instances just as clear evidence of vertical movement is displayed. Subsequently (3) shear-faulting along Caledonoid lines displaced the Charnoid faults by about three-quarters of a mile. These structures are believed to have resulted from a single phase of movement, occupying a brief interval of time: they were described as being 'contemporaneous in a protracted sense' (E. B. Bailey, 1954). The fold-and-fault pattern was probably caused by a major Armorican compressional force from a southerly direction being resolved into Caledonoid and Charnoid components by reason of the presence of a deep-seated resistant

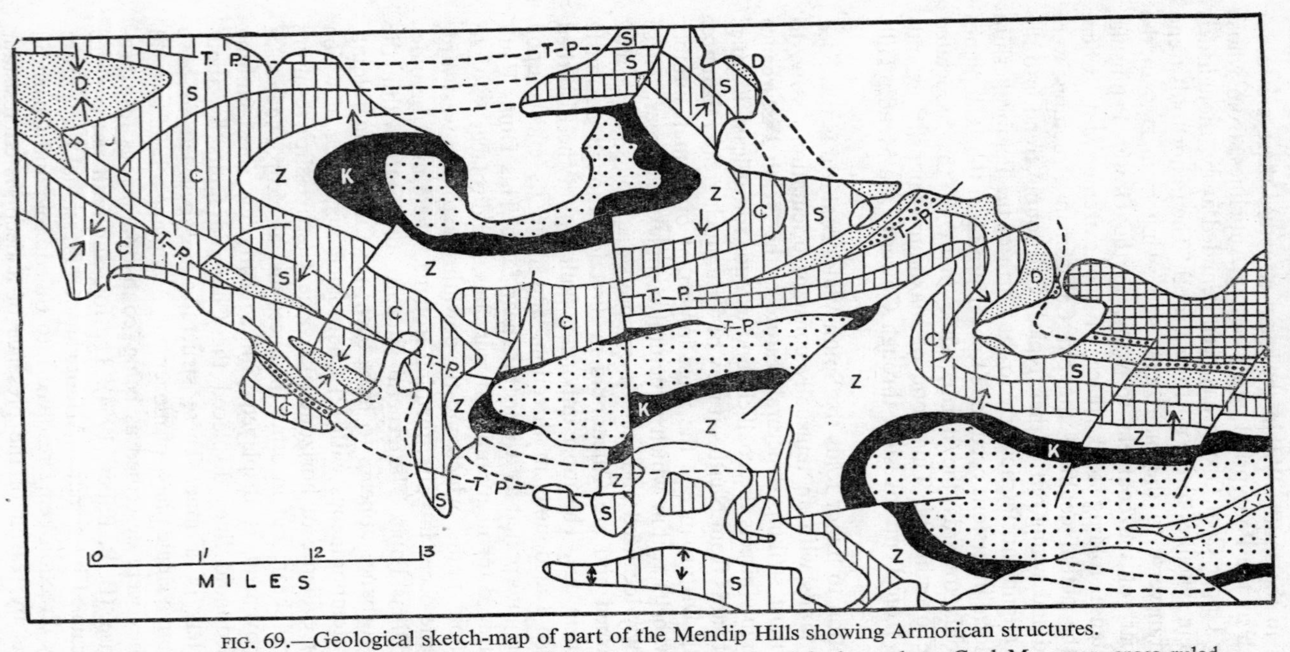


FIG. 69.—Geological sketch-map of part of the Mendip Hills showing Armorican structures. O.R.S. shown by coarse stippling; Silurian, in S.E., small dashes; Millstone Grit, large dots; Coal Measures, cross ruled. The zones of the Carboniferous Limestone shown by letters D S C Z K with the outcrop of K in solid black. The areas left blank are occupied by Triassic and Jurassic strata. T–P = thrust-planes.

(*After Dr. F. B. A. Welch, in Q.J.G.S.*, **85** (1929) and **85** (1933).)

mass. In other words these Armorican structures were controlled by Caledonian structures in the sub-Devonian foundation.

In the **Mendip Hills** in Somerset, east-to-west anticlines pitching at both ends ('periclines') bring the Old Red Sandstone and, in one case, Silurian rocks to the surface in four folds arranged *en echelon* (Fig. 69). The main folding of the Mendips involves the whole of the Carboniferous, but not the Trias, and therefore belongs to Phases III/IV. The fact that the component anticlinal folds are *periclines* is significant: it indicates that folding in two directions at right angles was involved in developing the structure. An early phase definitely belongs to the Caledonian orogeny, for the Upper Old Red Sandstone oversteps on to Silurian rocks. Therefore the Mendip area was involved in folding followed by an erosion interval sufficiently protracted for the whole of the Middle and Lower Old Red Sandstone to be removed prior to the Upper O.R.S. transgression. Precisely the same structural relationship is seen elsewhere along the Lower Severn Axis, at Tortworth, for example. During the Phase III/IV folding pressure was directed northwards as the periclines are asymmetric, with steeper northern limbs, which are locally overturned. This is best seen in the synclinal **Radstock basin,** where at Vobster vertical or overturned Coal Measures display extraordinary contortions. These structural complexities occur at the point where Armorican and Caledonian fold-axes cross. Farther to the north a belt of intense compression (the Farmborough Compression Zone) crosses the Bristol Coalfield along a line parallel to the Mendip axis. Within it the compressed measures have found relief by extensive overthrusting.

The eastward continuation of these Armorican structures beneath the cover of Mesozoic and Tertiary strata in South-East England was long ago envisaged by Godwin-Austen and other geologists, and led to the ultimate discovery of the buried Kent coalfield.

As might be expected, the Armorican structures in Devon and Cornwall show the effects of the northward drive even more clearly. The major fold is the great **Mid-Devon Synclinorium,** flanked by Devonian rocks and occupied by the Carboniferous 'Culm', which in the western coastal sections are seen to be strongly, often isoclinally folded. Similarly along the North Devon coast in the neighbourhood of Ilfracombe and Combe Martin, folding is intense.

The pale-weathering limestones are sharply bent into V-shaped folds, often fractured by faults and with the axial planes pushed over towards the north, indicating the operation of a northward-directed pressure (Fig. 70). In some cases the closely packed folds have had the middle limbs completely pinched out (Fig. 71); while the isolated lenticles of limestone have been rolled over and over until they have assumed a cylindrical form. No wonder that in earlier times they were mistaken for fossil tree trunks.

By carefully measuring round the contortions of one of the curious 'wriggly bands'—intensely folded thin limestones—Dr

FIG. 70.
Minor folds in the Devonian rocks at Combe Martin, North Devon.
The folds are overturned towards the north (left).
Hangman Head in the distance.

FIG. 71.
Armorican Minor Structures in North Devon.
The drawing shows isoclinal overfolds and minor thrust-planes in a Middle Devonian Limestone in slates near Ilfracombe.

J. W. Evans showed that in the neighbourhood of Ilfracombe the compression at this period resulted in a shortening in a north-south direction of the order of 40 per cent. On the clay rocks this compression produced a different effect: they flowed, as it were, and a strong nearly vertical cleavage resulted. Although less perfect than in the North Welsh slate belt, the cleavage was sufficiently good to allow the slates to be exploited for roofing purposes in several different localities, notably at Delabole, Cornwall.

In **Cornwall** it is much the same story (Fig. 72). According to Miss Hendrick's interpretation of the structure, the Devonian rocks here are fan-folded, with the axes diverging slightly from a point in the Channel near the Eddystone. Again the folds are overturned towards the north and associated with overthrust faults. The most significant of these is the thrust-zone which passes through the Lizard District and the Bolt Head-Start Point area in South Devon. Within this zone sheared lenticles of Lower Palaeozoic rocks, including Wenlockian and Ordovician, have been thrust from the south over younger Devonian rocks. This thrusting seems to have been the culmination of the movement which produced a higher degree of 'regional metamorphism' than anywhere else in southern England, and which, in the Lizard District, was accompanied by the intrusion of ultrabasic serpentine masses. Thus we have passed southwards from a zone of symmetrical folding through one of overfolding with increasing metamorphic effects, to a thrust-zone associated with the development of crystalline schists. The Lizard-Start thrusts play a role in relation to the Armorican structures analogous to that of the Moine thrusts to the Caledonian structures, only the orientation is different.

The east-to-west trend characteristic of Armorican structures in the south of Britain gives place farther north to a north-to-south trend, best seen perhaps in the Malvern Hills. In effect, when seen from a distance, the Malverns give the impression of a small mountain chain, out of all proportion to their actual height. They separate two very different types of country: rolling, hilly country occupied by Palaeozoic rocks to the west, and the flat Vale of Evesham occupied by Mesozoic strata to the east. Beneath the latter the older rocks are almost certainly folded on the same structural plan as in the Malverns themselves. Here the folds strike north-south, they are overturned towards the west and are associated with reversed faults—all resulting from a drive from east to west. It is inconceivable that these two grains—Armorican and Malvernoid—were developed at the same time: the latter is older than the former.

We have already noted the effects of the crossing of two fold-systems in the Mendip Hills area: from a slightly different angle it is important to notice a tendency for old-established fold-axes to re-establish themselves at a later date, causing re-folding along the same, or nearly the same line. Some of the Malvernoid folds are instructive in this connection. One of them, the Lower Severn Axis, follows the southern shore of the Severn Estuary, but to the northward swings into alignment with the Malvern axis. It was apparently initiated during the Lower Palaeozoic as at one point (Tortworth) Cambrian unconformably underlie Silurian rocks. Elsewhere in this zone important folding occurred at the acme of the Caledonide orogeny, in pre-Upper O.R.S. time. Later still renewed movement

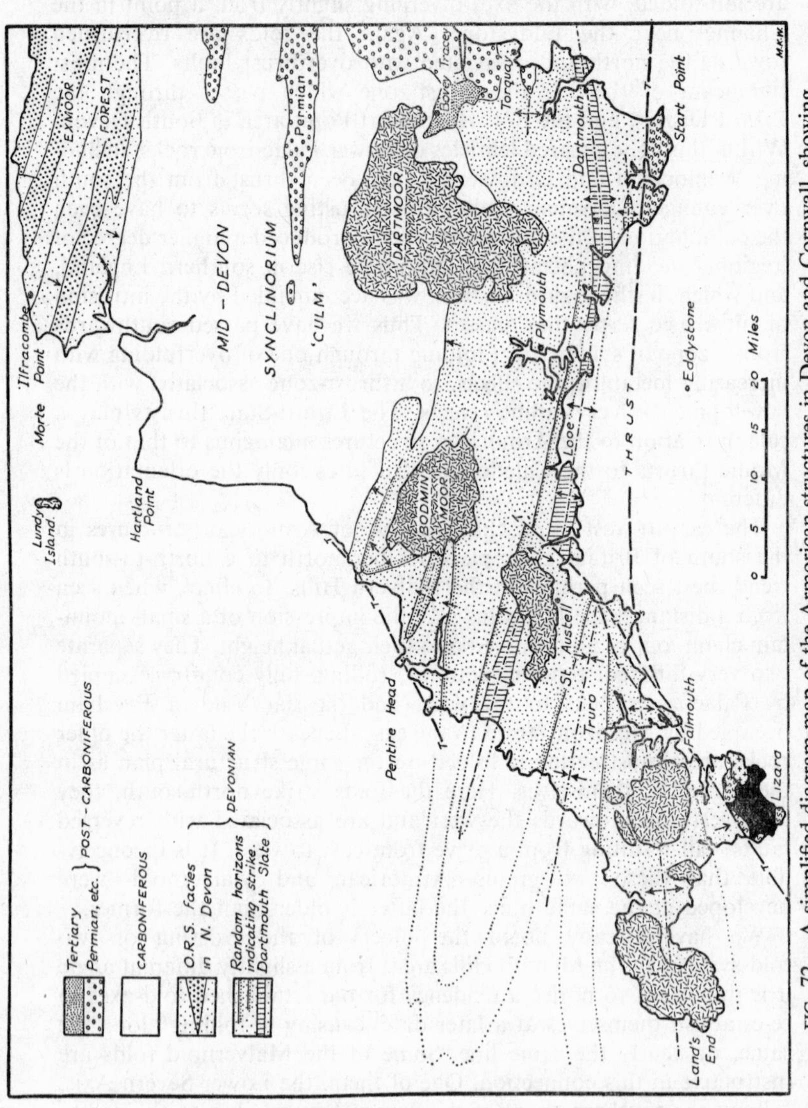


FIG. 72.—A simplified diagram-map of the Armorican structures in Devon and Cornwall, showing

in pre-Morganian time led to the removal of Ammanian Coal Measures and overstep by the Morganian. A similar sequence of events has been unravelled in the case of the **Usk axis**, a fold of similar trend to the Upper Severn Axis, and like it, changing its direction along the strike, from Caledonoid to Malvernoid. At the point selected for the diagrammatic section Lower Palaeozoic rocks are too deeply buried to show evidence of Caledonian ancestry; but a very complete record of Armorican movements can easily be read into the section (Fig. 73).

The Malvernoid trend is again displayed in the southern Pennines, the broad anticline of the Derbyshire Dome being the chief fold; but there are minor parallel folds, especially to the west and south-west. The amplitude of the folds increases from east to west, so that in the more westerly synclines Coal Measures are preserved, in the North Staffordshire coalfield. As we have seen, the axes in the latter area trend rather north-east to south-west. There is little doubt that the concealed Carboniferous rocks which underlie the Cheshire Plain are folded in a similar manner. On the eastern flank of the southern Pennines again, shallow synclines alternate with sharper anticlines, some of which, the Ashover anticline for example, are well exposed; others have only been discovered during the intensive exploration of these parts in the search for oil during the war years. They are concealed under the cover of gently dipping Permo-Triassic and younger rocks.

A close study of coalfield structures in the north of England, has shown the dominance of two directions: Caledonoid in the west and Charnoid in the east, the line of separation being determined by the great faults which flank the Pennines on the west. The former trend is clearly shown in the Lancashire coalfield and the adjacent area to the north. In the heart of the coalfield the Rossendale anticline, with a north-north-east to south-south-west axis brings Namurian to the surface, while the Clitheroe anticline, the Skipton anticline and the Bowland Forest syncline are prominent among the several strong folds which affect the rocks in the area between the coalfield and the Craven faults. These Lancastrian folds emerge from beneath the Triassic cover north-west of the Lancashire coalfield and terminate against the Craven faults. Farther to the north the structure is dominated by the tilted block of the northern Pennines which is bounded by fault-zones that determine the position of the westward-facing fault-line scarps (Fig. 50). The dips are normally gentle and easterly on the fault-block itself, except near its western margin where the Carboniferous rocks are upturned, locally into a sub-vertical position; they are sometimes even overturned and overthrust. This zone of intense compression has been termed the **Dent Line** by Selwyn Turner, who has traced it from near the Scottish border southwards to the Permo-Trias of western Lancashire. The existence of such structures, of

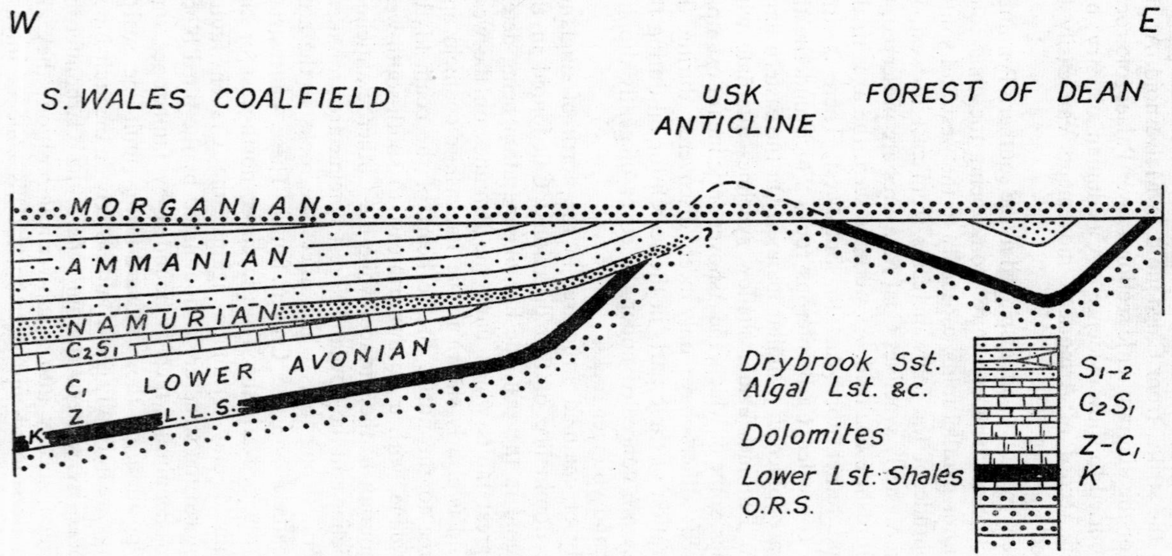

W E

S. WALES COALFIELD

USK ANTICLINE

FOREST OF DEAN

MORGANIAN

AMMANIAN

NAMURIAN

$C_2S_1$

$C_1$ LOWER AVONIAN

Z

K

L.L.S.

Drybrook Sst. $S_{1-2}$

Algal Lst. &c. $C_2S_1$

Dolomites $Z-C_1$

Lower Lst. Shales K

O.R.S.

FIG. 73.

Diagram-section from South Wales Coalfield across the Usk Anticline to the Forest of Dean. (*After T. N. George.*)

Inset: The Avonian succession in the Forest of Dean. For clarity the succession in the Forest of Dean between L.L. Shales and Drybrook Sst. (stippled) is left blank in the horizontal section.

Armorican date but Caledonoid trend, suggests a difficulty in dating structures in areas where Carboniferous and later rocks do not occur. Thus the grain of North Wales, as we have seen, is definitely

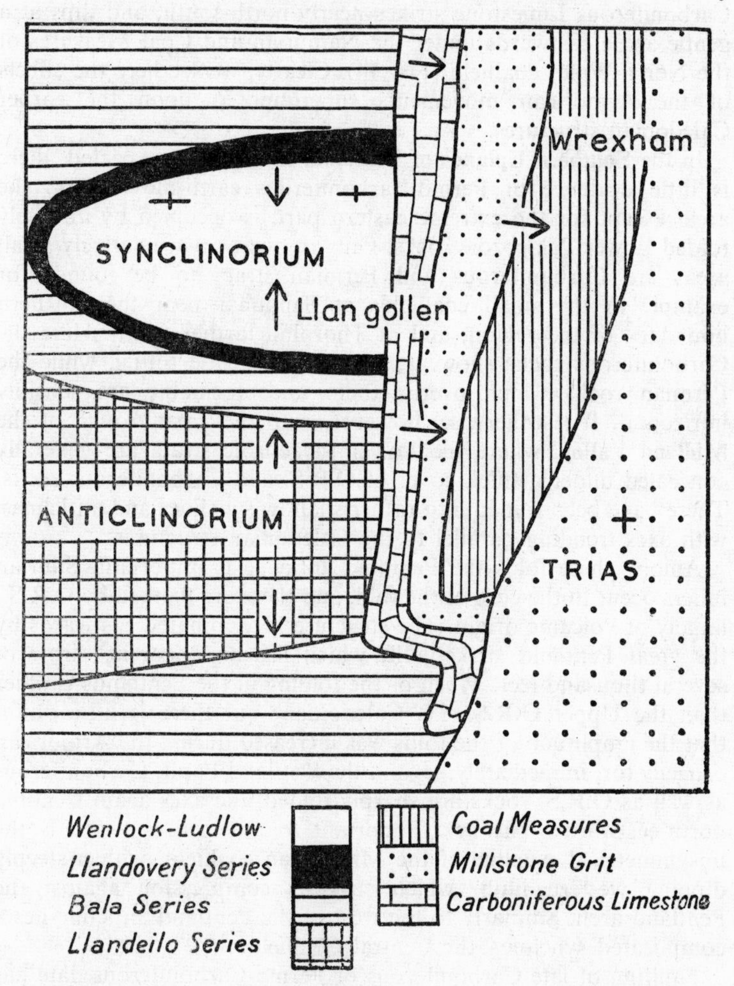


FIG. 74.
Diagram of the structure of the Llangollen District, North Wales, showing the effects of folding at two periods. Faults omitted.

Caledonoid, and we have interpreted this as being due to Caledonian earth-movements. But if the same grain in Lancashire dates from the Armorican earth-movements, why not in Wales too? The answer is to be seen in the Llangollen district, where strongly folded

Silurian slates and grits can be traced up to the unconformably overlying Carboniferous rocks: the former strike approximately east-west (a local modification of the Caledonoid direction); but the Carboniferous Limestone strikes nearly north-south, and dips at a gentle angle eastwards under the Namurian and Coal Measures of the North Wales coalfield (Fig. 74). Clearly, we see here the effects of the Armorican movements superimposed upon the earlier Caledonian structures.

In the **Southern Uplands of Scotland,** as might be expected, there is little evidence of Permo-Carboniferous earth-movements: the area, except for the extreme eastern part, is occupied by intensely folded Lower Palaeozoic rocks. Only in one or two relatively small areas are Carboniferous and Permian strata to be found—for example in the small coalfields at Sanquhar near the northern boundary of the region, and at Thornhill farther south. Here the Carboniferous rocks show at most only a gentle tilting, while the Permian rocks which overlie them unconformably are sensibly horizontal. It is otherwise, however, with the great trough of the **Midland Valley,** where the Lower Palaeozoic strata are generally concealed under a thick cover of O.R.S. and Carboniferous rocks. These have been folded into rather shallow synclines and anticlines, with axes trending parallel to the Caledonian structures.

Among these folds the Pentland anticline is important. Silurian inliers occur in the core of the fold, and these are flanked by O.R.S., largely of volcanic origin. The structure is terminated eastwards by the great Pentland strike-fault, which has an apparent throw of several thousand feet. Much of the folding in the Pentlands is older than the Upper O.R.S., i.e. Caledonian; but there is little doubt that the amplitude of the folds was increased during the Armorican orogeny for, immediately beyond the Pentland Fault, Carboniferous as well as O.R.S. rocks are sharply folded, the axes again trending north-eastwards. The next important fold to the eastward is the unsymmetrical syncline of the Midlothian coalfield, with a steeply dipping western limb, which suggests compression against the Pentland arch. Similarly to the west of the Pentland anticline lies a complicated syncline—the Central Coalfield.

Faulting of late-Carboniferous or Permo-Carboniferous date has played an important role in determining the present disposition of the rock-groups and hill masses in this region. According to their trend they fall into three groups:

1. Caledonoid in trend, e.g. the Pentland Fault.
2. Armoricanoid in trend, later than the folding and intimately connected with the injection of the east-to-west quartz-dolerite dykes which form an important feature in parts of the Midland Valley.

One of the most striking east-west faults is the Ochil Fault which forms the spectacular fault-scarp at the southern end of the Ochil Hills.

3. The third group, north-west to south-east in trend, is thought to be Tertiary.

## THE ARMORICAN IGNEOUS ROCKS

One other aspect of the Armorican orogeny remains for consideration. The crust found relief not only in folding and faulting, but also in the movement of magma of granitic composition which rose into the folded rocks. The act of intrusion may well have occupied a considerable interval of time, for each of the masses now exposed is a plutonic complex, built up of successive intrusions, differing somewhat in texture and composition. One variety, the so-called 'giant granite', is a particularly handsome rock containing scattered well-shaped white feldspar crystals up to 7 inches in length. The West of England granites are most suitable for building-stone, bridge construction and other engineering work. Thus London Bridge was built of granite quarried on Dartmoor, while many buildings in the Metropolis were made of, or faced with, these granites. They are better known to the public, however, by reason of their influence upon the scenery: the rolling uplands of Dartmoor, with their rocky tors and steep-sided, well-wooded valleys have been sculptured in the largest of these intrusions. The Dartmoor granite is the easternmost of six intrusions belonging to this period, the others in succession being the Bodmin Moor, St Austell, Falmouth, Land's End and Scilly Isles granites (Fig. 72). There are several smaller intrusions lying beyond the main outcrops, while the granites themselves and the altered slates (killas) and other rocks into which they were intruded are cut by numerous dykes and sills of granitic composition, but naturally of finer grain. These are the 'elvans' of the quarrymen and miners. The small island of Lundy, consisting almost entirely of granite, lies off the coast of North Somerset, and might be expected, from its geographical situation, to be another Armorican granite complex. However, geochronological measurements have proved it to be Tertiary.

Not only do the granites impart a distinctive character to the scenery of South-West England, but also they have played an important part in the economic development of the area. The St Austell granite, in cooling, was in places profoundly affected by magmatic vapours, which converted the granite into soft china-stone or even china-clay. Man-made scenic features in the form of great white dumps of waste material (consisting chiefly of quartz grains), and near-by deep excavations bear eloquent testimony to the vast amounts of china-clay (kaolin) which the granite has yielded for use in the potteries or for export from such towns as Fowey.

Over a wide belt of country the Cornish granites and the killas are cut by dyke-like lodes carrying tinstone (cassiterite), wolfram and sulphidic ores of zinc, lead and iron. Unfortunately the hey-day of Cornish mining seems to have passed, and with few exceptions the mines are derelict and the miners' cottages deserted and in ruins.

In the lodes the different minerals are arranged in zones concentric with the upper surfaces of the granite masses with which they are associated, this distribution depending upon the temperature of formation of the different ore-minerals. It is significant that a similar succession of zones has been established in the lodes of another English locality, the Alston block of the northern Pennines, where lead and zinc ores have been mined for upwards of ten centuries, nearly six hundred metalliferous lodes having been discovered in this period. By analogy with Cornwall one was justified in inferring that the northern Pennines were underlain by yet another granite, not yet uncovered by denudation. As the lodes cut Carboniferous, chiefly Yoredale, rocks, and as some of the ore minerals occur as detrital grains in the basal Permian sediments, the hidden granite was regarded as parental to the lodes and both were thought to be Armorican. A geophysical survey of the area revealed large negative anomalies of gravity which were correctly interpreted as indicating a hidden granite.[1] In 1960 a boring was sunk at Rookhope in Weardale and gave surprising and completely unexpected results. The buried sub-Pennine granite was found; but as its upper surface was deeply weathered it must have been uncovered and exposed when the Pennine block was finally drowned in late-Viséan times. Further, its petrographic affinities were with the Caledonian, not Armorican granites of other parts of the country. Finally, and conclusively, its radiometric age was found to be 362 m.y., which is a Caledonian age. The boring also proved that a number of mineral veins cut the granite: they are identical with those cutting the Yoredale rocks. There can be no doubt that the area of mineralization was determined by the presence of the granite, though the former is Armorican or later, while the granite is Caledonian. The granite cannot fill the role of parent to the lodes unless some part of it or the deep-seated source of both had been reactivated much later.

A similar anomaly has been disclosed by radiometric dating of some of the mineral veins in the West of England. The spatial

[1] Bott, M. H. P., and Masson-Smith, D., 'Interpretation of a gravity and magnetic survey of the Alston Block,' *Q.J.G.S.*, **113** (1957), 93.

relationship between the granites and lodes is self-evident; but some of the lodes in Cornwall have 'ages' as young as 50 m.y.—i.e. Tertiary.

A similar geophysical survey of the Askrigg Block to the south of the Alston Block and its underlying Weardale granite has been interpreted as indicating the presence of another granite mass apparently intrusive into 'Basement' rocks.

The West of England granites, especially the Dartmoor granite (see p. 113), have attracted the attention of geochronologists. Improvements in technique lead to 'new' figures becoming available from time to time. As presumably the latest are more reliable than earlier measurements, there would not seem to be much significance in averages; but for what it is worth, the average age of the Dartmoor granite over ten years prior to 1962 was $280 \pm 10$ m.y. The Land's End granite was 'almost certainly emplaced at the same time', though its K/A age is 250 m.y. and its Rb/Sr age, 270 m.y. The most remote date is 303 m.y. measured on biotite from the granite building the Scilly Isles. Evidently granitic intrusion during the Armorican orogeny was spread over a long interval of time.

In northern England occurs the best-known *minor* intrusion in the whole of the country. This is the great **Whin Sill,** a quartz-dolerite sheet, the outcrop of which is almost unbroken over a distance of nearly 200 miles. It builds the Farne Islands, off the coast of Northumberland, whence one branch of the outcrop extends a short distance north-westwards; but the main outcrop trends south-westwards, until the Carboniferous escarpment of the western Pennines is reached in the neighbourhood of Brampton. Here the outcrop turns south-eastwards along the scarp to near Brough, then eastwards to a point near Middleton-in-Teesdale, where it thins out. Obviously the Whin Sill must underlie a great area in Northumberland, Durham and Yorkshire. Locally in this area dykes occur, in composition and texture much like the Whin Sill rock, and presumably derived from the same magmatic source. These dykes are Caledonoid in direction, as are the faults with which they are associated. Dykes of Whin Sill type are much more prominent, however, in the Midland Valley of Scotland. Some of the dykes were intruded along important faults, the faulting and intrusion occurring shortly after the folding of the Carboniferous rocks in this region. A noteworthy feature is the extraordinary constancy in the direction of the dykes, some of which are traceable, as prominent east-to-west ridges, for very long distances.

## REFERENCES

Rather than reading accounts of Armorican structures in the Memoirs, Regional Geologies and various papers, the student is advised to supplement this chapter by the study of appropriate geological maps, amongst which the following 1-inch sheets of the Geological Survey are particularly useful.

Gower Peninsula, Cork Harbour, Stoke-on-Trent, Whitehaven, Aidrie, Alnwick, Haverfordwest, Newport, Wrexham.

Useful maps and sections will be found also in the Regional Geologies, notably in the volumes describing the English Midlands, South Wales, Northern England and the Midland Valley of Scotland.

The following papers deal with special aspects:

CHARLESWORTH, J. K. *Historical Geology of Ireland* (Oliver & Boyd, Edinburgh, 1963), chapter X ('Armorican Orogeny').

FALCON, N. L. 'Tectonic History of the Malverns,' *Geol. Mag.*, **74** (1947), 229.

GEORGE, T. NEVILLE. 'Devonian and Carboniferous foundations of the Variscides in North-West Europe,' in *Some aspects of the Variscan fold belt* (Manchester University Press, 1962).

GEORGE, T. N. 'The Namurian Usk Anticline,' *Proc. Geol. Assoc.*, **66** (1956), 271.

LEES, G. M., and TAITT, A. H. 'The geological results of the search for oilfields in Great Britain,' *Q.J.G.S.*, **101** (1945), 255.

OWEN, T. R. 'The structure of the Neath Disturbance . . .,' *Q.J.G.S.*, **109** (1953), 333.

WELCH, F. B. A. Describes the structure of the Mendip Hills in two papers, *Q.J.G.S.*, **85** (1929), and **89** (1933).

## CHAPTER XIV

# THE CONTROL OF SEDIMENTATION DURING THE MESOZOIC AND TERTIARY ERAS

DURING the search for water, coal, oil and other mineral deposits of economic importance, many deep borings have been made into the Mesozoic and Tertiary rocks in England. The information from these borings of the thicknesses and nature of the beds penetrated is of great value. In the preceding chapters we have attempted to deduce the main factors which controlled sedimentation in the Palaeozoic. In particular we have considered the significance of areal variations in thickness and lithology. Individual outcrops of a particular formation may be small; but owing to the strongly folded and faulted nature of the beds, each horizon outcrops in a sufficient number of widely scattered localities for it to be possible to obtain a picture, in broad outline at least, of its areal variation. But we cannot do this from outcrop evidence alone for large parts of the Mesozoic and Tertiary successions. Only small areas of England have been significantly affected by earth-movements since the Armorican movements. Over much of the country the dips of the post-Carboniferous beds are extremely gentle, folds are widely spaced and of small amplitude, whilst faulting is insignificant. The outcrops of the beds may be wide, but their pattern is often very unhelpful. For example, the outcrop of most of the Jurassic System is restricted to a broad belt stretching from Dorset to east Yorkshire. To the east the beds disappear beneath younger strata, to the west and north they have been removed by erosion except for a few widely scattered outliers. When beds can only be studied along a straight line, it is not easy to determine at what angle the present strike cuts across the upwarps and downwarps that were operative as controls of sedimentation during the Jurassic Period.

Fortunately there is now sufficient sub-surface data available for the Mesozoic and Tertiary formations to be regarded as three-dimensional units, whose areal variations in thickness and lithology can be studied. Sections can be continued far down-dip from the outcrop through borings.

Even where beds are completely hidden by younger rocks, sections can still be drawn, provided that there are sufficient borings sited approximately along a straight line. The information obtainable when the results of borings are plotted in various ways on maps is often more valuable. The simplest type of map is of the areas underlain by a certain horizon (Fig. 66). This map indicates the position and shape of the contemporaneous upwarps, on which the bed was either not deposited or from which it was removed by erosion soon after deposition. More precise information as to the position and behaviour of contemporaneous upwarps and downwarps can be obtained from an isopachyte map showing variations in thickness, or by a map showing the strata of different ages on which the bed rests. This can be supplemented by various types of maps depicting changes in lithology. Contour maps can be drawn to show the form of a particular surface, usually either the base of a certain formation or a thin and easily recognizable horizon. The first will show whether the formation was deposited on a markedly irregular surface or on a plane of erosion. If one can be reasonably certain that the surface that is contoured must have been originally horizontal, then its present disposition must be due to the effects of post-depositional earth movement (see Fig. 116).

A series of such maps drawn at as closely spaced horizons as the data permits gives a picture of the framework within which sedimentation took place. Moreover it distinguishes between those features which were persistent and those which were operative for only short periods.

The latest development extends the study of the Mesozoic and Tertiary strata from the land areas across the submerged continental shelf. With modern sampling techniques, it is possible not only to dredge up rock samples from the sea floor, but also to core into the softer parts of the sea bottom to depths of several feet. Such cores provide not only material for palaeontological, especially micropalaeontological investigation, but they are much more likely to come from actual seacrops than are dredged samples which might have been transported in a variety of ways to the place where they were obtained. Geophysical methods of investigation are now used offshore as well as on land. In shallow-water areas with alternating beds of hard and soft rocks, echo sounding apparatus set to impinge on the sea floor at a very oblique angle can be used to trace the submerged scarp and strike-vale topography, so that detailed geological mapping can be continued for some miles offshore. In deeper water, other techniques, particularly seismic shooting, are used to probe the depths of surfaces of discontinuity separating rock units of differing physical properties. But, as on land, from geophysical methods alone the age of the beds on either side of a surface of discontinuity can only be inferred. Actual samples are the only way of fixing age precisely and these can be obtained only by boring. Till very recently offshore borings round the coasts of Britain had been restricted to a few localities close inshore; but during 1965 the picture has changed completely. An extensive search for exploitable deposits of oil and gas in the North Sea area is being made, and has already yielded promising results. Publication of the scientific results is eagerly awaited.

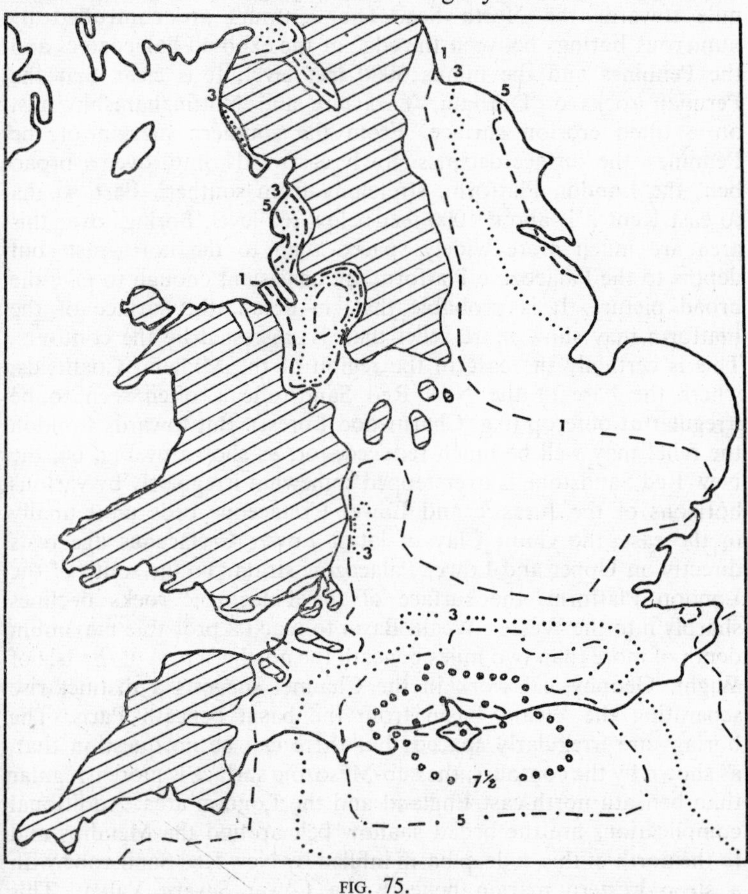


FIG. 75.

Structure contour-map of the surface on which the Buried Permian and post-Permian strata rest. (*After P. E. Kent.*)

| | |
|---|---|
| Lined | — Outcrops of Carboniferous and earlier rocks. |
| Dashed Line | — 1000 foot contour. |
| Dotted Line | — 3000 foot contour. |
| Dot-Dash Line | — 5000 foot contour. |
| Circles | — 7500 foot contour. |
| Circle-Dash Line | —10,000 foot contour. |

Fig. 75, a structural contour map of the basal surface of the Permian and post-Permian strata, summarizes the effects of all the deformations that have affected Mesozoic and Tertiary rocks. The form of the buried sub-Mesozoic surface cut across various divisions of the Palaeozoic and Precambrian rocks differs considerably beneath different regions in England. In the north-east this surface slopes regularly downwards at an average gradient of 150 feet per mile towards the North Sea. The contours are controlled by numerous borings between the edge of the exposed Palaeozoics and the Pennines and the minus 3000 feet level. It is clear that the Permian rocks of Durham, Yorkshire and Nottinghamshire rest on a tilted erosion surface. From the southern margin of the Pennines, the surface declines slowly eastwards, until over a broad belt, the London Platform, stretching from southern East Anglia to east Kent it is about 1000 feet below sea-level. Borings over this area are much more widely spaced than to the north-east, but depths to the Palaeozoic Platform are consistent enough to give the broad picture. It is probable that, in detail, the surface of the Platform may show more relief than is suggested by the contours. This is certainly the case in the region of the Midland Coalfields, where the base of the New Red Sandstone is often seen to be irregular at outcrop (e.g. Charnwood Forest). But towards London the relief may well be much reduced, for, as shown by Fig. 66, the New Red Sandstone is overstepped somewhat irregularly by various horizons of the Jurassic and Lower Cretaceous beds until finally in the east, the Gault Clay of latest Lower Cretaceous age rests directly on Upper and Lower Palaeozoic strata. To the south of the London Platform, the surface of the Palaeozoic rocks declines sharply into the Wessex-Weald Basin to reach a probable maximum depth of more than two miles beneath the northern part of the Isle of Wight. Geophysical work in the Channel suggests a distinct rise separating the Weald Basin from the basin beneath Paris. The borings are irregularly spaced; but there can be no question that, as shown by the contours, the sub-Mesozoic surface is more irregular than beneath north-east England and the London area. Additional complications are the broad shallow belt around the Mendips and to the north of this, a deep basin infilled by New Red Sandstone with a steep western margin beneath the Lower Severn Valley. This Severn Basin is the most southerly of a series of basins extending northwards to the Solway along the west side of the broad Pennine uplift. They are all infilled with several thousand feet of New Red Sandstone. They are probably fault-bounded on at least one side, whilst around Formby in south Lancashire, the deep borings are sufficiently closely spaced to show that the New Red Sandstone rests on a markedly uneven surface cut across various horizons of Carboniferous rocks.

So far we have described only the major form of the sub-Mesozoic surface and have not considered its development. In the Midland Coalfields, in the Mendips and also in the north-western basins, the New Red Sandstone must have been deposited on a markedly irregular surface, though the initial irregularities have been accentuated in many places by post-Triassic faulting. In north-east England, on the other hand, the sub-Permian surface more nearly approaches a plane. The reasons for these differences are explained below.

We have no evidence as to the form of the sub-New Red Sandstone surface beneath south-eastern England: on the London Platform and over its southern flanks, the New Red Sandstone is overstepped by later rocks. The geophysical evidence indicates that the western Channel is underlain by several thousand feet of New Red Sandstone. The same is suggested for parts of Cardigan Bay and the Irish Sea. Indeed it is probable that the main pattern of land and sea areas around the coasts of Wales and western England dates from New Red Sandstone times. During the Jurassic and Lower Cretaceous Periods the emergent London Platform separated the north-eastern and Wessex-Weald basins of deposition. The London Platform was finally submerged at the beginning of Upper Cretaceous times and the transgressing seas must then have spread far across the present Palaeozoic areas of western Britain, but owing to later erosion it is impossible to say how far.

In early Tertiary times the general setting was drastically altered. The Wessex Basin continued as a downwarp, but uplift was the dominant tendency over the former Wealden Basin, whilst contrariwise the site of the former London Platform was downwarped to become the London Basin. To the west and north there seems to have been broad general uplift and slight south-eastward tilting. The mid-Tertiary earth movements only affected the area south of the London Platform and the Mendip Shallows, in particular depressing the Palaeozoic floor still further beneath the southern part of the Wessex Basin. It is possible that much of the movement along the post-Triassic faults of the Midlands and northern England may have occurred then. The Pliocene and Pleistocene deposits again show a different tendency, with the beds thickening and inclining north-eastwards towards the southern North Sea Basin. The effect of this was to depress what had been in Mesozoic times the north-eastern part of the London Platform.

The tendency for retardation and even reversal of the sense of movement with time, that we have noted in the case of the Weald and the London Platform, operated also over smaller areas. In the very sparingly fossiliferous New Red Sandstone, through which it is extremely difficult to trace definitive horizons, this is difficult to demonstrate. But in the Jurassic rocks with better lithological and fossil control the case is different. The Lower Jurassic succession, in particular, becomes extremely condensed and indeed sometimes completely absent over three stretches of their main outcrop. These areas of thinning, in the Mendips, around the Vale of Moreton in Oxfordshire and Market Weighton in Yorkshire, used to be considered, when only outcrop evidence was available, as relatively narrow 'axes of uplift', due to posthumous movement along fold-axes which had been established in Armorican or even earlier times. Recent work has shown, however, that changes in facies and fauna, as well as in thickness, do not take place along a narrow belt (as is implied in the older conception of a single, sharply defined axis), but are much more gradational. At some horizons the greatest changes occur on or very near to the 'axis', at others well to the north or south of it. Further, the sub-surface data now shows that these 'axes' have not ancestors in the Palaeozoic. This is particularly clear in the case of the Market Weighton structure, for as Fig. 75 shows, there are no signs of displacement of the sub-Permian surface as it is followed across the so-called 'axis'.

The floor on which the Jurassic Beds were deposited was restless with a tendency to downwarp in certain areas, in other areas for periods of uplift, producing a shifting pattern of minor basins and 'schwellen' to use an apt German term. The Market Weighton Schwelle was active, though not always in precisely the same place, from early Jurassic to the end of Lower Cretaceous times. It was the most persistent of the schwellen, for only the Lower Jurassic and part of the Middle Jurassic strata were affected by the Mendip Schwelle. The influence of the Vale of Moreton or Oxford Shallows can be traced only in Lower Jurassic rocks. The effect of even more localized 'axes of uplift' on the sedimentation of the Jurassic rocks can be recognized at a number of horizons, for instances in the Inferior Oolite of the Cotswolds (p. 347).

The pattern of outcrops of the Cretaceous, particularly the Lower Cretaceous beds, is not so favourable for the recognition of 'axes'; but again in certain areas one can demonstrate the presence of local minor axes of contemporaneous uplift, both on a very small and a fairly broad scale.

The general depositional setting of the Tertiary rocks was different from that of the Mesozoics. Continental beds interdigitate eastwards with shallow-water marine or even brackish water strata. The boundary between the two facies was constantly shifting eastwards and westwards across the London and Hampshire Basins. Simple 'axes of uplift' of the Mesozoic type have not been recognized; but over the London Platform a number of north-to-south monoclinal folds have been traced by changes in the lithology or thickness of the Tertiary beds. These flexures may well be the superficial expression of movement along faults in the Palaeozoic floor, the movement being intermittent and spread over a long period of geological time. An analogy would be a skin of plasticine resting on the blocks of parquet floor and accommodating itself to vertical displacements of the blocks.

When dealing with the New Red Sandstone, we suggested that the Irish Sea and the western part of the English Channel may have

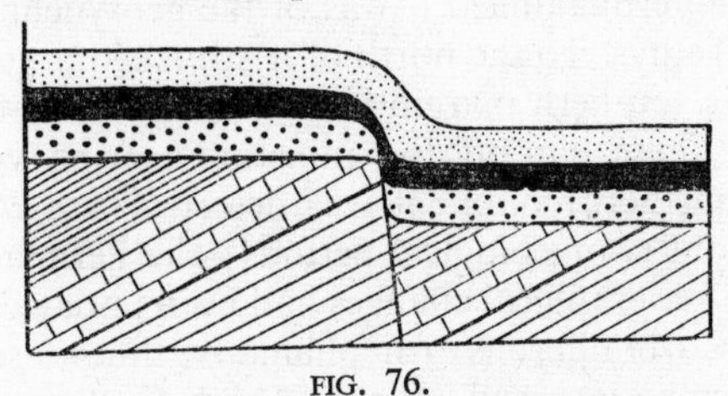

FIG. 76.
Diagram-section showing monocline in surface strata overlying normal fault in buried older rocks.

had a very long history as downwarped areas dating from the beginning of Mesozoic times. As yet we have little clear evidence regarding the later history of the Irish Sea Basin. It is perhaps significant that on the floor of the English Channel there are now known to be seacrops of beds around the Cretaceous-Tertiary boundary, which do not outcrop on the mainland of England. Again, as we shall see repeatedly from Permian to late Cretaceous times, there are strong resemblances in lithology and fauna between the beds outcropping in north-east England and in western Germany. This suggests that the North Sea Basin did not originate as an Upper Tertiary downsag, but that it was a significant and major element of the palaeogeographic setting of Mesozoic times.

## REFERENCES

DONOVAN, D. T. *The Geology of the British Seas*. (University of Hull, Inaugural Lecture, 1963.) Useful summary with bibliography.

GEORGE, T. N. 'Tectonics and Palaeogeography in Southern England,' *Sci. Prog.*, **50** (1962), 192–217.

GEORGE, T. N. 'Tectonics and Palaeogeography in Northern Ireland,' *ibid*, **51** (1963), 32–59. Both with comprehensive bibliographies and useful maps based on borehole data.

KENT, P. E. 'A structure-contour map of the surface of the buried pre-Permian rocks of England and Wales,' *Proc. Geol. Assoc.*, **60** (1949), 87–104.

## CHAPTER XV

# THE PERMO-TRIAS (1): THE PERMIAN PERIOD

As already stated, the building of the Armorican-Hercynian mountain chains ushered in a period of continental conditions over northern Europe. The sea was pushed far to the south of its position in early-Carboniferous times: it was of the geosynclinal type and is known as the Tethys. To the north of it stretched a great land-mass crossed near its southern margin by the roughly east-to-west chains noted above. These cut off the moisture-bearing winds, so that much of the northern continent was desert. These conditions persisted throughout two geological periods—the Permian and Trias—and indeed the geographical changes had been initiated in the British area in late-Carboniferous (Stephanian) times; so that three systems are really involved in this **Third Continental Period.** In parts of Britain (and elsewhere) a profound unconformity separates the Carboniferous from later rocks; but elsewhere and notably in the English Midlands certain Red Beds tend to bridge the gap and it is often difficult on account of the absence of fossils to prove their exact age. These Red Rocks are considered below. The same problem arises in even more acute form, in some parts of the country, when one seeks to find a rational line of demarcation between the Permian and Trias. There is no question that in Cumberland and the South-West of England the two are inseparable except on a purely arbitrary basis, and it is pointless to try to separate them. As a consequence of this difficulty, an increasing body of opinion in this country favours combining the Permian and Trias into one system, for which the name **New Red Sandstone** is widely used. The case for combining the two has been fully stated by R. L. Sherlock, who suggested the name 'Epeiric System', though neither of these two names is an improvement on 'Permo-Trias'. To call the Permian of Durham 'New Red Sandstone' is absurd. The main argument against combining the two systems is palaeontological. On two separate occasions a shallow sea spread over part of Europe, giving intercalations of marine sediments in the dominantly aeolian deposits. The first occasion was late in the Permian Period, and the second at about the middle of the Triassic Period. The faunas of these marine beds have little in common: indeed, while the marine fauna of the Permian is in the nature of a survival from the Carboniferous Period, that of the marine Trias of the Alps is strongly Mesozoic in character. As the marine Trias is absent from Britain, this very strong evidence tends to be overlooked, while the lithological similarities of parts of the continental facies of the two systems tend to be unduly exaggerated.

In this account we follow historical precedent in keeping the Permian separate from the Trias where this is practicable.

The general classification of the Permian of North-West Europe is into:

3. Thuringian Series.
2. Saxonian Series.
1. Autunian Series.

The **Autunian** is named from the Autun Basin in the Central Massif of France, where the series forms the natural continuation of the underlying Stephanian. In Britain, beds of this age have been proved to occur among the Red Rocks of the Midlands, but elsewhere they are represented by the unconformity which separates Carboniferous from Permo-Trias. This is largely true also for the Saxonian, so that the Permian of North-East England belongs to the Thuringian Series of the Continental classification.

The Permian of England is best studied in County Durham, which may be regarded as the type-area for the British Isles. Even here, however, the Permian rocks at outcrop do not much exceed 800 feet in total thickness. From the coast of County Durham the Permian outcrop stretches southwards to Nottingham (Fig. 79). The succession is most complete in the northerly parts of the outcrop, but the individual members thin southwards. Borings put down well to the east of the existing outcrop have passed through higher beds than any actually exposed, and there is a general increase in thickness eastwards, towards what was evidently the centre of the basin of deposition. It is believed that the edge of this basin lay not far west of the present outcrop. Its boundaries extend out into the North Sea, toward Germany, where the Permian is very closely similar even to minor points of detail.

We will look first at the Permian rocks of Durham, and then at their equivalents on the west side of the Pennines.

## THE PERMIAN OF NORTH-EAST ENGLAND

Numerous borings show that the Permian rocks rest on a plane of erosion sloping gently eastwards and cutting across various divisions of the Coal Measures. For twenty-five feet or so the Coal Measures beneath the sub-Permian surface are patchily reddened, though the overlying Permian beds themselves are not reddened. This reddening, caused by the oxidation of iron compounds, must be pre-Thuringian in age. It is interpreted as due to the formation of thick red soils under hot-humid conditions. These soils may have supported rain-forests which would have protected them from erosion; but when increasing aridity killed off the trees, erosion of these soils from the upland areas may well have been an important factor in giving the highest Permian and Triassic rocks their characteristic colour.

The Permian of County Durham (Fig. 77) comprises the four members:

4. (Upper) Permian Marls } (=Zechstein in Germany).
3. Magnesian Limestone }
2. Marl Slate (=Kupferschiefer in Germany).
1. Yellow Sand.

The basal member is only locally developed, and nowhere exceeds 150 feet in thickness. The sand is aeolian, and was probably deposited originally as sand-dunes on the pre-Permian land surface, but was slightly later redeposited by the advancing waters of a Permian Sea, which at its maximum development extended from North England to Thuringia in Germany. The real basal deposit of the Permian Sea is the **'Marl Slate',** a calcitic bituminous siltstone. Both in England and Germany this horizon has yielded well-preserved ganoid fish and drifted plant fragments, but little or no benthos. The bed contains much finely disseminated pyrite, often in the form of minute spheres which are believed to represent sulphur bacteria living in the stagnant bottom muds of shallow lagoons. Submarine springs discharging mineralized water are believed to have been the cause of the bed's abnormally high content of lead, zinc and, particularly in Germany, of copper hence the corresponding German term, Kupferschiefer. The metals were deposited either through bacterial activity or by reaction with the iron sulphide already present. Mass death of fishes may have occurred when the poisonous bottom waters rose into the planktonic zone.

The overlying **Magnesian Limestone** is unique in the English stratigraphical column. Where best developed, it is about 800 feet in thickness and is usually subdivided into Lower, Middle and Upper Magnesian Limestone. As the name implies, the rocks are chiefly limestones consisting essentially of the mineral dolomite (carbonate of magnesium and calcium), but including some calcite also. At certain levels marl takes the place of Magnesian Limestone, while gypsum, anhydrite and rock-salt deposits also occur. Towards the centre of the basin these salt deposits make up an increasingly large proportion of the total thickness of the Upper Permian. Thus, a recent boring at Aislaby in northern Yorkshire passed through 1810 feet of Permian, nearly 800 feet being salts.

In recent lists of fossils recorded from the Magnesian Limestone of this country by C. T. Trechmann, the Lower Beds are shown to

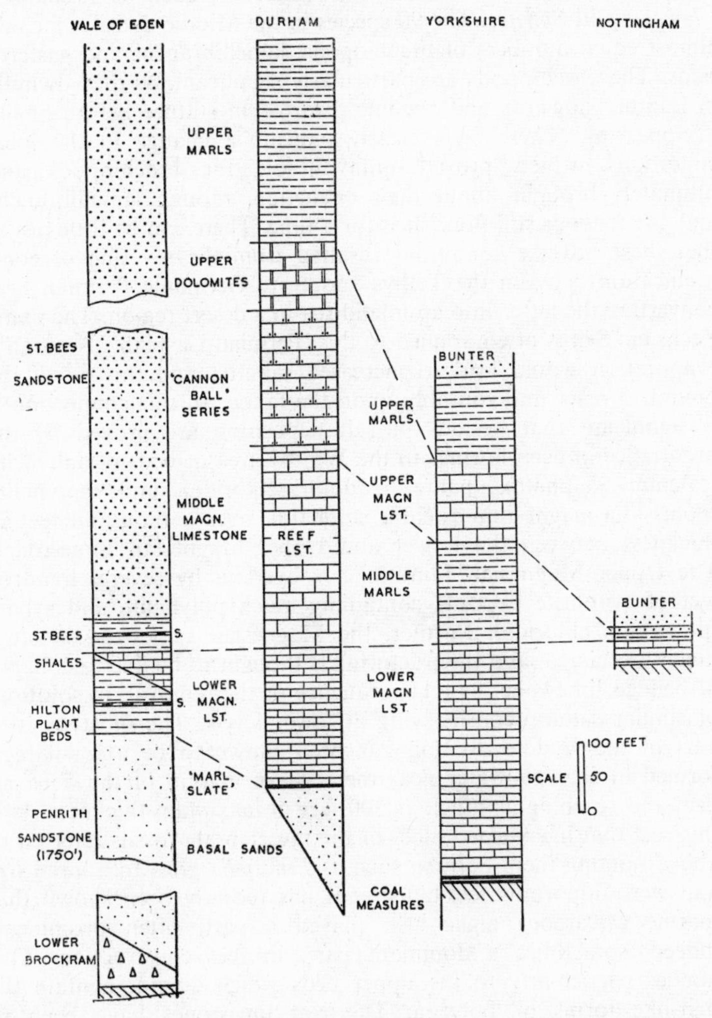


FIG. 77.

Comparative sections of the Permian with part of the Trias in northern England. (See also Fig. 82.)
s—salt deposits; x—passage-beds.

contain 44 species of invertebrates, the Middle Beds 90 species and the Upper Beds only 7. These figures emphasize the meagre nature of the Permian fauna compared with those of other systems, but it is not the figures alone which are significant: of the species in the Lower Beds no fewer than 16 are brachiopods, belonging to genera which were important in the Carboniferous, such as *Productus*, *Chonetes* and *Spirifer*. The 90 species in the Middle division include almost equal numbers of brachiopods, lamellibranchs and gasteropods. The brachiopods are particularly significant, as they dwindle in number upwards and become dwarfed in stature before finally disappearing. These facts clearly indicate a change in the local conditions, which proved unfavourable for brachiopods and ultimately brought about their extinction, though lamellibranchs and gasteropods still flourished for a time. There can be little doubt that these adverse conditions resulted from the severing of communication between the Tethys and Brito-Germanic Permian Sea, converting the latter into an inland sea in a desert region. The name Zechstein Sea is often applied to this 'Permian Caspian'. Naturally, evaporation would lead to increased salinity, and this would be bound to react unfavourably upon the fauna. In this connection it is significant that periods of salt deposition are proved by the occurrence in deep borings in the Whitby area of beds of anhydrite (calcium sulphate), halite (sodium chloride) and polyhalite (potassium-magnesium-calcium sulphate), over a thousand feet in thickness between the Lower and Upper Magnesian Limestones. The Upper Magnesian Limestone is overlain by several hundred feet of evaporite deposits containing much polyhalite and sylvite (potassium chloride). Further, the Magnesian Limestone is often much brecciated, and the fracturing is thought to be due to collapse of bedded limestones as a consequence of the removal, in solution, of similar saline deposits lying at lower levels. The most massive part of the Middle division has been shown to be a fossil reef, formed in shallow water near the western margin of the Permian Sea, and reaching as much as 300 feet in maximum thickness. It is this reef that has yielded most of the invertebrate fossils referred to above: among them *Polyzoa* such as *Fenestella* grew to a large size and were important reef-binders. It has recently been shown that marine calcareous algae also played a part, often prominent, indeed, sometimes a dominant part, in reef construction. This applies particularly to the upper beds which do not contain the mat-like forms of polyzoa. The reef limestones have been so affected by recrystallization that the delicate microscopic algal structures are rarely recognizable; but the limestones often show coarser structures closely similar to the 'algal heads' and laminated 'algal sheets' found at many other horizons in limestones, whose algal origin is generally accepted.

Interesting rock types in the Upper division include 'flexible limestone', the concretionary or 'Cannon Ball Limestone', and, at the top, some 100 feet of oolitic dolomites. The Cannon Ball Limestone is remarkable for the variety of calcitic concretions of all shapes and sizes occurring in the rock (Fig. 78). The concretions are embedded in a dolomitic matrix which proves less resistant to weathering than the former: consequently they stand out prominently from the weathered surfaces. By whatever process they may have been formed, it is clear that the original deposit was a more or less homogeneous mixture of dolomite and calcite which,

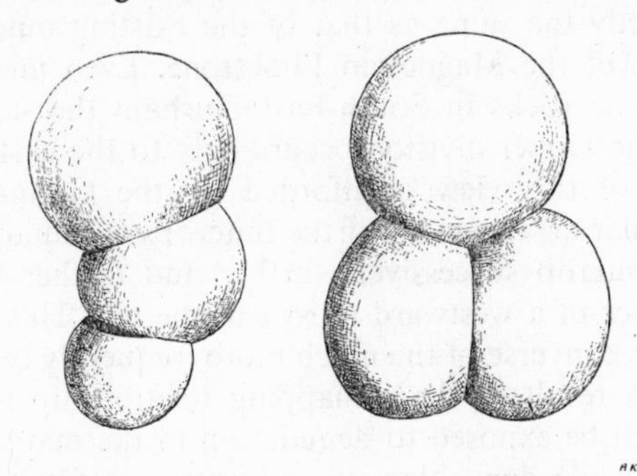


FIG. 78.

Cannon-ball concretions from the Upper Magnesian Limestone, Durham. The concretions figured measure 4 inches in height, but others of much larger size occur in these rocks.

after accumulation, developed a tendency for the two minerals to separate by segregation. This tendency was stronger in pure carbonate rocks than in certain impure argillaceous limestones which occur, and was apparently facilitated by the presence of organic remains and by salt, for fossils as well as traces of gypsum crystals are frequently discovered in the concretions.

The Magnesian Limestone forms an escarpment that transgresses the Coal Measures beneath (see Figs. 64 and 65). The outcrop of the Upper divisions lies to the east, the reef in the Middle division occupies a more or less central position in the outcrop and forms a series of prominent knolls up to three miles wide, while the lowest beds crop out farther to the west. The highest Permian rocks are not exposed at the surface, but have been proved in numerous borings through the overlying Trias. As the beds now have a gentle easterly dip, this arrangement of the successive members might reasonably be accounted for as the normal result of the recession of the escarpment in the direction of dip. But, as a general rule, in the course of such recession outliers are left behind, and the significant thing is that, in the present case, there are no such witnesses of the former extension (to the westward) of the beds. It has been inferred, therefore, that the occurrence of the reef knolls between the outcrops of the Lower and Upper divisions, and of the latter still farther to the east, resulted from formation in the waters of a shrinking sea. If this were the case, the retreat would be eastwards, that is, away from the Pennines, and each successive stratum would be laid down over a smaller area than those beneath, the feather edges of the successive beds would occur farther and farther to the east: in other words, their disposition would be exactly the same as that of the existing outcrops of the three divisions of the Magnesian Limestone. Even underneath the cover of Triassic rocks in South-East Durham the same arrangement holds: the Upper division occurs only to the east of the reef. Confirmation of this view is afforded by the German Permian, for here a similar arrangement of the outcrops is found, except that higher beds outcrop successively farther and farther to the west, bearing evidence of a westward retreat of the sea. This relationship is 'off-lap', the converse of the much more frequently seen 'overlap'. One important result of the off-lapping relationship is that lower beds might well be exposed to denudation in the marginal parts of such a basin, while deposition of sediment, or of salt, was taking place contemporaneously in the more central parts.

Further, this would give a concentric disposition of 'evaporites' (that is, products of evaporation in an enclosed basin) in the order of their solubilities—the least soluble being deposited first, and the most soluble being precipitated only after evaporation was almost complete. Therefore the least soluble evaporite would mark the margins of the basin, the most soluble, the centre. In terms of minerals, this means that carbonates of calcium and magnesium, as calcite or dolomite, would be laid down marginally, and would pass laterally into anhydrite, this in turn into rock salt and finally into potassium salts such as polyhalite (Fig. 79). These last are commercially important in many parts of Germany, and recently have been discovered in boring operations in the East Riding of Yorkshire. In vertical sequence this would give rise to a 'cycle of desiccation' involving basal limestone or dolomite, succeeded by anhydrite, and that in turn by rock salt and possibly potash salts. The cycle would be closed by a change of conditions involving increased precipitation, that would result in a layer of clay or 'marl' being deposited on the salt. For a variety of reasons a cycle might be incomplete; but S. E. Hollingworth believes it possible to express the Permian

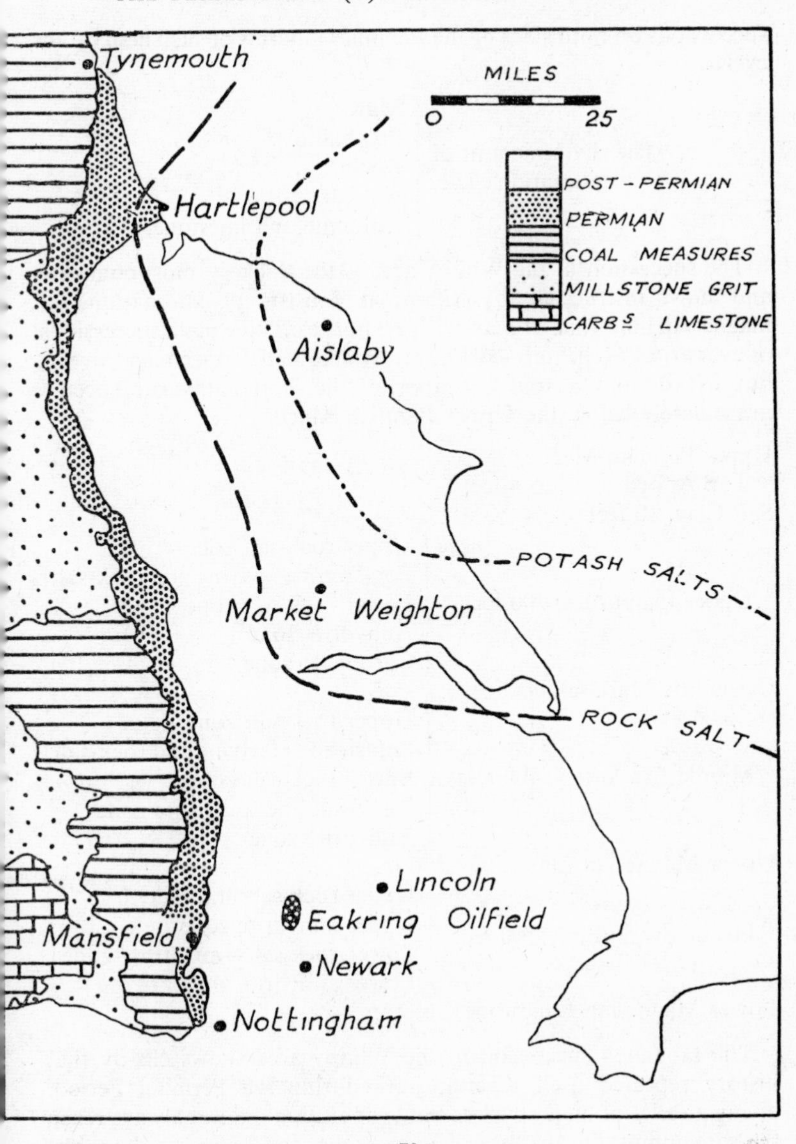


FIG. 79.

Sketch-map showing the Permian outcrop in North-East England and the approximate western limits of the deposits of rock-salt and potash salts. In the Eakring Oilfield, oil occurs in the higher parts of the Millstone Grit at a depth of about 2000 feet.

successions on both sides of the Pennines in terms of such **desiccation cycles.**

| | |
|---|---|
| The rhythmic unit of a desiccation cycle. | Marl.<br>Polyhalite.<br>Rock-salt.<br>Anhydrite.<br>Dolomite or Limestone. |

The succession in the Whitby area is the thickest, most complete and most instructive in Britain: it consists of alternations of magnesian limestone or marl with evaporites. Three main successions of evaporites occur, termed Lower, Middle and Upper respectively; but in addition a fourth evaporite, the Top Anhydrite, occurs immediately below the Upper Permian Marl.

| | |
|---|---|
| Upper Permian Marl | |
| Top Anhydrite, 2 to 4 feet | |
| Salt Clay, 10 feet | |
| Upper Evaporites, 200 feet | Upper rock-salt zone<br>Potash zone (sylvine and rock-salt)<br>Lower rock-salt zone<br>Anhydrite zone<br>Carbonate zone |
| Carnallitic Marl, 60 feet | |
| Middle Evaporites, 400 feet | Upper rock-salt zone<br>Potash zone (sylvine and rock-salt)<br>Lower rock-salt zone<br>Rock-salt and anhydrite zone<br>Anhydrite zone |
| Upper Magnesian Limestone, 200 feet | |
| Lower Evaporites, 1100 feet | Upper rock-salt and anhydrite<br>Upper anhydrite zone<br>Lower rock-salt—anhydrite zone<br>Lower anhydrite zone |
| Lower Magnesian Limestone, 365 feet | |

The tabulated succession in the Whitby area shows clearly that history repeated itself several times during the Permian Period, giving a series of major cycles; but evaporation did not always reach the same point. On the other hand some of the 'zones' in the table, especially in the Middle and Lower Evaporites, are composite and consist of a number of minor cycles each comprising layers of carbonate, anhydrite and rock-salt. Such layering must be seasonal and implies periodic replenishment of the supply of brine when communication with the source of supply—the outer ocean—was re-established. Such replenishment might be, and probably was, due to climatic causes. Alternating periods of more, or less intense evaporation, or of drier and wetter seasons could account for the minor cycles at least. Such seasonal layering has been interpreted as annual in the case of a 2000 feet series of evaporites in the Delaware Basin in Texas and New Mexico. Interpretation has not reached this stage as regards the British Permian, and the durations of the cycles, major and minor, are at present unknown.

Study of thin sections has shown that originally the successions of salts were more complex than now, and that certain of the minerals now present are not those originally precipitated. Complex replacements have occurred, in part contemporaneously, through interaction between the salts and the residual brine and partly as the result of leaching by ground-water. Thus the potash zone in the Middle Evaporites originally consisted of carnallite (KCl); while the outlines of characteristic arrow-head twins of gypsum have survived, though the crystals themselves have been pseudomorphed by anhydrite, rock-salt and polyhalite, in the massive anhydrite zones in the Middle and Lower Evaporites. These salts are not completely successional: in some cases the periods of precipitation are lengthy and therefore some minerals are spread through much of the sequence of layers. This is especially true of rock-salt and to a less extent of polyhalite and anhydrite.

Recognition of the part played by circulating ground-water in causing certain more stable minerals to pseudomorph less stable ones raises the question of the extent to which the dolomite of the Magnesian Limestone may be secondary after original calcite, the alteration having been effected by magnesian solutions. K. C. Dunham has shown that the Lower Magnesian Limestone north of the Hartlepools Fault consists largely of secondary dolomite, but contains some large lenses of primary, sparsely fossiliferous calcite-limestone. There is not much doubt that even in the absence of such lenses, much of the Magnesian Limestone is secondary. The prime control in the formation of salt deposits is climatic: the necessary condition is that evaporation should exceed the amount of water contributed chiefly by the near-by ocean, perhaps augmented by fresh-water contributed by rivers and rainfall. Small-scale examples of the conditions and processes involved are provided by salinas, salt-pans and marginal lagoons, the standard case being the 'gulf' of Karabugaz, marginal to the Caspian Sea. The vastly greater Permian evaporites in Texas and New Mexico presumably differ only in scale.

If this picture of the conditions existing in Permian times is an accurate one, it follows that westwards from Durham aeolian conditions must have been experienced during the period of formation of the Magnesian Limestone, and it would be reasonable to expect to find desert sandstones and breccias contemporaneous with the latter elsewhere in northern England. This is actually the case west of the Pennines.

Before going into details it may prove instructive to glance at the sediments forming on the surface of an existing desert such as that which occupies the greater part of Chinese Turkestan and includes the Lop Nor basin. This is enclosed by high mountains, at the foot of which thick bouldery gravel forms an outer zone round the desert. This 'piedmont gravel' is the coarse detritus that is brought down from the hills by temporary streams resulting from cloudbursts or heavy seasonal rains, and is deposited where the velocity of the running water is suddenly checked by the change of gradient. Inside the piedmont gravel zone is the belt of moving sand—the region of sand-dunes which from time to time encroach upon the gravel, and at others retreat towards the more central parts of the basin (Fig. 80). Inside the sand-dune belt the surface deposits are variegated clays, while deposits of mineral salt characterize the innermost parts of the basin. These features may readily be recognized in the British Permo-Trias.

Turning now to the west of the Pennines, Permian rocks occur in Cumberland, Westmorland and Lancashire and are well developed in the Eden Valley, which is flanked eastwards by the prominent escarpment or *cuesta* of Lower Carboniferous rocks. In this part of the country there is apparently perfect conformity throughout the Permo-Trias and we have to consider three principal formations: in downward sequence the St Bees Sandstone, the St Bees Shale and the Penrith Sandstone. The chief member of the Permian succession is the **Penrith Sandstone,** which is a medium to coarse-grained sand, bearing evidence of having accumulated under desert conditions: it exhibits dune bedding, while some bands consist of almost perfectly spherical grains. These are 'millet-seed sands', the typical product of the long-continued rolling to which wind-blown grains are subjected. Certain bands are loosely cemented by secondary silica deposited in such a way that each grain has acted as a nucleus round which the cementing silica has been deposited to form small, perfect quartz crystals. Such rocks are distinguished as 'crystalline sandstones'. Some of the harder beds of sandstone are useful as building stone. By contrast, other layers are bright red and too soft to be of any economic value: the cement in these is iron oxide. There is little doubt that the Penrith Sandstone represents the 'belt of moving sand' referred to above. At the base and towards the top of the Penrith Sandstone in the Eden

FIG. 80.—An impression of the Permian landscape during the formation of the Permo-Triassic Dune Sands; the 'belt of moving sand' in an existing desert, the Namib, South-West Africa.

Valley coarse breccias occur, known as **'brockrams'.** They do not occupy any definite horizon, and the name refers to a facies

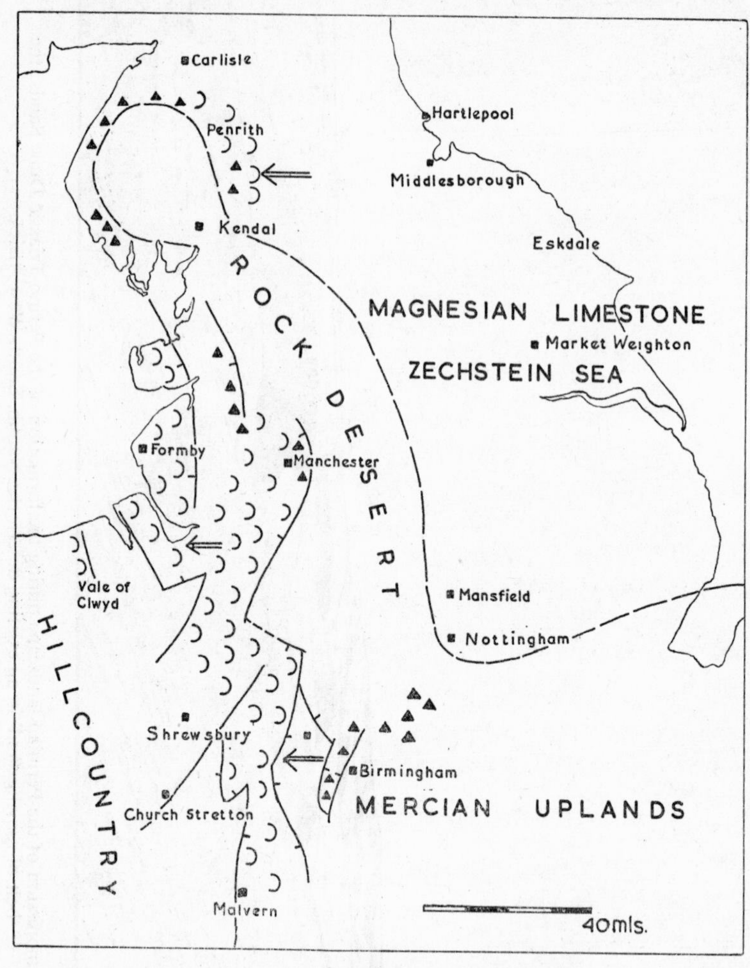


FIG. 81.

Sketch-map showing palaeogeographical features in the Permian Period. (*After L. J. Wills.*)

Desert sand dunes in north-western and west Midland areas; breccias shown by black triangles; the margin of the Zechstein Sea shown by broken line—its position west of the Pennines doubtful.

rather than to a stratigraphical formation. By analogy with the existing desert referred to above, the brockrams represent the piedmont gravel fans, and they might be expected to thicken towards the source of supply, and in the opposite direction to pass laterally into desert sands. It is at least suggestive that 2 to 3 feet of brockram on the Cumberland coast thicken to hundreds of feet inland and represents perhaps the whole of the Permian. While much of the material in the brockrams consists of Carboniferous rocks, a significant admixture of Ordovician (Borrowdale) volcanic rocks seems to indicate derivation from the Lake District area, rather than from the Pennines.

A striking feature of the Permian of north-western England is the remarkable variation in thickness that it—and particularly the Penrith Sandstone—displays. This is probably due to the existence of fault-bounded troughs, of which the Eden Valley is an example, into which the sediments from the mountainous uplands were poured. Thus the Penrith Sandstone varies in thickness from a maximum of 800 feet to nothing on the margins of the Cheshire Plain but swells out to 2360 feet in the Formby boring.

One of the problems of the western Permian is the local occurrence of a thin Magnesian Limestone. It is fossiliferous, and the few species recorded occur also in the Middle Magnesian Limestone of Durham, suggesting correlation with that division, though some geologists favour correlation with the top of the Lower Limestone as shown in Fig. 77. It appears to mark the maximum extension of the Brito-Germanic Sea, and it is difficult to resist the conclusion that at this time an arm of this sea spanned the Pennines possibly across the relatively low-lying Stainmore, though there is no direct proof of this, for there are no outliers connecting the Appleby district (where the western Magnesian Limestone is thickest), with the Durham outcrops.

This western branch of the Zechstein Sea extended westwards into Northern Ireland (Carrickfergus in Co. Antrim) and southwards into the Manchester district, where thin Magnesian Limestone is underlain by the Manchester Marls. These are red marls but contain typical Permian marine fossils such as *Schizodus* and *Pleurophorus*. These marls therefore occupy the same position relative to the Magnesian Limestone as the Hilton Plant Bed and the lower part of the St Bees Shales. The former contains obscure plant-remains.

The Magnesian Limestone of north-western England must be regarded as an intercalation in the **St Bees Shales** which both underlie and succeed Magnesian Limestone. The latter, however, is certainly not younger than *Middle* Magnesian Limestone. The part of the St Bees Shales lying above it must therefore be of the same age as the Upper Magnesian Limestone of the main outcrop. By the same kind of reasoning, the lower parts of the St Bees Shales must be of Lower Magnesian Limestone age as the succession is unbroken.

Figure 77 suggests the correlation of the Upper Permian Marls with the St Bees Shales as both occupy analogous stratigraphical positions, above Magnesian Limestone and beneath red sandstones usually regarded as basal Triassic in age. Within the limitations outlined above this correlation may be partly true; there is some degree of lithological similarity—both are at least argillaceous and both contain important saline deposits. But the upward range in time of the St Bees Shales is unknown—the top of the formation is not dated; and there is no guarantee that the change from an argillaceous into an epeiric facies took place simultaneously on both sides of the Pennines. Indeed it seems to us much more likely that the Upper Magnesian Limestone with the overlying Upper Marls is represented by the lower part of the St Bees Sandstone of the western areas. The equivalence in time of different members of the Permo-Triassic succession follows inevitably if the picture of the general conditions that we have drawn is a true one; and it must be true if drawn on a sufficiently large canvas.

## THE RED ROCKS OF THE ENGLISH MIDLANDS

As we have already seen, the Productive Coal Measures in the Midlands are succeeded by red beds laid down under very different conditions from those obtaining when the former were in process of deposition. The earliest indication of things to come is afforded by the **Etruria Marls** which were preceded by premonitory 'Malvernian' earth-movements; but these did not permanently destroy the Coal Measure type of environment and of sedimentation, for the red marls are succeeded by the Newcastle Group of normal grey measures with some valuable coal-seams, and of unquestionably Upper Carboniferous age (*Tenuis* Zone).

A much more fundamental change separates the Newcastle Group from the overlying Keele Beds, which were at one time thought to be Permian on account of their lithology; but the discovery in them of Stephanian plant-remains proved them to be Carboniferous. By a disastrous misuse of terms they were consequently grouped with the 'Upper Coal Measures', to which they bear not the slightest resemblance in lithology, faunal content or mode of origin. The same fate has befallen group after group of these red beds until, as one writer triumphantly declared recently, the Permian has now been removed from geological maps of the Midlands. Those who agree with this point of view are blinding themselves to the facts of facies variation. In point of fact the youngest Carboniferous rocks in Britain exhibit *two* fundamentally different facies: in places they are normal coal-measures; elsewhere they are of 'red-rock' facies. There is no recognized name for the latter, which is to be deplored, and we think that Sherlock's term 'epeiric' meaning 'continental' is appropriate. True he suggested the name for a System, to replace 'Permian and Trias'. Actually this epeiric facies includes rock-groups belonging to three different systems—the highest Carboniferous, the Permian and the Trias—but they combine to form one distinctive chapter of geological history: in that sense they are indivisible; together they constitute the **Third Continental Phase,** closely associated with the Armorican earth-movements. They cannot be combined to form one System, however, for the latter must be bounded by time-planes, while the Third Continental Phase has a strongly diachronous base.

The **Keele Beds** have been described above, and here it is only necessary to stress one very important fact: that in lithology they differ fundamentally from genuine Coal Measures. In place of the coal seams, underclays, shale roofs, mudstones and sandstones, the Keele Beds are red marls, red sandstones, red and purple shales, fine breccias, cornstones and thin ostracod- and *Spirorbis* limestones. Near Bridgnorth they bear evidence of another significant change in the incoming of breccias and limestone-chert-conglomerates resembling those characteristic of higher formations. They prove uplift of the western parts of the Mercian Highlands, whence these rocks were derived.

The Mercian Highlands, in the English Midlands, exerted a profound influence on sedimentation from Keele times onwards. In their immediate neighbourhood distinctive coarse-grained breccias were deposited as wedges banked up against and extending away from the highlands, forming piedmont gravel fans. The earth-movements continued spasmodically over a long period of time: there are therefore many such breccias which pass laterally into finer grained red sandstones and marls. They are often isolated from one another and in the absence of the usual stratigraphical criteria correlation is a special problem. One common-sense principle has proved useful—it involves making quantitative estimates of the varying proportions of materials of different ages present in the rocks. With the passage of time progressively older strata would have been exposed by denudation and laid under contribution in ever increasing amount. Therefore, other things being equal, an older breccia contains a higher proportion of younger rock debris and vice versa.

The **Enville Group** contains thick local wedges of so-called

Calcareous Conglomerate in which cobbles and pebbles of Carboniferous Limestone and chert are dominant over other materials derived from the Mercian Highlands, and including Wenlock and Woolhope Limestone, Llandovery (Rubery) Sandstone, Cambrian (Lickey) quartzite and even Precambrian igneous rocks. These are delta-fan deposits, carried down by torrents from the uplands.

In the **Clent Group** the most significant rocks are breccias consisting of large angular blocks of locally derived rocks, the majority of which are of Precambrian and Lower Palaeozoic age, with only a subordinate admixture of younger Palaeozoic material. Therefore on the evidence of included fragments the Clent Breccias are younger than the Enville Group. The latter, indeed, are often grouped with the Keele Beds. The two together reach the very considerable thickness of 4000 feet, in down-faulted basins.

With one exception the exact ages of these red-rock groups has not been established; but in finer-grained material in the **Corley Beds** at one locality in Warwickshire the remains of Autunian plants including *Walchia* have been found and prove their true Permian age.

From Keele times onwards aridity was increasing rapidly and the lithological details of the rocks clearly indicate accumulation in a desert environment, and the production of an extensive desert plain of low relief over the site of Nottinghamshire and Yorkshire. Ultimately this low-lying region was flooded by the advancing waters of the Magnesian Limestone Sea in relatively late Permian times (Fig. 81).

## THE 'PERMIAN' IN DEVONSHIRE

The 'Permo-Trias' is splendidly developed in **Eastern Devonshire** where it outcrops on the coast, forming the red cliffs in the vicinity of Dawlish, Teignmouth and Paignton, so familiar to travellers on the 'Great Western' branch of British Railways. Near Babbacombe the red sandstones and breccias are faulted against pale-weathering Devonian limestones, the contrast affording a most striking geological picture. Inland the rocks weather to a bright red soil that is singularly fertile and of considerable depth, as Devonshire escaped the Pleistocene glaciation, which in other parts of the country removed the mantle of soil, exposing the bed-rock over wide areas. The fertile soil, the congenial climate and the differential weathering of the limestones and igneous rocks, as compared with the softer Permo-Trias, account largely for the beauty of Devonshire scenery.

The difficulty of separating the Permian from the Trias is as acute in the case of these Devonshire rocks as with those west of the Pennines and in the Midlands: agreement as to where the line should be drawn has not been reached—some geologists even believe that the true Permian is unrepresented. In this account we shall follow the official view and describe as 'Permian' the lower part of the succession, and as 'Trias' the remainder.

The rocks falling into the former division include the same types, formed under the same conditions, as those already described from Cumberland and Westmorland, viz. breccias (comparable with the brockrams), red, false-bedded sandstones, marls and clays. Curiously enough the lowest member of the succession is a clay, the Watcombe Clay, up to 200 feet in thickness. As this bed lies beneath well-joined sandstones and breccias its outcrop determines a spring line, and is difficult to negotiate on the coast in any but the driest weather. For a long time it has been used as the raw material for a local pottery industry. The most striking of the Permo-Triassic rocks are undoubtedly the overlying breccias and breccio-conglomerates, consisting locally of huge blocks set in a sandy matrix, which is removed by the sea and gives rise to the residual boulder beds occurring at the foot of the cliffs, for example, at the Ness, immediately south of Teignmouth. It requires no strength of imagination to picture the conditions under which they were formed. As a proportion of the blocks are rounded it is clear that they were brought down by torrential streams from the then mountainous interior and deposited on the edge of a desert area stretching for an unknown distance southwards. The included fragments are largely of Devonian rocks; but locally a high percentage consists of igneous rocks, including porphyries which might well have been connected with the uprising Dartmoor granite, though the latter was not uncovered until long after this period. In addition, there are fragments of volcanic rocks which cannot be exactly matched in Devonshire at the present time, and appear to represent a spread of lavas that were completely destroyed, save for these relics. In the absence of the Watcombe Clays these breccio-conglomerates rest directly, and with strong unconformity, upon the underlying Devonian rocks. The unconformity is extensively exposed on the shore south of Torquay, for example, and although the older rocks are stained red with iron-oxide from the overlying strata, the marked difference in lithology and in attitude enables the observer to appreciate the fact that the surface of separation was an irregular pre-Permian land surface.

Above the breccio-conglomerates a thick series of false-bedded sandstones occur, and these pass upwards into red marls with a maximum thickness of 500 feet. The marls are succeeded by the

Budleigh Salterton Pebble Beds (see p. 325) which are commonly and quite arbitrarily regarded as marking the base of the Trias.

In the Exeter district Permian lavas occur in a number of small outcrops and appear to have been erupted from cones, as yet not located, on to a desert floor where they were weathered in a curious way. As might be expected, they bear a strong superficial resemblance to some of the Old Red Sandstone lavas which in Scotland were poured out under much the same conditions.

The pebble-content of the long tongue of New Red Sandstone infilling the Crediton Valley to the north of Dartmoor, is interesting. The lowest beds yield only sandstones and shales identical with the Carboniferous ('Culm') sediments; but at higher levels pebbles of untourmalinized lavas occur, followed by tourmalinized slates and lavas, and finally of sanidine and of micrograpite, indicating that the metamorphic aureole of the Dartmoor granite was first uncovered, then, somewhat later, coarse-grained dyke rocks were laid under contribution, and perhaps even the granite itself.

### THE 'PERMIAN' IN SCOTLAND

The most interesting aspect of the **Scottish Permian** is the evidence for intense volcanic activity, particularly in the western parts of the Midland Valley. In the Mauchline Basin in Ayrshire, although the Permian rocks rest unconformably on Barren Coal Measures, the two have been gently folded together. The lower member of the succession consists of 500 feet of basic lava-flows and 'ashes', associated with desert sandstones. By far the greater part of the succession consists of the dune-bedded desert sandstones—the Mauchline Sandstone, 1500 feet thick, and widely used as a road metal. Some sixty volcanic vents pierce the Carboniferous rocks of the Ayrshire coalfield and on very strong evidence are correlated with the basic lavas. In the eastern part of the Midland Valley, East Fife also is famous for the hundred or more volcanic vents that have been discovered; but it is uncertain how many of these are of Permian age—some presumably were associated with the earlier volcanic outburts; but those few which cut Coal Measures are certainly Permian.

In the Southern Uplands strata referred to the Permian on the evidence of their desert lithology and reptilian footprints occur in a number of basin-like areas. In the Sanquhar and Thornhill coalfields strongly current bedded red desert sandstones associated with breccia bands rest unconformably, though with slight discordance of dip, on Lower Westphalian Coal Measures; but southwards they transgress on to the strongly folded Lower

Palaeozoic rocks and reach the Solway Firth south of Dumfries. As their original attitude has been practically undisturbed by subsequent earth-movements the contrast is very striking. Far to the north, on the shores of the Moray Firth near Elgin another small basin of Permian sandstones occurs and is famous for its fauna of reptiles including *Gordonia*, *Geikia* and *Elginia*. These Elgin Sandstones may be either late Permian or early Triassic in age.

## REFERENCES

The Regional Geologies: 'Northern England' covers the Permian and Permo-Trias of both the main outcrop and the Eden Vale occurrences; 'South-West England'.

WILLS, L. J. *Concealed Coalfields* (Blackie, 1956).

The following papers deal with special topics:

DIX, E. 'The flora of the highest Coal Measures in Warwickshire,' *Geol. Mag.*, **72** (1935), 555. Proves the Permian age of the Corley (Enville) beds.

DUNHAM, K. C. 'Syngenetic and Diagenetic Mineralization in Yorkshire,' *Proc. Yorks. Geol. Soc.*, **32** (1960), 264. Excellent summary of evaporites with comprehensive bibliography.

DUNHAM, K. C. 'Neptunistic Concepts in Ore Genesis,' *Econ. Geol.*, **59** (1964), 1. Conditions of deposition of the Kupferschiefer and its possible relation to the Pennine ore field.

HOLLINGWORTH, S. E. 'The correlation of the Gypsum-Anhydrite Deposits . . . in the North of England,' *Proc. Geol. Assoc.*, **53** (1942), 141.

SMITH, D. B. 'Observations on the Magnesian Limestone Reefs of North-Eastern Durham,' *Bull. Geol. Surv.*, **15** (1958), 71. Evidence for algal structures.

VERSEY, H. C. 'Petrography of the Permian rocks in the southern part of the Eden Valley,' *Quart. Journ. Geol. Soc.*, **95** (1939), 275. Deals with the provenance of the brockrams, the nature of the red colour of the beds and their heavy-mineral content.

WILLS, L. J. 'The Palaeogeography of the Birmingham country,' *Proc. Geol. Assoc.*, **46** (1935), 211, especially those parts dealing with the Red Rocks of the Midlands.

## CHAPTER XVI

# THE PERMO-TRIAS (2): THE TRIASSIC PERIOD

THE Trias covers a larger area in England than any other System: it floors the Midland and Cheshire Plains, and from the Midlands a broad outcrop extends north-eastwards to the Durham coast, while to the west of the Pennines another outcrop stretches north-westwards through Lancashire into Cumberland and Westmorland. In addition the Trias ranges through Gloucester and South Wales into Somerset and Devon, while there are outlying patches in Scotland, notably near Elgin.

Had this system been named in Britain, it would certainly not have been called Trias, the System of three divisions, for in these islands it is capable of division into two series only; but in Germany, the home of the Trias, it is divided into three series:

3. The Keuper.
2. The Muschelkalk.
1. The Bunter.

In the Alps and southern Europe generally the Trias was laid down under marine conditions, this region being then occupied by the Tethys. During the Muschelkalk Period this sea spread northwards, depositing marine limestones over Germany and an area stretching as far as Heligoland and eastern France. This marine incursion did not reach the British Isles, however, where the whole of the Trias, like the Bunter and Keuper of Germany, accumulated under 'continental conditions' in an area of inland drainage.

In Britain the Trias forms a thick irregular sheet of detritus burying the land surface that resulted from the Armorican orogeny. We have already visualized this surface as being one of very diversified topography. Probably every hill of Palaeozoic rocks that rises above the general level of the Midland Plain to-day already existed as part of the Mercian Highlands in Triassic times. The rocks of the Permian and Trias together represent the wastage from the Armorican uplands. Old Red Sandstone history repeats itself in the Trias, and in the imagination we can witness the gradual degradation of the hills, and see the mantle of rock-waste creeping higher and higher up the valleys, until over a great area all the surface irregularities were obliterated and a low-lying plain produced over which the sea advanced at the opening of the succeeding epoch. It follows that the Trias forms an overlapping series, the higher beds covering a much larger area than the lower ones, while the formation as a whole is strongly unconformable to the older rocks. In general, the picture we have drawn carries the implication that the higher parts of the Trias will be of finer grain-size than the lower parts: in many localities the System comprises arenaceous rocks, sandstones and conglomerates below, and finer-grained argillaceous sediments above. The practice has been to use the term Bunter for the former, and Keuper for the latter; but probably the real relationship is not as simple as this. Under desert conditions rock disintegration is very rapid in exposed highland areas, and extensive screes of coarse angular debris, like the Permian Brockram, accumulate at the foot of the steep slopes. Fossil screes formed in this way can often be seen in the Trias, plastered against the slopes of Palaeozoic rocks and consisting of locally derived fragments. Where they abut against Carboniferous Limestone, the fragments are of this rock; where sandstone or quartzite, these in turn predominate. Such is the Dolomitic Conglomerate ('Dolomitic Breccia' would be a far more appropriate name), which is banked against the pre-Triassic Carboniferous Limestone uplands in the South-West Province. Now it is obvious that such screes would continue to form as long as the essential conditions persisted: they are not constant in their horizon—on the contrary, provided that the hills were originally higher than the formation is thick, breccia formation would persist throughout the whole geological period. One of the big problems of the Trias concerns the extension of this argument to include the other rock-types, the sandstones and the 'marls'. In existing deserts we can witness the *contemporaneous* formation of piedmont gravel (potential breccia and conglomerate), dune sands (potential sandstones), variegated clays (potential marls and shales) and salt deposits. These are essentially the rock-types of the Trias, and we should be prepared, from a consideration of first principles, to find shales and marls in one locality occupying the same horizon and therefore of the same age as sandstones elsewhere and breccias along the then-existing margins of the desert. It would be surprising if this were not so; yet much controversy, violent at times, has centred round the questions of the status and correlation of the subdivisions of the Trias. These problems are capable of no simple solution. Fossils are exceedingly rare and the stratigrapher is thrown back upon lithology. Yet a simple application of the fact of lateral variation of lithological facies, proved in a score of cases for normal marine strata, shows how unreliable for the purpose lithology really is. The difficulty has arisen partly from the practice of using stratigraphical names in two senses. So long as we use the term Trias to designate a chapter of geological history we must recognize that it comprises three successive time-periods—the Lower Triassic, Middle Triassic and the Upper Triassic Periods. But these three names also signify characteristic assemblages of rocks: the Bunter rocks are typically sandstones, but not exclusively so, if our first principles are sound. Similarly the typical Muschelkalk rocks are marine limestones (in Germany), while the Keuper are so-called 'marls' and sandstones. Now in Britain, limestones of Muschelkalk age and Muschelkalk lithology are not present; but where the Triassic succession is unbroken as in Yorkshire, rocks of Muschelkalk age must be present, though whether of Bunter or Keuper lithology it is impossible to say. This is really the same as saying that in Britain the Muschelkalk consists of Bunter sandstones or Keuper marls, which is a rank absurdity, and illustrates yet again how impracticable it is to use lithological terms in a time sense. Reasoning on similar lines it should not surprise us to learn that although in some localities the Bunter lithology is well developed, in other districts it is quite impossible to separate Bunter from Keuper on lithological grounds. In other words, rocks of Bunter age have assumed Keuper lithology.

On the other hand, in parts of western Scotland pebbly sandstone immediately underlies the Rhaetic, so that here the converse is true, and rocks of Keuper age are of Bunter lithology. To stress the point still further, in Raasay, one of the Hebrides, Keuper (lithology) is sandwiched in between Bunter above as well as below.

Dr R. L. Sherlock, who made a long study of the problems of the Permian and Trias, urged stratigraphers to work *downwards from the top* instead of upwards from the base in attempting correlation of these strata, using the base of the Rhaetic as a datum plane. It is believed that at the close of Triassic times all the original irregularities must have been smoothed out, and when the Rhaetic Sea inundated the region of the Triassic deserts it rapidly advanced over a sensibly flat surface stretching from Spain to Scandinavia. The salt deposits in the Trias, to which attention is directed below, occur at several different levels, at approximately constant depths beneath the Rhaetic base over a wide area, suggesting that these also may be regarded as datum planes. If Sherlock's suggestion is accepted, it at once becomes apparent that some part of the 'Bunter' is equivalent to some part of the 'Keuper'. For this reason we will consider the sandstone facies ('Bunter') and the marl facies ('Keuper') separately, while admitting that they are, in part, the equivalents of one another. Following this line of reasoning to its logical conclusion, Sherlock went a good deal farther than this and took the extreme view that much of the Permian is merely the lateral equivalent of the Bunter, basing his conclusions on changes in the Permian rocks when traced from Durham through Yorkshire into Nottingham. In brief, the Magnesian Limestone of Durham becomes much reduced in thickness to the south, and in Yorkshire (Fig. 74) the middle portion has been replaced by marl (Middle Permian Marl). In Nottinghamshire all that remains is about 15 feet of Middle Marl resting on a few feet of Lower Magnesian Limestone with Marl Slate and local basal breccia. In some exposures the Middle Marl passes up through sandy marl into typical red Bunter Sandstone with no obvious break, and certainly with no

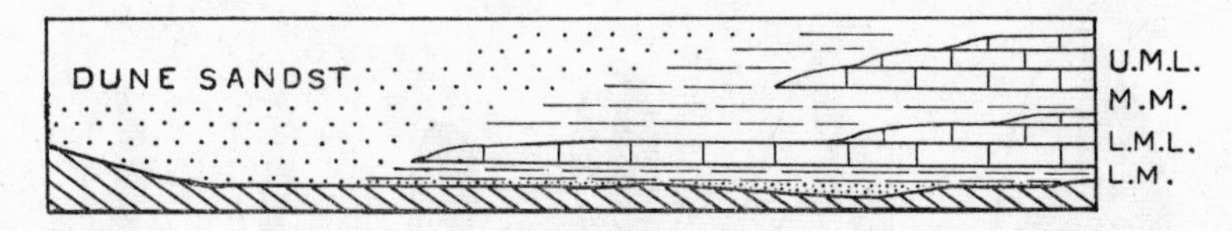


FIG. 82.
Diagram-section showing the variation (vertical and horizontal) displayed by Permian rocks between Yorks. (right) and Notts. (left).

M.L.—Magnesian Limestone (Upper and Lower).
M.M.—'Middle' Marl; L.M.—Lower Marl, the southern equivalent of the Marl Slate of Durham.

Time-planes are horizontal; the contemporaneity of (say) the upper part of the Lower Magnesian Limestone with the so-called Middle Marl, and farther south with Bunter (Dune) Sandstone is implicit in the diagram.

discordance of dip. These sections are interpreted as proving the equivalence of the Nottingham Bunter and the Durham Magnesian Limestone (Fig. 82).

**The Bunter Facies**

The rocks of Bunter facies comprise two chief types: soft, red sandstones and so-called pebble beds. A maximum thickness of 3000 feet is reached by these beds in Lancashire, but the two lithological types are most clearly differentiated in Shropshire and Staffordshire, where the lower Trias is traditionally capable of subdivision into:

3. Upper Mottled Sandstone.
2. Pebble Beds.
1. Lower Mottled Sandstone.

These lithological divisions are impersistent, however; the pebble-bed facies dies out north of the Ribble in Lancashire and north of Doncaster in Yorkshire, where the Bunter Sandstone is indivisible. Lithologically the sandstones are distinctive in colour, being bright red, mottled with green, yellow or white; they are normally soft and but loosely cemented. Strong current bedding of the type usually shown by sand-dunes has led to the belief that they were largely wind-transported. The occurrence in the sandstones of a large proportion of spherical millet-seed grains, about 0.5 mm. in diameter, and of wind-shaped pebbles (dreikanter), supports this view (Fig. 83). The rocks are coming to be known as the Dune Sandstones. They originated as 'barchans' in the Permo-Triassic desert and farther north, pass laterally into the mud-flats with salt deposits occupying the site of the Zechstein Sea in northern England.

The Pebble Beds are usually regarded as the most distinctive part of the Bunter, though they are very variable in the size, number

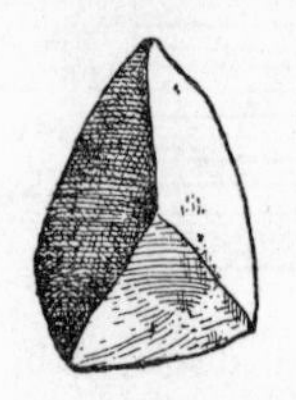

FIG. 83.

'Dreikanters' or Ventifacts: pebbles shaped by blown sand, thus indicating aeolian conditions.

These specimens consist of jasper, chalcedony, quartzite and rhyolite, and were collected in South-West Africa.

and distribution of the pebbles. Actually the name is a misnomer for much of the rock termed 'pebble beds'. It seems to have been given to sandstone somewhat harder than the Mottled Sandstone, somewhat browner in colour, and containing pebbles, not necessarily many, and at some horizons none at all. 'Pebble beds' without pebbles are indeed anomalous; but in the Liverpool district the 'Bunter Pebble Beds' are divided into a lower part with pebbles, and an upper part in which pebbles are scarce or absent altogether. Further, Sherlock says that the so-called pebble beds of the Manchester district would certainly 'be called Lower Mottled Sandstone if found across the Pennines' in Nottingham. Readers will by now recognize the symptoms and will know the remedy—not to name a time-division, Pebble Beds. Actually only in part of Staffordshire (Cannock Chase) are the pebbles closely packed, forming a polygenetic conglomerate.

The pebbles themselves, which vary in diameter from a quarter of an inch to eighteen inches, have been studied in the hope that they would furnish evidence of the rocks exposed to denudation at the time of their accumulation. This hope has not been fully realized. Many of the pebbles—some of them are cobbles or small boulders—have been matched with local rocks exposed in the Midlands to-day: these include Rubery (Llandovery) Sandstone, Lickey (Cambrian) Quartzite and Carboniferous cherts. Coarse- and fine-grained granitic rocks, lavas and schists of different kinds also occur in variety. A red grit has been referred to the Torridonian Sandstone of the North-West Highlands, but the 'red' Western Longmyndian is much nearer. The big problem of the pebble beds is the place of origin of certain liver-coloured quartzites which have not been exactly matched with any known outcrop, though speculation has ranged as far afield as the Scottish Highlands and Brittany. It is generally agreed that the pebbles are water-worn, of fluvial origin, deposited on a wide mountain-girt plain by swiftly flowing rivers swollen by flood waters. The difficulty of deriving them from any far-distant source is not insuperable: comparable instances can be found among existing rivers; but it is much easier and more likely that local sources now buried under the cover of newer rocks provided the 'unplaced' pebbles. Traced southwards from the Midlands the pebbly facies dies out, but reappears in Devonshire and Somerset, being strongly developed on the coast at Budleigh Salterton. Problems of provenance arise in this case also; for while there is no difficulty in deriving the many pebbles of Carboniferous Limestone found in these rocks in Somerset from the outcrop bordering the South Wales coalfield, and the cherts and Carboniferous Sandstones from the Culm to the west, there are many sandstones and quartzite pebbles, some fossiliferous, that match up exactly with Ordovician rocks occurring in France, but not anywhere in Britain, and a southerly source is strongly indicated.

The general inference to be drawn from these facts is that in early Triassic times at least two large river systems of considerable volume and velocity were responsible for spreading these sheets of pebbly gravel over the floor of part of the Triassic desert. There are no means of proving that the Bunter Pebble Beds of the English Midlands are of the same age as the Budleigh Salterton Pebble Beds of the Devonshire coast; but the change in vertical sequence from (Bunter) Dune Sandstones to fluvial Pebble Beds must have involved a climatic change, for these are large rivers and their presence indicates increased rainfall due, it is thought, to uplift of the area now covered by southern England.

From the point of view of the water supply of the Midlands the Bunter Sandstones are all-important. The amount of water which can be stored in a stratum depends upon the pore space available, and this is at a maximum in coarse-grained millet-seed sands. Particularly where covered by Keuper Marl, the Bunter is a natural underground reservoir which is tapped by countless wells and borings for water. The Bunter water is suitable for use in the brewing industry: Burton-on-Trent readily comes to mind as a centre dependent on this fact for its prosperity.

**The Keuper Facies**

This facies of the Trias comprises three rock-types: sandstones, so-called marls and mineral-salt deposits.

The Keuper sandstones differ from the Bunter both in lithology and origin. They are finer in grain, often well laminated, and consist of angular grains. On account of a fancied but rather far-fetched resemblance to 'watered silk' the laminated sandstones have been unfortunately named 'waterstones'. False bedding is common, and is of the normal deltaic type with well-developed top-set and fore-set beds. Lenses of marl are not uncommon in the sandstones, which are sometimes fossiliferous, yielding fish-remains including *Ceratodus*, a lung fish, plants, scorpions and rarely the footprints of amphibians.

In 1955 a marly band containing *Lingula* was found in Keuper Waterstones near Eakring in Nottinghamshire. One specimen was lying at right angles to the bedding planes and was clearly in the position of growth. Whilst lingulas are known to-day to tolerate a greater range of salinity than any other brachiopod, they have never been found living in anything approaching fresh water. We therefore have evidence of a period, perhaps only temporary, of marine or near-marine conditions during the deposition of the Keuper Waterstones. Closely comparable lingulas occur in both the Muschelkalk and Keuper in Germany, so there is a strong case for suggesting a temporary connection with the Triassic seas of Germany.

By far the most important rock-type in the Keuper facies is the so-called marl. It reaches a thickness of nearly 5000 feet under the Cheshire Plain, and although the local thicknesses are very variable, the lithology is remarkably constant over an area extending from Ireland to Bavaria. In Britain it is a unique deposit, better described as red mudstone than as marl, for marl is commonly understood to be a strongly calcareous clay soil; the Keuper Marl is but slightly calcareous and is not in the physical condition of clay. For the most part it is not stratified but structureless, breaking with a starchy fracture, and closely resembling loess. It consists largely of fine silt with an admixture of clay minerals and small dolomite crystals. The resemblance in physical characters to loess naturally suggests a common origin for both, and there are grounds for believing that the Keuper loess, like that which covers much of the surface of Asia with a thick mantle, originated in an arid region as rock flour that was transported by wind and was ultimately deposited as aeolian clay. Those parts of the Keuper loess which are stratified were presumably deposited in temporary lakes, or perhaps were resorted and interstratified with coarser detritus brought down from the uplands by freshets and spread over the surface of the Keuper plains by flood waters. The sandy intercalations (skerries) are greenish or grey in colour, they are often strongly false bedded, they show ripplemarks and sun cracks and locally 'pseudomorphs' (really casts) of clay after rock-salt crystals, proving that the bodies of water in which they were deposited existed for only short periods, and were perhaps like the *vleys* which appear in the wet season in the African deserts. A much more extensive flooding is proved by the occurrence of a 40-foot sandstone band some 150 feet down from the top of the Keuper in parts of the Midlands. Best exposed in the Forest of Arden, this **Arden Sandstone** is noteworthy as being, for the Trias, richly fossiliferous. It has yielded the remains of coniferous and other plants, fishes and amphibians, as well as molluscs of doubtful generic affinities.

On the other hand, shrinkage of the Keuper 'lakes' is proved by the mineral-salt deposits that occur at several different levels. Gypsum, hydrated calcium sulphate, occurs at Newark and several places between Nottingham and Leicester at about 60 feet down in the Trias. At a little more than twice this depth the same mineral occurs in Leicester, Derbyshire and Staffordshire. At Chellaston in Derbyshire compact gypsum has been worked as alabaster for a very long time. Now apart from carbonates, gypsum is the first of the mineral salts to be deposited from an inland sea or salt lake undergoing rapid evaporation; but even so, the mineral is not deposited until the volume of water has been considerably reduced. A further degree of desiccation is proved by the occurrence of thick deposits of rock salt (sodium chloride) in the Keuper of Cheshire, Lancashire, North-East Ireland, the Isle of Man, Staffordshire, Worcester and Somerset. Long before the accidental discovery of rock salt in Cheshire in 1670, when searching for coal, salt had been obtained by evaporating brine from salt springs in this country perhaps as far back as pre-Roman times. In spite of the enormous quantities that have been taken out of the Trias, latterly by pumping out the brine, not by mining the rock salt, for use as a condiment and preservative, for exploitation in the chemical, alkali, glass and soap industries and in metallurgical operations, the supply is still adequate to the demand. The removal of so much material from underground has left its mark on the surface: the Cheshire Plain is dotted with lakes occupying the sites of local subsidences. A recent boring, specially sunk to prove the amount of rock salt present at depth, has shown that the Keuper Marl contains two saliferous groups described as 'rock salt with subordinate beds of marl', the higher over 1300 feet and the lower over 600 feet in thickness. The marls above, below and separating the saliferous groups contain numerous subordinate beds of gypsum and anhydrite. In Worcestershire, Droitwich has been a centre of the salt industry from the earliest times; but the exploitation of the Somersetshire salt-field is a comparatively modern venture. The salt here is known to underlie the Bridgwater flats at the foot of the Polden Hills, of Lias, which rise so prominently above the plain.

Our last glimpse of Triassic times shows us the incoming of a climatic and geographical change. Towards the top, the Keuper Marl loses its red colour and becomes green, indicating less arid conditions, probably due to the gradual approach of the sea. The change appears to have set in earlier in the south than in the north, for the **Tea Green Marls** in part underlie the top gypsum horizon, while elsewhere they start some distance above it. This is an apparent anomaly as it is difficult to reconcile moister conditions with salt deposition.

The Triassic rocks as a whole are soft and easily denuded. As a consequence the Palaeozoic floor on which they rest is slowly being uncovered, and the buried hills are being stripped of their cover of marl. On the flanks of Exmoor and the Quantock Hills in Somerset, of the Mendip Hills farther north, and particularly in the Charnwood Forest district of Leicestershire, details of the sub-Triassic landscape can be studied, The rugged crags of Precambrian rocks in the last-named area are believed to have stood, much as they do to-day, as inselberge ('island-mountains') locally dominating the Triassic desert (Fig. 84). Quarrying operations, as well as natural wear and tear, have re-excavated some of the wadies—steep-walled valleys ripped in the hills in Triassic times. There is no feature of this kind more stimulating to the imagination than the smoothed but grooved surface of Mountsorrel granite against which the Keuper Marl is banked. In Professor Watt's view, blown sand was the agent responsible for grooving the granite; but Dr Raw has pointed out that the surface is not polished, and as an alternative suggests that the grooves mark different levels at which the waters of the Keuper Lake stood. The quartzite and other pebbles in the Keuper in this region are not dreikanters (Fig. 83); they are not sand-blasted, but they have been chipped in a distinctive manner as a consequence of exposure to the rapid changes of temperature to which they were subjected when lying on the surface of the desert. Either explanation is quite consistent with the picture of the local conditions, deduced from the lithology and distribution of the rocks: there must have been Keuper lakes, or there would be no salt

FIG. 84.—Inselberge landscape. An impression of the Charnwood Forest region in Keuper times. Actually the Lion Mountains, South-West Africa.

deposits; there must have been wind erosion, particularly in early Triassic times, witness the dreikanters and millet-seed sand. The question is complicated by Dr F. Raw's clear demonstration of the fact that rock surfaces exposed in Charnwood Forest during the Pleistocene Period were sand-blasted by strong winds blowing constantly from the north-east.

**Palaeowinds and Palaeomagnetism**

Distinctive features of the New Red Sandstone are the presence of thick beds of fossil dune sands and of evaporite deposits. In no other part of the British Stratigraphical Column are these so well developed. Dune sands occur in the Elgin area, Ayrshire and Dumfriesshire in Scotland; they are spectacularly developed in the Penrith Sandstone and in the Western Midlands and are to be found in the most southerly outcrops in Devonshire. Study of their false-bedding reveals a remarkable consistency in the direction of the foresets proving that these barchan belts were deposited by winds blowing persistently from an easterly direction (see Fig. 81). Dune movement in modern deserts (Sahara, Arabian, Australian, etc.) is clearly related to the general circulation of the atmosphere. In the inter-tropical Trade Wind belt the dunes travel from an easterly, in more northerly or southerly latitudes, from a westerly direction. If we assume that the general circulation of the atmosphere was the same in Permo-Triassic times as it is to-day (and short of a complete reversal of the direction of the earth's rotation, it is very difficult to see why this should not be the case), then the logical deduction is that Britain must have been in much lower latitudes then than it is to-day.

The evaporite horizons in the British Permo-Trias are but the western fringe of a much thicker salt-rich succession extending across Holland, Germany and the western parts of Poland. Such extensive evaporite deposits are forming to-day only in regions of considerable evaporation (high summer temperature, low rainfall and appreciable wind movement) in a belt certainly extending well beyond the Tropics, but scarcely to the present latitudes of the British Isles.

So far we have been following the classical method of the Doctrine of Uniformitarianism (the Present is the Key to the Past) in attempting to interpret fossil sediments from the conditions of to-day. During the past fifteen years or so, the development of the study of palaeomagnetism has provided a new geophysical line of investigation which is very relevant to our present discussion. As an igneous rock containing an appreciable amount of ferromagnetic minerals cools past a critical point, known as its Curie point, it acquires and retains a magnetic moment aligned in the direction of the earth's magnetic field at that time. During the deposition of sedimentary rocks detrital magnetic particles are aligned parallel to the then existing magnetic field. If carefully orientated specimens of magnetic rocks, either igneous or sedimentary, are collected and the declination and inclination of their contained magnetic fields are measured, then it is possible to deduce the position of the earth's magnetic pole at the time of their formation. These pole positions show very considerable variation for rocks of the different Systems. But unfortunately ferromagnetic minerals, such as magnetite and haematite, are present only in significant amounts in a very limited range of rocks—the basic and intermediate hypabyssal and extrusive igneous rocks and brightly coloured sedimentary rocks, mainly of the continental 'Red Bed' facies. Even then, the determinations made at any one locality may not be sufficiently consistent to give fossil pole positions that can be used with any degree of confidence. There are therefore many limitations, at present, to the information that can be obtained from palaeomagnetism. The significance of palaeomagnetic determinations in the Theory of Continental Drift is outside the scope of this book.

A considerable number of determinations of magnetic pole positions have been made for the Permo-Triassic Red Beds in Europe and the United States. These give fairly consistent results, indicating that the northern magnetic pole was then situated near the present position of the Japanese archipelago. If the continents were at that time in the same relative position as they are to-day, the Equator would run through the Mediterranean across Spain to Newfoundland and would then slant across the United States to the southern tip of California. With such a position of the Equator, the widespread dune sands and evaporite deposits of the British Isles and Germany would fall well within the Intertropical Trade Wind Belt.

## REFERENCES

As for the Permian System, and in addition:

NAIRN, A. E. Editor. *Descriptive Palaeoclimatology* (Interscience, London, 1961), especially Chapters III, IV, V and VII.

SHOTTON, F. W. Discusses, in particular, the dune-sands and directions of prevalent wind in the Permian deserts, *Liv. and Manch. Geol. Journ.*, **1** (1956), 450–465.

## CHAPTER XVII

# THE RHAETIC

THE Rhaetic Series constitutes a set of passage beds between the continental Keuper beneath and the marine main Jurassic rocks above. As with 'passage beds' in other parts of the stratigraphical column, there has been much discussion both as to the status of the Rhaetic and as to the systematic position of the beds.

The Rhaetic beds of the Tethyan region yield ammonites which are Triassic, not Jurassic, in their affinities. Ammonite specialists therefore recognize a Rhaetian Stage as the topmost stage of the Triassic System. Elsewhere in western Europe, the Rhaetic beds contain a distinctive fauna though without ammonites. In some countries the Rhaetic beds interdigitate with strata of Keuper lithology; in others, as in Britain, they overlie the typical Trias and pass upwards into beds yielding a Jurassic fauna. In Britain, the Rhaetic was clearly accumulated under special conditions, whilst the environment was changing from the deserts of the Triassic to the shallow seas of the Jurassic Period. This is our justification for treating the Rhaetic as a separate series rather than following the ammonite specialists in grouping it with the Trias, or the custom of most British geologists in regarding it as the basal member of the Jurassic System.

The Rhaetic are shown to have been deposited during a period of transition by abnormalities both in lithology and in their faunal contents. They are not normal marine strata, but were accumulated under lagoonal conditions, that is, in bodies of shallow water cut off probably by low barriers from the open sea. The surface upon which the Rhaetic beds were deposited was one of low relief, rendered so by the long-continued denudation of the Permo-Triassic Period and by the accumulation in the original valleys and hollows of great thickness of sandstones and marls. But it was not a completely flat surface: at a number of localities in England the Rhaetic beds change their lithology and thin out against masses of pre-Triassic rocks which must have stood as islands above the Rhaetic lagoons. The largest of these islands where these characters can to-day be studied is the region of the Mendips, but there are numbers of smaller ones in the belt of country lying between the southern margin of the South Wales coalfield and the Severn estuary.

Although the Rhaetic Series is usually less than 50 feet in thickness, it is divisible into five groups of beds (Fig. 85) in the classical outcrops of Somerset and Gloucester, of which the best-known occur at Aust Cliff, near the southern entrance to the Severn Tunnel, and Westbury Garden Cliff, on the opposite bank of the Severn. In these river cliffs erosion of the soft Keuper Marls undermines the harder

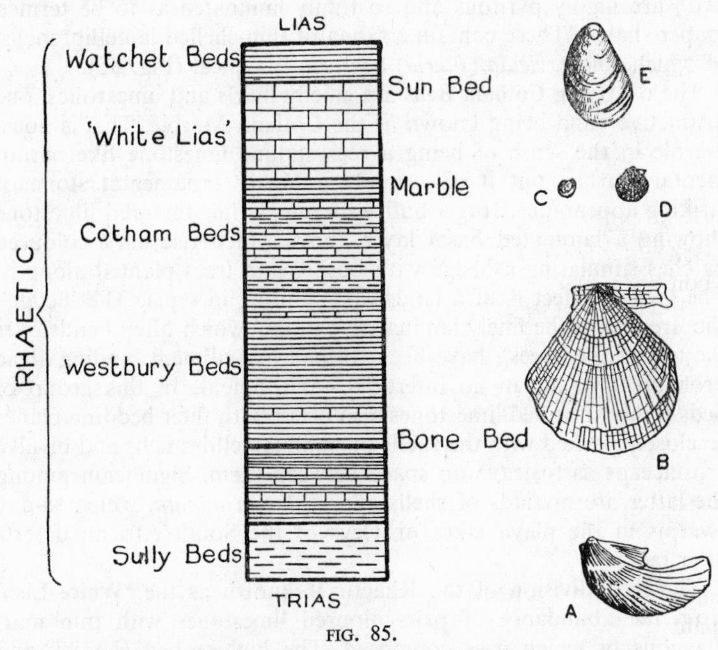


FIG. 85.

The Rhaetic succession, together with characteristic fossils:

A. *Rhaetavicula* (*Pteria*) *contorta.*
B. *Chlamys* (*Pecten*) *valoniensis.*
C. *Euestheria minuta.*
D. *Pseudomonotis fallax.*
E. *Liostrea* (*Ostrea*) *liassica.*

Rhaetic rocks, which fall in large slabs from the higher parts of the cliffs.

Prominent among these are fragments of the well-known **Rhaetic Bone Bed,** a highly pyritous layer an inch or two in thickness and rich in the remains of amphibians, reptiles and fishes. It is evidently a condensed deposit: although thin, it represents a considerable period of time. In some localities the 'bone bed' is at the actual base of the Rhaetic, and thus constitutes an organic basal conglomerate comparable with the Ludlow Bone Bed at the base of the Downtonian Series. In other areas, notably in the Severn estuary littoral, any thickness up to 20 feet of grey marl may separate the Rhaetic from the Keuper. These **Sully Beds** represent local infillings of the original hollows, and the strata which come above are much more extensive, showing that sedimentation later took place more uniformly over a much wider area. Above the 'bone bed' a series of black shales occurs and these, like the 'bone bed', are highly pyritous and so thinly laminated as to be termed 'paper shales'. These contain a fauna of thin-shelled lamellibranchs, of which *Rhaetavicula* (*Pteria*) *contorta* is typical (Fig. 85).

The overlying **Cotham Beds** are chiefly marls and limestones, one distinctive band being known as the Cotham Marble. This is not a marble in the sense of being a recrystalline limestone like monumental marble, but it is certainly a highly ornamental stone of striking appearance. It is a buff, exceedingly fine textured limestone showing a laminated basal layer above which rise dark coloured patches simulating a hedge with bushes and trees planted along it. The general effect is of a landscape painting in sepia. The 'hedge', the 'trees' and the finely laminated 'canopy' which often bends over the top of the 'trees', have been formed by sediment binding algae probably growing in an intertidal environment. In this group of beds thinly stratified limestones also occur with their bedding planes so closely packed with the shells of small lamellibranchs and bivalve crustaceans as to leave no space between them. Significant among the latter are myriads of shells of *Euestheria minuta*, which to-day swarms in the playa lakes or vleys of the South African deserts after rain.

The next division of the Rhaetic is known as the **'White Lias'** from the abundance of pale-coloured limestones with thin marl divisions of which it is composed. The highest bed is thick and massive enough to be quarried locally as a building stone, known as the 'Sun Bed'.

It is a curious coincidence that the highest member of the Series, the **Watchet Beds** consisting of oyster-bearing marls, is practically restricted to those localities where the lowest member of the Rhaetic succession, the Sully Beds, also occurs.

The succession just briefly described is that typical of the type-area of South-West England; but it is significant that when the beds are traced north-eastwards to Yorkshire, in no one locality is the succession complete. Local breaks cut out a few feet of beds here, and a few feet there, in a manner which we shall study in fuller detail in the main Jurassic System. Such minor breaks are termed **'non-sequences'**, and they suggest that the subsidence of the land in relation to sea-level, which later allowed the Jurassic seas to inundate the greater part of England, was by no means continuous or uniform, even over relatively small areas.

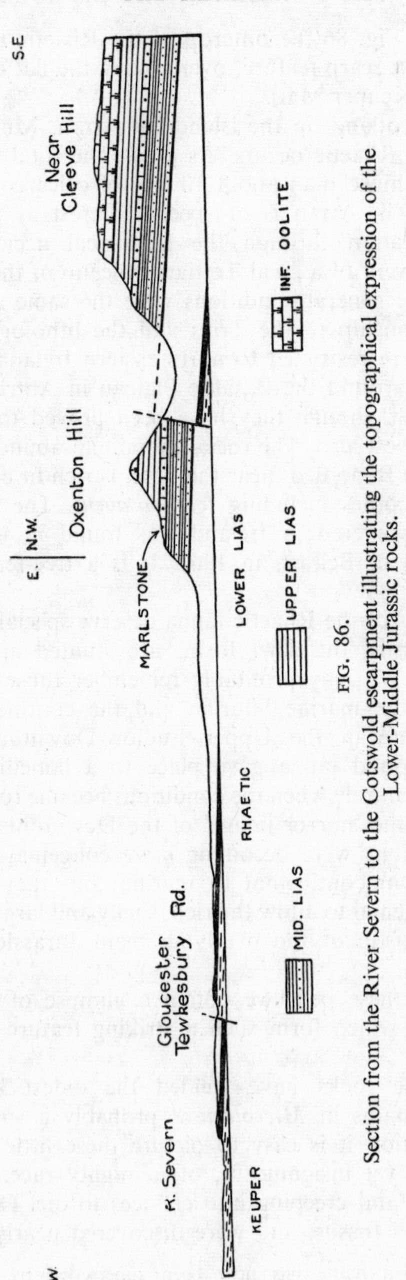


FIG. 86.

Section from the River Severn to the Cotswold escarpment illustrating the topographical expression of the Lower-Middle Jurassic rocks.

As shown in Fig. 86 the outcrop of the Rhaetic beds is usually marked by a low scarp-feature, overlooking the flat country on the outcrop of the Keuper Marls.

In western Scotland, in the islands of Arran, Mull and Skye, a very attenuated Rhaetic occurs. As a rule the total thickness does not amount to more than about 10 feet of calcareous sandstones. The occurrence in Arran is of special interest as the beds have survived denudation through the geological accident of being engulfed in the vent of a great Tertiary volcano of the caldera type.

In Ireland the general conditions were the same as in England, so is the relationship to the Trias and the lithology and faunas. Rhaetic strata are restricted to north-eastern Ireland and occur in small outcrops around the Basaltic Plateau in Antrim, to the east of Lough Neagh, though they have been proved to occur, below surface, to the west also. The rocks contain an abundant molluscan fauna, while the Bone Bed, near the base, is rich in bones and teeth of fishes and reptiles including *Ichthyosaurus*. The first Mesozoic plant to be discovered in Ireland was found in the Rhaetic at Waterloo north of Belfast, in 1961. It is a tree-fern, *Otozamites bechei*.

Three features of the Rhaetic fauna deserve special notice: of the invertebrate fossils, the chief forms are stunted and thin-shelled lamellibranchs. We may profitably remember those other passage beds, between the marine Silurian and the continental Old Red Sandstone, where in the Upper Ludlow-Downtonian rocks an expiring brachiopod fauna gave place to a lamellibranch fauna, which died out entirely when the conditions became too uncongenial. The Rhaetic is the 'mirror image' of the Downtonian in the sense that the conditions were becoming *more* congenial to animal life in changing from continental to marine; but they were not yet sufficiently congenial to allow the rich, shelly and largely brachiopod fauna characteristic of the overlying main Jurassic to enter the Rhaetic lagoons.

Secondly, in these beds we obtain a glimpse of the first great aquatic reptiles which form such a striking feature of the Liassic fauna.

Thirdly, these rocks have yielded the oldest known British mammalian remains in *Microlestes*,[1] probably a small marsupial. In the imagination it is easy to picture these little creatures, the forerunners, as yet insignificant, of a mighty race, living on the Mendip Island, and creeping into crevices to die. Only their teeth have survived as fossils, and were discovered nearly one hundred

[1] This well-known name has now been superseded by *Hypsiprymnopsis rhaeticus*.

years ago in Rhaetic-filled fissures in the Carboniferous Limestone near Frome in Somerset. Persistent sifting of the material from some of these shallow fissures yielded to C. Moore no fewer than 70,000 teeth and small bones of vertebrates, amongst which were twenty-nine teeth of *Microlestes* and a related type. Recently other fossiliferous fissures have been discovered in the Mendip Hills and also on the other side of the Bristol Channel in Glamorgan, South Wales. One fissure at Pant in Glamorgan proved to be amazingly fossiliferous: in addition to over one thousand triconodont teeth it has yielded hundreds of jaws and many vertebrae, skull- and long bones. The mode of articulation of the jaw definitely proves the creature to have been a mammal, while other features of the skull strongly suggest that it was a monotreme—a primitive egg-laying mammal—and therefore ancestral to the Australian duck-billed *Platypus* and spiny ant-eater, *Echidna*, the only living monotremes.

## CHAPTER XVIII

# THE JURASSIC PERIOD

THE Rhaetic beds are followed conformably by a thick succession of strata comprising the main Jurassic System, which has been divided into a number of major stratigraphical 'Series' based originally upon their lithological characters. Several of the stratal names applied to these divisions by the pioneer English stratigrapher, William Smith, in the period 1794 to 1796 are still widely used; but a parallel set of chronological divisions, the names of which all end in the uniform termination 'ian', have been introduced. These are based upon the faunal characters of the beds and are of wider application than the English stratal terms. Further, Oppel and others working on similar lines have subdivided the main 'stages' into a large number of 'zones', and these in turn into 'sub-zones'. We have already used these terms, for example when studying the graptolitic facies of the Ordovician; the Lower Carboniferous is divided into coral and brachiopod zones, while the goniatite zones of the Carboniferous are proving invaluable in working out the details of the succession and structure; but in the Jurassic System the process has been carried a good deal further and has been applied with a higher degree of accuracy than in the Palaeozoic Systems. This is explained by the fact that the ammonites in the Jurassic have proved more delicate time-indices than perhaps any other class of animal. They were evolving rapidly, and distinctive changes in those characters by which species and varieties are recognized were developed quickly, and in the short periods of time so required, only small thicknesses of sediment accumulated. Thus a zone in the Jurassic may be defined as a bed (or beds) of rock identified by their faunal contents and named after one distinctive species of ammonite. The fauna is the invariable element, but both the thickness and the lithology of the zones are subject to wide variation. In the Lias alone there are seventeen zones and no fewer than fifty-two sub-zones. Although the latter are by no means uniform in thickness, it is instructive in this connection to note that the total thickness of the Lias averages 500 feet, which suggests the figure of 10 feet as being the average thickness of a Liassic sub-zone.

The Jurassic rocks include many different types, but broadly speaking they comprise alternations of clay or shale with sand and limestone, with a marked preponderance of clay and limestone.

It is often possible to recognize a rhythm (in upward succession) of clay-sand-limestone, though the several members of the rhythm may be of very different thicknesses, and individual rhythms (or cyclothems) may be traceable for but limited distances. Throughout the main English outcrop, which stretches across country from the Dorset coast to that of Yorkshire, the strata are inclined gently to the east or south-east. The well-marked clay divisions are the most consistent in their lithology and give rise to broad flat vales, while the limestone groups, on the other hand, form steep escarpments facing west, with long, gentle, easterly directed dip slopes.

Primarily, the Jurassic rocks are grouped into three major divisions, the Lower, Middle and Upper respectively.

## THE LOWER JURASSIC

The Lower Jurassic is co-extensive with the **Lias,** a formation comparatively well known as it is splendidly exposed in parts of the English coast that enjoy a measure of popularity as seaside resorts, and also on account of the spectacular reptilian remains obtained from these beds, which figure prominently in museum collections.

For more than a century the Lias has been divided into Lower, Middle and Upper groups, based originally on changes in lithology, but subsequently restated in terms of ammonite zones. Of these three divisions the **Lower Lias** is most consistent in its lithology, while the Upper Lias is so exceedingly variable that any summary statement of its characters is very difficult to make.

Rather less than the lower half of the **Lower Lias** consists of rapid alternations of bluish marl or shale with pale grey argillaceous limestone. This interstratification is extraordinarily regular and suggests a rhythmic, possibly a seasonal cause for the banding, though it has been suggested that this remarkably regular interstratification of clay and limestone is not an original feature, but that the two types of sediment were separated subsequently to deposition. Hallam has shown (1960) that the banding must be primary. Certain of the limestone beds contain abundant trace fossils, that is structures produced by organisms moving on or below the surface of soft sediment. Some are vertical U-shaped burrows, others are branching structures either ramifying along a bedding plane or at an angle to the bedding. These burrows, infilled by sediment from a higher level, produce a mottled appearance to the rock surfaces. Burrows can often be seen to cut across or through one another and, as with dyke swarms in igneous rocks, a relative chronology can be worked out. The important point is that at numerous levels in the Blue Lias the base of a marl seam can be seen to rest on a slightly eroded surface of limestone. Clearly erosion of the limestone and the planing off of its burrows must have occurred before the deposition of the marl. Further, whilst the marl and limestone bands contain a rich and varied benthonic fauna, the interstratified paper shales are largely barren, though rich in bituminous matter. This again must be an original feature and must reflect the change from aerobic to anaerobic conditions on the sea bed. This portion of the Lias is called the 'Blue Lias', and in many localities it is quarried for paving slabs, for example at Street in Somerset, while they are prominent also in the pavements of Glastonbury, near-by. The name Lias is a corruption of 'layers' and obviously refers to the layered nature of this part of the succession. It was an old quarryman's term, adopted by William Smith in 1799 in his first 'Table of Strata'. In the south of England the Blue Lias is exploited also in the manufacture of hydraulic cement. In the quarrying operations large numbers of skeletons, often complete, and innumerable bones and teeth have been obtained of the giant reptiles of the period, to which further reference is made below. Less spectacular, but of far greater value to the stratigrapher, are the ammonites which occur frequently preserved in full relief in iron sulphide or in stained calcite. In Whitby and Lyme Regis until recently there were picturesque old shops in which almost the sole wares displayed were the ammonites and other fossils collected locally.

Above, the Blue Lias limestones are subordinate to clay and shale, and in the Lower Lias, as a whole, blue clay is much the most abundant rock-type. In Lincolnshire, however, the Blue Lias is separated from the dominantly argillaceous facies by some 25 feet of ferruginous oolitic limestone—the Frodingham Ironstone.

The Lower Lias retains these general characters throughout the whole outcrop, which extends from the coast at Lyme Regis to the Yorkshire coast at Whitby, Robin Hood's Bay and Redcar. It forms an easily followed belt of low-lying, flat ground, often swampy, for the Lias gives rise to a heavy tenacious clay soil. The outcrop forms the Ilminster flats and much of Sedgemoor south of the Mendips, and to the north the Vale of Gloucester and the Vale of Evesham. Still farther to the north the outcrop expands in the neighbourhood of Rugby to some 10 miles across, but then narrows to less than a quarter of a mile in the neighbourhood of Market Weighton. Beyond this belt of minimum thickness the outcrop once more expands to the Yorkshire coast. Such variations may be due to changes in the angle of dip of the beds, in the general case, but with the Lias it is due to actual variations in thickness. From Chard in Dorset the Lower Lias thins from 540 feet to 300 feet at Ilminster;

near Radstock, just north of the Mendips, the beds are very variable in thickness, at maximum less than 200 feet, but often less than 50 feet with some zones unrepresented. Traced farther northwards the beds increase rapidly to over 500 feet in the Gloucester-Cheltenham district and near Evesham they reach a maximum of 960 feet. These figures serve to illustrate the order of the variation in thickness: similar changes take place as the beds are traced into Yorkshire. The cause of the variation was undoubtedly *differential subsidence* of the sea floor on which the Lower Lias was deposited. The importance of this phenomenon during Jurassic times cannot be overestimated (see p. 298): it governed sedimentation in the sense of controlling the thickness of sediment that accumulated in any given period either on the stable areas (the 'shallows'), or in the intervening troughs.

In addition to the main Mendip uplifted area, there appear to have been a number of other 'islands' of Carboniferous rocks that were not submerged in this period: they had formed inselberge against which the Keuper sediments had been banked, they had stood as islands above the Rhaetic lagoons, and they still persisted in at least early-Liassic times. Each zone in turn, when traced up to these 'islands' in the belt of country lying between the South Wales coalfield and the Severn estuary, changes in lithology from the normal clays with interbedded limestones into calcareous littoral rocks consisting largely of shell debris and material derived by marine erosion from the Carboniferous Limestone.

The **Middle Lias** on the average is much thinner than the Lower division, it comprises two zones only, and is divisible into two main lithological units: a relatively thick series of clays passing up into sands succeeded by a thin, essentially limestone group. The latter is termed the Marlstone. Variations in thickness due to uplift in the three areas referred to above are to be noted in the Middle Lias also, the beds being completely absent in the neighbourhood of the Mendip and Market Weighton 'axes'.

While the Lower Lias, as we have seen, forms extensive flats like those which, in Gloucestershire, stretch from the foot of the Cotswold escarpment to the Severn, the Middle Lias forms the lower part of the escarpment itself, often projecting as a shelf by reason of the greater durability of the Marlstone (Fig. 83). Further many outliers of Middle Lias occur west of the main escarpment, forming prominent hills rising abruptly from the Lower Lias plain. Similarly, the Lower Lias stretches southwards from the Mendips across the almost 'dead level' Sedgemoor; but the general monotonous flatness is relieved by the steep-sided Glastonbury Tor, and farther to the

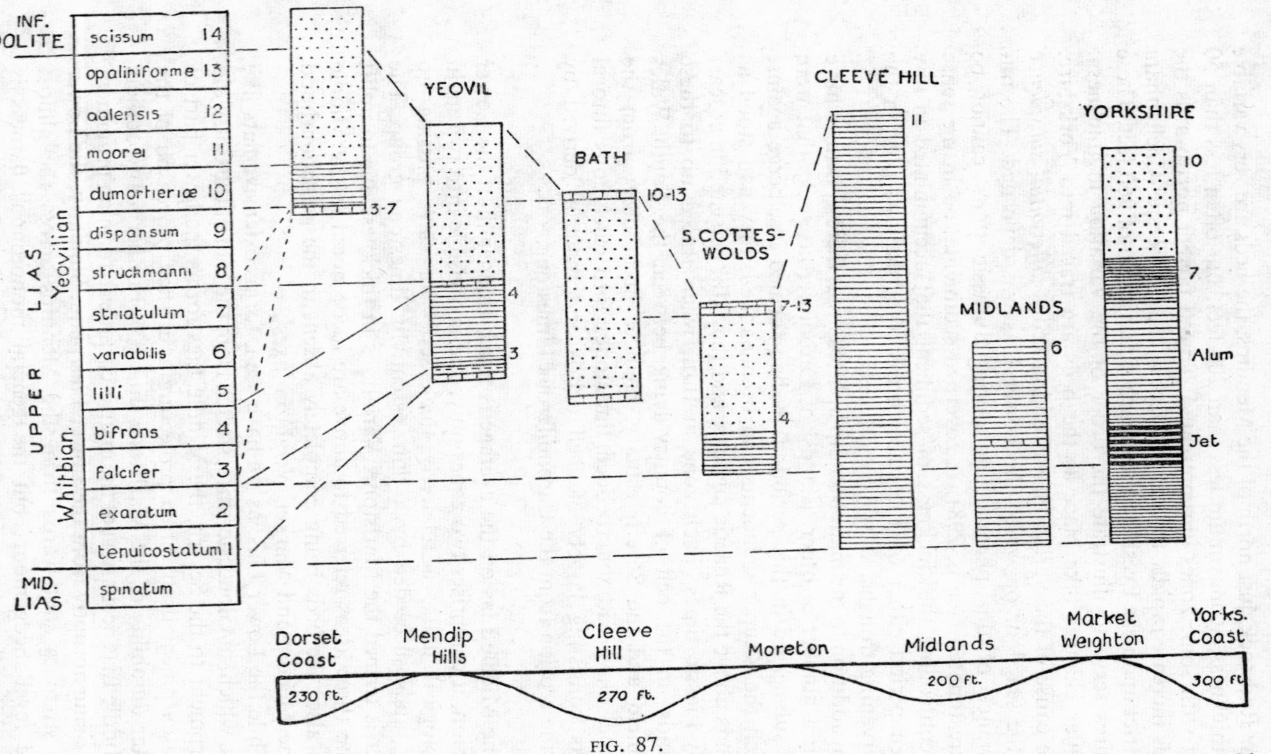


FIG. 87.

Diagram showing the variation in zonal development and in lithology of the Upper Lias between the Dorset coast and the Yorkshire coast.

The division between Whitbian and Yeovilian is placed between zones 4 and 5.

... the Mendip, Moreton and Market

west by Brent Tor, while nearer to hand the hog-backed Polden Hills lie parallel to the Mendips. All these are outliers of Middle Lias.

In the Midlands the Marlstone includes valuable ironstones near Banbury, at King's Sutton and at Melton Mowbray, while in Yorkshire it expands into the 'Ironstone Series', comprising over 100 feet of alternating shales and ironstones. The famous seams of the Cleveland district in Yorkshire, occurring on this horizon, were among the most valuable bedded iron-ores in the country. The Cleveland iron-ores are the most westerly parts of a band which extends on this, and somewhat higher horizons south-eastwards into Lorraine.

The **Upper Lias** is so extremely variable that it is difficult to summarize the facts in a small compass: it is impossible to obtain a comprehensive view of the variations in thickness and lithology of the several divisions without going much deeper into the details of the zoning than is permissible in a work of this scope. In general, however, the Upper Lias consists of sands above, resting on clays and shales, and these in turn upon shales and limestones. The shales and clays are much thicker in the northern than in the southern parts of the outcrop. Thus in North Yorkshire the Upper Lias Shales reach nearly 300 feet in thickness; on the Dorset coast, at the other extremity of the outcrop, this is reduced to 70 feet. The beds in Yorkshire include the Alum Shales, once widely used in the manufacture of alum, and the Jet Shales, which yielded the lumps of compact lignite termed jet, which is capable of being turned or carved into ornaments which take a good polish. Fashions have changed since jet ornaments were popular with our great-grandparents, and the once-flourishing industry which was centred at Whitby is practically extinct. Evidence of the industry can still be seen, however, in the line of continuous workings marking the outcrop of the Jet Shales. At one locality only in Yorkshire, at Blea Wyke on the coast, do sands occur above the Upper Lias Shales: elsewhere in these northern outcrops the overlying Middle Jurassic strata lie upon an eroded surface of the shales, proving the junction to be a non-sequence.

On the Dorset coast the Upper Lias comprises the following members:

| | |
|---|---|
| Upper Lias Sands . . . | 150 feet |
| Upper Lias Shales . . . | 70 feet |
| Junction Bed . . . | 5 feet |

Middle Lias 'Marlstone'.

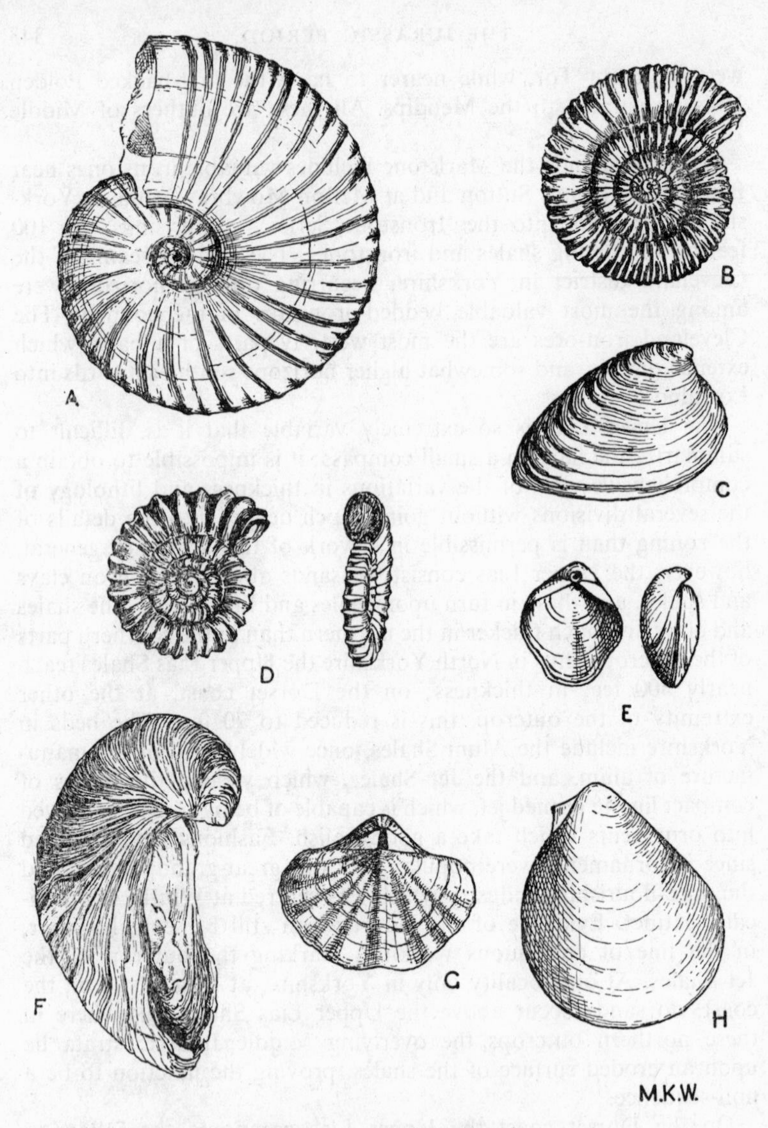


FIG. 88.—Fossils from the Lias.

A. *Amaltheus sp*. Zonal form in the Middle Lias.[1]
B. *Dactylioceras commune*. Upper Lias.
C. *Cardinia listeri*. Lower Lias.
D. *Promicroceras* (*Aegoceras*) *planicosta*. Lower Lias.
E. *Zeilleria leckenbyi*. Upper Lias (*after E. Neaverson*).
F. *Gryphaea arcuata*. Lower Lias.
G. *Spiriferina walcotti*. Lower Lias.
H. *Lima* (*Plagiostoma*) *giganteum*. Lower Lias.

[1] The keel is less clearly shown than in most specimens.

The study of the included ammonites has revealed some very interesting facts about the Junction Bed. Although so thin, it contains the faunas of the highest zone of the Middle Lias and the four lowest zones of the Upper Lias. These comprise the Whitbian Stage, and, as we have just seen, reach 300 feet in North Yorkshire. This is a particularly good example of a condensed sequence, and it is clear that within the limestone there must be bedding planes that represent long intervals of time, during which no sediment accumulated in this district. On some of the bedding planes the ammonites are seen in section, proving that wave action had planed off part of the stratum containing them. Sedimentation of a normal kind recommenced, however, later in Upper Lias times, when the overlying 70 feet of shale were formed.

In all the southern outcrops a sand formation separates the Upper Lias Shales from the overlying Middle Jurassic limestones; but the change from clay to sand and from sand to limestone took place at different times in different areas. The sands can only be mapped as one formation, but they differ in age from point to point, their boundaries transgress the time-planes and the formation is diachronous, representing a phase of arenaceous deposits spreading southwards from the Cotswolds. Not only do these sands belong to different zones in different localities, but they vary widely in thickness and have been given different local names. Thus they are the Bridport Sands on the Dorset coast, the Yeovil Sands in south Somerset, the Midford Sands in the north of the same county, and the Cotswold Sands in Gloucestershire. The significant facts are shown in the accompanying diagram (Fig. 87).

Now relating these facts of the lithology and distribution of the Lias to the palaeogeography of the period, it is evident that the Liassic Sea was shallow and of the epicontinental type; at its maximum extension it covered the greater part of England and South Wales. A gulf-like extension covered the western seaboard of Scotland, but the Highlands, together with Mid- and North Wales and the Cornubian Peninsula, presumably formed part of the Continent from which the copious supplies of muddy sediment represented by the Liassic clays and shales were derived (Fig. 89). Of the shores of the Liassic seas little is known apart from those of the islands in Somerset and South Wales. The Lias thins out against the London Platform as shown in Fig. 67, the second section.

## THE MIDDLE JURASSIC

Rapid variations in thickness and lithology similar to those shown by the Upper Lias, are exhibited even more markedly by the

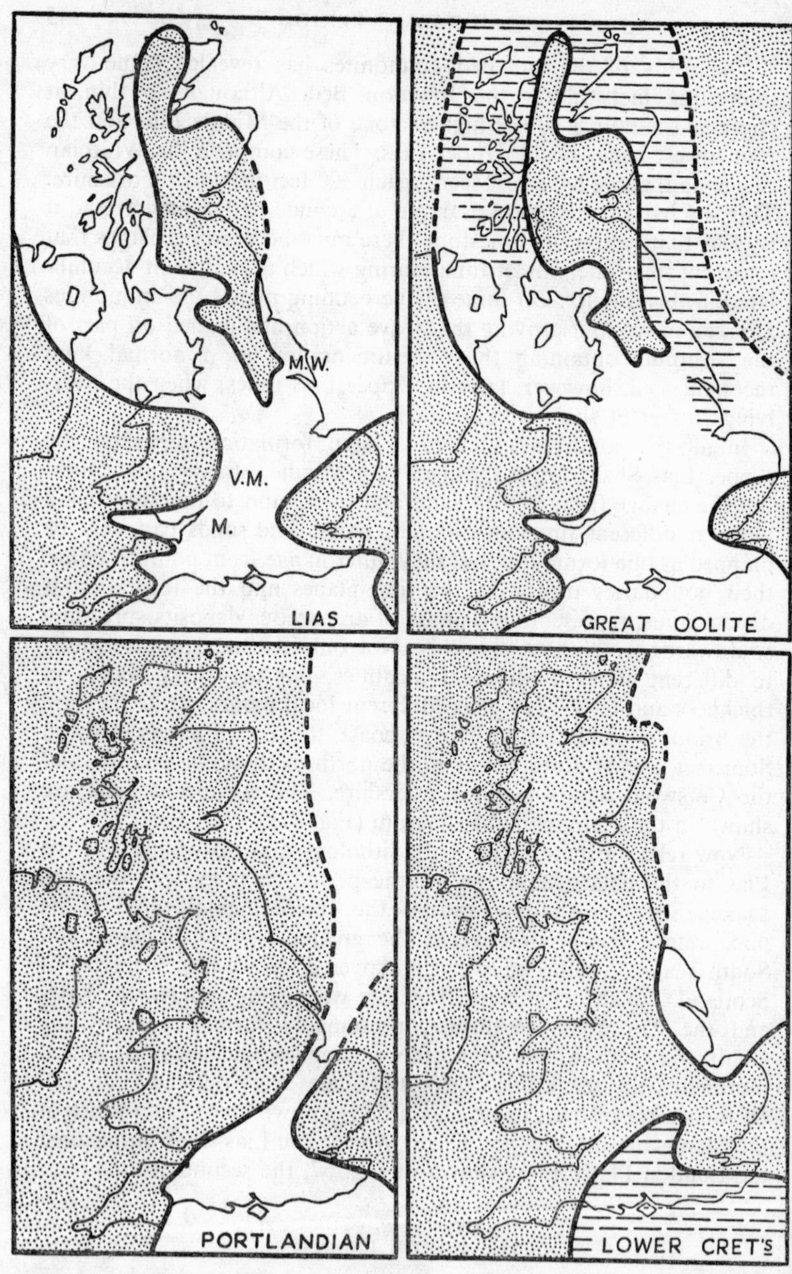


FIG. 89.—Maps to illustrate the changes in palaeogeographical conditions in Britain during the Jurassic and early-Cretaceous Periods.
Land areas, stippled; marine areas, blank; areas of deltaic sedimentation, ruled.
Position of the three major upwarps indicated by initials: M.W., Market Weighton; V.M., Vale of Moreton; M., Mendips.

Middle Jurassic rocks (Fig. 90). Before we can obtain a picture of the conditions under which these rocks were deposited, it will therefore be necessary to describe, in some detail, the succession in the type-area of the Cotswolds, and thence to trace the beds first southwards to the Dorset coast and then northwards to Yorkshire and Scotland.

The Cotswold Hills in Gloucestershire are composed of massive oolitic limestones, forming a fine cuesta rising to nearly 1100 feet O.D. at Cleeve Cloud and affording magnificent views across the strike-vale on the outcrop of the Lower Jurassic and Triassic rocks to the Malvern Hills and the high ground formed by the Palaeozoic rocks of the Forest of Dean and, in the far distance, Central Wales. This bold escarpment extends southwards from Cheltenham past Gloucester to Bath; but farther south it becomes much less impressive, and where it crosses the Mendips is scarcely discernible. Northwards from Cleeve Cloud it gradually diminishes in height when traced into Oxfordshire and Northamptonshire.

Originally the Oolites were divided into two main groups, the Inferior Oolite below and the Great Oolite above. The **Inferior Oolite** was so named from its position in the Bath district underneath the Great (or Bath) Oolite; but detailed study of the ammonite zones has proved the presence, in the Mid-Cotswolds about Cheltenham, of limestones lower than those at Bath, and reaching as much as 300 feet in thickness. These constitute the Lower and Middle Inferior Oolite; but even here, where the series is thickest, the succession is not complete: there are several breaks. In no known locality is the Inferior Oolite complete, and it is no exaggeration to say that in all localities the beds there developed represent only a fraction of the complete succession. One of the special lessons to be learned, perhaps better from this part of the stratigraphical column than from any other, is the significance and importance of 'non-sequences'. These vary widely in their importance: some are relatively insignificant breaks proved only by the most painstaking study of the succession of ammonites, and indicate local pauses in the process of sedimentation; others, by contrast, represent periods of earth-movements followed by erosion, and some of these have practically the status of major unconformities.

When the Inferior Oolite is traced along the Cotswold escarpment, two belts are discovered within which the Lower and Middle divisions are completely absent: these are the Moreton-in-the-Marsh district in the north and the district of the Mendip-Cotswold confluence in the south. As in Liassic times, these must have been belts of relative uplift, and in between them the sea-floor sagged downwards, allowing the accumulation of sediments of maximum thickness, thus

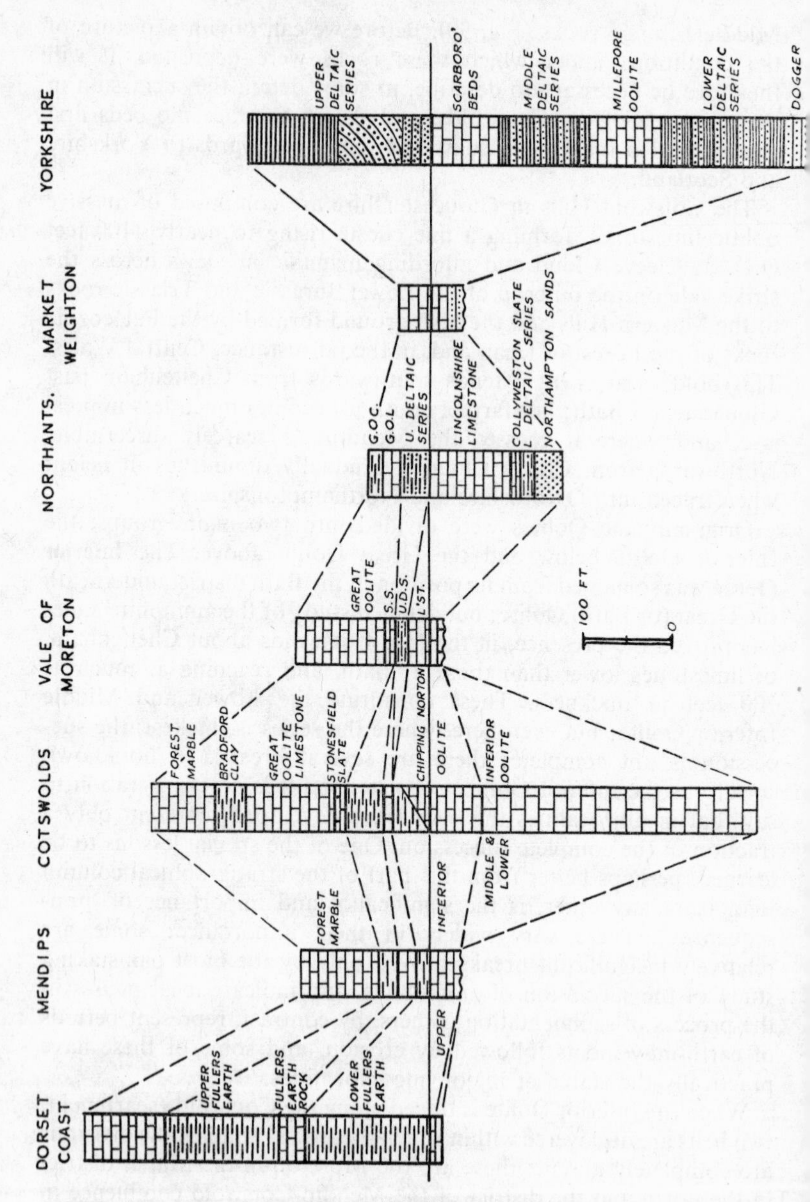


FIG. 90.—Diagram illustrating the variation in lithology and thickness of the Middle Jurassic rocks in England.

In the Northants. column G.O.C., Great Oolite Clay; G.O.L., Great Oolite Limestone.

reproducing in miniature the characteristics of a geosyncline. In the immediate neighbourhood of Birdlip to the south-west of Cheltenham, the Upper Inferior Oolite directly overlies the Lower Inferior Oolite; but to the south-west and to the north-east the Middle Inferior Oolite intervenes. Careful tracing of the local lithological units has proved the presence of a pre-Upper Inferior Oolite anticline—the Birdlip anticline—flanked by the complementary Painswick and Cleeve Hill synclines. The most important break in the Inferior Oolite succession therefore separates the Upper from the Middle and Lower divisions, and there is clear evidence that this break represents a long erosion interval during which the thickness of the beds was much reduced, or they were removed altogether. This episode of destruction and redistribution of the Lower and Middle Inferior Oolite is spoken of as the **Upper Bajocian denudation.** It was followed by a marine transgression, during which there was a marked extension of the area of sedimentation (Fig. 91), the Upper Inferior Oolite overstepping the Lower and Middle divisions on to Upper Lias, and in the Mendip region, on to Palaeozoic rocks. The effects of the Upper Bajocian transgression are very strikingly displayed in the Eastern Mendips. Here in Vallis Vale a shallow gorge has been cut through the oolites into the underlying rocks, thus beautifully exposing one of the most convincing unconformities in the country. The yellow Jurassic limestones form the higher parts of the extensive exposures on both sides of the valley, and rest in seemingly horizontal strata on massive-bedded Carboniferous Limestone, steeply inclined eastwards. The surface of unconformity is a flat and gently undulating plain, and by whatever process it was originally produced, it is clear that it was trimmed up and smoothed by the advancing waters of the Bajocian Sea. The top few inches of the Carboniferous Limestone are extensively bored by molluscs, the borings being filled with Jurassic sediment, while the surface is strewn with Jurassic oysters.

In the Inferior Oolites of the Cotswolds many different types of limestone occur, as well as more argillaceous 'calcareous marl'. Of the limestones, the most valuable are the freestones, which are soft, pale coloured, even-grained oolites. These are easily quarried by taking advantage of the bedding and well-developed master joints by which the rocks are traversed, and easily trimmed or carved into any desired shape, so they have consequently been widely exploited as building stones. The so-called 'grits' such as the Lower and Upper Trigonia Grit (named after a distinctive genus of lamellibranch which they contain) and the Clypeus Grit (named after a sea-urchin found abundantly in this rock (Fig. 92, E)) are misnamed: they are not grits in the official sense at all, as they are

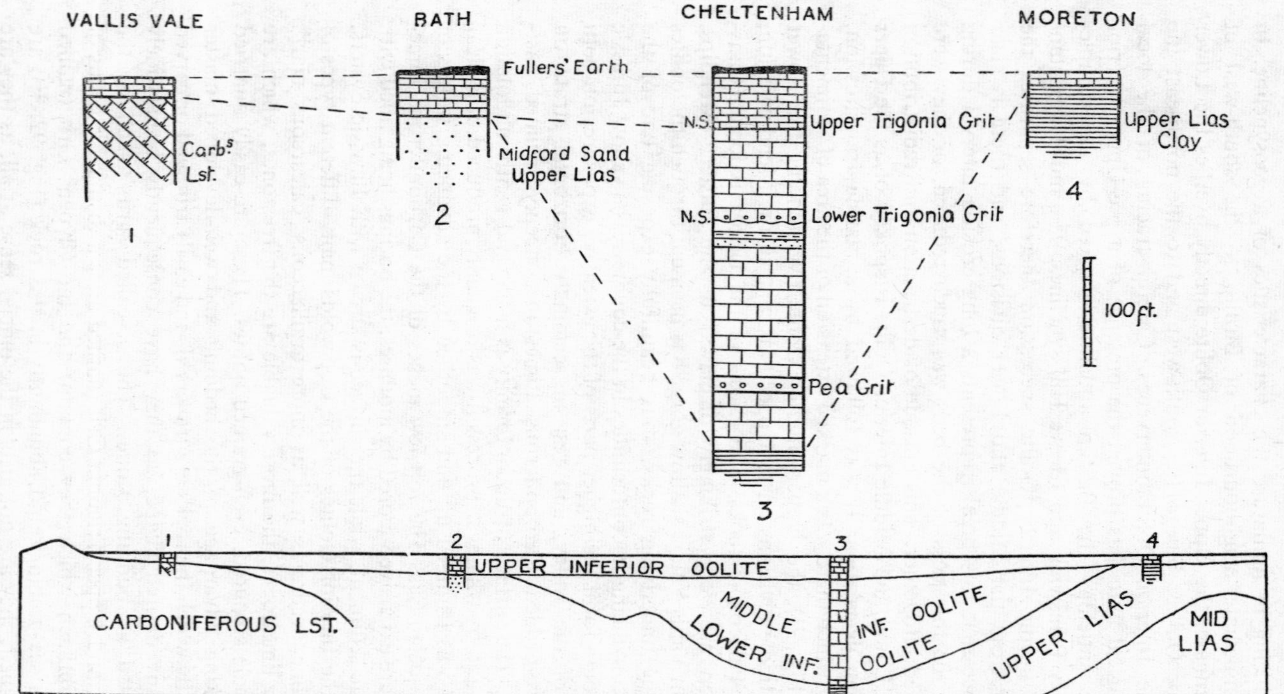


FIG. 91.—Scale sections of Inferior Oolite at Vallis Vale, Frome, Bath, Cheltenham and Vale of Moreton. Based upon these, a diagram-section showing the relations between the Mendip Hills and Moreton, and the results of the Upper Bajocian Transgression. N.S. = Non-sequence. (*After W. J. Arkell.*)

not arenaceous rocks but limestones. Their grittiness, such as it is, is due to the abundance of fragmental shells, and not to quartz grains; but it may be noted that the Upper Trigonia Grit, one of the most distinctive beds in the whole succession, is the basal member of the Upper Bajocian Stage, and is 'floored' by the most important non-sequence in the whole Inferior Oolite. Another distinctive rock-type is the 'Pea Grit', best known in the Cheltenham district. It is a coarse yellow pisolitic limestone built up of loosely aggregated ovoid bodies resembling crude and overgrown ooliths. Some of these pisoliths are encrusted with bryozoans, while algae have played a part in their formation, though there is a difference of opinion as to how important a part.

Both in lithology and faunal content the Inferior Oolite of the Cotswolds differs greatly from the underlying Lias. In place of the dominantly argillaceous sediments yielding abundant cephalopods with brachiopods and lamellibranchs restricted mainly to the more arenaceous layers, the oolitic limestones yield a rich and varied fauna of echinoids, brachiopods, lamellibranchs and gastropods; but unfortunately for the zonal palaeontologist, ammonites are infrequent. It is obvious that the beds were deposited under shallow water, marine conditions, on the floor of an epicontinental sea, the waters of which were clear and warm enough at times to allow corals to flourish.

The lowest part of the **Great Oolite Series** is of a very different lithological type from the underlying limestones, and in the southern Cotswolds consists mainly of blue-grey clays, yielding few fossils other than oysters. In the middle, a seam of massive, buff-coloured non-oolitic limestone occurs, containing an abundant fauna of brachiopods. These clays with the limestone are the Fuller's Earth Beds, which take their name from seams of commercial fuller's earth occurring in the higher part. This special type of clay is non-plastic, it breaks down readily in water and is put to a number of industrial uses depending on its adsorptive properties. It takes the fat out of wool—the process of 'fulling'—and the colour out of oil. It is still exploited in the Bath district for fulling purposes; but was formerly much more important when sheep-rearing and the attendant woollen industry were flourishing in the Cotswolds and other parts of the West Country. In the northern Cotswolds the Lower Fuller's Earth changes laterally into the Chipping Norton Limestone, a hard oolite containing minute abraded chips of lignite. Resting non-sequentially on the Chipping Norton Limestone is a distinctive greenish or chocolate-coloured clay, the Estuarine Clay, which can be traced into north Oxfordshire, where it yields abundant shells of the freshwater snail, *Viviparus*.

The next member of the succession is only a thin band, but it is very constantly developed in the Cotswolds, the type-locality being the village of Stonesfield in Oxfordshire, which gives its name to the **Stonesfield Slate.** The rock is finely laminated micaceous and calcareous sandstone or thinly bedded flags which were formerly extensively quarried and exposed to weathering during the winter

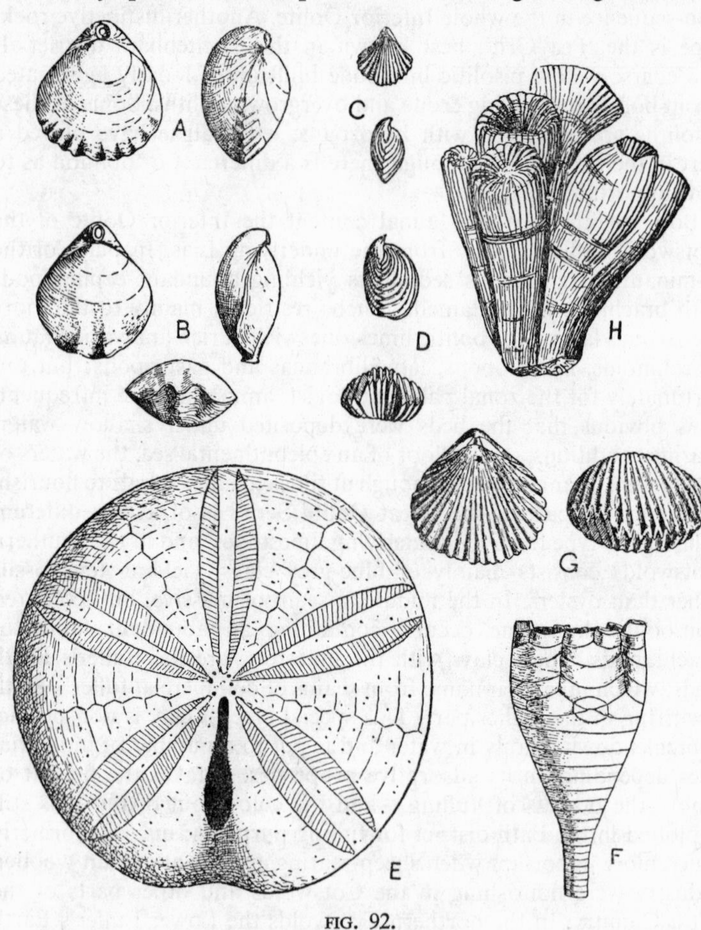


FIG. 92.

Jurassic fossils.

A. *Plectothyris* (*Terebratula*) *fimbria*. Inferior Oolite.
B. *Epithyris* (*Terebratula*) cf. *submaxillata*. Inferior Oolite.
C. *Rhynchonella* sp. Inferior Oolite.
D. *Kallirhynchia* (*Rhynchonella*) *concinna*. Inferior Oolite.
E. *Clypeus ploti*. Vesulian.
F. *Apiocrinites elegans*, previously *Apiocrinus parkinsoni*. Bradford Clay.
G. *Rhactorhynchia* (*Rhynchonella*) *inconstans*. Kimmeridge Clay.
H. *Thecosmilia* sp. Corallian.

months, after which treatment they could be readily split into slabs thin enough to be used for roofing purposes. Many of the old Cotswold manor houses, farms and cottages built of the local freestone are roofed, appropriately enough, with Stonesfield Slate, and the effect is distinctive and harmonious, adding charm to the beautiful Cotswold countryside. But the rock is definitely not slate in the true sense: it possesses no cleavage—the planes of easy splitting are the natural bedding planes. From an entirely different angle the Stonesfield Slate is one of the most fascinating of all the Jurassic rocks, on account of the extraordinary variety of fossils it contains: the remains of plants and insects are associated with reptiles of many kinds including turtles, crocodiles, flying reptiles and dinosaurs, and with more ordinary molluscs. Not the least significant are the lower jaw-bones of small mammals. This assemblage suggests that the beds were formed in very shallow, more or less land-locked lagoons.

The remaining members of the succession are, in the main, oolitic limestones, closely resembling those of Inferior Oolite age and evidently formed under the same conditions. They include several valuable seams of building stone, of which Bath Stone is the best known. Collectively the oolitic limestones on this level are referred to as the **Great Oolite Limestone,** while the highest rock in the Series is the **Forest Marble,** a strongly false-bedded shelly oolite which is named from the forest of Wychwood in Oxfordshire, where it was formerly quarried and polished as an ornamental stone. These two massive limestones are separated from one another by an intervening thin clay, the **Bradford Clay,** named from the type-locality, Bradford-on-Avon, near Bath. This clay is famous for its fauna of distinctive brachiopods of restricted vertical range, which give it value as a datum for correlation purposes; but it is probably better known on account of the beautifully preserved fossil crinoids it contains. The specimens of *Apiocrinites elegans* previously *Apiocrinus parkinsoni*, preserved in full relief, are world-famous (Fig. 92, F).

In the Mid-Cotswolds the highest part of the escarpment is capped by Inferior Oolite, the Great Oolite appearing some little distance from the scarp-edge, and thence forming the whole of the long dip-slope. Consequently the outcrop of the latter is out of all proportion to the thickness of the beds, and reaches a maximum width of 10 miles.

When the Oolites are traced southwards from the Cotswolds on to the Mendip 'shallows', they become reduced to less than a third of their former thickness. It will be seen from Fig. 90 that this reduction is mainly due, as already explained, to the complete thinning out of the Lower and Middle Inferior Oolite; but the Fuller's-Earth is appreciably affected too. Farther southward, in the Somerset-Dorset basin of deposition, the Great Oolite expands and is even thicker than in the Cotswolds, but the proportion of argillaceous material is much higher. The Fuller's-Earth Rock, for example, is here represented not by massive limestone, but by thin seams of 'stone' set in clay. At the same time the Inferior Oolite is extremely attenuated and variable in thickness. It rarely exceeds 30 feet, of which the greater part is composed of the Upper Inferior Oolite. As a result of this change in lithology, the Oolites south of the Mendips produce pleasant rolling country, sadly lacking the grandeur of the 'cuesta' of the Cotswolds.

The cuesta also diminishes in height as the beds are followed from the Mid-Cotswolds northwards. In the region of the Oxford 'shallows', the Lower and Middle Inferior Oolite are absent, while the Great Oolite Series is substantially reduced. This diminution in thickness continues into Northamptonshire, where the Forest Marble is represented by the Great Oolite Clay—a variegated clay yielding oysters, underlain by the Great Oolite Limestone, only 20 feet in thickness, cream in colour and somewhat marly. Below, the formation consists of variable clays with thin limestones, the upper part being marine; but the lower portion contains freshwater shells and plant remains. These lower beds clearly indicate a new type of physiographical environment, the significance of which is more fully considered below: meantime it may be noted that the term 'estuarine' is commonly applied to them.

The **Upper Estuarine Series** consists mainly of pale or greenish coloured clays and silty clays, interpreted as fluviatile marsh deposits. Locally the clays have been leached to the consistency of a fine clay by plant colonies growing in coastal swamps. Beds of shelly marl and argillaceous limestones containing oysters and lingulas as well as more typically marine bivalves were deposited during marine invasions of the coastal flats. The **Lower Estuarine Series** are fine sands, silts and clays, often containing vertical rootlets and locally worked for refractory purposes. Current-bedding and channelling are developed to some extent in the sands. Apart from plant debris and ostracods the beds are unfossiliferous. They are regarded as having been deposited on a low lying coastal plain or delta flat on the northern side of the London Platform.

From the north of Northamptonshire to Lincolnshire the Upper and Lower Estuarine Series are separated by a lenticular limestone, which gives rise to the strikingly straight escarpment of Lincoln Edge. This **Lincolnshire Limestone** is a very variable rock, consisting in part of false-bedded banks of broken shell-fragments, in part of luxurious coral-reefs, and was evidently formed in very shallow water. In the neighbourhood of Corby the Lincolnshire Limestone is divided into two parts, Lower and Upper, separated by an erosion-surface. The Lower Limestone is traversed by deep channels several hundred yards in width and individually traceable for several miles in a west-south-west to east-north-east direction. This is parallel to the line along which the limestone thins out, and also to the edge of the London Platform. Presumably the channels resulted from strong tidal or current scour in the neighbourhood of, and parallel to, the shoreline of the time.

The remainder of the Inferior Oolite Series differs considerably in lithology from that developed in the Cotswolds. Beneath the Lower Estuarine Series is the **Northampton Sand Ironstone Formation,** our chief source of iron ore. The main ore body, when fresh, is greenish to grey in colour and is composed of closely packed ooliths of the iron silicate, chamosite, set in a matrix of siderite (iron carbonate) and calcite with some chamosite. In natural outcrops the rocks are heavily limonitized, brownish in colour and often show 'box-stone structure'. Owing to variations in the mineral content of both ooliths and groundmass, the main ore body contains a wide range of rock-types grading into one another. The nature of the matrix is regarded as the primary feature in the precise classification of the ores, secondary subdivisions being based on the nature of the ooliths. Adjectival prefixes are given to the minerals of the groundmass and substantival prefixes to those of the ooliths. A 'sideritic limonite oolite' is, therefore, the term applied to a rock made up of limonite ooliths in a siderite matrix; whilst a 'sideritic chamositic chamosite oolite' contains chamosite ooliths in a matrix of chamosite and siderite. The main ore-body is underlain by non-oolitic or sparsely oolitic siderite mudstones, siltstones and limestone, which are not normally worked. In some parts of the ore field similar rocks overlie the ore body, in others they are separated from it by a development of chamositic or kaolinitic oolites and sandstones. The kaolinite ooliths are often flattened, giving a shaly appearance to the rock.

The Northampton Sands were clearly deposited in a shallow sea. They yield a fauna of brachiopods, thick-shelled lamellibranchs, echinoids, some corals and rare ammonites. The shells are often fragmentary, locally broken ooliths are abundant, beds of conglomerate and breccia composed of local materials are not infrequent, whilst there is clear evidence of channelling, though not on the same scale as in the Lincolnshire Limestone. In its westerly outcrops, the Northampton Sands become extremely sandy, whilst the same tendency is to be seen around Stamford and Wellingborough in its eastern limits. It is probable that the original basin of deposition was not very different from the present extent of the formation. Sandy detritus was trapped in the marginal zones, whilst in the central zone, largely the site of the present ore-field, chemical precipitation predominated over mechanical deposition. The precise conditions leading to the chemical precipitation of chamosite and siderite are still uncertain. Uniformitarianism cannot help us, for the iron content of the sea waters of to-day is clearly very much lower than it was during those periods of the geological past when bedded iron ores were being deposited.

The ore is exploited on a large scale in great open-cast workings, with faces up to a mile in length, and sometimes with as much as 80 feet of overburden above the ironstone. These fine exposures, particularly at Corby, together with the records of hundreds of trial boreholes put down in the exploration of the ironstone field, have been studied by the Geological Survey officers.

One interesting discovery is the presence in these beds of structures—sharp anticlines, step-faults, horst-like uplifts and trough faulting, resembling those usually ascribed to deep-seated tectonic movements. They are, however, merely superficial, dying out at shallow depth and are regarded as a result of the sculpturing of the existing landscape. The underlying Upper Lias clay is an incompetent rock. During the excavation of the valleys the clay was unable to support the weight of the overlying beds. As a result it has 'flowed' into the deepening valleys from beneath the hills on either side, with the formation of sharp folds faithfully following the changing course of the valleys. As the valleys deepened, this plastic flow of the clay left the edges of the sheets of competent rocks forming the plateaux unsupported, and they therefore sagged down towards the valleys as 'camber flaps', often with the formation of small fault-like dislocations. Similar structures can be expected to occur, though they have not often been described, in other areas where the same geological conditions occur. The necessary condition is the occurrence of beds of gently dipping sandstone or limestone resting on thick clays.

In the neighbourhood of the Market Weighton upwarp, the Oolites are hidden beneath the overstepping Upper Cretaceous rocks. Well-records, however, show that the beds are very attentuated, though the succession is not known in detail.

On the north side of the Market Weighton upwarp, the Cleveland Hills and the North Yorkshire Moors, often rising above the 1000-foot contour, are composed of Middle Jurassic rocks. The landscape is, however, very different from that of the Cotswolds, with their typical pattern of arable and pasture fields; with charming farm-houses built of the local warm-coloured stone; with some of the villages such as Bourton-on-the-Water architectural gems; with many fine buildings in the market towns dating from the time when the Cotswolds were the great sheep-walk of England. By contrast, in Yorkshire the rocks form barren, very sparsely populated moors, with the soil so poor that often even heather has difficulty in maintaining a foothold. Scenically, one is reminded of the moors on the Millstone Grit and the Coal Measures on the west side of the Pennines. There is good reason for this. The Middle Jurassic rocks of the North Riding consist in the main of sandstones and shales with, in their lower and middle portions, thin coal-seams underlain by seat-earths. The 'washouts', channelling and many other phenomena show that these beds were laid down under very similar conditions to the Upper Carboniferous of North England.

Unfortunately these beds were misnamed in the past the 'Estuarine Series'. In the early days of geology the distinction between the deposits laid down in the estuaries of large rivers and those formed by rivers building out deltas into shallow seas was not appreciated. The 'Estuarine Series' with their coal-seams, their current bedded sandstones, their evidence of anastomosing drainage channels should be more precisely called the **'Deltaic Series'.**[1] A rich flora has been obtained from them, an interesting member being the 'maidenhair palm', *Ginkgo*, which still flourishes in Japan.[2] In the highest beds the plants are nearly all drifted; but in the Lower and Middle Deltaic Series, rootlet beds of *Equisetites*, allied to the modern horse-tails, with the stems standing upright in the position of growth, have been found. This flora has a much more modern aspect than that of the Coal Measures, however. Conifers and cycads are important, whilst fruits and seeds of the earliest Angiosperms, the true Flowering Plants which compose the bulk of the existing flora, have been obtained.

At three levels at least, however, there is evidence of the sea having invaded the delta-flats. The Dogger (Fig. 90) is a marine sandstone, rich in iron carbonates; the Millepore Oolite is usually a calcareous sandstone taking its name from the abundant polyzoan, *Haploecia* (*Millepora*) *straminea*; whilst the Scarborough Beds are limestones and shales yielding marine fossils, including ammonites.

Evidence of the same episode of delta-formation is to be found

[1] It seems pointless to perpetuate this mistake, so the term 'Deltaic' is used in this account. The reader is warned, however, that in current geological literature the older term is still often used.

[2] Rare specimens are to be seen in English gardens, for example, at Kew.

in the scattered patches of Jurassic strata preserved beneath the Tertiary volcanic rocks along the west coast of Scotland and in the narrow outcrop along the shore of the Moray Firth in Sutherlandshire. In Skye, Raasay and Mull massive sandstones containing the ammonites of the Inferior Oolite are overlain by some hundreds of feet of sandstones and shales, very similar in all essentials to the Deltaic Series of Yorkshire and containing molluscs and plants. The molluscs range from typical marine forms through brackish (*Neomiodon*, *Liostrea*) to freshwater forms (*Unio*, *Viviparus*). The assemblages of the individual shell-beds are sharply differentiated and were clearly controlled by differences in the salinity of the waters. A close comparison can be made with the distribution of present-day faunas along the east coast of Texas. Here a string of low islands with channels between them separates a line of shallow estuaries and lagoons from the open-water of the Gulf of Mexico. During a spell of dry years the salinity of the waters in the lagoons steadily increases and they become colonized by brackish and finally marine forms. A period of land floods will drastically reduce the salinity and cause mass-mortality. On the east coast of Scotland only the equivalents of the Great Oolite are exposed. These are of the same deltaic facies and include a coal seam $3\frac{1}{2}$ feet in thickness, which is still exploited at Brora.

As will be seen from Fig. 89, in place of the extensive epicontinental seas of Lower Jurassic times, we must picture for the Middle Jurassic a relatively shallow, clear-water sea covering south and central England; but farther northward, rivers from a northern land-mass had built out deltas covering what are now the eastern and western coastal areas of Scotland. The eastern delta extended southwards into Yorkshire. One final word as to the behaviour of the areas of uplift, so important during the deposition of the Lias. The Market Weighton upwarp was clearly an unstable area throughout the whole of the Middle Jurassic; but the Mendip and the Vale of Moreton upwarps, whilst greatly affecting sedimentation during the deposition of the Inferior Oolite, had much less effect on the Great Oolite.

## THE UPPER JURASSIC ROCKS

It has long been customary to divide the Upper Jurassic strata of Britain into the following units, based primarily on lithology:

7. Purbeck Beds.
6. Portland Beds.
5. Kimmeridge Clay.
4. Corallian Beds.

3. Oxford Clay.
2. Kellaways Beds.
1. Cornbrash.

Dr. W. J. Arkell in his recent (1956) comprehensive work, 'Jurassic Geology of the World', classifies the Jurassic rocks of the British Isles as under:

| | *Stage* | *Formation* |
|---|---|---|
| Upper Jurassic | Purbeckian | Purbeck Beds |
| | Portlandian | Portland Beds |
| | Kimmeridgian | Kimmeridge Clay |
| | Oxfordian | Corallian Beds and upper part of the Oxford Clay |
| Middle Jurassic | Callovian | Middle and lower parts of the Oxford Clay, Kellaways Beds and Upper Cornbrash |
| | Bathonian | Lower Cornbrash and Great Oolite Series |
| | Bajocian | Inferior Oolite Series |
| Lower Jurassic | Toarcian | Upper Lias |
| | Pliensbachian | Middle Lias and upper part of Lower Lias |
| | Sinemurian | Middle part of Lower Lias |
| | Hettangian | Lower part of Lower Lias |

These stages are based on a most thorough investigation of the ammonite faunas and are intended for intercontinental (world-scale) comparisons and correlations. But, unfortunately, as we have already seen, purely palaeontological divisions do not always coincide with what may be termed the 'natural', and therefore long-established, divisions of the beds in a particular area. The Bajocian/Toarcian boundary follows closely the long-established division between the Lower Jurassic (Lias) and the Middle Jurassic (Oolites).

More recently (1962) at an international 'Colloquium on the Jurassic' it was recommended (a) that the boundary between the Lower and Middle Jurassic should be drawn at the top of the zone of *Graphoceras concavum*, that is, well within the Inferior Oolite and above the Lower Estuarine Series; (b) that the base of the Upper Jurassic should be drawn between the Callovian and Oxfordian Stages of Arkell and (c) that the Purbeckian Stage should be abandoned.

From the standpoint of the British stratigrapher, the Middle-Upper Jurassic (Callovian/Oxfordian) boundary, as defined above, is most unfortunate, for it is not only drawn within a great clay formation, the Oxford Clay, but it also places in the Middle Jurassic a considerable thickness of beds (Upper Cornbrash to the upper part of the Oxford Clay) which have previously been regarded by most British geologists as the basal portion of the Upper Jurassic.

This book is primarily concerned with the stratigraphy of the British Isles and, even at the risk of being thought parochial, we prefer here to follow what we regard as the 'natural' lines in Britain and to include the Callovian beds in the Upper Jurassic and the whole of the Oolites in the Middle Jurassic. When all said and done these stratigraphical terms were originally introduced to define English formations in their type-areas and remain the standards for comparison. We are, however, in agreement with the disappearance of the Purbeckian as a Stage. The Purbeck Beds are clearly a facies deposit laid down under special conditions and further, as will be shown below (p. 375), only the lower part of the Purbeck Beds is of Jurassic age.

The full succession of the Upper Jurassic, from the Cornbrash to the Purbeck Beds, is finely exposed in continuous coastal sections in Dorsetshire. Northwards and north-eastwards a wide overstep of Cretaceous rocks partly conceals the underlying Jurassic Beds, except at a few points where the former have been cut back farther than usual by denudation. For a short space in Dorset and again in Yorkshire the *whole* of the Upper Jurassic is so concealed, the Cretaceous resting directly upon Lias on the western side of the Wolds. North of the Wolds, however, the several divisions reappear from underneath the Cretaceous rocks, and spread out to cover wide areas in North Yorkshire.

In the Fen country of Cambridgeshire and South Lincolnshire parts of the Upper Jurassic succession are concealed under the superficial Fen deposits.

Of the main divisions the two great clay formations are most consistent in their lithological characters, but between them the Corallian shows great variation. In the south of England and in Yorkshire the latter beds are chiefly calcareous sandstones and shelly oolitic limestones, with locally coral-reef limestones; but in the central district, extending from Oxfordshire into South Yorkshire the Corallian is almost wholly clay, the Ampthill Clay.

Above the Kimmeridge Clay the deposits of Portlandian and Purbeck age are conspicuous in Dorset; they decrease in importance when traced to the north-eastward.

## THE CORNBRASH

The **Cornbrash,** one of William Smith's original stratal divisions, consists of less than 30 feet of marine limestones, sometimes rubbly or flaggy, elsewhere blue-hearted and massive, together with some ferruginous sandy marls. Though so thin, it forms a very important datum, for it can be traced from Dorset to Yorkshire and has been found in Raasay. The lower part contains ammonites, brachiopods and lamellibranchs of Bathonian (Great Oolite) aspect, but the fauna of the upper beds links on with that of the overlying Callovian Stage. The very important palaeontological boundary separating the Bathonian Stage (the top of the Middle Jurassic) from the Callovian Stage (the base of the Upper Jurassic) must therefore be drawn somewhere in the Cornbrash. Fortunately the marked faunal change between the Upper and the Lower Cornbrash coincides in southern and central England with a marked line of erosion, whilst in Yorkshire only the Upper Cornbrash is present, resting on the Deltaic Series and indicating the submergence of the delta-flats.

### THE KELLAWAYS BEDS AND OXFORD CLAY

The Oxford Clay, together with the underlying Kellaways Beds, forms a low-lying continuous vale, which was formerly well wooded. It 'floors' the Vale of White Horse, continues north-eastwards past Oxford to the Fens and the Peterborough district, skirts the Yorkshire Wolds and finally reaches the coast south of Scarborough.

The typical **Kellaways Beds,** which pass downwards into the Cornbrash, are essentially sands and calcareous sandstones, usually only a score or so of feet in thickness but increasing to 70 or 80 feet in Yorkshire. In the central area the rocks change their lithological characters, passing into clay, presumably indicating the existence of deeper water hereabouts.

The **Oxford Clay** is very much thicker, being some 600 feet in the south of England. In its lower parts the formation is well stratified, with a good deal of sandy sediment included; but higher up the sand fails, through increasing depth of the Oxfordian Sea, only to reappear towards the top, indicating the oncoming of the shallow-water conditions of the Corallian. Pyritized nodules and bands of septaria are frequent, and in the massive, middle part of the formation give the only indication of bedding.

In many parts of its outcrop the Oxford Clay is exploited for the manufacture of bricks, notably in the neighbourhood of Peterborough and Bedford, now the centres of an enormous brick-making industry. The well-known term 'Flettons' is derived from a village near Peterborough. As a consequence the exposures, in the form of vast open pits, are the best in Europe for this part of the Jurassic. In the course of making these excavations careful watch has been kept for fossils, and the fauna is well known. Ammonites are common at certain levels, and in the lower part of the clay are compressed, but still show their original outlines in remarkable perfection. This mode of preservation is very useful as the different types of *Kosmoceras*, the characteristic genus, are distinguished largely by the shape of the aperture of the shell. In addition to the ammonites, which again are used as indices of the several zones into which the formation is divided, reptilian remains in abundance and variety have been discovered. The land reptiles are represented by Dinosaurs, marine reptiles by types of crocodiles and by very many skeletons of *Ichthyosaurus*, *Pliosaurus* and *Plesiosaurus*, together with very many different types of fossil fishes.

The Oxford Clay of Yorkshire is different in both lithological and faunal facies from that of the south of England, the change taking place at the Market Weighton upwarp. Northwards from this place the clays tend to pass into thin ferruginous sandstones and sandy oolitic limestones, and at the same time types of fossils characteristic of the Russian Oxfordian replace the typical English forms.

Above the Middle Jurassic rocks of the coastal areas of Scotland, both Callovian and Oxfordian Stages are represented. On the Sutherlandshire coast the Kellaways rock forms the roof to the Brora coal, while above comes a considerable thickness of massive sandstones from which casts of the characteristic ammonites and other fossils have been obtained. In Skye and Eigg, on the other hand, the Oxfordian consists of blue clays, which represent only a small part of the complete formation, however.

## THE CORALLIAN BEDS

The rocks immediately above the Oxfordian differ strikingly from the latter, being sandy sediments succeeded by oolite limestones frequently associated with coral limestones, the whole reaching a thickness of 200 feet on the Weymouth coast, but usually being thinner than this.

The succession commences with the Lower Calcareous Grit, a series of poorly fossiliferous sands and grits, and is completed above by the somewhat similar Upper Calcareous Grit, which, however, is absent from the Oxford district. Between the two series of grits occur lenticular limestone formations, some beds of which are hard oolites, while others are marls with scattered oolitic grains.

These rocks were formerly known as the Coral Rag and Coralline Oolite; these names do give a reasonable idea of the chief lithological characters of the rocks, but they are not sufficiently comprehensive, for other types are present, while in places the limestones pass into clays and the names then become misnomers. It would carry us too far into the accumulated wealth of detail concerning these rocks were we to trace the variations in thickness and in lithology of the several divisions when they are followed along the strike. Among the outstanding features are, firstly, the occurrence at several different levels of true fringing coral reefs, at Steeple Ashton in Wiltshire, in the Oxford district, at Upware in Cambridgeshire, as well as in Yorkshire. As a fact the Steeple Ashton reef has never been exposed or quarried, but its presence beneath the soil is inferred from the phenomenal abundance of fossil corals on the surface of the fields—'every stone on the field is still a coral', and as they are in a better state of preservation than those obtained from any other British locality, the occurrence is little short of world famous. Detailed study in the Oxford district has shown that the reefs occur as irregular strips, separated from one another by outcrops of detrital limestone representing the wastage from the fringing reef due to marine abrasion. Many different kinds of 'perforate' corals occur in these reefs in the position of growth, and they are accompanied, as in modern reefs by an abundant fauna of sea-urchins, lamellibranchs and gasteropods, which flourish in these circumstances.

In one or two places the escarpment of the Corallian is broken, and it is found that here the limestones are temporarily replaced by clays, probably deposited by a river, the muddy waters of which would inhibit coral growth. It is interesting to note that these gaps in the escarpment are followed by railways and canals, and in one case by the Thames: here the course of the existing river has been determined by a Jurassic ancestor bringing mud *from* the London district!

A few miles north-east of Oxford the Corallian scarp ceases abruptly and is replaced by a flat clay vale: here on some existing geological maps the Kimmeridge Clay is shown in contact with the Oxford Clay; but actually this is incorrect as the Corallian is itself present in considerable force, having passed laterally into a clay formation, the **Ampthill Clay.** Recent detailed zonal work has shown, however, that only the few feet of ironshot limestones and marls forming the basal part of the Ampthill Clay are the equivalents of the highest Corallian limestones of Oxford. The great bulk of the Ampthill Clay is to be correlated with higher zones, present in Dorset and Yorkshire, but absent in Wiltshire and at Oxford. This facies persists along the outcrop, except for a brief return to the fringing reef facies at Upware, near Cambridge, into Yorkshire. In this county the Corallian, after disappearing at the Market Weighton upwarp, attains to a greater importance than anywhere in the south of England. The series outcrops on three sides of the Vale of Pickering and spreads out over the Yorkshire moors, to the west forming the impressive escarpment of the Hambleton Hills rising to over 1300 feet, thence extending eastwards through the Tabular Hills to the sea-coast in the neighbourhood of Scarborough. In facies the Corallian of Yorkshire resembles that of the south of England, though there are marked differences in the thicknesses of the beds and the succession in Yorkshire includes beds not present in the southern development.

Corallian rocks outcrop on both the eastern and western coasts of Scotland, but are indifferently exposed. In Kent, borings made in the course of exploring the buried coalfield have penetrated some 300 feet of Corallian beds. The most striking feature is a mass, 125 to 135 feet in thickness, of white coralline limestone, clearly representing fringing reefs formed close to the shore of the London Platform. Farther to the south, the recent trial borings for oil at Henfield in Sussex and at Portsdown, have passed through a dominantly argillaceous facies of the Corallian, representing the deposits formed well away from any coastline in the centre of the Wealden basin of deposition.

### KIMMERIDGE CLAY—KIMMERIDGIAN

The type-locality for the Kimmeridgian is Kimmeridge Bay on the Dorset coast, where this stage is finely exposed and reaches a maximum thickness of 800 feet. It is remarkably consistent in its lithological characters, being essentially a dark clay formation, with much true shale. Thin beds of argillaceous limestone are included, as well as bands of septarian nodules. These harder rocks extend out for a considerable distance from the shore, forming the 'Kimmeridge ledges', which in stormy weather constitute a danger to shipping. The formation is perhaps best known on account of combustible bituminous shales, exposed in the type-locality and known as the 'Kimmeridge Coal'. This bituminous shale has been used locally for fuel for a very long period of time, but there are several grave objections to its use: when burned it leaves a large quantity of ash, and in burning produces an offensive smell on account of its high content of sulphur. So much evil-smelling black smoke is produced that an ancient account states that the people working round Kimmeridge coal fires 'looked more like Furies than men'. The sulphur also militates against the use of the shale as a source of mineral oil, though even in recent years companies have been floated for its exploitation. Since 1960, however, a small productive oilfield has been developed around Kimmeridge. The oil-bearing strata are sands of the lower Corallian and also the Cornbrash.

The Kimmeridgian is covered by the Cretaceous at intervals along the outcrop, but appears to be completely developed in the neighbourhood of Swindon, where the clay was worked for brickmaking during the building of the town, and yielded abundant reptilian remains. Much of the Fen district is underlain by Kimmeridge Clay, which appears here and there as low islands rising through the superficial deposits. These have determined the sites of such towns as Ely, March and Chatteris. The influence of the Market Weighton upwarp is proved by the Kimmeridge Clay becoming very thin indeed: little more than 100 feet of shaly clays represent the whole of the Oxfordian and Kimmeridgian Stages. But northwards the formation thickens again and floors the Vale of Pickering, which was occupied by a large glacial lake during the Pleistocene Period. Consequently thick lacustrine deposits mask the Kimmeridge Clay, and it is only locally that the latter rises to the surface.

In discussing the Lower and Middle Jurassic rocks, we have repeatedly had occasion to refer to the effects of movement along narrow belts of uplift. Of these, only the Market Weighton upwarp was in operation during Upper Jurassic times. Variations in the thickness of the Kimmeridgian, however, give evidence of the existence of a broad zone of limited deposition stretching from the London Platform across the southern Midlands. On the Dorset coast the Kimmeridge Clay is some 800 feet thick; but at Swindon it is reduced to 300 feet; at Oxford 150 feet and at Cambridge to little more than 120 feet. To the north of this zone, however, it again expands, to over 300 feet in Lincolnshire, and reaches at least 400 feet in Yorkshire. Modern methods of study have shown that the variations in thickness are not due to the omission of large parts of the succession. Further, from Swindon to beyond Oxford the highest part of the Kimmeridgian is composed of sandy clays and yellow sands, often containing very large spherical 'doggers' (concretions) of hard gritstone as well as pebbles. According to the zonal palaeontologists, the 35 to 45 feet of dominantly arenaceous beds at Swindon represent some 400 feet of clay in the Dorset coast section. This is the reverse of the normal relationship between the thickness of arenaceous and argillaceous beds laid down in a given interval of time. Other factors have to be taken into account. The thickness of sediment deposited in a given time depends firstly on the relation between the rates of deposition and of subsidence of the sea-floor; and secondly on the grade-size of the detritus. If subsidence occurs as rapidly as sedimentation, or more so, the thickness of beds laid down is limited only by the supply of sediment. If, however, the rate of supply of sediment exceeds that of subsidence of the sea-floor, then the thickness will be limited by the speed at which the latter sinks. Further, if the sea be shallow, current action will winnow away the finer particles and transport them to areas of more rapid subsidence. Clearly Dorsetshire was an area of relatively rapid subsidence during Kimmeridgian times; but in the Midlands depression occurred more slowly, with the result that the beds are both thinner and more arenaceous than in Dorset. If this contrast between the two areas had been slightly more pronounced, the Kimmeridgian of the southern Midlands would have been a condensed sequence, with the fossils of possibly several zones occurring in the same stratum.

In western Scotland shales containing Lower Kimmeridgian fossils have been discovered in Skye and Mull; but it is in the Kimmeridgian of the east Sutherlandshire coast, near Helmsdale, that the main interest lies. This is the most northerly station of reef-building corals in Mesozoic Europe; but the corals are not lying in the position of growth, neither are they embedded in limestone—the normal matrix for corals—but in shales interbedded with coarse boulder-beds. The boulders are extremely large, often yards in diameter, while the largest, the so-called fallen sea-stack, is a mass of bedded Old Red Sandstone, measuring 50 yards in length, 30 yards in width and 10 yards in height. It lies on its side with the bedding planes vertical. As it is underlain by hundreds of feet of shales and boulder beds, it obviously cannot be a fallen stack, and some other explanation must be sought, which will, at the same time, account for the curious contradiction noted above in connection with the mode of occurrence of the corals.

Bailey and Weir have made the interesting suggestion that these extraordinary anomalies resulted from earthquake shocks caused by contemporary movements along a submarine fault-scarp. The scarp-face formed a submerged cliff-like feature of Old Red Sandstone separating two areas of essentially different types: an inshore shallow-water zone where reef-building corals, sea-urchins and oysters flourished; and a deep-water zone, beyond the fault-scarp, where black mud was accumulating. The inevitable result of an earthquake shock would be to detach joint-bounded blocks from the scarp-face; they would plunge into the mud below, causing contortion of the bedding planes—this is a special characteristic of these rocks. At the same time the tidal wave caused by the shock would sweep blocks of coral and the shells of sea-urchins and other organisms over the edge of the scarp into the deep-water muds at its foot. Intermittent movement along the fault must have occurred over a long period, for boulder beds of this type occur at many horizons in the Kimmeridgian, and make up nearly a third of the total thickness.

## THE PORTLANDIAN STAGE

The two highest units of the Upper Jurassic, the Portland Stage and the Purbeck Beds, are magnificently exposed in the fine coastal sections of the 'Isle of Purbeck' and the 'Island of Portland'. The former is best seen in the Isle of Purbeck, between St Alban's Head and Durlston Head, where the cliffs rise to above 500 feet O.D. The steepness of these cliffs is such as to make the rocks largely inaccessible, and this is due to the fact that the Upper Portlandian consists of hard, well-bedded limestones, while the Lower Portlandian consists of sands and sandy marls which are easily eroded by the sea, causing undercutting of the overlying rocks. There is a perfectly gradual passage from the Kimmeridge Clay into the overlying Portland Sand, and it is difficult to decide where to draw the line between them. The Lower Portlandian sands and marls, about 100 feet thick, are overlain by the Cherty Beds of the Upper Portlandian, which forms the floors of the quarries in which the well-known 'freestones', or Portland building stones are, or have been, quarried. The popularity of the Portland Stone dates from its selection, by Sir Christopher Wren, for building the new St Paul's Cathedral after the Great Fire of London. Since then it has been used in many famous buildings in London, including the British Museum, Somerset House and King's College, several of the Government buildings in Whitehall and a host of other less well-known buildings. In the best freestone are found huge ammonites ('*Ammonites*' *giganteus*), and it appears that these animals reached their maximum size in Upper Portlandian times.

Inland the Portlandian rocks are hidden for many miles beneath the cover of unconformable Upper Cretaceous strata. When they reappear in the Vale of Wardour, they have diminished considerably in thickness. The presence here in the Lower Portlandian of a bed containing scattered black, cherty-looking pebbles ('lydites') is significant, for it marks the most southerly appearance of the Upper Lydite Bed. This pebble bed contains phosphatized ammonites derived from the highest zones of the Kimmeridge Clay (here of the arenaceous facies), and clearly indicates a considerable non-sequence. At Swindon and in scattered outliers between Oxford and Aylesbury the calcareous Portlandian Beds become even more attenuated and are last seen just west of Leighton Buzzard. As will be shown later (p. 374), beds of Portlandian age, but of a different facies, are present in Norfolk and Lincolnshire.

In the south of the Kent coalfield deep borings have penetrated considerable thicknesses of Portlandian beds, which differ considerably

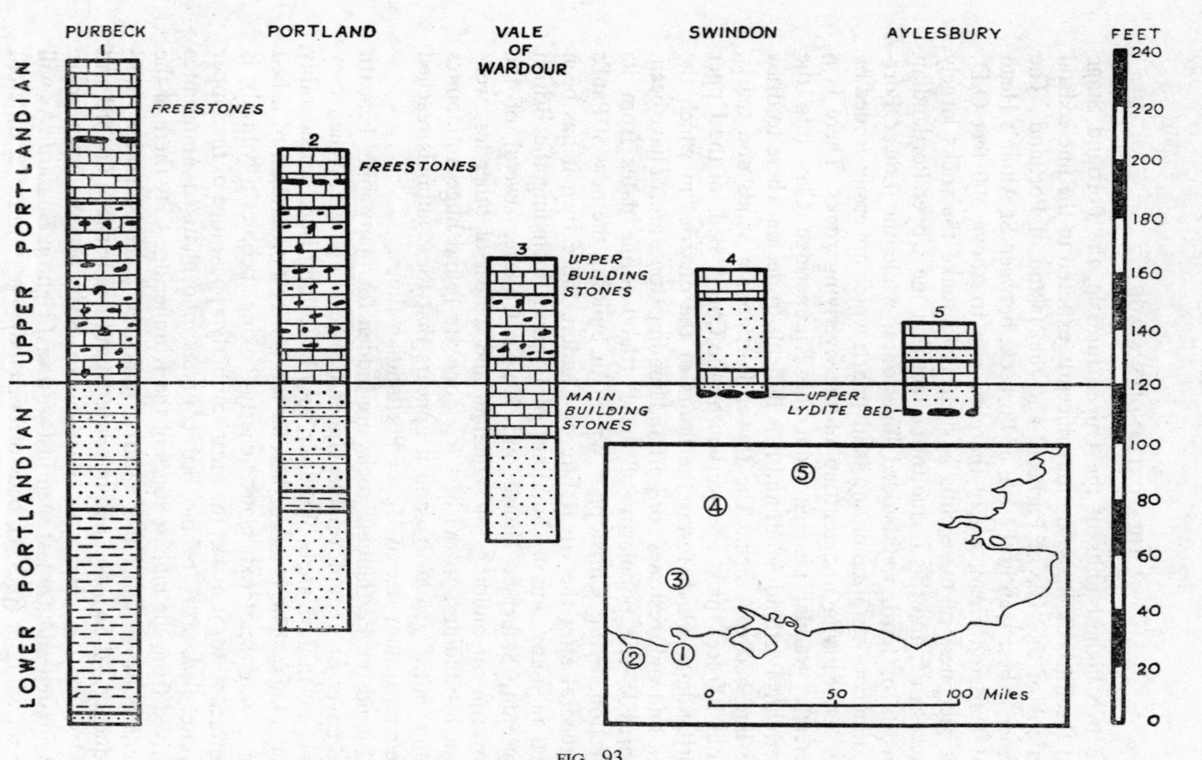


FIG. 93.
Vertical sections showing the variations in thickness and lithology of the Portlandian Beds.
Marls, broken lines; sands, dotted; sandstones, ruled and dotted; limestones, bricks; chert, black.

in lithology from those exposed in Dorset and elsewhere. The upper division is very sandy, without any freestones or chert, whilst the underlying beds are argillaceous and pass imperceptibly downwards into the Kimmeridge Clay. Just before the Second World War deep borings were sunk in the hopes of finding oil in south-east England. Seepages had been discovered in the Corallian and Wealden Beds of Dorset and in Pevensey Marshes in Sussex, whilst for many years the boring at Heathfield, Sussex, had yielded enough gas to light the station lamps. The anticlines of south-east England were found to be of the right type to contain oil, provided that suitable reservoir rocks occurred at depth. The Portlandian was regarded as the most likely reservoir rocks, for in some of the Kent borings the joints of the sandy limestones are impregnated with bitumen. Unfortunately the Portlandian was everywhere found to be of too argillaceous a facies. Oil was present; it could be extracted from the cores with chloroform, but the pores in the rock were too small to allow the oil to migrate freely and to feed wells. Whilst the economic return has been so disappointing, these very deep borings have been of great scientific value in affording detailed knowledge of the deep-seated geology of the area.

### THE PURBECK BEDS

The rocks of the highest group of the Upper Jurassic are perhaps the most interesting from the point of view of their origin. In their lithology and faunas they bear witness to a drastic change of geographical conditions, and the general inference to be drawn from their detailed study is that the closing phase of Jurassic geological history was much like the opening phase. It is largely true to state that the Purbeck Beds marks a return to Rhaetic conditions, in the sense that the rocks are not normal marine types but include some that were deposited in lagoons, some in freshwater, and some are actually fossil soils.

The type-area is, of course, the 'Isle of Purbeck', where they are much better developed than anywhere else in Britain, particularly in Durlston Bay, Swanage. Here they attain a thickness of 400 feet, which is not the maximum, however, as they reach 560 feet in, or rather under, Kent. In Dorsetshire they are conformable to the underlying Portlandian beds and to the overlying Wealden rocks. Although less than half the thickness they reach in Durlston Bay, the Purbeck Beds in the neighbourhood of Lulworth Cove, farther to the west, are exposed in such a way as to attract the attention of the most casual visitor. The rocks are inclined steeply landwards, and the resistant Portland Stone forms a natural barrier tending to resist the inroads of the sea; but the barrier has been breached at a number of points, and the sea having once gained access to the softer rocks behind tends to erode small oval-shaped coves in the Purbeckian and Wealden rocks. Both series are seen well exposed in steep cliff-sections in Lulworth Cove, Stair Hole and at other points, where the rapid alternations of different kinds of strata and the curious folds and contortions into which they have been thrown combine to make a most striking geological picture.

Inland from the coast, exposures are limited to excavations which have been made in the exploitation of some of the rocks for building and ornamental stone. The hills near Swanage are scarred with such pits and with heaps of waste material from the workings, and bear witness to one of the oldest stone-quarrying industries in England. 'Purbeck Marble' has been used for interior decoration for more than 700 years, and although the industry is now but a shadow of what it was formerly, the marble has been carried for church decoration as far as Scotland, Ireland and the Continent. The pillars of the nave of Salisbury Cathedral, for example, show what effective use can be made of the contrast between polished and unpolished Purbeck Marble.

In the Lower Purbeck Beds old land soils, the so-called 'Dirt Beds', occur, and contain the erect stumps and prostrate trunks of coniferous trees as well as cycads. The 'fossil forest', a short distance east of Lulworth Cove, is the best exposure where one of these old forest surfaces may be examined. Above the Lulworth forest bed a curious massive breccia, the 'Broken Beds', occurs, consisting of large and small angular fragments of thinly bedded limestones. This brecciation has been regarded as due to the caving in of the limestone, when the underlying trees decayed; but Dr Arkell has claimed that it was due to overthrusting during the mid-Tertiary earth-movements. He points out that in areas such as Portland, where the beds are horizontal, there are plenty of tree trunks but no 'Broken Beds'. He regards the old record of the presence of 'Broken Beds' in the Vale of Wardour as erroneous. West has recently (1964) shown that the Lower Purbeck Beds of Dorset, especially the 'Broken Beds', must once have contained considerable amounts of gypsum and anhydrite. He regards the beds as an evaporite series, in which primary gypsum has been converted to anhydrite as a result of increasing overburden. Other diagenetic changes included extensive silicification and calcification, for ghosts of gypsum or anhydrite crystals, mainly of microscopic size, are abundant in both the limestones and the cherts. Whilst West agrees with Arkell that the brecciation is essentially tectonic in origin and not really comparable with the solution breccias of the

Permian evaporite series of the Durham coast (p. 308), the presence of much anhydrite at this particular level in the Lower Purbeck Beds must have facilitated the failure of the beds under tectonic stress. Seams of secondary gypsum after anhydrite are developed at certain horizons, whilst in marly beds towards the top of the Lower Purbecks casts of cubes of rock-salt are not uncommon.

In the Middle and Upper Purbeck Beds the building stones and 'marbles' occur, the latter (in the Upper Purbeck) being thin beds of freshwater limestone with abundant remains of *Paludina* (*Viviparus*), a common type of freshwater gasteropod (see Fig. 112). The limestones are interbedded with marls and shales, some of which constitute the 'Insect Beds', containing a remarkable fauna of butterflies, beetles, dragonflies, locusts, ants and even aphids (green-fly).

The fauna of the Purbeckian is extraordinarily varied. The 'Cinder Bed', so-called from its appearance in the weathered state, is crammed with oysters, together with rare trigonias and the spines and radioles of the echinoid *Hemicidaris purbeckensis*. This assemblage indicates a brackish water, rather than a truly marine environment. Freshwater lamellibranchs like *Unio* and gasteropods like *Paludina* and *Limnaea* are abundant, particularly in the Upper Purbeckian. The fossil trees and many types of insects have been already mentioned. The remains of many unique forms of fossil fishes, turtles and crocodiles have been obtained from the Middle Purbeckian, while a 12-inch band at the base of this division has yielded mammalian remains.

The Purbeck Beds behave similarly to the Portlandian when traced north-eastwards. In the Vale of Wardour all three divisions are well represented, their total thickness being about 100 feet; but at Swindon only some 20 feet of strata rest with slight erosion on the Portland Stone. The Lower Purbeck is certainly present and perhaps the Middle division is also represented, though the evidence is inconclusive. Around Oxford and Aylesbury about the same thickness of marls and thin limestones occurs locally between the massive Portlandian limestones and sands which have hitherto been regarded as of Lower Cretaceous age. Recently (1962) however, at several outliers, these sands have yielded a fauna closely comparable with that found in the Cinder Bed of Dorset, but more varied in its molluscan assemblage and indicating more normal marine conditions. The significance of these discoveries and of other recent work farther northwards is dealt with in the succeeding chapter.

Anticlinal inliers of Purbeck Beds outcrop around Mountfield in Sussex and the beds have been penetrated by deep borings in other parts of the Weald. Whilst the rock types have a general resemblance to those of the Dorset coast sections and contain the same zonal sequence of ostracods, there are significant differences in detail. The 'Cinder Bed' is a well-marked datum in each area, but in Sussex the basal Purbeck beds, resting on the Portland Sandstone, are a gypsiferous series, with at least four seams of anhydrite or gypsum thick enough to be mined. At other horizons also, the succession in the Weald differs sufficiently from that found in Dorset to show that an unstable upwarp between Winchester and Portsmouth must have separated the Dorset from the Weald basin.

## REFERENCES

The Regional Geologies 'Bristol and Gloucester District' and 'East Yorkshire and Lincolnshire' contain excellent accounts of the detailed stratigraphy of these contrasting areas, in which the effects of contemporaneous earth-movement are so clearly shown.

ARKELL, W. J. *The Geology of Oxford* (Oxford University Press, 1947). An excellent account of a most important area. Many sections are described. Includes revision of his 1933 work.

ARKELL, W. J. *The Jurassic System in Great Britain* (Oxford University Press, 1933). This monumental work contains a very detailed and fully documented account of all that was known about the Jurassic rocks at the time of writing.

BAILEY, E. B., and WEIR, J. *Trans. Roy. Soc. Edin.*, **57** (1932), 429–467. The peculiar characters of the Kimmeridgian of Helmsdale ascribed to submarine faulting.

DAVIES, G. M. *The Dorset Coast: A Geological Guide* (Murby, London, 1956). A very useful guide to these classic sections.

HOLLINGWORTH, S. E., TAYLOR, J. H., and KELLAWAY, G. A. *Q.J.G.S.*, **100** (1944), 1–44. A full account and discussion of the origin of the superficial structures of the Northampton Ironfield.

KENT, P. E. *Proc. Yorks. Geol. Soc.*, **30** (1955), 197–227. Discusses the nature and influence of the Market Weighton structure.

WEST, I. M. 'Evaporite diagensis in the Lower Purbeck Beds of Dorset,' *Proc. Yorks. Geol. Soc.*, **34** (1964), 315–330.

## CHAPTER XIX

# THE CRETACEOUS PERIOD

### THE JURASSIC–CRETACEOUS BOUNDARY

In the Weald and in Dorset the non-marine Purbeck Beds are overlain by another thick group of non-marine rocks, the Wealden Beds. The two formations are perfectly comparable and the boundary between them is difficult to place: it is drawn in Sussex at the subtle change from shaly to sticky and more silty clays. Moreover the fauna of the lower part of the Wealden Beds is similar to that of the Purbeck Beds. Farther northwards in the scattered outliers in Wiltshire, Oxfordshire and Buckinghamshire the limestones and marls of the Purbeck Beds are overlain by a thin development of poorly fossiliferous sands and clays, the **Shotover Sands,** which have usually been correlated with the Wealden Beds. Overlying the Shotover Sands and overstepping across them to rest locally on Purbeckian, Portlandian, Kimmeridgian and even Corallian strata are patches of coarse sands yielding a marine fauna of late Lower Cretaceous age. The Shotover Sands and the older Jurassic rocks are affected by gentle folds and faults which do not disturb the marine Cretaceous rocks. From Leighton Buzzard to South Norfolk these marine Lower Cretaceous sands, the **Woburn Sands,** are much thicker and have an almost continuous outcrop. Nodule beds, containing both derived and indigenous fossils, are locally developed in the lower part of the Woburn Sands. In Norfolk and Lincolnshire, the equivalents of the Woburn Sands are separated from the Kimmeridge Clay by considerable thicknesses of sands and clays. In Norfolk the Kimmeridge Clay is overlain by the Sandringham Sands and in Lincolnshire by the Spilsby Sandstone, both with basal phosphatic nodule beds. The Market Weighton upwarp was still in operation, for the Spilsby Sandstone and the overlying beds thin out towards it and finally on the crest of the upwarp, late Lower Cretaceous beds overstep across the Jurassic rocks until they come to rest on the Lias. Farther to the north around Speeton, the Kimmeridge Clay is overlain nonsequentially by marine clays, the Speeton Clay, also with phosphate nodule beds prominently developed in its lower part.

Until very recently (1962) the Sandringham Sands of Norfolk, the Spilsby Sandstone of Lincolnshire and the lower part of the Speeton Clay of Yorkshire were all regarded as of very early Lower

Cretaceous age. Their basal phosphatic nodule beds were thought to contain a mixture of derived Kimmeridgian and indigenous Lower Cretaceous ammonites. It was believed that in late-Jurassic times an extensive uplift had occurred across the Southern Midlands separating the Weald-Dorset basin from a northern basin, which was submerged by a marine transgression in very early Lower Cretaceous times. The base of the Cretaceous System was regarded as everywhere clearly defined, except in the Weald and Dorset where the Wealden Beds pass down into the Purbeck Beds.

The Wealden Beds when traced southwards into the Paris Basin and then into south-east France, interdigitate with marine beds of unquestionable Lower Cretaceous age. The ammonite fauna of the Lower Cretaceous beds in France is, however, different from that of the Speeton Clay. In late Jurassic and early Cretaceous times there were two clearly defined faunal provinces in Europe: a southern province covering the Tethyan region, and a northern province extending across Germany and Poland to the Volga region of Russia. There was intermittent communication across Russia with the southern province and this enables the two different ammonite successions to be correlated. The marine Portlandian and marine Lower Cretaceous beds in southern England yield the ammonite fauna of the southern province, the Speeton Clay and its equivalents in Lincolnshire and Norfolk that of the northern province. We have already hinted at a difference between the faunas of Yorkshire and Southern England in earlier Upper Jurassic times, for example in the Oxfordian. Here we have a clear explanation of these differences.

This picture has been substantially modified by R. Casey. A new drainage channel at West Dereham in South Norfolk provided a temporary exposure of the richly fossiliferous phosphatic nodule bed at the base of the Sandringham Sands. Dr Casey's study of the ammonites obtained there, led him to re-examine the specimens found in the past from the Sandringham Sands and the Spilsby Sandstone and then to compare these with the ammonite faunas of the highest Jurassic and lowest Cretaceous beds of the Russian outcrops. He has shown that the English ammonites hitherto regarded as of lowest Cretaceous (Valanginian) age had been misnamed and that they are indeed identical with species occurring in the highest Jurassic rocks of Russia. The Spilsby Sandstone is therefore to be correlated with the Purbeck and Portland Beds. Moreover, a near-marine fauna of Middle Purbeck age has been found (1962) in the 'Lower Cretaceous' sands at two localities between Aylesbury and Leighton Buzzard.

Casey correlates the beds as shown on the opposite page.

| S. Lincs. | S. Midlands | Dorset | Volga Area |
|---|---|---|---|
| Claxby Beds | — | Wealden | Valanginian |
| Upper Spilsby Sandstone | — | Durlston (Upper Purbeck) Beds | Ryazanian |
| Mid-Spilsby Nodule Bed | Sands with Middle Purbeck Fauna | Cinder Bed | |
| Lower Spilsby Sandstone | Purbeck marls and thin limestones | Lulworth (Lower Purbeck) Beds | Volgian |
| ? Missing | | | |
| Basal Spilsby Nodule-Bed | Portland Sand Upper Lydite Bed | Portland Sand | |
| MISSING | | | |

He would place the Cretaceous-Jurassic boundary at the level of the 'Cinder Bed—Mid-Spilsby Nodule Bed'. In the entirely marine developments this level is marked by the incoming of *Tollia* (*Surites*) *spasskensis* and other Ryazanian forms. In the Weald and in Dorset the 'Cinder Bed' is an easily traceable 'marker horizon' and is eminently suitable for defining the boundary between the Purbeck and Wealden Beds.

In the Southern Midlands the 'Cinder Bed' horizon seems to be represented by the sands yielding a marine Middle Purbeckian fauna. The 'Mid-Spilsby Nodule Bed—Cinder Bed' horizon therefore marks a phase of transgression in the north (see Fig. 89) with the sea spreading southwards across the South Midland isthmus to bring a brief episode of brackish water conditions to the swamps of Dorset and the Weald.

Casey's suggestion would give a firm base for the Cretaceous System in England and one that is in line with the position of this boundary in other parts of Europe.

## THE LOWER CRETACEOUS

### 1. The Wealden Series

In the type area of the Weald of Kent, Surrey and Sussex, the Wealden Beds comprise two chief members: the Hastings Beds below, and the Weald Clay above.

The **Hastings Beds** consist of alternating clays and sands, and although both are unconsolidated and in the main not indurated, in both types of sediment hard rock-bands do occur, including thin limestones, sandstones and ironstones. On account of this diversity, the area where they outcrop, the central Weald, is one of considerable topographical relief and of extremely picturesque scenery. By contrast the Weald Clay outcrops on a broad, flat vale encircling the central tract, and in the western Weald reaching a width of about 20 miles.

The subdivisions of the Hasting Beds, together with their relative maximum thicknesses and lithology, are indicated in Fig. 94.

The basal beds are clays on the coast, but inland these pass laterally into, and are succeeded by, the **Ashdown Sand,** the thickest of the several divisions. In the type-area of Ashdown Forest, with Crowborough Beacon, 792 feet O.D. as the culminating point, these sands produce extensive pine- and heather-clad heaths.

The overlying **Wadhurst Clay** is the most interesting of the subdivisions, owing to its great variation in lithology. It is at this level that there is the greatest concentration of nodules of clay ironstone, which were formerly worked as ore. Numerous place-names such as Furnace Copse and Minepit Shaw and the picturesque hammerponds, sometimes with the remains of furnaces on their banks, recall the time when the 'Weald' was the great iron-producing area in England. The industry began to die out towards the end of the sixteenth century, owing partly to the increasing destruction of the forests which supplied the charcoal used as fuel, and partly to the exploitation of the 'Black Band' ironstones in the Coal Measures. Lenticular bands of calcareous sandstone, the Tilgate Stone, are particularly abundant in the upper half of the subdivision. It was from stone-bands near Cuckfield that Dr Mantell obtained the first remains of the great herbivorous dinosaur, *Iguanodon* (Fig. 105). Since that time large quantities of reptilian remains have been obtained from these rocks. The bedding planes of the sandstones in the Hastings Beds frequently show ripple-marking, sun-cracks, rain-pits and fossil footprints of terrestrial animals. They prove the existence of extensive sandy flats sufficiently soft to take the imprints, and later rendered sufficiently hard to retain them when covered by a fresh layer of sand or mud. Soil beds of *Equisetites*, traceable over considerable areas, prove the former existence of extensive swamps.

The **Tunbridge Wells Sands** bear a very close resemblance to the Ashdown Sands. Lenticular seams of variegated clay, of which the

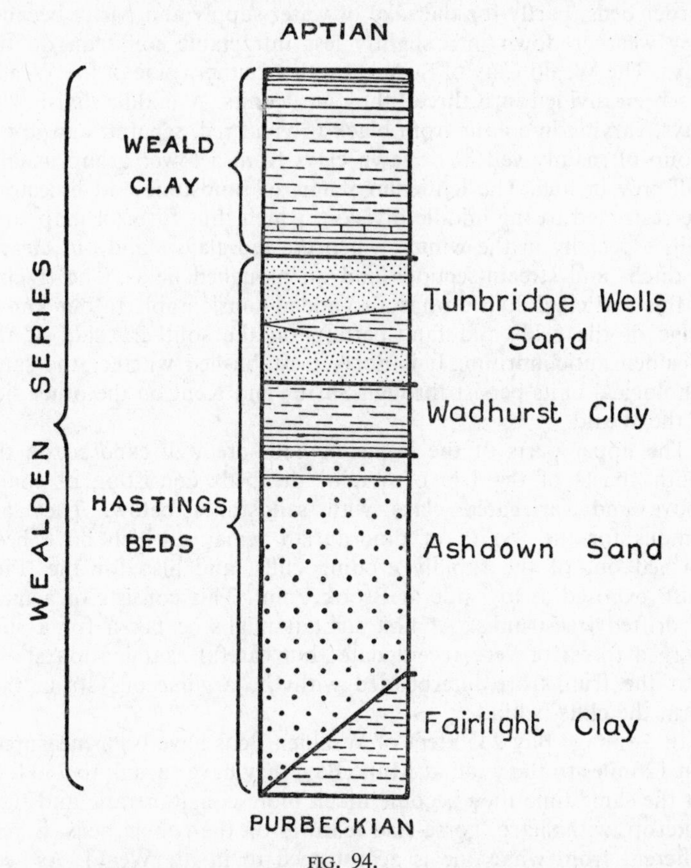


FIG. 94.
The Wealden (Neocomian) succession in South-East England.
The whole column represents 2600 feet of strata.
The impersistent clay in the Tunbridge Wells Sand Group is the Grinstead Clay.

Grinstead Clay is the most persistent, are developed at several horizons. Soil beds with *Equisetites lyelli* are even better developed in the Grinstead Clay than in the Wadhurst Clay. Locally the sands are irregularly cemented and then weathering produces the striking 'Sand Rock' scenery of Tunbridge Wells, West Hoathly and elsewhere.

The **Weald Clay** is a stiff, blue-grey clay becoming shaly at the top. Lenticular seams of Paludina Limestone, closely resembling 'Purbeck Marble', and of fine-grained sandstone also occur. Most of the settlements on the outcrop of the Weald Clay are sited on these harder beds, partly for the sake of water-supply and partly because they weather down into slightly less intractable soil than do the clays. The Weald Clay of Sussex, on the southern side of the Weald, has been divided into three lithological units. A middle division of clays, varying in colour from black to vivid red, separates an upper group of mainly yellow or fawn clays from a lower group usually buff-grey in hue. The lenticular seams of sandstone and limestone are restricted to the middle division, which thus forms a mappable unit, especially in the winter, when the red clays stand out clearly in ditch- and stream-sections and on ploughed fields. The tracing of this 'red clay' division has also added considerably to our knowledge of the fold- and fault-pattern on the southern side of the Wealden anticlinorium. It is not yet established whether the same lithological units persist through Surrey and Kent on the other side of the Weald.

The upper parts of the Wealden Beds are well exposed on the south coasts of the Isle of Wight, the beds consisting of shales above and variegated clays with sandstones below. They are famous for the wealth of dinosaurian remains which have been washed out of the rapidly eroding cliffs, and also for the 'Pine Raft' exposed at low tide at Brook Point. This consists of a mass of drifted tree-trunks. At first sight it might be taken for a submerged forest of very recent date; but careful examination shows that the trunks are interbedded with the argillaceous strata that form the cliffs behind.

In Swanage Bay 2350 feet of Wealden Beds have been measured; but 12 miles to the west, at Mupe Bay, they have shrunk to 750 feet. At the same time they become much more conglomeratic and their outcrop, with sharp, gorse-clad features on the pebble beds, is very different from what one is accustomed to in the Weald. As seen from Fig. 89 these pebble beds were laid down close to the margins of the area of deposition. The pebbles consist mainly of white quartz; but some of them carry tourmaline, and these, together with infrequent pebbles of radiolarian chert from the Culm Measures, show that the material was derived from the neighbourhood of the Dartmoor Granite.

As mentioned above (p. 373) the Shotover Sands used to be regarded as of Wealden age, but recent fossil discoveries in the Oxford-Aylesbury area suggest that these beds are in part of Middle Purbeck, in part of Aptian age. Farther to the east borehole evidence along the southern margin of the London Platform proves that the Wealden Beds overstep the bevelled edges of the higher Jurassic strata (Purbeckian to Bathonian) and finally, in the borings near Ramsgate, rest directly on Palaeozoic rocks.

### CONDITIONS OF DEPOSITION

The sedimentological features of the Wealden Beds in the type area, especially those of the Hastings Beds, have been studied in the greatest detail by P. Allen. They comprise the following megacyclothems:

IV { Middle and Upper Weald Clay<br>Horsham Stone<br>
III { Lower Weald Clay<br>Upper Tunbridge Wells Sand<br>
II { Grinstead Clay<br>Lower Tunbridge Wells Sand<br>
I { Wadhurst Clay<br>Ashdown Sand

The detailed succession of megacyclothems I and II is as under:

6. Thick siltstones and silty clays.
5. Thick dark coloured, ostracod-bearing clays.
4. Thin clays, with *Neomiodon* (*Cyrena*) shell beds.
3. Soil-bed with *Equisetites*, the rootlets penetrating downwards into a few feet of lenticular sandstones, siltstones and clays.
2. Pebble-bed, which may be locally merely a 'scatter' of small pebbles in a sandy matrix.
1. Thick sandstones.

The sandstones (Ashdown Sand, Upper and Lower Tunbridge Wells Sand) with their abundance of festoon bedding, washout structures, etc. are interpreted as deltaic deposits growing southwards from the London Platform into a freshwater lake during a period of falling lake level. Then as lake level rose, there was an abrupt lithological change into the clayey upper unit of the megacyclothem with a 'pebbly strand-line retreating northwards, followed successively by a silty shoreface, an offshore "fence" of green horse-tails, and open water with patches of "iron scum", pea-shells, water fleas and a muddy bottom'. After a period of lacustrine conditions, the lake level began to fall and the delta front spread southwards again.

The horizontal movement of the strand lines was considerable, for the southern limit of the Ashdown delta front can be fixed with precision near Hastings, whilst thirty miles to the north-west, rootlet beds of horse-tails were penetrated by the Warlingham boring. These cyclic sequences must be related to the transgressions and regressions during Valanginian, Hauterivian and Barremian times of the contemporary seas which covered much of eastern France. During one transgression the Hauterivian, the sea nearly reached the shore of the English Channel.

Detailed study of the pebble-beds has shown that large pebbles are narrowly restricted to winding zones which are believed to mark the courses of two rivers flowing off the London Platform, the one from the neighbourhood of Dover and the other from near Croydon (Fig. 95).

With the passage of time denudation bit deeper into the rocks exposed on the London Platform; consequently older material figures more prominently in the younger pebble-beds. Thus the sand of the eastern belt of the Top Ashdown Pebble-Bed contains among its heavy-mineral suite glauconite which is believed to have been derived from the glauconite-rich Portlandian then exposed on the edge of the Platform. The Lower Tunbridge Wells Pebble-Bed, which is well exposed around West Hoathley, Sussex, contains a great variety of pebbles including cherts and silicified limestones from the Carboniferous, and red-stained lavas and quartzites from the Old Red Sandstone as well as phosphatized ammonites ranging in age from Upper Kimmeridgian to Lower Portlandian.

The Weald Clay is mainly a lacustrine deposit. The London Platform must by now have been greatly reduced in relief and could only supply sandy detritus intermittently for short-lived deltaic episodes, represented by the Horsham Stone and other thinner and more lenticular sandstone horizons. The highest beds of the Weald Clay are dark-coloured shales yielding oysters, *Filosina*, echinoid spines, etc. indicating near-marine conditions comparable with those of the 'Cinder Bed'.

The Wealden Beds of Dorset and of the Isle of Wight show many differences in detail from those of the type area. In particular, they do not show any evidence of cyclothems, whilst the proportion of sand is greater and in Dorset distinctly pebbly horizons are common.

### 2. The Lower Greensand

Everywhere round the Weald, except in the south-east, the strike-vale on the outcrop of the Weald Clay is overlooked by the escarpment of the Lower Greensand. The name Lower Greensand was somewhat unhappily chosen; indeed it has been described as having 'its origin in a series of mistakes and misconceptions'; but it has become an integral part of the British stratigraphical nomenclature.

William Smith first applied the name Greensand, aptly enough, to certain beds in Wiltshire. The name was then extended to include certain strata exposed on the Kent coast, and not till later was it realized that the Greensand of Wiltshire overlies the Gault; but that of Kent is overlain by the Gault. Therefore it became necessary to distinguish an Upper from a Lower Greensand, with the Gault occurring in between.

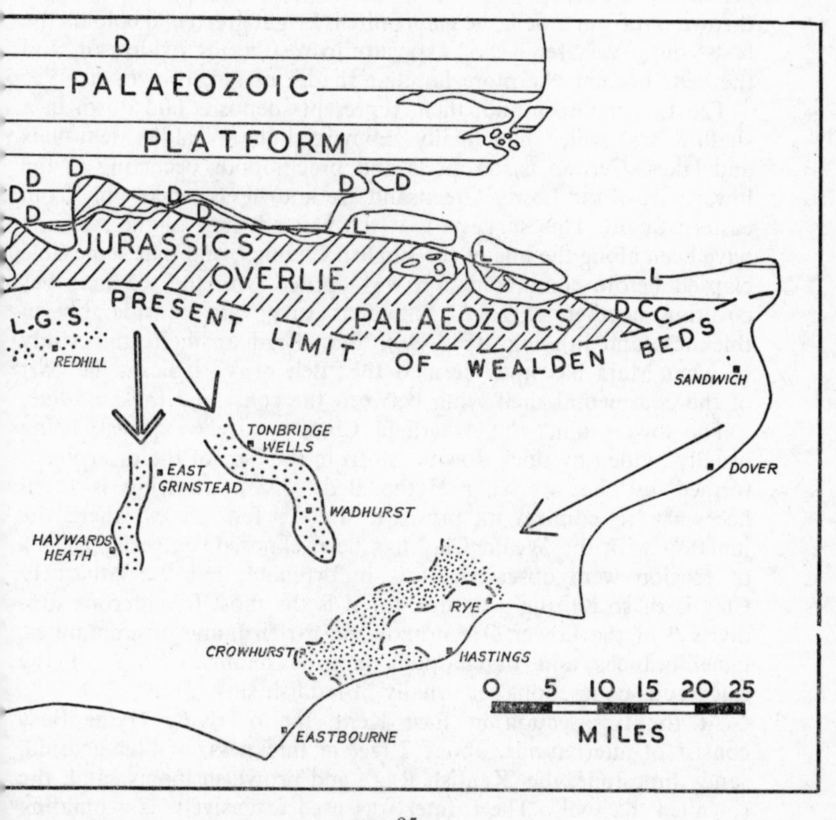


FIG. 95.

The rivers of the Wealden Delta. (*After P. Allen*).
Stippled—Areas where large pebbles are frequent.
L.G.S.—Pebble-beds in Lower Greensand near Westerham.
Double-lined arrow—Pebble-bed at top of Lower Tunbridge Wells Sand.
Thin arrows—Pebble-bed at top of Ashdown Sand.
Thin stipple—Sandy matrix of Pebble-bed rich in glauconite, garnet and apatite.
C—Boring proved Upper Carboniferous beds beneath marine Cretaceous.
D—Boring proved Devonian rocks beneath marine Cretaceous.
L—Boring proved Lower Palaeozoic beds beneath marine Cretaceous.

The Upper Greensand is more aptly named than the Lower Greensand, it usually has at least a greenish tinge; but the Lower Greensand, as well as containing some limestone and clay, is usually coloured red, brown, yellow or white, in fact, nearly every colour except green. The name has, however, one virtue: it does remind us that the beds are rich in glauconite and are therefore of marine origin, for glauconite is forming to-day only on submarine banks. When fresh, as in the sides of a newly made cutting or in material thrown out from a well, the glauconite is bright green and colours the beds; but a very few years' exposure to weathering oxidizes it, and the beds become the more familiar shades of red, brown, etc.

The Lower Greensand, then, represents deposits laid down in a shallow sea, which had finally submerged the Wealden delta-flats and lakes. Certain gasteropods and brachiopods occurring in the lower part of the Lower Greensand are known elsewhere only from eastern Spain. This suggests that the first advance of the sea may have been along the line of the English Channel, and that some time elapsed before communication was opened with the sea that was covering northern France. The beds vary very considerably in thickness and lithology (Fig. 96), and afford an interesting study of what Marr has aptly termed the 'Belt of Variables'—the part of the continental shelf lying between the coast and the mud-line.

The lowest unit, the **Atherfield Clay,** is rarely exposed, being usually hidden by thick downwash from the face of the escarpment formed by the overlying Hythe Beds. Deep augering is often necessary to confirm its presence. In the few places where the junction with the Weald Clay has been exposed, only slight signs of erosion were observed. It is unfortunate that the Atherfield Clay is of so retiring a nature, for it is the most fossiliferous subdivision of the Lower Greensand, and a rich fauna of ammonites, lamellibranchs and brachiopods can be hammered out of the calcareous concretions set usually in reddish silty clay.

At the type-section in East Kent, the overlying **Hythe Beds** consist of alternations, about 2 feet in thickness, of blue-hearted, sandy limestone, the 'Kentish Rag', and brownish loamy sand, the so-called 'hassock'. The former was used extensively as a building stone for London by the Romans. The beds are rather patchily fossiliferous. They produce a well-marked 'cuesta' with a belt of orchards along the clay-sand junction at the foot of the scarp-slope, and more orchards mixed with arable fields on the dip-slope. This type of country extends from the coast to the river Medway; but farther westward the escarpment begins to get higher, and the orchards and hop-gardens give place to extensive chestnut plantations and sandy heaths. This reflects the appearance of the 'arenaceous facies'—seams of spicular sandstone and some chert set in loamy sands. The height of the escarpment is largely controlled by the relative abundance and hardness of the stone-bands. It reaches over 800 feet O.D. to the south of Westerham; but between Reigate and Dorking, where the stone-bands completely fail (Fig. 96), the Hythe Beds produce only an insignificant feature. To the south and west of Dorking, however, the stone-bands reappear in force, and the escarpment reaches its maximum height of 965 feet O.D. at Leith Hill. From this well-known viewpoint a range of heather- and pine-clad hills sweeps round the western end of the Weald to the line of the river Arun near Pulborough. Here an abrupt change in lithology, back to the rag-and-hassock type, takes place, and consequently the arable cultivation on the dip-slope reappears. The ragstone, however, soon becomes very spasmodic in occurrence, and in East Sussex the Hythe Beds produce only a low 'feature'.

In East Kent the overlying **Sandgate Beds** are greenish, glauconitic loams forming a well-marked strike-vale at the foot of the dip-slope of the Hythe Beds. Inland from the coast they quickly diminish in thickness and become difficult to map as a continuous stratum. Near Godstone, in Surrey, however, they again thicken and at Nutfield consist of some 70 feet of grey spicule-bearing limestone interbedded with seams of fuller's earth. The former contains the ammonite, *Parahoplites nutfieldensis*, which is characteristic of this horizon. The seams of fuller's earth are the most valuable in the country, and were probably deposited in the quiet waters of a shallow lagoon. West of Dorking the facies changes: the lower Sandgate Beds consist of calcareous sands, patchily cemented into ragstone; while the upper beds are loams of considerable thickness and coloured red by iron-oxide formed from the abundant glauconite. In some exposures the cementing mineral in the sands is silica, in which case the 'doggers' are chalcedonic sandstones, or they may be partly siliceous and partly calcareous. Formerly it was thought probable that the silica was derived from spicules in the overlying beds; but it now appears that the spicules are present in insufficient numbers to provide all the silica, some of which may therefore have been directly deposited on the sea-floor contemporaneously with the sands, though some rearrangement of the silica by percolating water has taken place. These sands with stone-bands are the **Bargate Beds.** In places where the proportion of stone-bands to sand is high and the dip is small, as in the Godalming neighbourhood, these beds form extensive plateaux, usually under arable farming. The Bargate Beds yield an indigenous fauna including *Parahoplites nutfieldensis* and brachiopods, preserved in calcite, together with small phosphatized ammonites derived chiefly from the Oxford Clay, as well

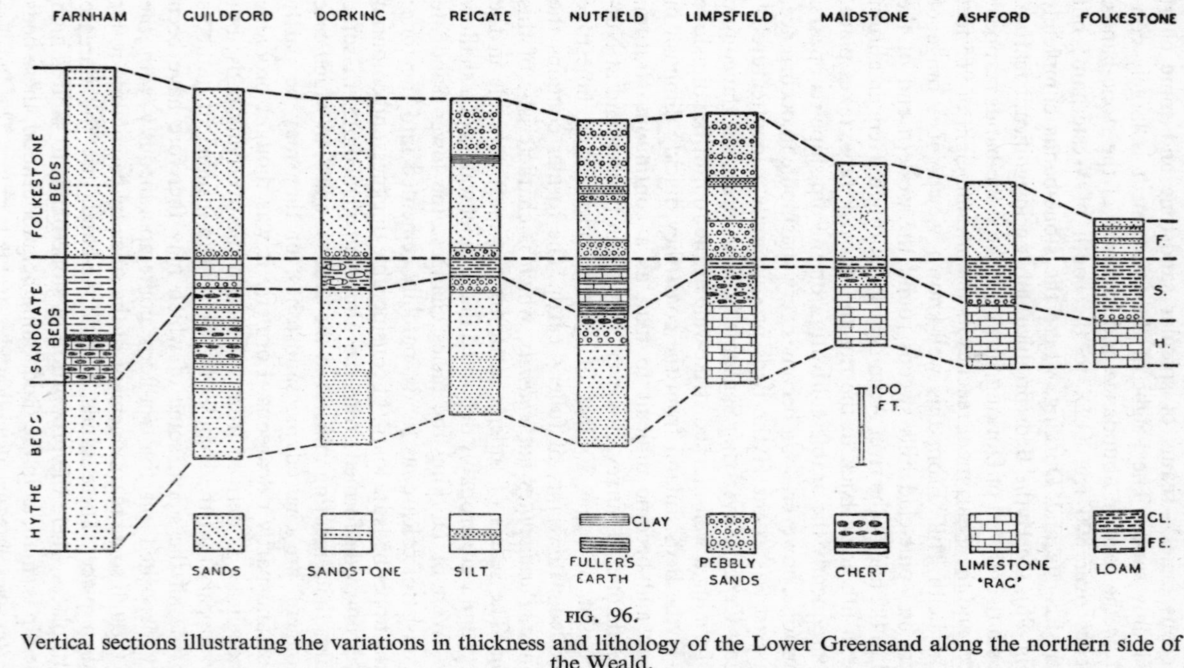


FIG. 96.

Vertical sections illustrating the variations in thickness and lithology of the Lower Greensand along the northern side of the Weald.

Current bedding is shown conventionally in the Folkestone Beds; close stippling indicates fine sand; GL = glauconitic, and FE = ferruginous.

as fish-teeth. Many abraded ooliths occur, too, and were apparently derived from the Great Oolite, then outcropping at the western end of the London Platform. Their coarseness of grain and pebbly nature, together with the strong current bedding they exhibit, prove the Bargate Beds to have been deposited in very shallow water—probably just off a spit forming the western boundary of the lagoon in which the fuller's earth was forming farther east.

The overlying **Folkestone Sands** are, in one sense, the most frustrating subdivision of the Lower Greensand. At the Kent coast they consist of coarse greenish sands, often cemented into seams of sandstone. This facies can be traced for some ten miles inland. Before Ashford is reached they have changed into a westward-thickening succession of dominantly unconsolidated sands,varying considerably in grade-size and colour, often strongly current bedded with the foresets sloping downwards from the north-west, and often with the true dip difficult to determine owing to the ramifying seams of ironstone. Locally seams of silt or clay occur, some thick enough to be mapped for considerable distances; and more rarely the sand has been cemented into hard sandstone or quartzite (Fig. 96). Their outcrop is marked by wide stretches of sandy heaths with conifers and silver birches revelling in the light soil. They usually produce a distinct 'feature' overlooking the strike-vale on the Sandgate Beds or, when this is absent, the dip-slope of the Hythe Beds. In places the ironstone is compact enough to give rise to steep-sided, conical hills such as the Devil's Jumps, to the north of Hindhead. One eminent naturalist once wrote of the hard black rock, present here, as basalt!

Until a few years ago the Folkestone Sands were regarded as unfossiliferous, and as having been deposited very probably under aeolian conditions, for many of the sand-grains are beautifully rounded and polished. The easily mappable junction between the Gault Clay and the Folkestone Sands was formerly regarded as marking the boundary between the Lower and the Upper Cretaceous beds. The basal sandy clays of the Gault yielded ammonites characteristic of the base of the Middle Albian Stage, and it was thought that these beds with their phosphatic nodules indicated a considerable non-sequence; and that the Folkestone Sands, though unfossiliferous, could be referred to the top of the underlying Aptian Stage, which includes the *nutfieldensis* fauna of the Sandgate Beds.

Within recent years, however, a large fauna has been collected from the sandstones of the type-section and immediately inland. The ammonites prove, firstly, that the sequence is condensed and broken by many non-sequences; and secondly, that the beds are nearly all referable to various zones of the Lower Albian Stage. It is only the basal beds that are of Upper Aptian age. If this is so, the very important Albian-Aptian boundary must be drawn somewhere within the Folkestone Sands. Except in East Kent very few fossils have been obtained from these beds: for, owing to their high porosity, percolating water has dissolved away the shells. Ammonites preserved in ironstone have, however, been found well up in the Folkestone Sands near Farnham. Again they belong to the Lower Albian Stage and are separated from the next datable horizon—in the loams overlying the Bargate Beds with the *nutfieldensis* fauna—by nearly 200 feet of unfossiliferous beds. It is to be hoped that further collecting will enable the base of the Albian Stage to be fixed with precision. The present position is that this stage-boundary is no longer of any practical importance so far as geological mapping is concerned, for it does not coincide with the base of a lithological division that can be followed in the field.

These discoveries raise anew the question of the conditions under which the beds were deposited. In East Kent they are clearly marine. The occurrence at Farnham of delicate siliceous sponges in current-bedded sands of a type that are elsewhere regarded as of aeolian origin is very puzzling. The most reasonable explanation is that the Folkestone Sands are in the main marine, laid down in very shallow water under the influence of powerful and persistent currents from a north-westerly direction. The abundance of well-rounded and polished sand-grains suggests that the sea was fringed by extensive sand-flats, which may have been submerged at times, and from which material may also have been blown by the wind. The fragments of wood that occur fairly frequently could have been carried by rivers from farther inland. The existence of temporary lagoons in this current-swept sea is indicated by glauconite-rich, persistent seams of clay and silt in the Reigate area.

Pebbly beds are locally developed in the Lower Greensand, particularly in the Folkestone Beds. The pebbles comprise the same types of cherts and silicified rocks as occur in the Lower Tunbridge Wells Pebble-Bed (p. 380). Derived Jurassic debris is plentiful only in the Bargate Beds of the Godalming neighbourhood. Its scarcity in the Folkestone Beds cannot be explained by supposing that the Jurassic cover of the London Platform had been completely removed, for in certain borings the Gault clay rests directly on Jurassic rocks. The attrition due to current- and wave-action on the floor of the Lower Greensand sea must have been much more severe than in the rivers meandering across the delta-flats of the Hastings Beds. As a result, although the pebble-beds of the Lower Greensand of the northern side of the Weald are considerably closer to the Jurassic outcrops of the Platform, they do not contain such a complete record of the beds under contribution, for only the harder constituents have survived as pebbles.

In the Isle of Wight the Lower Greensand reaches its maximum thickness of some 800 feet of beds. The cliffs to the east of Atherfield Point are richly fossiliferous and are the type sections for the detailed zoning by means of ammonites of the British Lower Aptian and most of the Upper Aptian stages. Fortunately the sections at Folkestone (p. 385) take the story on into the Albian above the level where ammonites fail in the Isle of Wight. The **Atherfield Clay** consists of about 80 feet of blue-grey silty clay, richly fossiliferous in some layers, notably the Perna Bed, a coarse sandstone at the base of the formation, named after the lamellibranch *Mulletia* (*Perna*) *mulleti*. The overlying **Ferruginous Sands** consist of greenish or rusty-coloured sands, rich in glauconite though this is often oxidized to limonite. These beds, richly fossiliferous both at Atherfield and at Shanklin, are the equivalents of the Hythe and Sandgate Beds of the Weald. The **Sandrock Series** continues the succession and consists of nearly 200 feet of white or yellow sand interbedded with laminated grey sand and blackish clay. They are correlated with the Folkestone Beds on lithological grounds, for similar laminated beds occur at the top of the Lower Greensand in the south-western Weald. The overlying **Carstone,** a pebbly sandstone varying widely in thickness, has yielded Lower Albian ammonites.

In Dorset less than 200 feet of marine Lower Cretaceous strata are exposed in the cliffs of Swanage and Worbarrow Bays. They represent a somewhat condensed sequence of the divisions recognized in the Isle of Wight; but in several particulars, notably in a great abundance of lignite, they indicate deposition closer to land. This is supported by the faunal evidence. Ammonites, plentiful in the Isle of Wight, are rarely found in Dorset, whilst there is a westward increase in the abundance of brackish water lamellibranchs and gasteropods. Finally, in the vicinity of Lulworth Cove the Lower Greensand disappears beneath the overstepping Gault.

Inland, in a few places such as the Vale of Wardour and at Calne in Wiltshire, the Lower Greensand appears for a short space from beneath the Upper Cretaceous cover. The best-known of these outlying patches is that near Farringdon in Berkshire. Here the beds consist of ferruginous sands and gravels, famous for their indigenous fauna of calcareous sponges, brachiopods and echinoids, *Parahoplites nutfieldensis* has been found here, while the brachiopods show many points of similarity to those in the Bargate Beds, so that general correlation with the Sandgate Beds of the Weald is proved.

Phosphatized Upper Jurassic fossils occur in addition. Locally the beds are cemented to form a unique sponge-conglomerate.

### 3. The Marine Neocomian

North of the London Platform the Lower Cretaceous rocks are of a very different nature from those of the Weald. On the Yorkshire coast at Speeton some 200 feet of bluish clay, the **Speeton Clay,** rest on Kimmeridge Clay. A phosphatic nodule-bed at the base of the Speeton Clay contains ammonites derived from the top zones of the Kimmeridge Clay. A few feet above the 'Coprolite Bed' the first indigenous ammonites, of earliest Cretaceous age occur. The remainder of the Speeton Clay represents a continuous section, though with minor nonsequences, ranging through the Valanginian, Hauterivian, Barremian, Aptian and into the Albian Stage.

The Speeton Clay has a very restricted outcrop beneath the Upper Cretaceous beds; but to the south of the Market Weighton upwarp, along the foot of the Yorkshire and the Lincolnshire Wolds, the Neocomian Beds reappear. Here they are of a very different facies: a variable succession of limestones, clays, sandstones and ironstones, obviously deposited in very shallow water, for drifted plant-remains are common and some of the beds show signs of having been churned up by worms. The Market Weighton upwarp was still active. The lower beds are overstepped northwards by the highest member, the **Carstone,** a coarse pebbly sandstone which finally rests on Lower Jurassic strata. This is the last time that we shall have occasion to refer to movement in this belt. It is worth recalling that it has been repeatedly mentioned as a major factor in controlling sedimentation from earliest Liassic to latest Lower Cretaceous times.

It used to be thought that the equivalents of the Portland and Purbeck Beds were not represented in the beds that separate the Kimmeridge Clay from the Red Chalk in the outcrops between the Wash and the Market Weighton upwarp. But as we have seen (p. 374) very recent work has shown that their basal member, the Spilsby Sandstone, is the time-equivalent of most of the Portland and the Purbeck Beds of southern England and therefore that the nonsequence represented by the phosphatic nodule beds overlying the Kimmeridge Clay is not nearly as great as was thought formerly.

The Neocomian rocks disappear southwards beneath the recent deposits of the Wash, and when they reappear on the Norfolk coast the succession is thinner than in Lincolnshire, with the basal beds, again resting on an eroded surface of the Kimmeridge Clay. The Carstone of Norfolk, in its basal beds, yields slightly rolled Lower Aptian ammonites, equivalent to those of the Atherfield Clay and the Hythe Beds. Barremian ammonites have been found

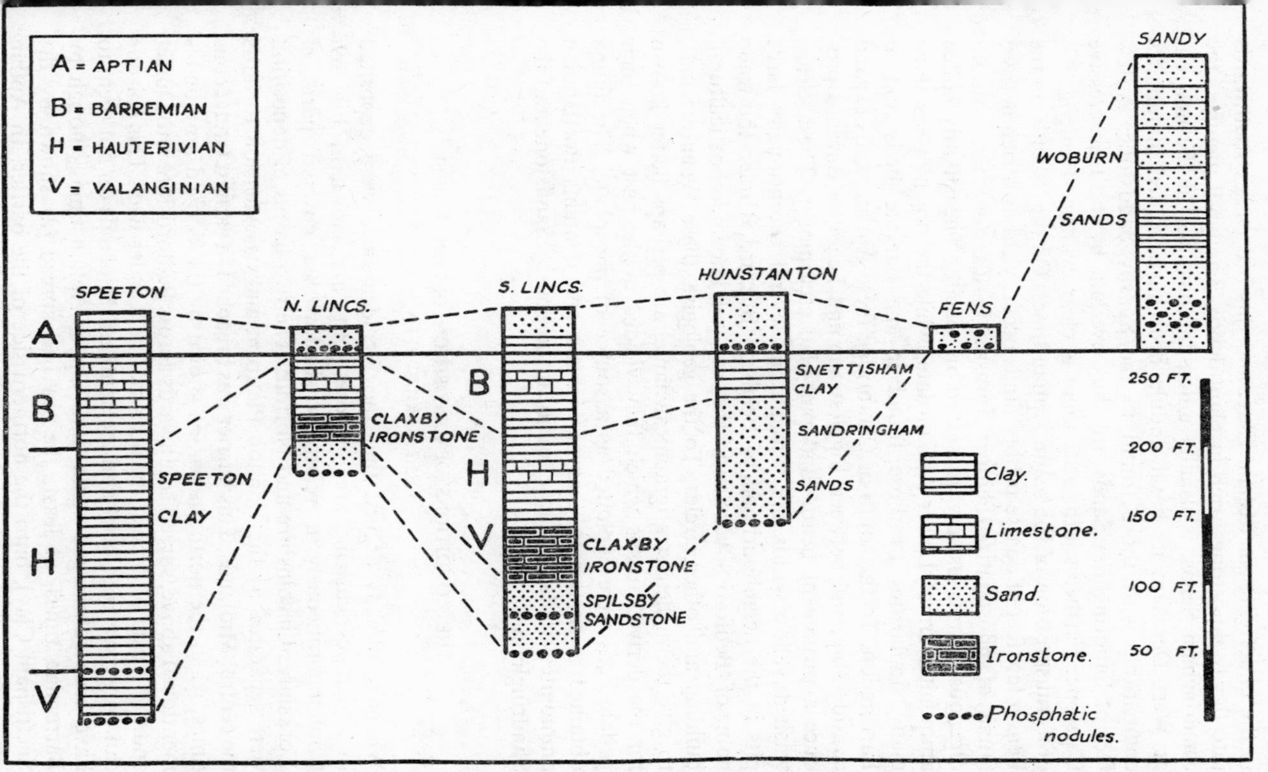


FIG. 97.—Vertical sections showing the variations in thickness and lithology of the Neocomian of the Northern Basin.

in the underlying **Snettisham Clay,** and this bed passes southwards into flaggy sandstones, rich in plant-debris. The basal member, the **Sandringham Sands,** is usually unfossiliferous; but in the new cut at West Dereham its basal nodule beds have yielded ammonites comparable with those found in the Spilsby Sandstone. A few feet of Sandringham Sands are thus overlain by the transgressive Carstone. Farther southwards there is clear evidence (see Fig. 97) of a transgression of the sea in Aptian times. On the 'islands' in the Fens a few feet of coarse pebbly sands occur, yielding a rich derived fauna of phosphatized Upper Jurassic fossils, together with indigenous forms, usually preserved in calcite. The slightly rolled ammonites are of Lower Aptian date, while the brachiopods show many similarities to those found in the Bargate Beds and at Farringdon. To the south of Cambridge these Aptian sands expand considerably, and between Biggleswade and Leighton Buzzard produce a prominent heath- and pine-clad escarpment. These clean-washed yellow sands are wrought in several exceptionally large pits in the neighbourhood of Leighton Buzzard. Under the trade name of 'Bedford Silver Sands' they are well known in horticultural, building and other circles. To the geologist, these **Woburn Sands,** to give them their stratigraphical name, are perhaps better known for the derived fossils which they yielded in the past when their pebble beds were exploited as a source of phosphate. The fauna obtained is similar to that of Upware and contains Portlandian ammonites similar to those found in the Spilsby Sandstone and the Sandringham Sands.

## THE CONDITIONS OF DEPOSITION OF THE LOWER CRETACEOUS BEDS

We have already argued that the Wealden Beds were deposited in a deltaic-lacustrine area, whose limits are shown in Fig. 89. Contemporaneously a relatively shallow sea covered parts of Yorkshire, Lincolnshire and Norfolk. The two basins of deposition were separated by the London Platform and its extension towards the central Midlands. This barrier was breached in earliest Cretaceous times, when the northern sea, as shown by the derived ammonites mentioned above, spread southwards across Bedfordshire into Dorset and the Weald to deposit the near-marine 'Cinder Bed'. This episode can only have been brief and the southern Midlands do not seem to have been submerged again until Upper Aptian times, though by Barremian times, at least, the sea had spread (as shown by the Snettisham Clay), onto the northern side of the barrier. In Aptian times we see first a transgression of the sea from the south or the south-west across the delta-flats, and then the submergence of the western part of the barrier and the joining of the two seas. This transgression from the south occurred in three stages. The basal beds of the Atherfield Clay in the Isle of Wight and the western part of the Weald are older than those in Kent. Therefore the first advance of the Lower Aptian sea, along the line of the English Channel, did not spread eastwards into Kent. The second surge of the sea into Kent was probably connected with the opening of a channel southwards to the seas over northern France. The upper part of the Atherfield Clay, the Hythe Beds and their equivalents were then laid down. In the south-east of the Weald, however, in the Boulonnais (which is the extension of the Weald into France), and underground along the edge of the London Platform, the Sandgate Beds overstep the Hythe Beds to rest, with a basal phosphatic nodule-bed, on an eroded surface of the Wealden. Indeed, in parts of the Boulonnais and beneath North Kent this overstep carries them across the Upper Jurassic on to Palaeozoic rocks. The scattered patches of Lower Cretaceous rocks beyond the Chalk Downs, notably those at Farringdon, are also to be correlated with the Sandgate Beds. The northward and westward transgression of the sea in Upper Aptian times was, therefore, far more extensive than that of the Lower Aptian, and resulted finally in union with the northern sea, which meantime had been spreading southwards from Norfolk across Cambridgeshire into Bedfordshire and beyond.

The shores of the northern sea must have lain near the existing Scottish coast, for erratic blocks found in the Pleistocene Boulder Clay of Fraserburgh and Moorseat in Aberdeenshire have yielded a rich fauna of Barremian and Hauterivian fossils. The soft nature of the sandstone in which the fossils are embedded and which was clearly deposited in very shallow water, proves that it cannot have withstood much transport. It is very probable, therefore, that Lower Cretaceous rocks are extensively developed beneath later deposits on the bottom of the Moray Firth.

There is evidence also of a minor phase of earth-movement affecting the margins of the areas of deposition. This phase is to be correlated with the **Younger Cimmerian** folding which is more strongly developed in the Upper Jurassic and earliest Cretaceous rocks of North Germany. Detailed mapping shows that in Wiltshire and Oxfordshire the Lower Greensand is not only unconformable on the higher Jurassic strata, but that it is undisturbed by the slight folds and faults affecting the latter. For example, near Calne an important fault cuts out the entire Corallian, Oxford Clay being thrown against Kimmeridge Clay; but the Lower Greensand passes across the fault without any disturbance. In the Boulonnais the movements are even more marked. Connected with the same period of activity was the renewal of movement along the Nuneaton and Charnwood axes. The first would account for the abrupt disappearance of the Lower Cretaceous beneath the Gault to the south-west of Leighton Buzzard. The second would explain the Lower Cretaceous beds overstepping at Sandy from Kimmeridge Clay on to Oxford Clay and then back on to Kimmeridge Clay. Inspection of a geological map shows that lines of Charnian trend through Leighton Buzzard and Sandy, when extended to the north-west, pass through the ancient rocks of Nuneaton and Charnwood Forest.

## 4. The Gault and the Upper Greensand

The change from Folkestone Sands to **Gault Clay** in the Weald is almost dramatically sudden, though there is no discordance of dip between the two formations. In parts of Sussex stiff blue clay rests directly on a sheet of ironstone capping the sands, but generally a few feet of sandy clay with phosphatic nodules separate clay from sand.

The Gault is richly fossiliferous and outstanding on account of its wealth of ammonites, particularly '*Hoplites*', some of which still show a beautifully iridescent shell, though many are preserved in iron sulphide. In addition to the ammonites, belemnites are common ('*Belemnites*' *minimus*), and the fauna also includes many lamellibranchs (*Inoceramus concentricus*, *I. sulcatus*, *Nucula pectinata*) and gasteropods, fewer brachiopods and occasional crabs and lobsters (Fig. 98).

The Gault is not a particularly deep-water clay, the maximum depth of the sea being estimated at about 200 fathoms. Thirteen ammonite zones, characterized mainly by species of '*Hoplites*', have been recognized, and detailed zonal work has shown that deposition was slow with many pauses. At the type-section at Folkestone the sequence is reasonably complete; but a few miles inland a conspicuous bed of phosphatic nodules and rolled fossils appears. This represents a major non-sequence separating Upper Gault (Upper Albian) from an incomplete Lower Gault (Middle Albian). The available evidence suggests that this, the most pronounced of the numerous breaks in deposition, is traceable throughout the Weald.

As is to be expected, the lithological contrasts between the Gault and the Folkestone Sands on the one hand and the Gault and the Chalk on the other, find expression also in topographical and ecological contrasts. The heathlands of the Lower Greensand, with woods of conifers and silver birches, give place to water-logged flats of the Gault with oaks much in evidence; and these in turn are

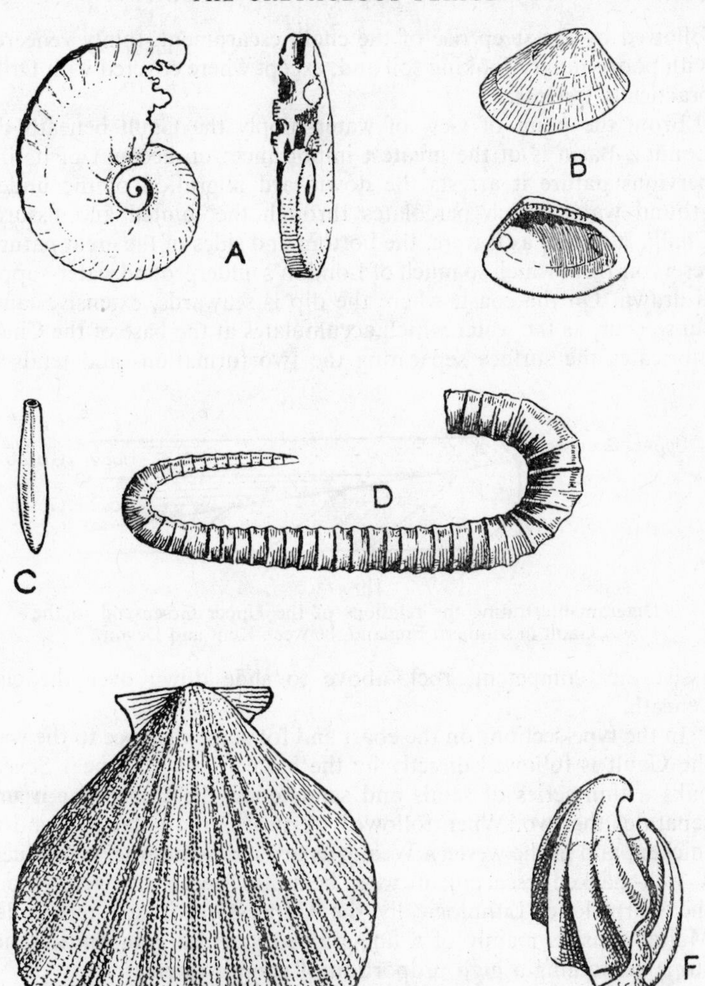


FIG. 98.
Characteristic Albian Fossils.

A. '*Hoplites*' (*Anahoplites*) *splendens*. Gault.
B. *Nucula pectinata*. Gault.
C. *Neohibolites* (*Belemnites*) *minimus*. Gault.
D. *Hamites* sp. Gault.
E. *Chlamys* (*Pecten*) *aspera*. Upper Greensand.
F. *Inoceramus sulcatus*. Gault.

followed by the steep rise of the chalk escarpment, thinly veneered with poor, hungry-looking soil and, except where covered with Drift, practically treeless.

From the point of view of water-supply the Gault beneath the London Basin is of the greatest importance: on account of its impervious nature it arrests the downward migration of the underground water which percolates through the jointed and fissured Chalk. It forms, as it were, the bottom and sides of the great natural reservoir from which so much of London's underground water-supply is drawn. On the coast, where the dip is seawards, extensive landslips occur, as the water which accumulates at the base of the Chalk lubricates the surface separating the two formations and tends to

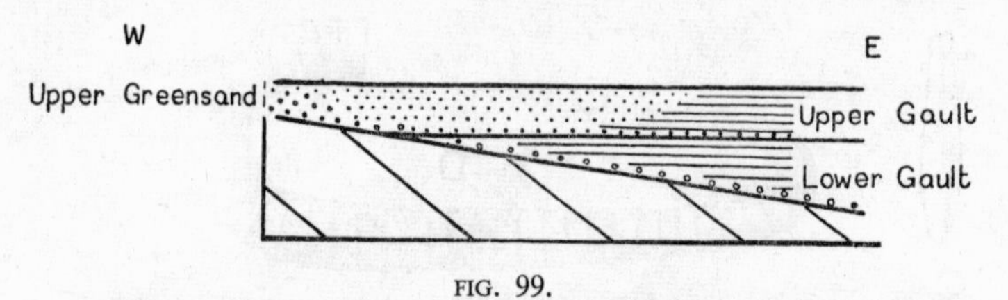


FIG. 99.

Diagram illustrating the relations of the Upper Greensand to the Gault in southern England, between Kent and Devon.

assist the 'competent' rock above to slide down over the clay beneath.

In the type-sections on the coast and for some distance to the west the Gault is followed directly by the basal Chalk; but near Sevenoaks a thin series of sands and sandstones, the **Upper Greensand,** separates the two. When followed westwards the latter is found to thicken, and in the western Weald, as around Selbourne, it produces a well-marked escarpment with beautiful beech 'hangers' along the scarp-slope. Lithologically the Upper Greensand, here called Malm, consists mainly of a fine-grained greenish glauconitic sandstone containing a high proportion of sponge spicules.

In the Isle of Wight this thickening of the Upper Greensand at the expense of the Gault continues, whilst beds of hard chert make their appearance. In Dorset the Gault becomes sandy and micaceous and increasingly difficult to distinguish from the basal beds of the Upper Greensand; indeed, in West Dorset and Devon it has proved impossible to separate the two. The beds of the Blackdown Hills to the south of Wellington are particularly well known. In the past, when they were extensively exploited for scythe stones made from the siliceous concretions in the sand, a rich fauna of beautifully preserved chalcedonic shells of molluscs was obtained. Specimens from here of *Protocardia hillana*, *Torquesia* (*Turritella*) *granulata* and other forms are to be found in most good collections. In Devonshire the Upper Greensand caps the Haldon Hills between the Exe and the Teign valleys. The beds are coarse-grained or even pebbly sands. They contain compound corals of littoral type, absent from the Blackdown Hills, and thick-shelled molluscs. Standing on the western edge of the Haldon Hills one looks across the Teign Valley to the tors of Dartmoor some five miles away. No trace of the Upper Greensand can be found along the flanks of Dartmoor, though the ground overtops the Haldon Hills where the beds are horizontal. Clearly the existing Teign Valley coincides closely in position with the shoreline of Upper Greensand times.

Study of the faunas of the Gault and Upper Greensand has shown that instead of being successive members of the Cretaceous System, they are the lateral equivalents one of the other, the Upper Greensand of the westerly outcrops being of the same age as the Upper Gault of the Kent coast, the lithology being governed by the conditions of sedimentation. In a shallow sea, the floor of which was undergoing progressive subsidence, we should expect higher zones to overlap lower ones, and, as time progressed to overstep on to the rocks outcropping round the margins of the sea; and clay in the lower beds more centrally situated should give place to sands in the marginal belt, and these should become pebbly as the shoreline is approached (Fig. 99). This is exactly how the Gault and the Upper Greensand behave: the overstep at their base produces perhaps the most striking unconformity in the whole stratigraphical column. In the Weald, the Isle of Wight and eastern Purbeck, the Gault rests on the Lower Greensand with a sharp lithological contrast but no discordance of dip. Near Lulworth, however, the Gault oversteps on to the Wealden Beds and then farther westwards on to lower and lower horizons. Clearly the great pile of Jurassic and Permo-Triassic rocks of West Dorset and Devon had been tilted eastward and, in some localities, slightly faulted and folded. An erosion surface was then cut across their basset edges probably during very late-Jurassic and early-Cretaceous times. The transgression carried the Middle and Upper Albian seas across this erosion surface, until the beds rest on every horizon between the highest Jurassic and the Carboniferous (Fig. 97). Indeed in the deep borings in South-East England, the Gault rests on Old Red Sandstone at many places in the central area, on slates of either Silurian and/or Cambrian age in the Harwich neighbourhood. Thus, with the exception of the Ordovician and the Precambrian, the tally of the systems below the Cretaceous is complete.

The sequence of lithological changes which have been traced between Folkestone and the Haldon Hills is repeated in the reverse order as the beds are followed north-eastwards from the Haldon Hills to Norfolk. To summarize, the Upper Greensand is best developed in Dorset and Wiltshire, the Gault first appearing as a mappable horizon near Beaminster in North Dorset, whilst the Upper Greensand finally thins out in South Bedfordshire.

At Cambridge the Gault is 150 feet in thickness, but when traced into Norfolk it becomes steadily thinner and more marly. Finally at Hunstanton on the Norfolk coast a striking and much portrayed cliff-section shows 4 feet of Red Rock or **'Red Chalk'** separating the basal Chalk from the Carstone. The Red Rock is a brick-red, rather nodular limestone, very gritty and containing scattered pebbles in the basal few inches. *Inoceramus sulcatus*, which is restricted to the Upper Gault, has been found 10 inches above the base, so it is possible that a very thin representative of the Lower

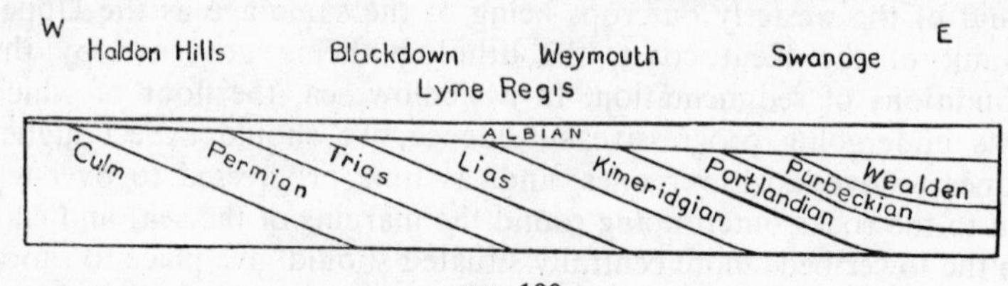


FIG. 100.
Diagram illustrating the Albian transgression in southern England.

Gault may also be present. The greater part of the Red Rock with its numerous *Neohibilites* (*Belemnites*) *minimus* is of Upper Albian date. It is clearly a very condensed deposit, representing in 4 feet the 150 feet of Gault at Cambridge and the 230 feet in Bedfordshire. A similar Red Rock overlying and perhaps overstepping the Carstone can be traced along the foot of the Wolds in Lincolnshire and South Yorkshire; but at Speeton it is represented by a very small thickness of variegated, often reddish, marls, which yield the characteristic fossils.

The peculiar characters of the deposits in Norfolk, Lincolnshire and Yorkshire must be due largely to their having been laid down far from a land-area. The sea cannot, however, have been exceptionally deep, for the conglomeratic basal few inches of the Red Rock and the nature of the minerals and pebbles present shows that the top of the Carstone must have been churned up by bottom currents. The striking colour of the matrix has been ascribed to lateritic mud.

Have we any evidence as to the position of the shorelines of the time? They can be located with accuracy in the Haldon Hills only. The transgression which submerged the London Platform and carried the sea to the edge of Dartmoor must also have extended far across the Midlands to the borders of Wales; but all trace of the littoral deposits of the sea, except in the Haldon Hills, has been stripped off by subsequent erosion.

English geologists usually regard the Gault and the Upper Greensand as the basal members of the Upper Cretaceous Series. This certainly has the advantage of emphasizing their transgressive nature; but it also involves splitting the Albian Stage, for the Folkestone Sands with their Lower Albian fauna would be grouped with the Lower Cretaceous, whilst the overlying rocks containing Middle Albian forms would be assigned to the Upper Cretaceous. Stages by definition, surely, are very important divisions of geological time, and why should a stage be split into two unequal divisions and allocated to two series? Moreover, just across the Channel in North France and Belgium, it is not the Albian rocks which transgress across the Palaeozoic strata of the Brabant Massif (the continuation of the London Platform), but those of the succeeding Cenomanian and higher stages. As Dr Spath has pointed out, the most persistent lithological change, both chronologically and areally, in the English Cretaceous rocks, occurs at the base of the Chalk, i.e. at the base of the Cenomanian Stage. We are therefore following Dr Spath and drawing the boundary between the Lower and Upper Cretaceous Series at the junction of the Albian and Cenomanian Stages.

## THE UPPER CRETACEOUS

### The Chalk

Although most other types of sedimentary rock are met with many times in the stratigraphical column, there is only one Chalk, the well-known and highly distinctive Upper Cretaceous rock. It is regarded by many as being typically English, for it is the Chalk cliffs of Kent or of the Isle of Wight that are first sighted by travellers entering our southern ports.

For the most part the Chalk is a singularly pure, dazzling white limestone, which, at nearly all points on its outcrop forms a prominent escarpment. The stratigraphical level of the hard bands in the Chalk, which really produce the escarpment, varies considerably in different parts of the outcrop and in some areas the escarpment is double (Fig. 101). In South-Eastern England it rings the Weald, forming the South Downs, reaching the sea in the magnificent cliffs at Beachy Head; also the North Downs, overlooking the Thames estuary and the London Basin, while farther to the north and west it rises to the surface again, forming the Chiltern escarpment overlooking the broad, flat clay vale extending away towards the Midlands. To the north-east the Chalk uplands continue through Norfolk, Lincs., into Yorkshire, forming the Yorkshire Wolds, and providing fine coastal scenery in the neighbourhood of Flamborough Head. Similarly, to the south-west the Chiltern Hills give place to the Berkshire Downs, the Marlborough Downs, and the deeply dissected plateau of Salisbury Plain, these uplands ringing the Hampshire Basin of Tertiary rocks in the same way as the North Downs and Chiltern Hills encircle the London Basin. In the Isle of Wight the rocks are well exposed, the 'Needles' being sea-stacks isolated by marine erosion from the main outcrop (see Fig. 113). It rises again from the sea-floor to form Ballard Point, the easterly extremity of the belt of high ground which crosses the 'Isle of Purbeck', reaching the coast once more in the neighbourhood of Lulworth, and there forming towering cliffs rivalling those built of the Jurassic limestones in the near neighbourhood.

Although the exact conditions of deposition of the Chalk are still under discussion, one thing at least is certain: the formation is marine throughout. As with the Albian Sea of the immediately preceding period, it is difficult to fix the margins of the Chalk Sea with any degree of accuracy. Except in the extreme east of Devonshire, where the lowest beds are coarse calcareous sandstones, there is nowhere in the English Chalk any indication of sedimentation under shallow-water conditions near to an existing coastline. But in parts of North-East Ireland and western Scotland the Chalk is represented largely by coarse-grained, highly glauconitic sands and sandstones, of Upper Greensand facies, but definitely containing the Chalk fauna. These rocks must have accumulated near the coastline. In so far as the Chalk was deposited under water considerably deeper than that of Albian times, the Chalk Sea must surely have spread over a wider area: the 'Cenomanian transgression' carried the sea perhaps far beyond the boundaries of its Albian predecessor, until probably only the highest points of the Welsh, Cumbrian and Scottish uplands remained unsubmerged as islands. It has been suggested that the '2000-foot peneplain' of Wales represents the erosion-cut surface on which the Chalk was deposited. Others regard this surface as of pre-Triassic or pre-Tertiary date.

In regard to the stratigraphical limits of the Chalk, the base is in many places a plane of erosion, and the lowest beds contain phosphatic nodules and rolled fossils derived from underlying rocks. Similarly, beneath the cover of Tertiary rocks in the London and Hampshire Basins the top of the Chalk is everywhere a plane of erosion, and although the angular discordance between the two formations is so slight as to be imperceptible in even extensive exposures, the plane of separation represents a great time-break, the significance of which is considered more fully below.

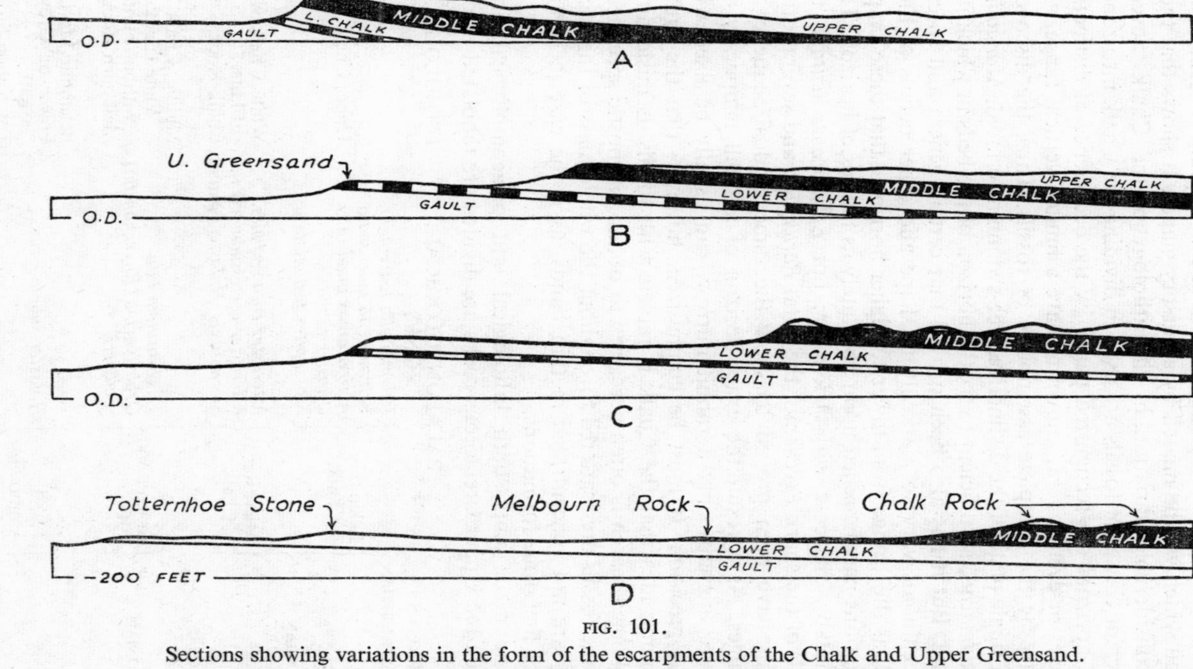


FIG. 101.

Sections showing variations in the form of the escarpments of the Chalk and Upper Greensand.
A. near Dorking; B. near Shaftesbury; C. near Marlborough; D. near Cambridge.

Fig. 103 should be carefully studied as this diagram contains much detail which will be missed by a cursory glance. It shows that there is considerable variation in the lithology of the Chalk. Several different classes of fossils are used in dividing the Chalk into zones, and horizons are recognized partly by the occurrence of distinctive species or even genera, known to have a limited vertical range, and partly by the complete assemblage of fossils. Thus, the discovery of a single plate of the distinctive, free-swimming crinoid, *Marsupites testudinarius*, is sufficient to fix the horizon of the beds in which it is found. But it has also been proved that certain genera and species of echinoids vary so markedly in shape and other details of their shell as they range from lower to higher horizons, that these shape-variations may be relied upon absolutely as indices of horizon. This is notably the case with *Micraster*; but *Echinocorys scutata*, the teeth of the shark *Ptychodus*, the coral *Parasmilia* and several other forms have been proved to show the same gradual sequence of changes. As a result the exact horizon of a small temporary exposure, perhaps only a rabbit burrow, can usually be fixed with great precision. It must be emphasized, however, that the rather common idea that the Chalk is replete with fossils, is misleading. Prolonged search is often necessary to obtain diagnostic specimens, for the fossils are scattered throughout the whole mass of the rock; they are not concentrated in thin bands, as is the case in several other limestone formations.

The main units, both lithological and palaeontological, into which the Upper Cretaceous rocks are divided are tabulated below.

| STAGES | | PALAEONTOLOGICAL ZONES | LITHOLOGICAL |
|---|---|---|---|
| MAESTRICHTIAN | | | |
| SENONIAN | Belemnite Chalk. | *Belemnitella lanceolata.*<br>*Belemnitella mucronata.*<br>*Actinocamax quadratus.*<br>*Offaster pilula.*<br>*Marsupites testudinarius.* | Upper Chalk<br>or |
| | Micraster Chalk. | *Micraster coranguinum.*<br>*Micraster cortestudinarium.*<br>*Sternotaxis* (*Holaster*) *planus* | White Chalk with Flints.<br>Chalk Rock. |
| TURONIAN | Brachiopod Chalk. | *Terebratulina lata*<br>*Orbirhynchia* (*Rhynchonella*) *cuvieri.* | Middle Chalk or White Chalk without Flints.<br>Melbourn Rock. |
| CENOMANIAN | Ammonite Chalk. | *Holaster subglobosus.* | Belemnite Marl.<br>Lower or Grey Chalk.<br>Totternhoe Stone. |
| | | *Schloenbachia varians.* | Chalk Marl.<br>Glauconitic Marl. |

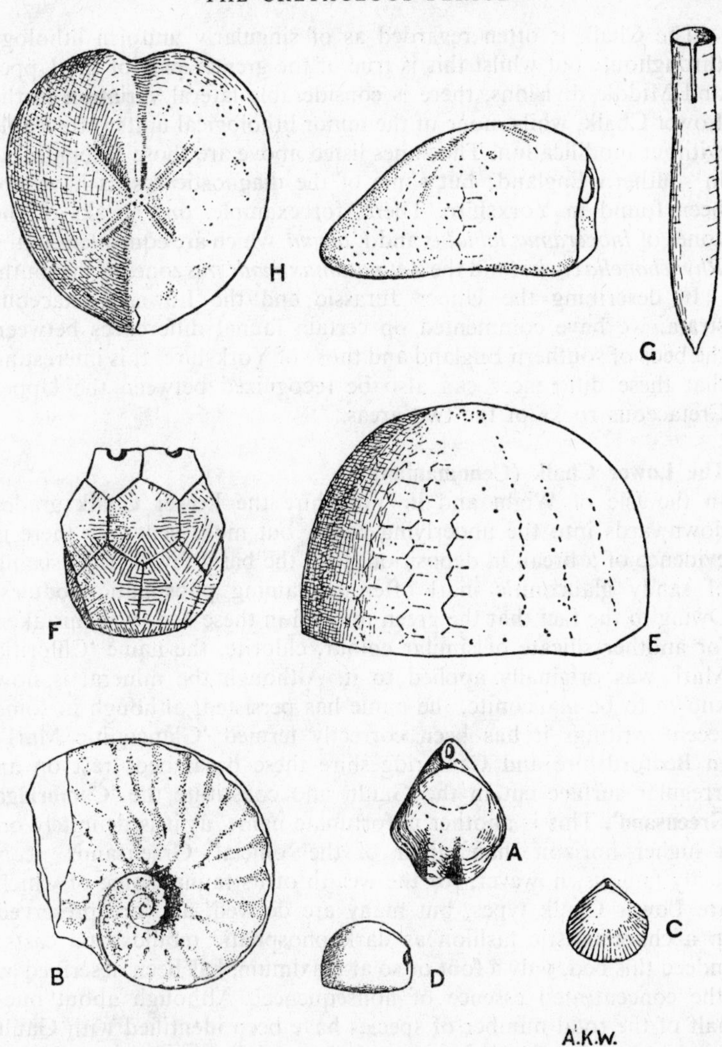


FIG. 102.

Fossils from the Chalk. Zonal forms marked.*

*H. *Micraster coranguinum*. Upper Chalk.
*G. *Belemnitella mucronata*. Upper Chalk.
*F. *Marsupites testudinarius*. Upper Chalk.
E. *Echinocorys scutata*. Upper Chalk.
*D. *Offaster pilula*. Upper Chalk.
*C. *Orbirhynchia* (*Rhynchonella*) *cuvieri*. Middle Chalk.
*B. *Schloenbachia varians*. Lower Chalk.
A. '*Terebratula*' *biplicata*. Lower Chalk.

The Chalk is often regarded as of singularly uniform lithology throughout; but whilst this is true of the greater part of the Upper and Middle divisions, there is considerable lateral variation in the Lower Chalk, whilst none of the minor lithological units is traceable without modification. The zones listed above are those recognizable in southern England; but some of the diagnostic fossils have not been found in Yorkshire. There, for example, one speaks of the zones of *Inoceramus labiatus* and *I. lingua*, which are equivalent to the *Rhynchonella cuvieri* and the *Actinocamax quadratus* zones of the south.

In describing the Upper Jurassic and the Lower Cretaceous strata, we have commented on certain faunal differences between the beds of southern England and those of Yorkshire. It is interesting that these differences can also be recognized between the Upper Cretaceous rocks of the two areas.

**The Lower Chalk (Cenomanian)**

In the Isle of Wight and in Yorkshire the Lower Chalk grades downwards into the underlying rocks, but more generally there is evidence of a break in deposition, with the basal few feet consisting of sandy glauconitic marl often containing phosphatic nodules. Owing to the fact that the green mineral in these beds was mistaken for another silicate of similar colour, chlorite, the name 'Chloritic Marl' was originally applied to it. Although the mineral is now known to be glauconite, the name has persisted, although in some recent writings it has been correctly termed 'Glauconitic Marl'. In Bedfordshire and Cambridgeshire these basal beds rest on an irregular surface cut in the Gault, and constitute the **'Cambridge Greensand'.** This is another unfortunate name, as it is definitely on a higher horizon than either of the 'official' Greensands. It is justly famous, however, for the wealth of its fauna, some of which are Lower Chalk types, but many are derived, and are preserved in a characteristic fashion as dark phosphatic moulds and casts: indeed this bed, only a foot or so at maximum, has been described as 'the concentrated essence of nonsequence'. Although about one-half of the total number of species have been identified with Gault forms occurring in the type-sections at Folkestone, many others have not been discovered in the Albian rocks of any other English locality. Among the most striking of the fossils are the remains of reptiles, both terrestrial and marine, and birds.

Another feature of the bed is that in the past, when the nodules were extensively worked as a source of phosphate, it yielded large numbers of erratic boulders. Professor L. Hawkes has examined those that are preserved in the Sedgwick Museum at Cambridge. The boulders range up to 2 feet in length and up to 1 cwt. in weight though it is extremely probable that larger blocks were left behind in the pits and only fragments collected. The great majority of the erratics consist of arenaceous rock-types, quartzites, greywackes and sandstones, many of them of Lower Palaeozoic aspect. Numerous pebbles of igneous and metamorphic rocks are also present and some of these are distinctive enough to be traced back to their parent rock-mass. Pebbles of riebeckite-microgranite exactly match the rocks of Mynydd Mawr in Carnarvonshire, whilst a banded hornstone is very similar to some of the Arvonian (Precambrian) pyroclasts occurring to the north of Snowdon. Some of the spherulitic and flow-banded rhyolites may well have come from the Uriconian (Precambrian) lavas of Shropshire. Certain radiolarian cherts are very similar to those of South-West England, whilst some of the vein-quartz pebbles can be matched in the same region. Certain igneous rocks, however, cannot be paralleled in any known British locality; but one of them, an olivine-basalt, compares closely with certain basic lavas in South Norway. Given that the horizon has been correctly identified, how can one explain this assemblage, drawn from such a wide range of probable sources, occurring in a deposit which was clearly laid down far from any coastline? There are only two possible explanations: either the boulders were carried by floating ice, or drifted entangled in the roots of trees. There is, however, no evidence of any glaciation of North-West Europe in Cretaceous times; on the contrary, palms were flourishing in Silesia and figs in Greenland. The most reasonable explanation, therefore, is that the boulders were transported in the roots of trees. The concentration of boulders is due first to the Cambridge Greensand being an extremely concentrated deposit representing a very long period of time, and also most probably to currents flowing into an eddy similar to that of the Sargasso Sea, but considerably smaller, for the Cambridge Greensand can be traced only for some 50 miles along the strike from near Ely into Bedfordshire.

The same explanation accounts for the erratic blocks which have been found very occasionally embedded in the Chalk. We may instance a boulder of nordmarkite (a rare type of syenite) found at Betchworth in Surrey and most probably derived either from the Oslo region or from Ben Loyal near Assynt in North-West Scotland.

Above the Glauconitic Marl much of the Lower Chalk, particularly the Varians Zone, is grey and marly, due to the presence of a much larger proportion of land-derived silt and clay than is found in the typical white Chalk. This is the **'Chalk Marl'** and it was evidently deposited in shallower, muddy water, which gradually deepened and cleared as time went on. The natural mixture of lime and clay in some of the beds of the Chalk Marl is ideal for the manufacture of

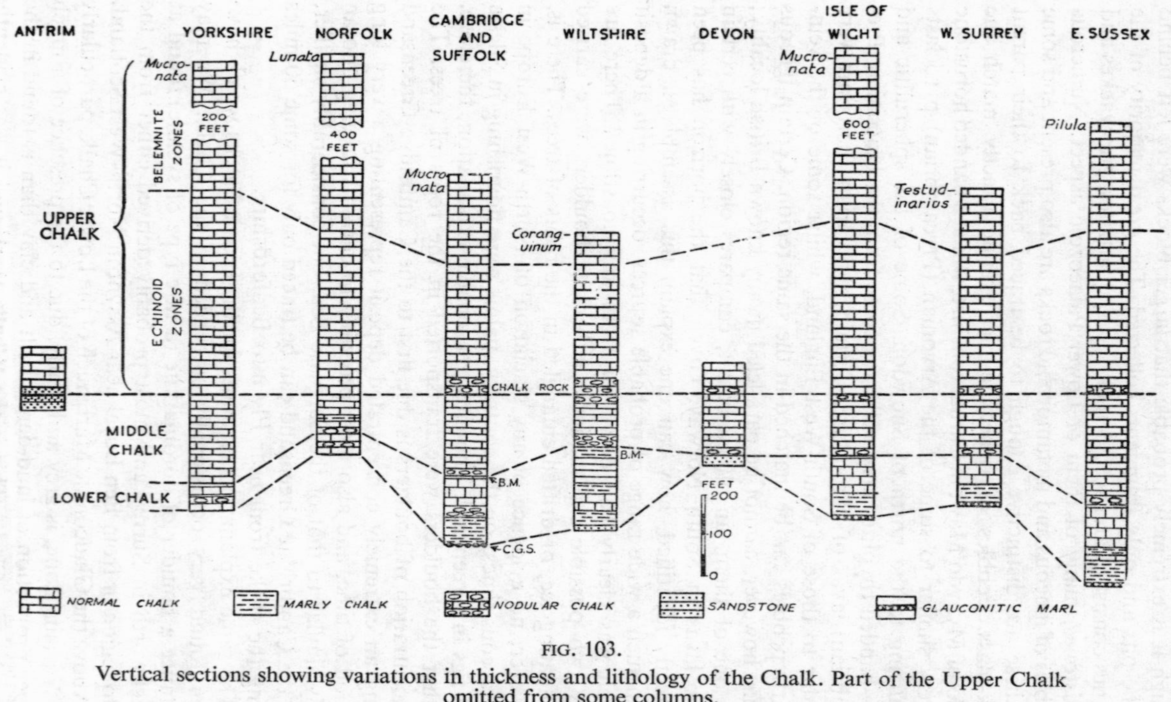


FIG. 103.

Vertical sections showing variations in thickness and lithology of the Chalk. Part of the Upper Chalk omitted from some columns.

B.M., Belemnite Marl; C.G.S., Cambridge Greensand.

The zone lying immediately below the Tertiary is named in each case.

cement, and these beds have been extensively exploited, notably in the mouth of the Medway Gap in Kent. Another big concentration of the cement industry occurs round Gravesend; but here the very pure limestone of the Upper Chalk is artificially mixed with either London Clay or Thames mud. At the top of the Lower Chalk one or more thin but widely traceable seams of marl occur. This is the **Belemnite Marl,** yielding *Actinocamax plenus*.

**The Middle and Upper Chalk (Turonian and Senonian)**

The greater part of these stages consists of white, rather blocky Chalk, the incoming of flints coinciding, in general, with the base of the Upper Chalk. Resting on the Belemnite Marl in the Chilterns and Cambridgeshire are a few feet of massive, nodular, often knotty Chalk. This is the Melbourn Rock, lithologically the most persistent of the three 'rock' horizons in the English Chalk. A similar lithological variant, the Totternhoe Stone, occurs in the middle of the Lower Chalk, whilst at the base of the Upper Chalk is the Chalk Rock. The effects of these three hard bands, when well developed, on the topographical expression of the Chalk, can be appreciated from Fig. 101. It is suggestive that these three 'rocks', together with some minor ones at other horizons, are best developed in Cambridgeshire and the northern Chilterns, where the Cambridge Greensand occurs. The rocks, with their nodular structure due to current action, evidently represent periods of very slow deposition. We have seen that in highest Jurassic and Lower Cretaceous times a broad uplift affected the southern Midlands. Clearly this tendency was revived at times, in the same locality, during the deposition of the Upper Cretaceous strata.

The Chalk Rock, though not so widely traceable as a lithological unit as the Melbourn Rock, is characterized by a distinctive fauna, which occurs at the same level in Yorkshire, in beds of normal Chalk lithology. This *reussianum* fauna (named after the ammonite, *Hyphantoceras reussianum*) is very different from that found in the normal white Chalk above and below. It consists of numerous ammonites, gasteropods (rare elsewhere in the Chalk), lamellibranchs, some restricted to this sub-zone, and in particular, sponges, such as *Ventriculites* and corals. Clearly this is a shallow-water fauna and this conclusion is corroborated by the frequent occurrence in the Chalk Rock of erosion surfaces, often phosphatized and with glauconite-infilled borings.

The Belemnite Chalk varies greatly in thickness (Fig. 103). In East Devon it is completely absent, the highest zone of the Chalk on the hills behind Sidmouth being that of *Micraster cortestudinarium*. This is due to the recent denudation of the higher zones, however.

Elsewhere the highest Chalk is overlain by Tertiary beds. There must therefore have been considerable pre-Tertiary erosion of the Chalk. In the London area, in particular, the whole of the Belemnite Chalk (nearly 800 feet thick in the Isle of Wight and Norfolk), is often missing. Actual discordance of dip between the Chalk and the Tertiary strata cannot be demonstrated in any one exposure; but it can be proved by following the edge of the Tertiary rocks for perhaps a score of miles and finding that they overstep from one

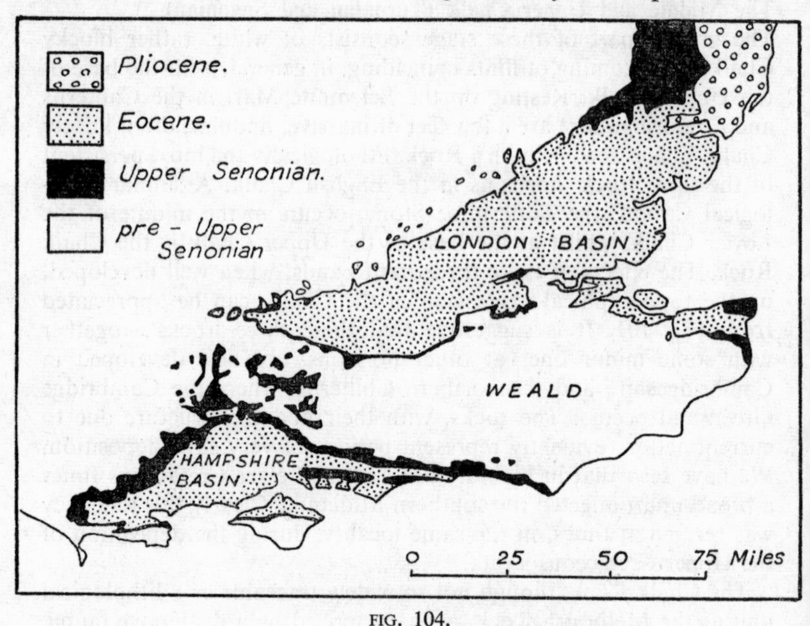


FIG. 104.
The Eocene overstep of the higher Chalk divisions.
(*After S. W. Wooldridge and D. L. Linton.*)

zone of the Chalk on to another (Fig. 104). A big break is, of course, suggested by the complete change in lithology and faunal contents, but of this more anon. Further, in many exposures the surface of the Chalk immediately underlying the Tertiary rocks is smooth and deeply bored by rock-drilling molluscs—clear proof that the surface was cut in solid chalk, not in soft ooze.

At the moment the chief significance of the break is that at Trimingham, Norfolk, the *Belemnitella lanceolata* Chalk—formerly known as the '*Ostrea lunata* Chalk'—the highest zone preserved in the British Isles, consists lithologically of quite normal Chalk, obviously laid down under a considerable depth of water. There is no evidence of the beds having been deposited during a phase of shallowing such as must have occurred before the cutting of the extensive erosion plane of the type indicated above.

To obtain a complete picture of the end of the Cretaceous Period we have to go beyond the boundaries of this country. The whole of the kingdom of Denmark is underlain by Chalk which forms majestic cliffs in the south-east and facing the Baltic Sea. By comparison with the English Chalk the significant fact is that the lowest zone there exposed is the highest normally seen in England, i.e. the *Mucronata* Zone, while above it comes a whole Stage, the Danian, which is quite unrepresented in this country. The Danian Chalk, rich in brachiopods, corals and with biohermal masses built largely of bryozoa was clearly deposited during a phase of shallowing. Above it comes a series of glauconitic marls and non-calcareous clays that are regarded as Tertiary though older than English rocks of this age. Together with the Danian Stage they go far towards filling the gap which separates our Chalk from the overlying Eocene.

Whilst only the Lower Maestrichtian is present on the land surface of the British Isles, chalks of Upper Maestrichtian and Danian age have been proved within the last few years in core samples from the floor of the English Channel between the Isle of Wight and the coast of Brittany. They are overlain and overstepped by beds of Middle and Upper Eocene age. As more submarine data become available it is clear that our present picture of the distribution of land and sea areas during latest Cretaceous and early Tertiary times will have to be modified.

In Antrim the Cretaceous is extensively developed. It consists of the Hibernian Greensands below, yielding Cenomanian and Lower Senonian fossils, and the White Limestone above, of Upper Senonian and Lower Maestrichtian age. The Greensands rest on Triassic and Liassic rocks. They outcrop around the present coast from east of Londonderry to the south of Belfast. Inland they are overstepped by the White Limestone, an unusually hard variety of pure chalk, and this rests, in places with a thin basal conglomerate, on Dalradian schists. The White Limestone is several hundred feet in thickness and it is clear that the Upper Cretaceous seas must have extended far beyond the present outcrops. One chance glimpse of their former extent is the presence of White Limestone, proved by both lithological and palaeontological evidence, in a depression, possibly a former swallow hole, in the Namurian rocks near Killarney, in south-west Eire.

### CONDITIONS OF FORMATION

Except for part of the Lower Chalk which may contain up to 50 per cent. insoluble residue, the formation is singularly free from land-derived sediment. It is a limestone of unique purity, at some levels containing less than 1 per cent. of insoluble material. From this fact it might reasonably be argued that it was deposited far from land, beyond the reach of even the finest mud carried in suspension by the sea-water. This would carry with it the implication that it is a deep-sea deposit. In quite early days these conclusions appeared to gain support from the occurrence, in almost any sample, of the shells of foraminifera. The view was widely accepted, therefore, that the Chalk is a fossil foraminiferal ooze, comparable with the deep-sea globigerina ooze which covers nearly a quarter of the surface of the globe at the present time. Actually the proportion of recognizable foraminiferal shells is small, whilst the study of the macrofossils, particularly of the mollusca, of the Chalk shows an absence of really deep-water forms. As we have already seen, there is evidence in the lithology as well as in the fauna that certain parts of the Chalk were deposited in relatively shallow water, at least within reach of current action, though it is well to remember that even in these so-called shallow-water phases there is no oolitic structure, no dolomitization, no corals to speak of, and certainly no strong current bedding such as that seen in the Jurassic limestones at several different horizons.

With the highest powers of an ordinary microscope, Chalk is seen to consist of shell-fragments of varying size, set in a powder which is too fine-grained to be resolved. This powder has been compared with the aragonitic oozes dredged up from shoal waters off the coasts of the Bahamas and Florida, and therefore the Chalk has been regarded as being in large part a chemical precipitate. Recently, however, this powder has been studied under the much greater magnification of the electron microscope, and is found to be entirely organic in origin, being composed of either broken fragments (coccoliths) or complete skeletons (coccospheres) of certain pelagic calcareous algae. They are exceedingly minute, less than four microns (0.004 mm.) in diameter.

The depth at which the nearest modern analogues to the fauna of the Chalk live suggests that the depth of the Upper Cretaceous Sea never exceeded about 150 fathoms. If that were the case, it would be necessary to explain away the absence of terrigenous sediment, and in attempting to do so two suggestions have been made: first, that the Chalk Sea was surrounded by rainless, desert coasts, or alternatively that the surrounding land was completely base-levelled. In the first case there would be no rivers to carry land-waste into the sea; in the second, although rivers may have existed, they would be so sluggish that they would be incapable of carrying any load in suspension. On this point we should remember that the great thickness of the Chalk points to the existence of great continental land-areas from which a continuous and copious supply of calcium carbonate in solution was derived throughout the period. How was it transported if not by rivers?

The strongest support for the theory of desert coasts is to be found in the peculiar Upper Cretaceous rocks of Antrim and some of the Western Isles. Here a thin development of Senonian Chalk of normal lithology rests apparently directly on the Cenomanian. The latter consists of glauconitic sands containing many perfectly rounded sand-grains, whilst the Senonian is mainly of normal Chalk lithology, though it is strongly silicified, and in places contains cracks filled in with sand containing many 'millet-seed' grains. The silicification of limestone and the abundance of 'millet-seed' grains are features of many modern deserts. It has, however, been suggested recently (1961) that most of the 'millet-seed' grains in the White Sandstone of Loch Aline near Mull are too large for their rounding to have been caused by wind action. Extremely vigorous submarine sorting is more probable. Highly rounded sand-grains are often to be found in the small amounts of insoluble material in the English Chalk.

It is therefore probable that both theories contain some truth. There is no evidence of major folding of the land areas bordering the British basin of deposition in Mesozoic times. Prolonged denudation uninterrupted by major orogenetic movements must lead to peneplanation. The evidence given above from North-East Ireland and western Scotland indicates that these land-areas must have been, in part, deserts; but if the theory that the erratic boulders now found in the Cambridge Greensand and the Chalk were transported in the roots of floating trees is correct, some rivers must have traversed the desert belt, as does the Nile to-day. These rivers would have carried in solution the great quantities of carbonate needed for the skeletons of the organisms which built up the Chalk. The average coccolith content of the Chalk is over 60 per cent.; and comparison with the coccolith content of the calcareous oozes forming to-day on parts of the floor of the Atlantic suggests that 'the living coccospheres must have been nine times more abundant in the Chalk Sea than they are at present in the Atlantic Ocean'. The solubility of calcium carbonate decreases with rise of temperature, so that the high temperatures inferred from other evidence would have been very favourable for coccoliths. Curves showing the inferred variation of temperature during the deposition of the Chalk indicate that the highest temperatures were reached during the Lower Senonian—it is precisely this Chalk which is most even-textured and has the highest content of coccoliths. These palaeotemperature curves were based on Urey's $0^{16}/0^{18}$ method. Sea-water contains two isotopes of oxygen, $0^{16}$ and $0^{18}$, whose proportions are believed to be dependent on temperature. Calcium carbonate secreted by organisms will contain these two isotopes and might therefore provide a record of the temperature of the waters they inhabited. Measurements on scrapings of shells of living marine organisms kept in thermostatically controlled baths gave encouraging results, though it was found that certain species only grew shell during a part of the local temperature range and hence did not record the true mean temperature of the waters they lived in. After investigating a variety of fossil materials it was decided that belemnites with their massive guards made of radiating fibres of calcite were the most promising. They also gave more consistent results than those obtained from the shells of oysters, inocerami, brachiopods, etc. Published results suggest that the Upper Cretaceous seas were warm temperate with an average temperature close to 20° C (72° F). The agreement of these palaeotemperatures with other geological evidence suggests that the basic assumption that the ionic composition of the sea-water of the Mesozoic was similar to that of to-day, perforce untested, is probably valid.

The general lithological characters of the Chalk imply a steady deepening of the sea throughout Lower and Middle Chalk times, but with minor halts for the formation of the 'rock' bands. A more pronounced phase of shallowing is indicated by the Chalk Rock. After this, deepening continued steadily, as is shown by the very uniform lithology of the Upper Chalk. The Chalk Sea probably reached its maximum depth of about 150 fathoms during the deposition of the *Marsupites testudinarius* zone. Then followed some slight shallowing; but to obtain evidence of the final shallowing of the sea we have to cross the North Sea.

There has been considerable discussion as to the mode of formation of the flints, so characteristic of the Upper Chalk. The majority must have been formed either during or shortly after the deposition of the Chalk, for partly rolled flint pebbles compose the transgressive basal bed of the Tertiary strata. Some authors claim that the flints were deposited contemporaneously with the chalk-ooze, masses of silica-gel being precipitated whenever the concentration of silica in the sea-water reached certain limits. There are numerous difficulties in accepting this hypothesis and it is much more probable that the flints originated during the phase of uplift indicated by the stratigraphical break at the base of the Tertiary beds. According to this view the Chalk, as deposited, contained a certain amount of opaline silica, partly as sponge skeletons and loose spicules and partly as scattered globules of inorganic origin. Alkaline groundwaters percolating through the Chalk would be able, under certain conditions, to dissolve the opaline silica and when conditions changed, would precipitate it, perhaps to replace the soft calcareous ooze infilling the shell of an echinoid or other fossil or, more commonly, to form one of the bizarre-shaped nodules lying along a bedding plane. A separate period of flint formation is shown by the infrequent occurrence of thin sheets of flint, infilling joints or small fault planes and cutting the bedding at a high angle. The mid-Tertiary movements must have given rise both to fissuring of the Chalk and to conditions suitable for a second period of ground-water circulation.

## REFERENCES

ALLEN, P. *Geol. Mag.*, **91** (1954), 498–508. The geology and relief of the London Platform deduced from the study of the pebble-beds in the Hastings Beds.

BAILEY, E. B. *Geol. Mag.*, **61** (1924), 102–116. The arguments for desert shorelines to the Chalk sea.

BLACK, M. *Proc. Geol. Soc.*, **1499** (1953), 81–86. The only published account of the results of studying the Chalk under the electron microscope.

CASEY, R. *Bull. S.E. Union. Sci. Soc.* **117** (1963), 1–15. The position of the Jurassic-Cretaceous boundary.

CHATWIN, C. P. 'The Hampshire Basin and adjoining areas,' *Brit. Reg. Geol.* (1948), Mem. Geol. Surv.

CHATWIN, C. P. 'East Anglia and adjoining areas,' *ibid.* (1948). Both these volumes contain good accounts of the Cretaceous rocks; but the bibliographies are restricted to official publications.

GALLOIS, R. W. 'The Wealden District,' *Brit. Reg. Geol.* (1965), Mem. Geol. Surv.

HAWKES, L. *Q.J.G.S.*, **99** (1943), 93–104. Discussion of the erractics in the Cambridge Greensand.

KIRKALDY, J. F. *Proc. Geol. Assoc.*, **50** (1939), 379–417, and **74** (1963), 127–164. The English Cretaceous beds below the Albian, together with comprehensive bibliographies.

SMITH, W. E. *Proc. Geol. Assoc.*, **72** (1961), 91–134. The shallow water Cenomanian beds of South Devon.

SPATH, L. F. 'Gault ammonites Pt. XIV,' *Mem. Pal. Soc.* (1943). Stratigraphical conclusions together with full bibliography.

TAYLOR, J. H. 'Sedimentary Features of an Ancient Deltaic complex: The Wealden Rocks of south-eastern England,' *Sedimentology*, **2** (1963), 2–28, comparison with modern deltas.

WILSON, V. 'East Yorkshire and Lincolnshire,' *Brit. Reg. Geol.* (1948), Mem. Geol. Surv.

## CHAPTER XX

# THE TERTIARY ERA

POST-CRETACEOUS geological time is most conveniently divided into two unequal parts: a longer, earlier period, and a shorter, later one. There is no uniformity in the naming of these major divisions, but the two terms, Tertiary and Quaternary, are usually applied to them in this country. Together, these two time-divisions constitute the **Cainozoic Epoch**—the epoch of modern life. It should be noted that some authorites incorrectly regard 'Tertiary' as synonymous with 'Cainozoic'.

The Tertiary Era is in turn divided into four shorter periods: in order, the Eocene, the Oligocene, the Miocene and the Pliocene. These are successive chapters of geological history; they are also the names of the Tertiary Systems, which are the youngest of the Solid formations and are practically restricted to South-East England. On the other hand, the Quaternary strata are Superficial, resting on all older formations and occurring in all parts of the country.

The marked lithological difference between the Chalk and the overlying Tertiary beds bears witness to a great change in conditions: to the withdrawal of the sea from the British Isles area, while the plotting of the Chalk zones in different parts of the country proves that the Cretaceous strata were uplifted, tilted, and suffered considerable erosion (Fig. 104). We are familiar with the general proposition that such a break involves changes in the faunas in the two sets of rocks involved, but from this point of view the post-Chalk, pre-Eocene break stands supreme. In no other comparable case were the changes so complete, nor was the extinction of the older fauna so thoroughly effected.

Since the Armorican revolution at the close of the Carboniferous Period reptiles had dominated the animal world. From the first few amphibians which ventured to spend part of their lives on dry land for the first time in the late-Carboniferous and Permian Periods had sprung the hosts of reptiles that in the process of time had become adapted to every type of habitat. In the sea the great marine saurians, *Ichthyosaurus*, *Plesiosaurus* and many others, had enjoyed an existence from the Lias onward. On land the dinosaurs held sway. Among these amazing terrestrial reptiles were forms which moved on two legs and which had adopted the erect carriage.

Some of these were vegetarian and relied upon their agility and speed when attacked by their natural enemies. Others were bipedal carnivorous reptiles, and there is no mammal living which reached such a great size or was so formidably armed with tooth and claw as the 'Terrible Reptile', *Tyrannosaurus*. Another great group of dinosaurs includes the huge 'Thunder saurian' *Brontosaurus*, *Atlantosaurus* and *Diplodocus*, measuring some 80 to 90 feet from snout to tail. So huge were these apparently defenceless dinosaurs that they probably lived immersed in the waters of lagoons. This manner of life would afford them protection from the great carnivorous types and at the same time would to some extent counterbalance their unwieldy bulk. Yet another highly specialized group includes many heavily armoured types with most bizarre forms, which look more at home in the pages of *The Humours of History* than in a reputable text-book (Fig. 105).

Even the air had been conquered by the reptiles, and the flying *Pterodactyls*, like great completely bald birds of repulsive aspect and with reptilian heads and teeth, were abundant in the Jurassic, and attained to large sizes, with a wing span of 18 feet, in the Cretaceous. The Jurassic and Cretaceous Periods together are well named the 'Age of Reptiles'. Held in the background, as it were, by this overwhelming dominance of the reptiles were a few still primitive mammals. As we have seen, these had first appeared in the Trias; but for them evolution seemed to stand still.

With the passing of the Cretaceous, however, there was an almost complete reversal of the roles of reptiles and mammals. The dinosaurs, adapted to so many different modes of life and of world-wide distribution, became completely extinct: not one survived into the Eocene. Neither is there any trace of the great marine saurians, nor of the flying reptiles. At the same time the changes that brought extinction to so many races gave an impetus to mammalian evolution. With the disappearance of their formidable competitors the mammals increased greatly in importance, and although in form and size they bear but little, if any, resemblance to their living descendants, the ancestry of most living forms has been traced back step by step to the early-Tertiary.

The wholesale extinction in the pre-Tertiary interval did not affect the reptiles only, but among the invertebrate animals equally important, though naturally less spectacular, changes were effected. Thus the ammonites, which, judging from their abundance at some levels in the Jurassic and Cretaceous, must literally have swarmed in the seas of those periods, did not survive the Cretaceous. With them passed the hosts of belemnites. On the other hand the other molluscan orders, the lamellibranchs and the gasteropods show a notable increase in numbers and in variety of forms—a tendency that has persisted until the present time.

In the plant world, too, the differences between the Cretaceous

FIG. 105.

Extinct Mesozoic reptiles:

A. *Pterodactyl*, a flying reptile.
B. *Stegosaurus*, an armoured dinosaur, 25–30 feet in length.
C. *Diplodocus*, an amphibious dinosaur, 80 feet in length.
D. *Triceratops*, an armoured dinosaur, 25 feet in length.
E. *Iguanodon*, a herbivorous dinosaur, 30 feet in length.

(*M. K. W., after photographs of restorations in W. E. Swinton's 'The Dinosaurs'; Pterodactyl from brush-drawing by Alice B. Woodward.*)

and Tertiary floras are as striking in their way as those in the animal kingdom, though the break occurs in the Cretaceous. A list of the Tertiary flora reads much like a present-day plant catalogue, and the Eocene landscape was clothed with trees, ferns and flowering plants of modern aspect. Important newcomers were the grasses which first appear in the Eocene: their advent was doubtless a contributory cause of the rapid evolution of the hoofed mammals.

So in these several ways the Eocene was indeed the 'dawn of the recent'.

The present outcrops of the Tertiary rocks occupy two synclinal basins floored by the Chalk. The larger of these, bounded by the converging Chalk hills of the Chilterns and the North Downs, and truncated eastwards by the North Sea, is the **London Basin.** The smaller is the **Hampshire Basin,** lying to the south of the South Downs and Salisbury Plain. In Tertiary times these two now separated basins were united, and a glance at the geological map of Europe shows them to be merely a portion of a larger area of Tertiary strata covering in addition the Paris Basin and much of Belgium. This larger area of Tertiary sedimentation is the Anglo-Gallic Basin.

## THE EOCENE SYSTEM

The Eocene strata cover a wide range of lithological types indicating many changes in the conditions of accumulation, but the broad outlines of Eocene geography persisted throughout the period. Roughly a line joining the Wash and Torquay separates a region in which no Tertiary sediments occur from one in which they accumulated to a considerable thickness. The region north-west of this line was part of a continental land-mass which suffered denudation and supplied detritus throughout the period. Of the configuration of this land we have no positive information; but there are good reasons for believing it to have been one of low relief and extensive plains. It is difficult to realize that even the mountains of North Wales as we know them to-day were non-existent at this time. The sculpturing of this picturesque region from an up-warped portion of the pre-Eocene peneplain is essentially a Cainozoic phenomenon.

At least one great river (it has been significantly named the Eocene Mississippi) drained this land, spreading sand and gravel over the low-lying coastal plains across which it meandered before emptying its waters into the Eocene Sea. Where the river met the sea in the region of London a wide delta-flat extended seawards. Beyond the delta a shelf-sea stretched eastwards far into France. Had it been possible, a traverse from a point on the Eocene continent to one in the Eocene Sea would have shown a transition from aeolian, through fluviatile and deltaic environments, and ultimately into the shelf-sea. This is true for all horizons in the Eocene; in other words, each and every Eocene formation is liable to exhibit four different facies in different parts of its outcrop. Further, the conditions we have visualized were not stable throughout the period, but the position of the shoreline, and hence of the several lithological zones, was continually changing. Naturally towards the centre of the basin, and in the hinterland, slight warping of the crust would produce no appreciable effect.

It must be realized that the usual 'imperfection of the geological record' applies to the Eocene just as to other Systems; but from the wealth of data amassed since these strata were first seriously studied, two guiding principles emerge which do much to clarify the study of Tertiary stratigraphy. First, the lateral variation in a west-to-east direction from continental into marine; and secondly, the significance of the vertical variation can best be appreciated if

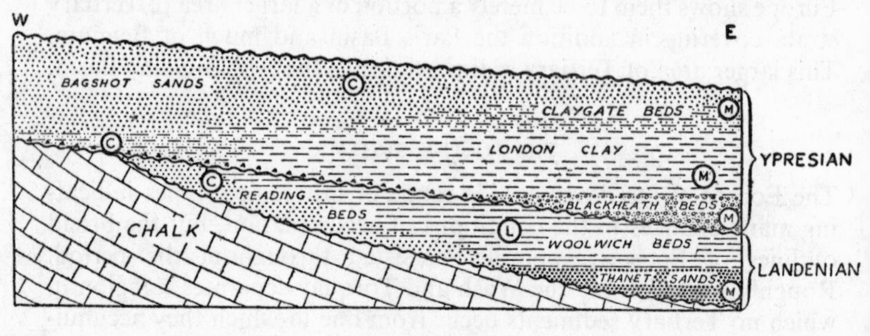


FIG. 106.

Diagram showing details of the Lower Eocene Cycles of Sedimentation in the London Basin.

The facies is indicated by the letters M, marine; L, lagoonal; C, continental.

the beds are regarded as having been deposited during successive **cycles of sedimentation.** Ideally, each cycle represents one complete swing of the pendulum, as it were, from continental through marine and back to continental conditions again. It comprises, first, a marine transgression ushering in the marine phase. The latter was terminated by the spreading of continental conditions from west to east, pushing back the sea. The next cycle started with the succeeding marine transgression. The cycles are not bounded by time-planes, for they are defined in terms of changing conditions, and changing conditions demand time for their accomplishment. In other words the cycle-boundaries are diachronous. It follows that each marine phase is represented by a wedge of strata, in England thinning westwards. The normal relationship during the marine transgression will be overlap of lower by higher divisions; during the regression, offlap will be the rule (Fig. 106).

This cyclic treatment was developed by French and Belgian geologists, and was later applied by L. D. Stamp to the Tertiary strata in Britain. Five complete cycles—five rounds in the conflict between marine and continental conditions—are recognized in the Eocene, and one in the Oligocene; but in France the record is more complete, the Montian cycle partly filling the gap above the English Chalk, the Stampian and other cycles completing the Oligocene.

The history of the Eocene Period commenced with a down-warping of a portion of the pre-Eocene floor, allowing the sea to spread westwards thus initiating the **Landenian Cycle** and depositing sands to a maximum thickness of 90 feet in East Kent. Westwards the thickness diminishes steadily to 60 feet in the great pits at Charlton on the outskirts of South-East London, where they were exploited for the manufacture of amber-coloured glass and for use in iron and brass foundries. Evidence of a marine origin for these **Thanet Sands** is afforded by the presence of glauconite and by a fauna of marine molluscs and fish-remains. The basal stratum is full of unworn, green-coated flints and is known as the Bull-Head Bed. This first Eocene marine invasion did not penetrate far inland, for the Thanet Sands thin out entirely in Surrey (at Horsley) and northwards in Suffolk, where they are overlapped by the succeeding Woolwich and Reading Beds.

The 'double-barrelled' title of the **Woolwich and Reading Beds** expresses the fact that they exhibit quite different facies in these two districts.[1] The only constant member of the succession is the basal bed of glauconitic, sandy clay which contains many well-rounded flint pebbles, where it rests on the Thanet Beds; but where it over-laps on to the Chalk, like the Bull-Head Bed, it contains *unworn* flint nodules. This basal marine-bed indicates a further spreading westwards of the Eocene Sea; but the incursion must have been short-lived for in the western outcrops the typical Reading Beds consist of yellow and white sands averaging 30 feet in thickness and of continental facies. They are succeeded by a rather greater thick-ness of mottled clays, also of non-marine origin. The Reading Beds are unfossiliferous save for impressions of leaves in the clay bands. It is stated that the sands show dune-bedding in the neighbourhood of Reading itself; but elsewhere they show current bedding of the normal deltaic type, and the beds are regarded as having accumu-lated on the delta-flat of the 'Eocene Mississippi'. The delta was traversed by several distributaries, the shingle-filled channels of which are sometimes cut across in quarrying operations. Bands and

[1] In studying the Lower Tertiary strata it will be found that this nomencla-ture is unnecessarily complicated—'unnecessarily' in the present state of knowledge and for our present purpose. Each and every different lithological facies bears a place-name dating back to the time before correlation was effected. They are names, however, which are very widely used, and it is difficult to avoid their introduction. They are more popular than the names of the cycles of sedimentation to which they belong.

lenses of clay-breccia which occur in the sands were probably produced by the distributaries cutting laterally into the stratified clays and sands of the delta.

Reading Beds of this type occur all along the northern edge of the London Basin in Hertfordshire and Essex, while beyond the main outcrop several outliers occur far up on the dip-slope of the Chalk in the Chiltern Hills. That of Lane End, near High Wycombe in Buckinghamshire is of particular interest, for it is one of the few places where the marginal facies of the Reading Beds has escaped erosion. Clay-breccias and pebbly sands, often filling channels, are exceptionally well developed; whilst the abundance of well-rounded quartz pebbles and the nature of the detrital grains in the sands prove that locally, at least to the north-west, the Chalk had been breached and the Lower Greensand exposed.

The Reading Beds are rarely seen in natural sections, but they yield valuable brick-making materials, and scattered pits, some of very large size, occur on the outcrop. Local cementation by silica has affected the sand in some places, the indurated masses remaining as residual boulders long after the softer sands have been denuded away. These are termed 'sarsens'. Similar cementation of the flint-pebble beds has produced the Hertfordshire Pudding Stone, a siliceous conglomerate containing many rounded flint pebbles (many of which are beautifully colour-banded) embedded in a yellowish or white quartzite matrix.

The equivalents of the Reading Beds in East Kent are entirely marine; but in the west of that county and in Surrey, and typically in the Woolwich district, the lithological facies is different, though the mere names of the rock-types in the Woolwich Beds are the same as in the Reading Beds to the west: they are interbedded clays, sands and flint-pebble beds. In contrast with the Reading facies the Woolwich Beds are fossiliferous, yielding a somewhat varied assemblage of marine fossils in the lower beds; but the upper division contains large quantities of shells belonging to a very small number of species in the Woolwich 'Shell Beds'. The commonest types are *Corbicula* (*Cyrena*) *cuneiformis* and *Melania*, as well as lignite bands and the impressions of leaves. Neither the fossil assemblage nor the lithology is typical of normal marine conditions, and it is often stated that estuarine conditions are indicated, though this implies that the great Eocene River at this time had both an estuary and a delta. Now, from their lithology, the Reading Beds are believed to have been laid down under deltaic conditions; and it is impossible for a delta to pass seawards into an estuary, for quite different geographical conditions are involved in the development of these features. The Woolwich Beds of the type-area were laid down in shallow lagoons on the seaward side of the Reading Beds delta, while still farther east glauconitic sands were accumulating in the open sea over the site of East Kent (Fig. 107).

The marine transgression that ushered in the succeeding **Ypresian Cycle,** spread rapidly across the lagoons and delta-flats and reached at least as far west as Hungerford. In the eastern part of the London Basin the cycle commences with the **Blackheath Beds.** These vary from pebble beds consisting of ovoid pebbles of flint and very occasionally of quartzite, set in a minimum of sandy matrix, to yellow sands with occasional strings of pebbles. The lithological terms, 'Blackheath Pebble Beds' and 'Oldhaven Beds', have been applied in the past to the pebbly and the sandy facies respectively. In some places they are cemented to form a ferruginous or calcareous sandstone, which is often richly fossiliferous. The fauna includes the few brackish-water forms of the Woolwich Shell Bed, associated with numerous marine types such as *Glycimeris* (*Pectunculus*) *plumsteadiensis*. These beds, especially when of the pebbly facies, although resting conformably on the underlying Landenian strata, frequently occur in deep channels which, in places, cut right through the Woolwich Beds to the Thanet Sands below. Southwards (as well as westwards) the Blackheath Beds overlap the Landenian, and on the crest of the North Downs near Caterham rest directly on Chalk, even on Middle Chalk. Their occurrence on such a low horizon may, however, be due partly to the removal in solution of higher parts of the Chalk after these highly porous pebble beds were deposited.

With regard to origin an upwarp of part of the floor of the shelf-sea, over the site of the Weald, caused shallows within which the Upper Chalk suffered active erosion and contributed the myriads of flint pebbles; while the rare quartzite pebbles were evidently derived from the cemented portions of the Reading or Woolwich sands. The almost ideal ovoid shape of the majority of the pebbles and the absence of angular ones indicates that they were worked over by wave action for a long period of time; while the surface cracks commonly exhibited by them bear witness to the severe battering they experienced. If further evidence of shallow-water conditions were needed it is afforded by the channels, produced by strong current, or tidal scour, referred to above.

West of Croydon and a little to the north of the Thames, the Blackheath Beds disappear abruptly, the **London Clay** resting directly on the Landenian deposits. In such areas the basal beds of the London Clay are sandy, and in places, as at Lane End, include pebble beds which 'channel' down into the Reading Beds.

The clay above these beds is very uniform in lithology: a monotonous blue-grey clay which weathers yellowish-brown in the surface

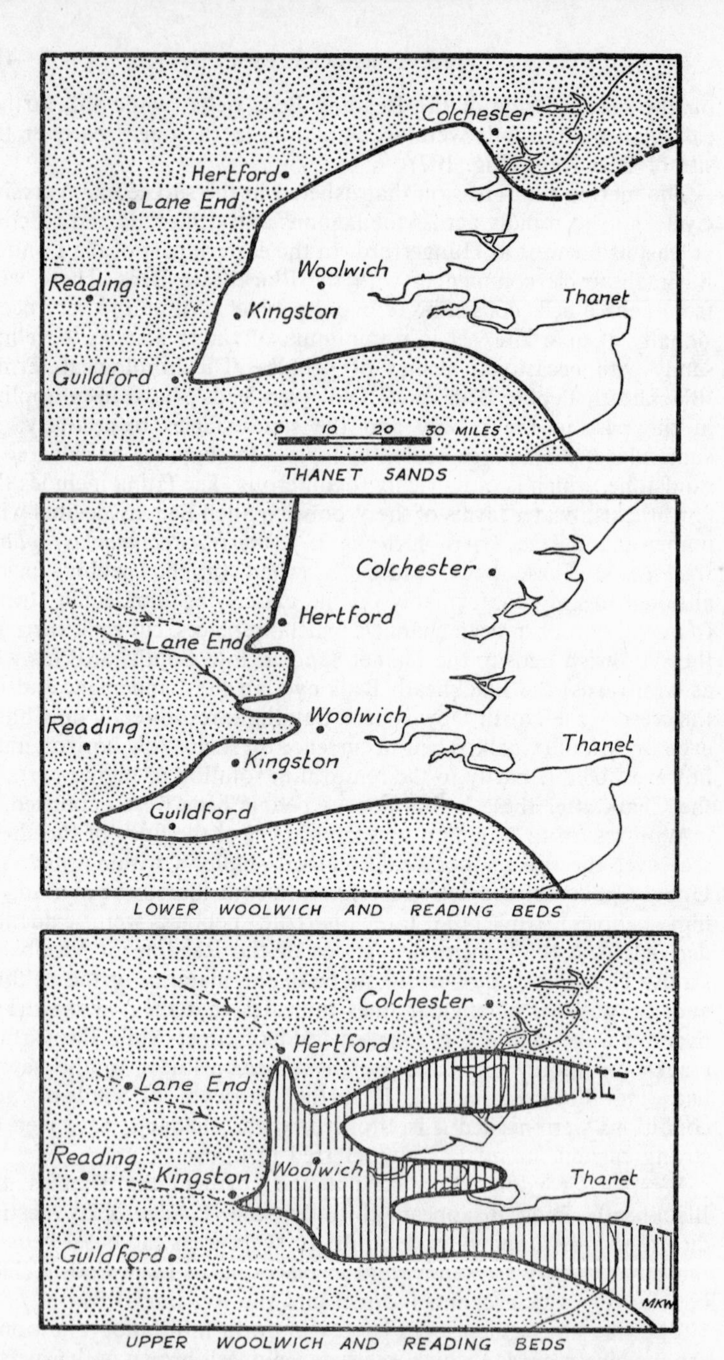


FIG. 107.—Maps to illustrate the changes in Palaeogeography in the London Basin during the Landenian Cycle. (*After S. W. Wooldridge.*)
Land, stippled; lagoon, shaded; sea, blank; rivers indicated by broken lines.

layers. The monotony is broken only by layers of large septarian nodules which occur on several horizons, and which are important, for when broken open they are found sometimes to be crowded with fossils. The greater part of the clay is unfossiliferous, though careful collecting by a number of enthusiastic workers on this unpromising material has resulted in the discovery of a host of fossil shells, more than a hundred species of fishes and such interesting forms as crabs, turtles, crocodiles, birds and curious mammals, together with plant-remains. The latter are valuable indicators of the climatic conditions, which must have been much warmer than at present, for the flora included oak and almond, magnolia and laurel, while *Nipadites*, the stemless palm, is living still, but is restricted to the Malay Archipelago. The whole assemblage is regarded as characteristic of the tropical rain-belt. The plant- and animal-remains derived from the land occur at the bottom and top of the London Clay, where the incoming of sand indicates a shoaling of the water, and, in the case of the top 50 feet, a passage into the overlying Bagshot Sands. These passage beds are the **Claygate Beds,** which in the type-area in Surrey, consist of rapid alternations of sand and clay in thin beds. Apart from the sandy base and top, the London Clay is undoubtedly the normal marine blue clay of the period, and is estimated to have been deposited in about 100 fathoms of water. If it survives long enough to participate in the next orogenic period, it will be converted into blue slates indistinguishable (except for the fossils) from the Cambrian slates, while the Claygate Beds will ape the Lingulella Flags of the Cambrian System.

The London Clay, which is nearly 600 feet in thickness near Southend, thins steadily westwards to little over 300 feet near Windsor, just over 100 feet near Kingsclere and to only a few feet near Hungerford. At the same time the clays in the extreme west contain a very appreciable admixture of sand and silt, and this, with the presence of much finely disseminated glauconite, indicates approach to, but not the proximity of, the coastline.

The Claygate Beds pass up quite gradually into the **Bagshot Beds,** which to-day occur as a much-dissected sheet of sand forming high ground, well drained, contrasting strikingly with the heavy water-logged, low-lying country underlain by the London Clay. In North London, Highgate Hill and Hampstead Heath are capped by Bagshot Sands, which also occur many miles to the east, capping the Rayleigh Hills in Essex. In their natural state these hills of Bagshot Beds are clad with heather, gorse and coniferous trees, and afford extensive views out over the surrounding London Clay flats.

In lithology the Bagshot Sands closely resemble the fluviatile Reading Beds, consisting of current bedded, pale-coloured sands, with thin seams of pipeclay and occasional spreads of small pebbles. Again fossils, other than plant-remains, are absent, and the beds obviously constitute the continental facies of the Ypresian Cycle. The junction of the Bagshot Sands and underlying London Clay must be diachronous. At the beginning of the cycle the sea had spread quickly over the lagoons and deltas to the western limit of the basin, as a result, presumably, of the sinking of its marginal parts; but thereafter sediment was poured in by the rivers more quickly than the sea-floor sank to accommodate it. Therefore the deltas extended farther and farther eastwards, pushing back the sea. In the extreme west of the basin the marine episode must have been very transient: in a few places continental Bagshot Sands rest on continental Reading Beds, with no intervening marine strata. The line of the present Lea Valley coincides with the boundary between continental and marine Bagshot Beds: on its western side the beds are of the type described above; on the east they are sands of finer grain and very occasionally yield casts of marine molluscan shells.

So far no mention has been made of the Eocene Beds of the Hampshire Basin. This is deliberate. Cycles of sedimentation and the principles underlying this concept can be best illustrated by the Landenian and Ypresian beds of the London Basin. In the Hampshire Basin the Landenian is represented only by Reading Beds and Woolwich Beds of the lagoonal facies. Inroads of the sea have destroyed that part of the Basin in which marine Thanet Sands and the marine type of Woolwich Beds might be expected to occur. Even the lagoonal type is present only in the extreme east, from Newhaven to Worthing. The great bulk of the beds separating the Chalk of the Hampshire Basin from the London Clay are closely comparable in lithology with the Reading Beds of the London Basin; but in the Dorchester neighbourhood they change abruptly to a gravelly facies, yielding pebbles of Upper Greensand chert, evidence that farther westwards the Chalk had been breached.

The overlying London Clay was laid down in considerably shallower water than the stiff clays of the type-area. In Hampshire the beds are mainly silty clays, whilst fine sands and even beds of flint pebbles are locally developed. Again, the London Clay thins westwards and also becomes more sandy, while in the extreme west, near Cranborne, it oversteps the Reading Beds to rest on the Chalk. There are marked faunal differences between the London Clay of the London and the Hampshire Basins. For example *Glycimeris brevirostris* and *Cardita* (*Venericor*) *planicosta*, which sometimes form veritable shell-banks, and *Turritella*, which is locally extremely abundant in Hampshire, are absent or very rarely found in the

London Basin. These differences can be explained if the Ypresian transgression occurred in stages. During the first stage only the eastern portion of the London Basin was submerged by a relatively cool-water sea spreading in from the North Sea Basin. A later advance of the sea covered the western portion of the London Basin and the Hampshire Basin, and a connection along the line of the present English Channel was opened with the Tethys. Warm-water molluscs, brachiopods and polyzoans invaded first, the Hampshire, and later, the London Basin, for there they occur only in the higher parts of the London Clay. Palms, mangroves and other plants, together with the occasional carcases of animals living in the tropical rain forests along the southern shores of the sea, were drifted westwards by the currents from the Tethys and finally sank, waterlogged, onto the muddy sea-floor of Sheppey.

The overlying Bagshot Sands are of marine facies to the east, but of fluviatile facies to the west of the Test Valley. In the Bournemouth neighbourhood they expand to over 500 feet in thickness and consist of a lower division rich in seams of pipeclay (hence the potteries round Poole); and an upper division, the Bournemouth Freshwater Beds, which provide us with a very good example of a fossil delta.

Plant-remains in the clay beds indicate a continuation of the tropical to subtropical conditions that had persisted through earlier Eocene times: the leaves recorded including fig, *Eucalyptus*, *Acacia*, palms, ferns, the 'monkey puzzle' tree (*Araucaria*) and *Aralia*. The plants named all grow in England in favourable situations to-day, the last-named being a popular parlour plant of our grandparents' times, but none of them is indigenous to these Islands, though they flourish luxuriantly in warmer climates.

In the Dorchester area the Bagshot Beds, like the local Reading Beds below, assume a gravelly facies, and contain pebbles of Palaeozoic rocks, radiolarian chert, schorl-rock and silicified Purbeck Limestone, which indicate extensive denudation of the Cretaceous strata, uncovering the older rocks beneath. These Bagshot Gravels overstep the Reading Beds and London Clay, and come to rest directly on high zones of the Chalk; while farther westwards gravels usually regarded as of Bagshot age occur on the Chalk Downs of Dorset and eastern Devon and overlie the Upper Greensand of the Blackdown Hills and Haldon Hills near Exeter.

The close of Bagshot times marks the completion of the Ypresian Cycle. Over the greater part of the London Basin no beds higher than the Bagshot Sands occur; but in its western parts and particularly in the Hampshire Basin the Bracklesham and Barton Beds are developed and are referred to three cycles, in order the Lutetian, the Ledian and the Bartonian.

The picture given above may, however, be an over-simplification. It is now known that a species of Nummulites, *N. planulatus*, is restricted to the lowest part of the Bracklesham Beds of the Isle of Wight and the adjacent mainland. There are also strong lithological and faunal resemblances between these beds and much of the so-called 'Bagshot Sands' of the western part of the London Basin. In the Paris Basin and Belgium, the beds yielding *N. planulatus* are named the Cuisian and are regarded as of equal status to the underlying Ypresian and the overlying Lutetian. It has been claimed that the Bagshot Sands of both the Hampshire and the London Basins are entirely of Cuisian age; but unfortunately these beds are almost barren of fossils, and it remains for the future to settle this problem of the Ypresian-Cuisian relationship in southern England.

In the Hampshire Basin the higher Eocene cycles are represented mainly by greenish sandy clays, often yielding marine molluscan shells in great variety. Washing of samples of the clays often yields the small coiled shells of the foraminifera, *Nummulites*. This is of considerable importance for these forms are of much greater value than bottom-living molluscs, in correlating the Tertiary beds of different parts of the Anglo-Gallic Basin. Indeed continental geologists often refer to the Eocene and Oligocene Systems as the 'Nummulitique'. The lower part of the Bracklesham Beds yields *N. laevigatus*, the upper part *N. variolarius* and the Barton Beds *N. prestwichianus*, formerly called *N. wemmelensis*. This is the real justification, combined with certain differences in the molluscan faunas, for regarding the Lower Bracklesham Beds as the marine facies of the **Lutetian,** and the Upper Bracklesham Beds as the marine facies of the **Ledian,** cycle.

The **Bracklesham Beds** consist, in East Hampshire and extreme West Sussex, of some 300 feet of sandy clays, locally richly fossiliferous. At the western end of the London Basin, although the lithology is much the same, the thickness is much less—some 70 feet only, and fossils are sporadic. Near Bournemouth current bedded sands and lenticular masses of flint shingle occur at the top of both Lower and Upper divisions, indicating littoral conditions; but even in the west of the Hampshire Basin the Bracklesham Beds are not true continental deposits; they were laid down on the seaward side of deltas extending into the Lutetian and Ledian seas. At Alum Bay at the western end of the Isle of Wight they consist of finely laminated sands, standing vertically in the cliffs, and containing bands of lignite. On account of their distinctive colouring they prove an attraction even to people of no geological interests. Many visitors to Alum Bay fill bottles with the sands and carry them away as souvenirs of their visit, thus in a small way contributing to the already rapid erosion of the cliffs. Twenty miles to the east at Whitecliff Bay, the Bracklesham Beds are very different: they consist of dark coloured glauconitic clays and sandy clays with shell-bands full of *Cardita* (*Venericor*) *planicosta* and other marine fossils. A careful comparison of the Eocene strata, so clearly exposed, in these two fine coast sections, provides a most convincing demonstration of the underlying theme of the stratigraphy of our

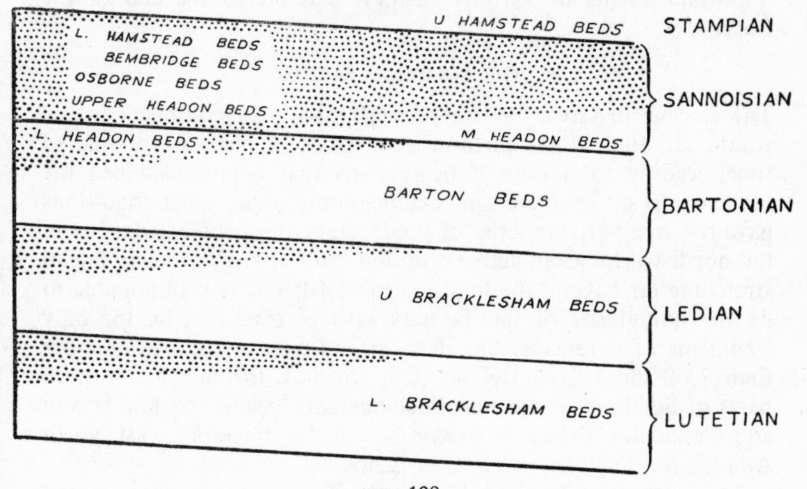


FIG. 108.

Diagram showing the later Tertiary Cycles of Sedimentation in the Hampshire Basin.

Continental facies, stippled; marine facies, blank; certain thin marine intercalations in the Sannoisian are omitted.

Lower Tertiary beds: the dominance of non-marine beds in the west, but of marine beds in the east.

The highest of the Eocene strata are the **Barton Beds,** the type-locality being on the sea-coast in Christchurch Bay. Resting conformably on the underlying Bracklesham Beds, they are divided for purposes of description into Lower, Middle and Upper Barton Beds. The Lower Barton Beds are green clays with sandy partings. The overlying Middle Barton Beds are chiefly clays, while the Upper Barton Beds are sands. The latter stretch into the western end of the London Basin,[1] giving rise to the heather- and gorse-covered Bagshot Heath. As repositories of fossils the Middle and Upper Barton Beds are without equal among the Tertiary strata; more

[1] Unfortunately the palaeontological evidence concerning the age of the 'Barton Beds' of the London Basin is inconclusive: there is even some justification for correlating them with the Upper Bracklesham division.

than 500 species of gasteropods and lamellibranchs have been recorded from these beds, many of them being allied to forms living now in the Australian and Japanese seas (Figs. 109 and 110). Evidence of the withdrawal of the Bartonian Sea is afforded by the incoming of brackish-water fossils towards the top of the Barton Beds, while marine fossils are absent from the overlying Lower Headon Beds. This eastward withdrawal was one of the most important events in Tertiary history, and marks the end of the Eocene.

### THE VOLCANIC FACIES

The Eocene in Great Britain presents two great contrasts: in the south, although slight earth-movements took place from time to time, leading to marine transgressions that counterbalanced the tendency to silt up the basin, sedimentation under quiet conditions gave rise to a variable series of sands, clays and pebble beds; but in the north volcanoes in active eruption built up a great lava plateau stretching far beyond the limits of these Islands. It is impossible to fix the boundaries of the Tertiary lava plateau exactly, for only fragments of it remain; but these extend over a distance of more than 2000 miles from Ireland (Co. Antrim), through the western parts of Scotland to the Faroe Islands and Iceland, to Jan Mayen and Greenland. Evidently Britain lay on the fringe of a vast North Atlantic (or Thulean) volcanic province.

At one time it was thought that the Tertiary lavas were erupted from a series of fissures aligned roughly north-west to south-east; but the more modern view is that they were the products of several immense volcanoes of the central type. This localization of the volcanic forces at isolated points led to the gradual building up of lava cones or domes which, on account of the fluidity of the magma, were relatively low, but each one spread out over a wide area. With few exceptions the Tertiary lava-flows are basaltic in composition; and although some are as much as 100 feet or more in thickness, they average 20 feet. They are exposed to advantage in the coast sections, where each flow is seen to consist of a massive central portion sandwiched in between a slaggy top and base. Inland this gives rise to a distinctive terraced type of scenery; for the massive parts of the flows are more resistant to weathering than the slaggy parts, so that the former appear as steps on the hillsides. Some of the Tertiary basalts are world-famous on account of the remarkably regular columnar jointing which they exhibit, notably at the Giant's Causeway in Antrim and Fingal's Cave, Staffa. A total thickness of 6000 feet of basaltic lavas has survived in Mull; the original thickness must have been much more. Bearing in mind the fact that the

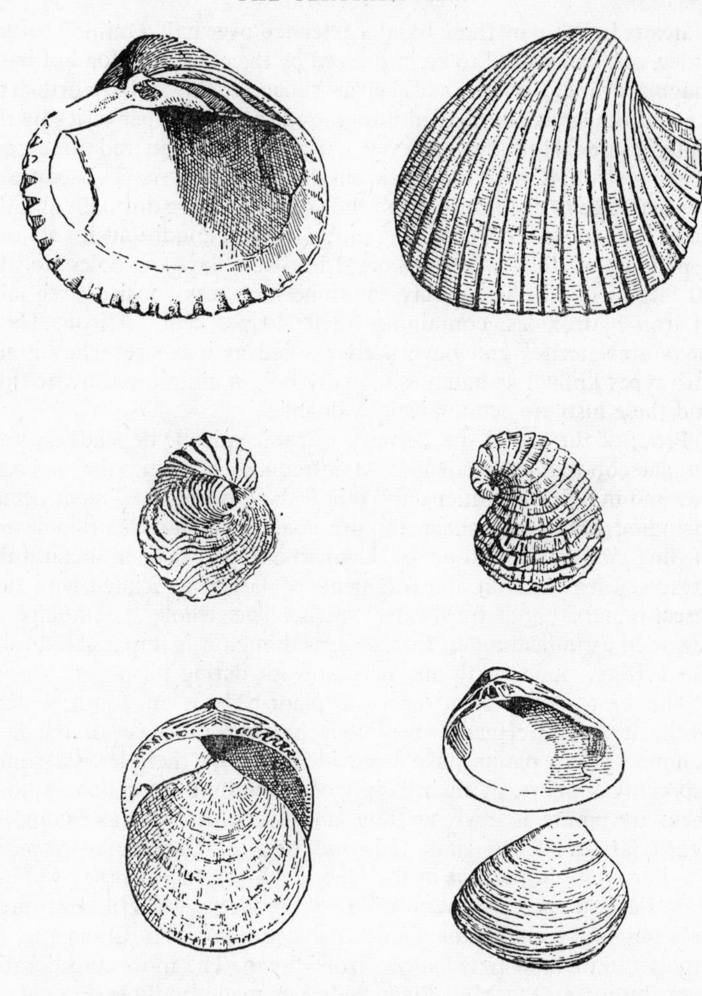


FIG. 109.
Eocene lamellibranchs:
Above: *Cardita* (*Venericor*) *planicosta*, Bracklesham Beds.
Centre: *Chama squamosa*, Barton Beds.
Bottom, left: *Glycimeris* (*Pectunculus*) *plumsteadiensis*, Blackheath Beds.
Bottom, right: *Corbicula* (*Cyrena*) *cuneiformis*, Woolwich Shell Beds.

plateaux built up by these basalts extended over half a million square miles, one cannot fail to be impressed by the enormous load of basic magma erupted at the surface, as subaerial flows. In North-East Ireland the lavas are divided into a lower and an upper series by the 'Interbasaltic Horizon'—a level marked by a bright red zone contrasting strongly with the black basalts. This level marks a pause in the sequence of eruptions, when the volcanoes were dormant and the flows lay exposed to weathering under tropical conditions for so long a period that they were converted into red clays or 'boles' locally 90 feet in depth. These clays in some instances consist essentially of iron hydroxides, containing up to 40 per cent. of iron. These clays are laterites and have been worked as iron ore. They grade into types known as bauxites, equally rich in aluminium hydroxide, and these also are economically valuable.

Proof of the age of the Tertiary volcanic episode depends entirely on palaeobotanical evidence. At infrequent levels in the volcanic pile and in a few localities only, thin beds of normal sediment occur, including sandstone, shale, impure coal or lignite and thin layers of fine-grained limestone of lacustrine type, rich in beautifully preserved leaves, fruit and fragments of wood, associated with rare insect-remains and freshwater shells. The whole assemblage is regarded as indicating an Eocene age, though it is impossible to use the Tertiary plants with any precision for dating purposes.

The best-known occurrence of plant-beds is in south-western Mull, at Ardtun Head, where they lie near the base of the lava column. Many plants have been identified by their leaves, some, especially conifers, by their fruit, some even by their pollen. Among them are plants as lowly as fungi and liverworts, and as exalted as near-relatives of the giant redwood trees of California—*Sequoia*. Conifers were important in the Hebridean forests, but they were of Far Eastern types, not related to modern western European varieties, and included the maidenhair tree (*Ginkgo*) of China and the highly ornamental *Cryptomeria* from Japan. The most considerable contribution to the Mull Plant-Beds was made by flowering plants, however, among them several forms of oak, plane, hazel and *Cornus*, all again of Far Eastern types. *Magnolia* lent colour to the scene, and the rounded leaves of the lotus floated on the lakes.

The significance of these occasional intercalations of normal sediments lies in the proof they afford that the volcanoes were not continuously in eruption: they were from time to time dormant sufficiently long for forests to become established on the basaltic plateaux, only to be destroyed by later eruptions.

At one point in Mull can be seen what remains of the trunk of a tree of considerable size, embedded in basalt, and carbonized by the

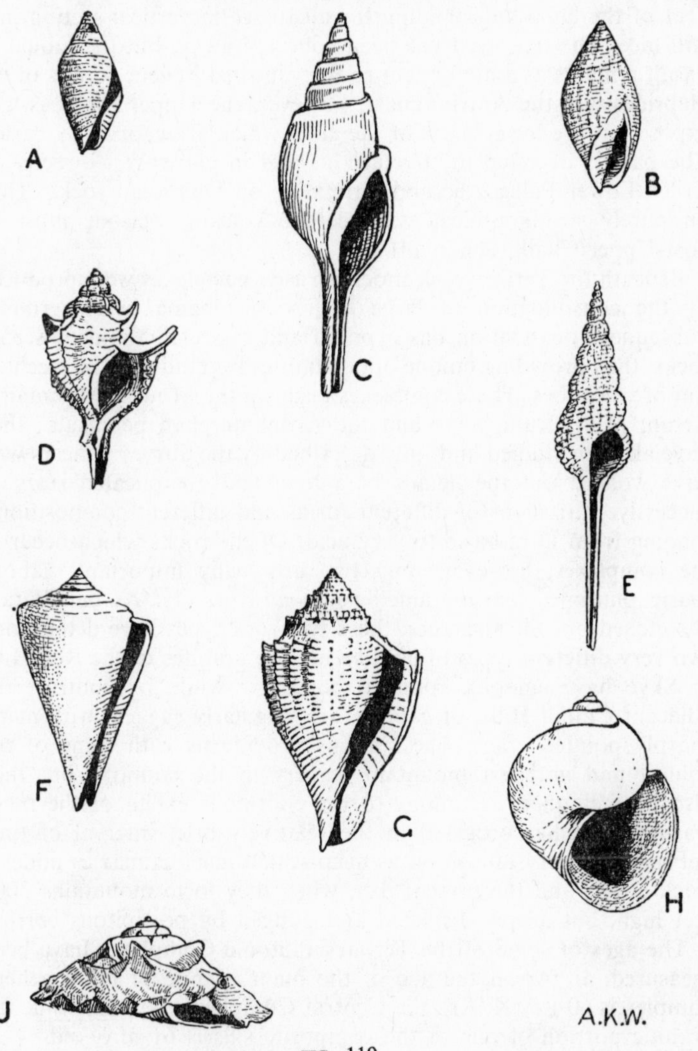


FIG. 110.

Gasteropods from the Eocene Barton Beds:

A. *Conorbis dormitor*.
B. *Mitra*.
C. *Clavilithes longaevus* (also in Bracklesham Beds).
D. *Murex asper*.
E. *Fusinus porrectus*.
F. *Leptoconus edwardsi* previously *Conus deperditus*.
G. *Athleta* (*Volutospina*) *luctator*.
H. *Natica* sp.
J. *Xenophora agglutinans*.

heat of the lava, but standing for all to see in vertical section in a cliff-face. The tree itself has been collected away, but the mould in basalt remains as a monument to the vanished Eocene forests of the Hebrides. On the Antrim coast, however, the Upper Chalk is well exposed in the lower parts of the cliffs which are capped by basalt. The basalts overstep the Cretaceous and in places rest directly on Trias, Lower Palaeozoic and ultimately on Dalradian rocks. Thus on purely stratigraphical evidence the volcanic episode must be post-Upper Chalk (Senonian).

Beneath the Tertiary volcanoes **intrusive complexes** were produced by the consolidation of large bodies of magma below ground. Subsequent denudation has exposed and dissected the deep-seated rocks, thus providing unique opportunities for studying the mechanism of volcanoes. These complexes occur in the Mourne Mountains, Arran, Mull, Rum, Skye and the Ardnamurchan peninsula; they have all been studied and fully described by the Survey Officers who have worked out the details of a long and complicated story of successive intrusions of different forms and different compositions, ranging from ultra-basic to very acid. Of the rocks which occur in the complexes, however, only two are really important, gabbro (basic plutonic, coarse-grained rock) and granite. As denudation has etched out the structure, these two rock-types have determined two very different types of land form. The granites of the Red Hills in Skye have smooth, rounded contours; while by contrast the adjacent Cuillin Hills, of gabbro, are singularly rugged, with many sharply pointed crags. The Cuillins provide us with some of the wildest and grandest mountain scenery in the country; but they also bear eloquent testimony to the enormous extent of the rock-wastage that has occurred in the relatively brief interval of time between their crystallization as deep-seated igneous masses under a thick cover, and the present day, when they form mountains 3000 feet high, but deeply dissected and gouged by precipitous corries.

The ages of some of the Tertiary Plutonic Complexes have been measured. In Arran the age of the outer granite of the northern complex is $60 \pm 5$ (K/Ar), the Central Complex is $60-63$, while the granitic portion of one of the composite sills is 61 m.y. old.

The closing phase of Tertiary igneous activity took the form of the injection, over the whole area, of multitudes of basic dykes which in general are constant in the direction in which they strike (Fig. 111). In the main there is little deviation from north-west to south-east, but some of the dykes extend into northern England, where they swing more nearly east-to-west. They occur in a belt of country narrowing westwards, bounded by the Acklinton dyke on the north and the Cleveland dyke on the south, both of these being

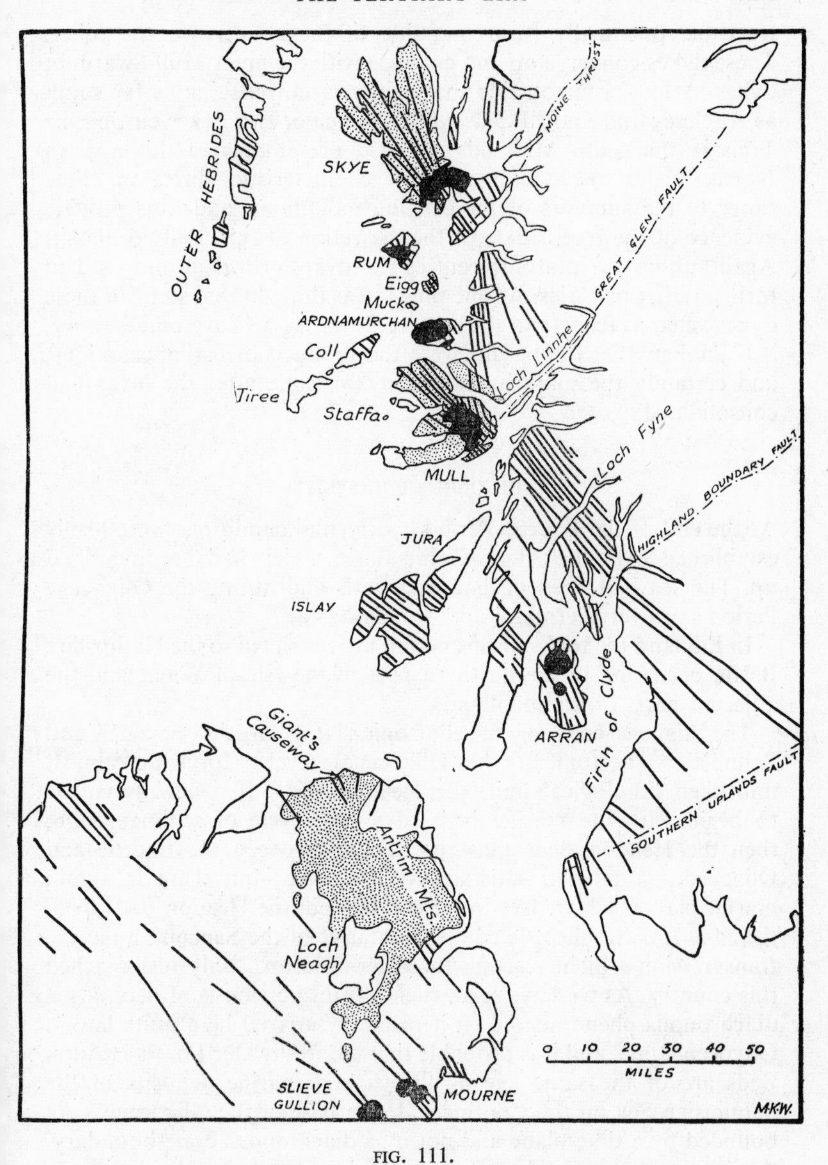


FIG. 111.

Tertiary igneous rocks of Scotland and Northern Ireland. Plutonic centres, black; lavas, stippled; dyke-swarms shown conventionally.

(*Based on maps by officers of the Geological Survey.*)

traceable practically from one side of the country to the other. These dykes converge on and coalesce with the great Mull Swarm of dykes. A few occur outside the main swarm, reaching as far south as Anglesey and Snowdonia; while the one or two dykes cutting the Trias in the south Midlands are also presumably of this age. In North Wales they maintain the characteristic direction, they range to the summits of the existing mountains, and thus provide evidence of the recent date of the dissection of this uplifted massif. Again, about the plutonic centres the dykes crowd in and tend to form a radiating series. At one time it was thought that some of these dykes acted as feeders to the surface flows; as we have noted above, it is unlikely that the basalts were the products of fissure eruptions, and certainly the majority of the dykes came after the lavas had consolidated.

## THE OLIGOCENE SYSTEM

At the end of the Eocene Period continental conditions were firmly established over the Anglo-Gallic Basin which had become silted up. The sea had been pushed eastwards and during the Oligocene Period lay over Germany and Russia.

In England the rocks of this period are restricted to the Hampshire Basin, occurring in the northern part of the Isle of Wight and the adjacent parts of the mainland.

The highest beds of the Bartonian (top of the Eocene) and Sannoisian (bottom of the Oligocene) Cycles form an almost unbroken lithological unit, the Headon Beds. If a new system is to begin with the marine beds of a new cycle of sedimentation, then the Headon Beds must be divided between the Eocene and Oligocene—a most unsatisfactory procedure—but there is a thin marine clay which wedges into the middle of the Headon Beds from the east. It is the short-lived representative of the **Sannoisian** marine transgression which, starting in eastern Europe, only just reached this country. As we have seen, such a transgression is of necessity a diachronous phenomenon, so it probably arrived here quite late in Oligocene time, and it is probable that the freshwater Lower Headon Beds are of the same age as the earliest marine deposits of the Sannoisian Sea on the Continent. If the base of the Oligocene were bounded by a time-plane and not by a diachronous cycle-boundary, the whole of the Headon Beds could be regarded as belonging to that System. It is, of course, not the first time that this difficulty has been encountered; but whichever principle is followed in drawing the Systematic boundary, the fact remains that the physical conditions in Lower Headon times were identical with those in Upper

Headon times—conditions quite unlike those encountered at any previous time, but which persisted throughout the Oligocene, giving the rocks of this period a distinctiveness, both in lithological type and in fauna. For these reasons we prefer to include the whole of the Headon Beds in the Oligocene, recognizing, however, that the Lower Headon Beds constitute the continental facies of the Bartonian Cycle.

In the Lower **Headon Beds** lamellibranchs and gasteropods of brackish and freshwater types are abundant, proving beyond doubt that these marls were deposited in freshwater lakes that from time to time were brought into communication with the sea, probably as a consequence of slight sinking of the area, giving brackish-water lagoons and 'estuaries'. Some of the most abundant shells are almost identical with existing freshwater snails found in our ponds and lakes to-day. Thus at the top of the Lower Headon Beds is a cream-coloured limestone crowded with the shells of *Limnaea longiscata*. This is very similar to the living *Limnaea stagnalis*, one of the commonest and largest pond snails. Limestones of this type recur in the Middle and Upper Headon Beds. The same evidence of origin is afforded by the Unio Bed, for *Unio* still lives in lakes and rivers, and is one of our freshwater 'mussels'. Similarly the 'Chara Bed' is crowded with the remains of this still-living freshwater alga. To complete the picture, water-lilies and other aquatic plants flourished in the Headon lakes, on the banks of which palm trees grew. Rapid burial under silt and mud has led to the preservation of the leaves of these plants in Leaf Beds, while the trunks of the trees contributed to the formation of beds of lignite. The contemporary vertebrate fauna is well represented in a Crocodile Bed and in a Mammalia Bed near the base of the Headon Beds, this latter having yielded bones of birds, mammals and reptiles. The mammals are all types of extinct genera and include the tapir-like *Palaeotherium*, the pig-like *Anthracotherium* and the primitive carnivore, *Hyaenodon*.

During the period of deposition of the Middle Headon Beds the sea spread over the area, depositing sandy glauconitic clays containing marine shells and some corals. Westwards these marine beds fail, and continental conditions were soon re-established, and the Upper Headon Beds, as noted above, consist of the same lithological types, containing the same brackish and freshwater fossils, as the Lower Headon Beds.

The **Osborne Beds** are practically restricted to the Isle of Wight, and are of freshwater origin throughout, consisting chiefly of clays and marls, but with beds of limestone at intervals. The fauna is like that of the underlying Headon Beds, consisting largely of freshwater snails, *Limnaea*, *Viviparus* and *Planorbis*. Some of the limestone bands are again rich in the remains of *Chara*.

The thickest of these very distinctive limestones in the Oligocene is the overlying **Bembridge Limestone,** cream coloured and 20 feet in thickness, including thin partings of marl. The fauna is essentially the same as in the Oligocene limestones from lower levels, but with

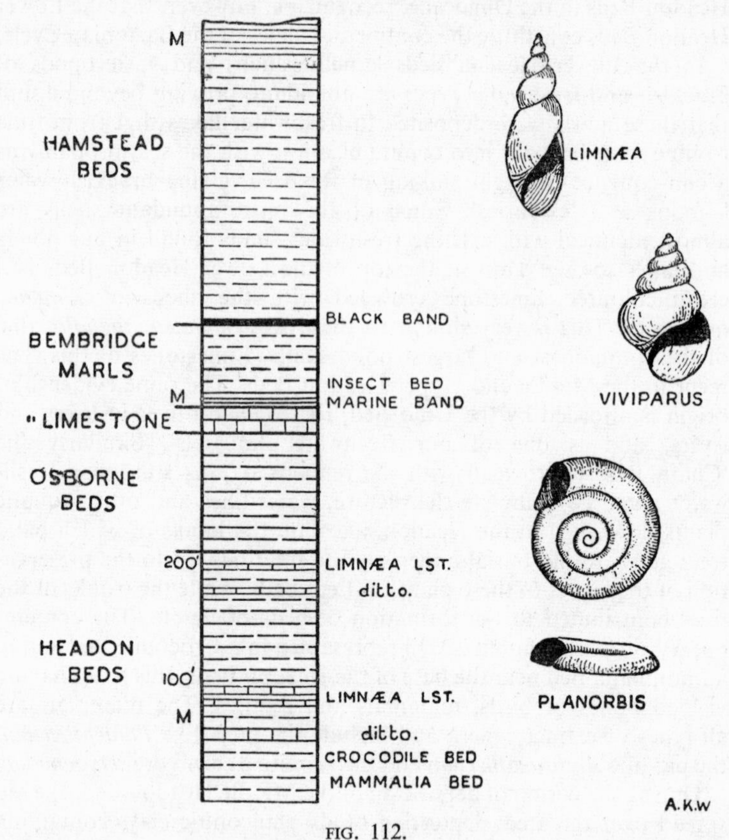


FIG. 112.

Vertical section through the Oligocene strata of the Isle of Wight, with the characteristic freshwater gasteropods, *Limnaea longiscata*, *Viviparus lentus* and *Planorbis euomphalus*.

Marine horizons marked 'M.'

the addition of land snails and the remains of several types of swamp-dwelling mammals closely allied to hippopotamus (*Hyopotamus*, etc.). A slight change in the physical environment brought large quantities of mud into the region where previously the water had been clear, and led to the accumulation of about 100 feet of **Bembridge Marl.** Among other fossils, oysters and the lamellibranch *Mya* occur in certain beds which must have been marine, though at other levels both freshwater and land snails occur. Probably the most interesting bed in the Bembridge Marls is the Insect Bed from which twenty species of insects have been obtained. These fossils are associated with plant-remains which prove parts of the delta to have been forest-clad, with oaks, beeches, conifers and ferns all in evidence.

The highest of the Oligocene strata and the youngest Tertiary rocks to have survived denudation in the Hampshire Basin are the **Hamstead Beds,** which form a continuation of the Bembridge Marls below, but with a greater range of lithology, as shales and sands vary the monotony of the marls, which are largely of freshwater origin. A significant band is the 'Water-lily Bed', whilst at the base occurs the 'Black Band', a carbonaceous loam with rootlets penetrating downwards into the weathered top of the underlying Bembridge Marls. The top 20 feet or so of the Hamstead Beds are, however, marine clays yielding oysters, *Corbula subpisum* and other marine fossils. Applying the cyclical concept they are regarded as the basal member of the **Stampian Cycle.**

Outside the Isle of Wight and the neighbouring parts of the New Forest, Oligocene rocks occur at only a few widely scattered localities. Creechbarrow, a prominent hill and fine viewpoint, lying just to the north of the Chalk Downs which cross the Isle of Purbeck, is capped by limestones yielding the fauna of the Bembridge Beds. Other isolated lake basins of Oligocene date may be represented by pockets of pipeclay at Petrockstow in North Devon and at Flimston in South Pembrokeshire. No fossils have been found and the age suggested for these deposits is based on their lithological similarity to the deposits of the **Bovey Tracey Basin** (see Fig. 72, p. 284), between Dartmoor and Newton Abbot in eastern Devonshire.

This outlier is found in a long, flat-bottomed valley in which the little town of Bovey Tracey is situated. Borings through the valley floor have proved the presence of at least 650 feet of Oligocene, the underlying floor not being reached. The marginal deposits are gravels and coarse sands full of flints from the Chalk and chert from the Greensand which caps the near-by Haldon Hills. Away from the margins of the depression the strata rapidly become fine-grained and include much pale-coloured pipeclay, which is particularly abundant towards the base. There is no doubt that this outlier of Oligocene strata occupies the site of a large lake, at least 40 to 50 square miles in area, dominated then as now by surrounding hills of granite, Devonian limestones and Culm. The high ground was drained by rivers heavily charged with sediment, a large part of which was deposited in the lake as in a settling tank. The valuable pipeclays

FIG. 113.

Sketch of part of the Isle of Wight, showing the steeply inclined Chalk at the Needles, succeeded by the vertical Eocene strata in Alum Bay, and the nearly horizontal Oligocene farther north.

(*A. K. W., from the diorama in the Geological Museum, London.*)

consist of redeposited kaolin derived from the Dartmoor granite, and are of considerable economic value in the pottery industry. Interbedded with the clays and silts are bands of lignite, consisting largely of the remains of the giant conifer, *Sequoia*, the famous redwood of the existing forests of California. This is associated with cinnamon and other trees, and it is thought that the lignite bands represent 'pine rafts' of logs floated down into the lake, ultimately becoming water-logged and sinking to the bottom.

The dating of these Bovey Tracey Beds depends upon the interpretation placed on the evidence of the fossil plants. Some geologists refer them to the Miocene Period (Aquitanian Stage).

## THE MIOCENE PERIOD—'THE ALPINE STORM'

The Oligocene Period witnessed the accumulation of at least many hundreds of feet of lacustrine and marine sediments in southern England: there may originally have been much more than the 650 feet which survived denudation in the Hampshire Basin, for a great stratigraphical break separates the Hamstead Beds from the Superficial deposits resting upon them, two whole geological periods, the Miocene and Pliocene, being unrepresented. In eastern England Pliocene beds do occur, resting on a nearly flat surface cut indiscriminately in different Cretaceous and Tertiary strata. The latter by contrast are not only warped, but locally are strongly folded, faulted and in places overthrust. It is clear that these effects must have been produced in the interval between the Oligocene and the Pliocene, that is, in the Miocene, by important earth-movements. Similar considerations in other parts of the world have shown that the Miocene ranks with the Caledonian and the Armorican as the third great period of mountain-building movements of the first magnitude, when profound changes were effected in the distribution of sea and land and in the configuration of the earth's surface. These earth-movements have been named Alpine, for the Miocene witnessed the emergence of the Alps on the site of the Mesozoic Tethys. Not only the Alps, however, but most of the existing mountain-chains were thrown across the world at this time, including the Himalayas, the western chains of the Americas and, in Europe, the Carpathians and the Pyrenees.

In southern Europe the strata were thrown into great overfolds which were severed from their roots and carried in successive 'slices' (nappes) northwards for many miles along thrust-planes. At the same time the strata suffered intense regional metamorphism. The region of Britain lay on the margin of the area affected by the Alpine storm and consequently the metamorphism and structures incidental to mountain building are absent. Thus, although the Tertiary strata of the Isle of Wight are standing on end (Fig. 113), they are still just sands and clays, in much the same physical condition as when first deposited. Naturally the Miocene movements have left their impress most clearly in southern England, where the Mesozoic and Tertiary strata outcrop; elsewhere in this country effects must have been produced, but they are difficult to disentangle from those of the earlier Armorican movements. Geological and topographical maps of southern England bring out most clearly an

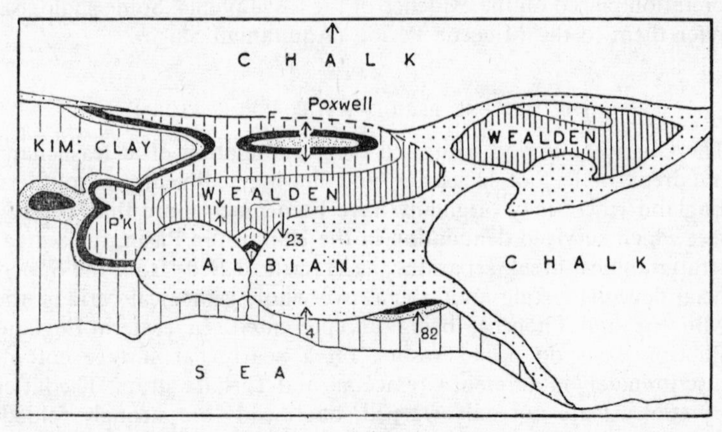


FIG. 114.

Geological sketch-map of part of the Weymouth district, showing gently folded Albian-Cenomanian rocks on strongly folded Jurassic strata. (*Based on the* 1-*inch Geological Survey Map, Weymouth sheet.*)

east-to-west grain. As we have seen, this is due, in such regions as the Mendip Hills, to Armorican folding (see Fig. 69); but in eastern England it results, just as clearly, from the Alpine movements. Subsequent denudation has laid bare the structures in the coastal belt of Dorset (Fig. 114) in a most striking fashion. Here to the east of Weymouth the mapping demonstrates two periods of folding: an earlier, in which rocks up to and including the Wealden were involved; and a later, along parallel but not identical axes, when even the Cretaceous were affected, though the amplitude of the folds was less (Fig. 115). In this area, it can be proved that there were two periods of faulting. Certain faults affect the Jurassic, but not the higher Cretaceous rocks; other faults are clearly post-Cretaceous in age. In one case, at least, there is evidence of reversal of movement along a fault-zone. The fault shown in Fig. 114 on the north side of the Poxwell anticline is, at the surface, a reversed fault. A shallow boring proved Portlandian Beds resting on Upper Greensand. Another and deeper boring passed through the same fault-zone at a depth of about 1600 feet and showed that Oxford Clay to the south is in contact with Forest Marble and Fullers' Earth to the north. In the Jurassic rocks, therefore, this fault-zone is a normal fault with a downthrow of over 500 feet to the south; but the downthrow must originally have been greater (see Fig. 115), for in the mid-Tertiary movements the block to the south of the fault-zone was moved upwards over the block to the north. Elsewhere in the same area there are two closely parallel faults, the one, a normal fault of pre-Upper Cretaceous age downthrowing south, the

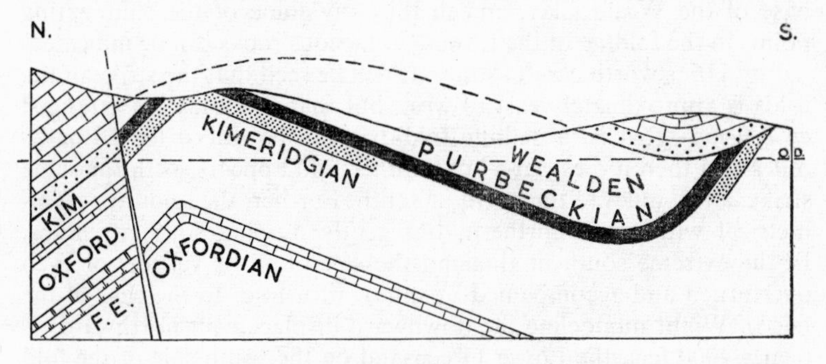


FIG. 115.

Diagram-section through the Poxwell anticline, interpreting the structure as due to two periods of folding: the earlier, pre-Albian, the later, post-Cretaceous.

Note that the fault is normal for the Jurassic, but reversed for the Cretaceous. (*After A. H. Taitt and P. E. Kent.*)

other a post-Upper Cretaceous reversed fault hading south. Combine this complication with a rapid overstep of the Upper Greensand on to various horizons of the Jurassic beds and it is not surprising that in places the relations of the beds have proved extremely difficult to unravel. Dr G. M. Lees has suggested that these complicated tectonics, which are restricted to quite a small area, may have been facilitated by a buried salt deposit, presumably in the Trias.

Whilst attention is naturally focussed on the zone of most intense folding running through the Isle of Wight and the Isle of Purbeck, a complete view of the nature of the disturbances produced by the Alpine earth-storm can be obtained only by studying their effects over a wider area. This can best be done by contouring a surface, originally horizontal or nearly horizontal, which has been deformed by the movements. The obvious one to select is the sub-Eocene peneplain, which has the advantage of being traceable over wide areas. When below ground-level, the top of the Chalk is recorded with precision in well-logs; whilst where it has been removed by recent erosion its height can be estimated with confidence, from a knowledge of the slow lateral variations in thickness of the different zones of the Chalk beneath the unconformable Tertiary beds. As seen from Fig. 116 the variations in height of this surface can be traced throughout the Hampshire Basin, mid-Wessex, the London Basin and the North and South Downs. Over the Weald, however, it cannot be followed with any approach to comparable accuracy. Contour lines there must be drawn on other surfaces, for example the base of the Weald Clay, and in this way some of the culminating points in the folding of the Lower Cretaceous rocks can be indicated.

Fig. 116 is worth careful study. It will be seen that the strike of the folds is approximately east to west, but that the folds are arranged *en echelon*—that is, a definite fold-axis can be traced for 10 or 20 miles and then it dies out—but another fold appears, with the same strike, a few miles to the north or south. Further, the folds are asymmetrical with steep northern, but gently dipping southern limbs. In the extreme south of England the steep limb is vertical or even overturned and accompanied by minor thrusting. In the case of the Isle of Wight monocline the downward displacement northwards is nearly 4000 feet, the Lower Greensand on the south side of the fold being at the same height above sea-level as the Hamstead Beds on the north side. In Wessex and the Weald the asymmetry is usually only a matter of a few degrees, the northward dip being perhaps 10 to 15 degrees, the southward, 5 to 10 degrees.

There is a very important difference between the disturbances in the London Basin on the one hand and in Wessex and the Weald on the other. In the first case, folds are few and of slight amplitude (less than 200 feet); in the other, folds are more numerous and often exceed 600 feet in amplitude, whilst strike-faulting is more pronounced. Surely here we have a reflection of the deeper-seated geology of the two areas. In the London area, the Palaeozoic rocks lie about 1000 feet below sea-level; but under the southern and central Weald the depth of the Palaeozoic floor normally exceeds 3000 feet and at Portsdown drilling stopped at 6332 feet below O.D., just after entering the Trias!

This great pile of uncompacted Mesozoic strata reacted to the pressure from the south in a manner very different from that of the relatively thin cover overlying the resistant block of the London Platform. The line separating the two types of folding runs east-to-west from the Vale of Pewsey through Kingsclere to just south of Guildford, and thence roughly along the scarp-face of the North

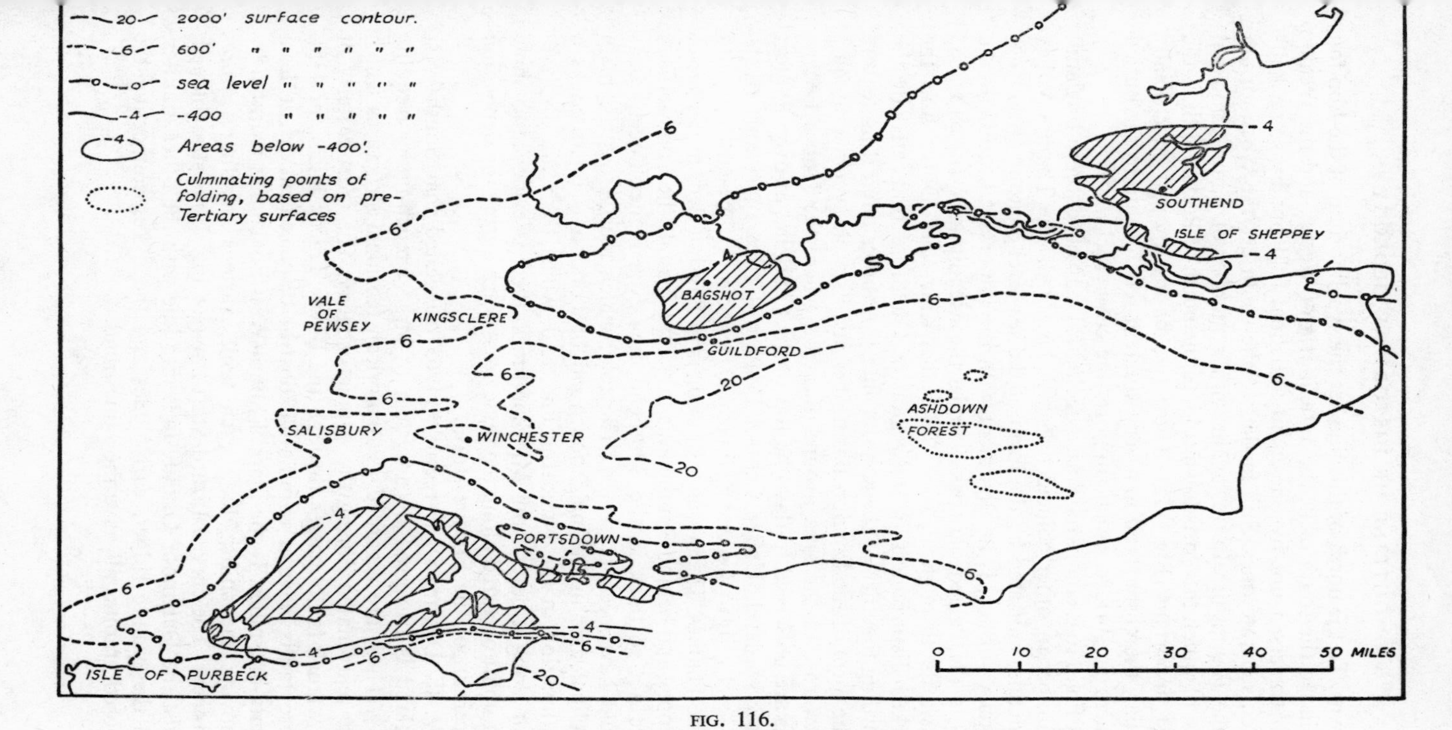


FIG. 116.

Contour map of the sub-Eocene Peneplain to show the nature and effects of subsequent earth-movements. Areas below −400 feet shown by oblique ruling. (*After S. W. Wooldridge and D. L. Linton.*)

Downs. To the north of this line lies the synclinorium of the London Basin; to the south of it, the anticlinoria of Wessex and the Weald, each traversed not by one main anticlinal fold but by some half-dozen separate ones. Still farther to the south lies the synclinorium of the Hampshire Basin, again with a number of minor anticlinal axes, of which the Portsdown fold, to the north of Portsmouth, is the most important (Fig. 115). These two basins, though superficially similar, therefore stand in a very different relationship to the buried Palaeozoic surface which supports the cover rocks.

If Fig. 116 is compared with a geological map of southern England, a number of other coincidences will be noted. The Thames Valley Anticline, indicated by the form of the sea-level contour of the sub-Tertiary surface, is in alignment with the important Cardiff-Bristol axis in the Palaeozoic rocks; whilst the Mendip axis can be traced eastwards through Pewsey Vale, the Kingsclere Dome and the marked disturbances in the region of Guildford (indicated by the crowding together of the contour lines). Another interesting feature is the form of the London Basin: it is not a simple syncline pitching eastwards. In the area around Bagshot, where the Upper Eocene beds are preserved to-day, the top of the Chalk lies at over 400 feet below sea-level. Under Central London it rises approximately to sea-level, only to descend again to 400 feet below O.D. near the mouth of the Thames. The presence of outliers of Bagshot Beds in the Isle of Sheppey and behind Southend is thus explained. If the London Clay were not so thick in the Southend area even higher Eocene beds would have been preserved. The fold, which must cross the main synclinal axis in the neighbourhood of London is regarded as a continuation of the Nuneaton line, and, whilst the main displacement along it dates from Miocene times, there is evidence to show that uplift occurred along the same cross-warp during the deposition of certain of the Eocene strata.

W. R. Dearman has recently (1963) suggested that South-West England is traversed by a system of large wrench-faults trending NNW. These are regarded as Armorican tensional structures which were rejuvenated during the Alpine orogeny. The most easterly of the wrench-faults passes through the Bovey Tracey Basin (p. 435). These faults have a cumulative dextral displacement of at least twenty-one miles. If the map of South-West England is redrawn by removing the shifts along each fault, various puzzling features disappear. The curved Lizard-Start line (see Fig. 72) is straightened, whilst the Dartmoor Granite falls into line with the other granites, and the granite ridges, early lodes and the dykes connecting the exposed granites all have the same trend.

## THE LENHAM BEDS AND THE CRAGS

The study of these beds introduces new problems and new methods of investigation, for the story is written not so much in a succession of strata that accumulated during the period, as in the denudation effects produced.

Long-continued denudation of a land-surface tends towards the production of a flat surface by planing off the irregularities. Ultimately a plain is developed, rising gently inland, and traversed by sluggish rivers which are well graded from source to mouth.

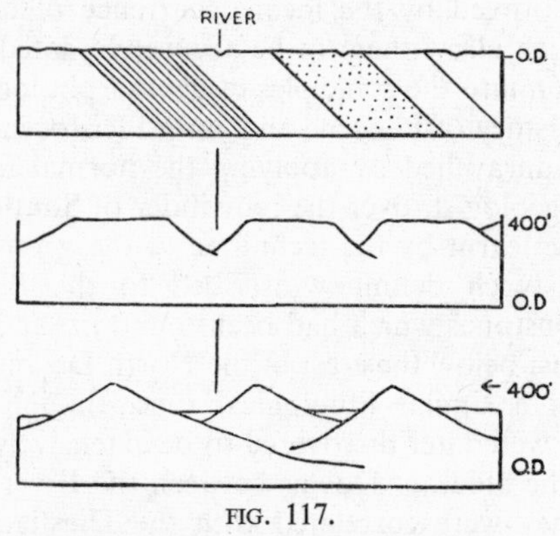


FIG. 117.

Stages in the destruction of a peneplain.

Top section: the peneplain.
Middle section: the dissected peneplain.
Bottom section: landscape showing accordant summit levels.

Such a condition demands stability for a long period of time, and in practice the ideal is rarely, if ever, attained. The resulting surface is nearly, but not quite, a plain; certainly not a *plane* in the strict sense, and has been called a **peneplain.** Later elevation of the area will cause rejuvenation of the river system and the process of destroying the peneplain is commenced; but the evidence of peneplanation will persist in the landscape for a very long time. In the first stage of downcutting, the rivers will deepen their valleys, but wastage of the slopes will be slow. The landscape will be characterized by plateau-like features—the relics of the peneplain—on the 'interfluves' between the valleys. The interfluves will be progressively reduced in size through lateral cutting by the rivers, until in the penultimate stage of destruction the plateaux as such may have disappeared and the only evidence of the former existence of the peneplain may be isolated hills with accordant summit levels (Fig. 117). It is important to note that all plateaux are not dissected peneplains: many are developed in horizontal strata, particularly when hard and soft strata are interbedded, the plateaux at different levels then coinciding with the harder rocks; but if the flat surface is cut indiscriminately in inclined strata through hard and soft alike, showing complete independence of the structure, the plateau may be safely regarded as an uplifted peneplain.

In Britain peneplains occur at several different levels. Each represents an attempt at base-levelling. No two at different elevations in the same area can be of the same age; the highest must be the oldest and the lowest the youngest of the series, a general truth which is proved by the local occurrence of deposits on the 'platforms', which allow them to be accurately dated.

This digression into the principles of geomorphology is necessary: for whilst the history of Pliocene and early Pleistocene times in East Anglia can be unravelled by applying the normal methods of the stratigraphical geologist, over the remainder of South-East England far more can be learnt by the technique of the geomorphologist.

In 1858 Prestwich definitely ascribed to the Pliocene certain fossiliferous ironstones which had been found in sands filling a pipe in a chalk pit just below the crest of the North Downs at Lenham in Kent. Sands of a similar lithological type, though unfortunately unfossiliferous, were later discovered to be extensively developed on the surface of the block of Downs between the River Stour and the Kent coast. They were correlated with the Diestian (Lower Pliocene) of the Low Countries. Subsequently it was shown that these **Lenham Beds** yielded a suite of detrital grains easily recognized and different from that of the Eocene sands. This was very fortunate, for much of the dip-slope of the North Downs is mantled by sandy and clayey deposits of widely different modes of origin and age.

In the extreme east of Kent the outliers of Lenham Beds occur as low hills above a very striking surface cut across different zones of the Chalk, and declining gently northwards from a height of about 550 feet O.D. on the crest of the escarpment. This surface is clearly distinct from, and younger than, the sub-Eocene surface which is more steeply inclined (Fig. 118). The Lenham surface bevels the crest of the North Downs at a height of about 620 feet westwards from Lenham to the Medway gap; but farther to the west the Downs rise to above 800 feet, and in place of the bevel a flat bench cut into the Chalk can be traced at approximately the same level, and about a mile behind the crest-line of the Downs. At the back of the bench a pronounced change of slope occurs, and clearly represents a line of old sea-cliffs, now much degraded. In places sands occur on the bench and these contain the same distinctive suite of heavy minerals as the Lenham Beds in East Kent. At Netley

Heath in Surrey marine fossils have been obtained from the sands. The fauna is of slightly later date than that at Lenham, and is correlated with the Red Crag of East Anglia, described below. Cobbles of flint and pebbles, including spicular chert in small quantities derived from the Hythe Beds to the south, occur in the

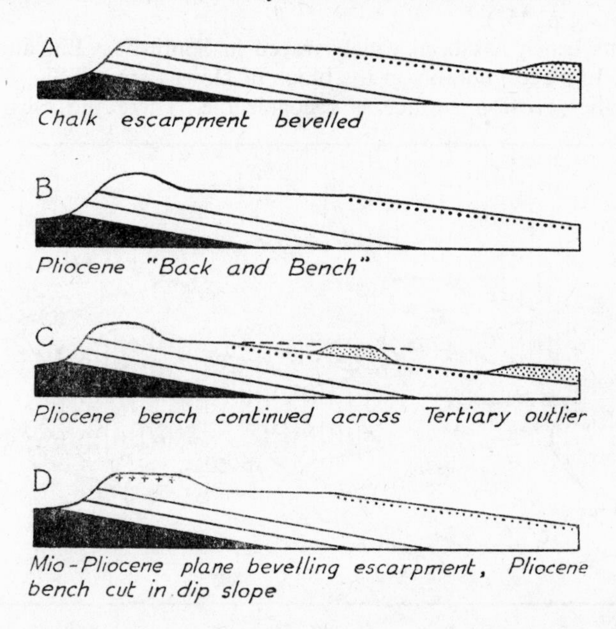


FIG. 118.

Sketch-sections illustrating the relations of the Lenhamian shelf in parts to South-East England. (*Mainly after S. W. Wooldridge and D. L. Linton.*)

A. East Kent (South on the left, North on the right).
B. West Kent and East Surrey (North to South).
C. Chilterns (N.W. to S.E.).
D. Wessex (North to South).

(Chalk, white, with major divisions indicating the dip; Eocene, stippled; dots indicate the sub-Eocene plane, and crosses the Mio-Pliocene plane.)

sands. Obviously the Lower Greensand material could only have been transported to its present position before the existing topography was developed: there could have been no Chalk escarpment and no strike-vale on the outcrop of the Gault, but a gently inclined surface falling towards the *north*, down which rivers carried the chert pebbles.

Passing now from south to north of the Thames Valley, a similar feature, comprising a bench and a degraded sea-cliff behind it, can be traced along the dip-slope of the Chiltern Hills. Locally it is thinly veneered with sands yielding the characteristic heavy minerals of the Lenham Beds. The bench is normally cut in Chalk; but at Lane End in Buckinghamshire both Reading Beds and London Clay are capped unconformably by shingle (Fig. 119). At Rothamsted Red Crag fossils have been obtained, though from a slightly lower level (see p. 453).

This bench has been widely traced in South-East England (Fig. 119). In places, notably in the block of Downs around Shaftesbury, a higher erosion surface is recognizable. There the escarpment

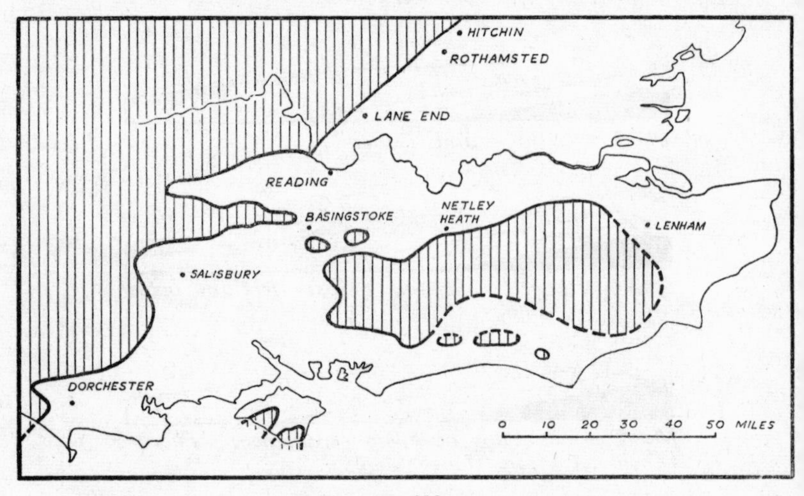


FIG. 119.

The probable extent at the 'Pliocene' Sea in South-East England. (*After S. W. Wooldridge and D. L. Linton.*) The continuous line surrounding the land areas (shaded) indicates where 'Pliocene' beach features are preserved.

is bevelled at a height of 750 to 800 feet O.D., while the 'Pliocene' bench and degraded cliff behind it that we have been tracing occurs lower down the dip-slope at about 650 feet. The higher erosion surface is widely developed in southern England. Its extent at any one locality may be limited to a few square miles; but the general accordance of the summit levels at about 800 feet is very impressive. Clearly this 800-foot peneplain is older than the Lenham Beds feature: it truncates the folds produced during the Alpine orogeny, and is referred to as the Mio-Pliocene erosion-surface. This, then, is the highest and oldest of the erosion surfaces younger than the Miocene folding. Presumably it was produced by long-continued sub-aerial erosion. Uplift to the extent of approximately 150 feet then took place, followed by a period of stillstand long enough for a new erosion surface, graded to the new base-level, to be developed.

As this surface is backed by old sea-cliffs and is locally floored with sand or shingle containing marine fossils, the whole region must have been depressed to allow the sea to spread widely over southern England. The duration of this last marine transgression of these parts of the country is indicated by the difference in age between the Diestian fossils of Lenham and the Red Crag fossils of Netley Heath and Rothamsted.

So far we have traced the 'Pliocene' coastline along the Chalk Downs of South-East England and have found that the distinctive bench rises very gradually westwards from a height of about 550 feet O.D. in East Kent to about 650 feet O.D. in Dorset. In the central Weald there are extensive areas rising above 600 feet O.D., but no trace of a bench or of shingle has been found. This is scarcely surprising, for the Chalk is much more resistant to erosion and also contains much more durable material for shingle, in the form of flint, than do the Hastings Beds of the central Weald. Fortunately the extent of the 'Pliocene' submergence of the central Weald can be inferred from another line of reasoning, which also provides additional and very strong arguments for the existence of this marine episode.

The rivers of Wessex and the Weald are not only transverse to the Miocene folds over wide areas, but they often seem to take an impish delight in cutting across a fold just at its point of greatest amplitude! This relation can be explained only if we suppose that the existing transverse drainage originated *after* the recession of the 'Pliocene Sea'. The direction of the streams would then be controlled by the slope of the uplifted sea-floor, on which a thin veneer of deposits rested unconformably on the planed-down, folded Cretaceous and Tertiary rocks. The unconsolidated deposits would be soon stripped off the greater part of the area, and the drainage would then be superimposed on the older strata. Sufficient time has elapsed since for a considerable amount of adjustment to the structure of the pre-Miocene rocks to take place, with subsequent streams etching out the strike of the softer layers. The old transverse drainage can, however, be reconstructed with very considerable accuracy, by using the evidence of the numerous wind-gaps in the region.

A different relationship occurs in places, notably in East Surrey and West Kent, to the south of the area where the crest-line of the Downs rises above the 'Pliocene' bench, as described above. Clearly here the 'Pliocene Sea' did not extend as far south as the existing Chalk escarpment. On what was the land-area of Lenhamian times, the existing drainage is dominantly along, and often closely related to, the structural lines produced by the Alpine earth-storm. In other words, we are seeing a portion of the drainage (admittedly somewhat modified by later and minor adjustments to structure), which originated on the warped land-surface of Miocene times. It is possible to trace the approximate extent of the submergence of the Weald, in Lenhamian times, by following on a map the change from a dominantly transverse to a dominantly longitudinal drainage pattern. The recent discovery of fossiliferous 'Pliocene' deposits on the South Downs near Beachy Head is supporting evidence for the general accuracy of the reconstructed Lenhamian coastline.

A final and very important point is the fact that both the Mio-Pliocene and the 'Pliocene' erosion surfaces maintain virtually the same height above existing sea-level, within a margin of about 100 feet, when followed from Dorset to East Kent, and from the Chilterns to the South Downs, distances of 180 and 75 miles respectively. There can, therefore, have been no important subsequent transverse warping of South-East England. We shall return to this point later.

The Pliocene and early Pleistocene beds of East Anglia are known as the **Crags.** This is the local name for shelly sands and is apt enough for the lower part of the succession, which consists of sands, often current bedded, full of shells, sometimes complete, but in other layers finely comminuted. Three divisions are recognized: the **Coralline Crag,** whitish or faintly yellow in colour below; and the well-known strongly ferruginous **Red Crag** above, and to complete the succession, the more variable **Icenian Crag.** The Crags are clearly shell banks deposited in very shallow water. The Coralline Crag, except for a few tiny patches, is restricted to the neighbourhood of Aldeburgh; but the Red Crag oversteps it, and over a wide area in Suffolk, rests directly on Cretaceous or early-Tertiary beds (Fig. 120). Even when the Red Crag overlies the Coralline Crag, the junction is accompanied by marked signs of erosion, with the Red Crag sometimes banked up against low cliffs of the older division, from which boulders up to a ton in weight have fallen.

At the base of whichever Crag rests unconformably on the older rocks is the **Suffolk Bone Bed** or **Nodule Bed,** only a foot or so in thickness, but containing an extraordinary range of constituents, 'the sweepings of a land surface'. They include igneous rocks, Jurassic material, Cretaceous fossils and flints, together with septaria, molluscs and teeth of fish and land mammals from the London Clay. Much of this material is much water-worn and phosphatized and this applies also to the teeth of sharks, whales, seals and land animals, including *Mastodon,* a primitive elephant, which are probably indigenous forms. In addition the famous **Boxstones** occur in this bed—rounded cobbles of coarse brown sandstone, often containing molluscan casts. A very large fauna has been obtained from them, but nothing resembling it has been found anywhere else in the country, and at different times the Boxstones have been referred to the Oligocene, the Miocene and the Lower Pliocene.

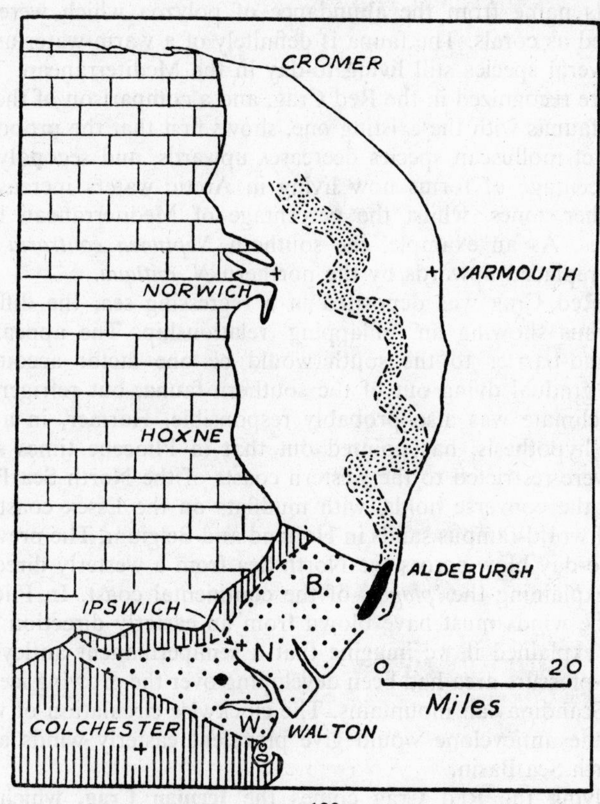


FIG. 120.

Map of the Crags of East Anglia. (*Mainly after Harmer*.)[1]
Icenian Crag, blank, with probable course of distributary, in which the Chillesford Beds were deposited, in light stipple.
Red Crag, heavy stipple. Zones are indicated by capital letters:
B. = Butleyian.
N. = Newbournian.
W. = Waltonian.
Coralline Crag, black; Eocene, vertical shading; Chalk, 'bricks'.

Their precise age is still a matter of opinion. Reference will be made in the next chapter to the 'eoliths', claimed by some as very

[1] Borings have proved the presence of Crag, probably Norwich Crag, completely hidden beneath Pleistocene deposits and occupying a considerable area to the south-west of Hoxne. See Woodland, A. W., War Time Pamphlet of Geol. Surv. No. 20. Pt. 10 (1946), Fig. 7.

primitive flint-implements, which occur in the Nodule Bed and at other horizons in the Crags.

Both these Crags are extremely fossiliferous. The Coralline Crag takes its name from the abundance of polyzoa which were first described as corals. The fauna is definitely of a warm-water aspect, with several species still living to-day in the Mediterranean. Three zones are recognized in the Red Crag, and a comparison of the successive faunas with the existing one, shows first that the proportion of extinct molluscan species decreases upwards, and secondly that the percentage of forms now living in Arctic waters increases in the higher zones, whilst the percentage of Mediterranean forms decreases. As an example, the southern *Neptunea contraria* (Fig. 121) is replaced upwards by the northern *N. antiqua*.

The Red Crag was deposited in a regressing sea, the different zones thus showing an 'offlapping' relationship. The appearance of a land-barrier to the south would be one factor accounting for the gradual dying out of the southern fauna, but refrigeration of the climate was also probably responsible. Harmer, in a very elegant hypothesis, has pointed out that in Pliocene times shelly sands were restricted to the western coasts of the North Sea Basin. To-day the converse holds, with mudflats on the Essex coast, but miles of world-famous sands in Holland and Belgium. The prevalent winds to-day blow across the North Sea from a westerly direction, hence explaining the '*plages*' of the continental coast. In Pliocene times the winds must have blown from an easterly direction. This can be explained if we imagine that a semipermanent anticyclone or high-pressure area had been developing over the growing ice-caps of the Scandinavian mountains. The clockwise circulation of winds round the anticyclone would give prevalent easterly winds across the North Sea Basin.

Overlying the Red Crag comes the **Icenian Crag,** which was deposited under different conditions. The 'Rhine-Thames' drainage system was building out a great delta into the shallow sea in which the true Crags were laid down. The basal member, the **Norwich Crag,** consisting of even-bedded, laminated sands and clays, covers large areas in Norfolk and North Suffolk. Its fauna is of a very shallow-water, marine character, and it represents the 'bottom-set' deposits laid down in front of the growing delta. The succeeding **Chillesford Beds** have a sinuous outcrop (Fig. 120) and are regarded as having been deposited in one of the distributaries of the delta, which had now encroached on to East Anglia. The very numerous flakes of mica in these beds are assumed to have been derived from the mica-schists of the Ardennes. Evidence of a slight southward advance of the sea is given by the overlying **Weybourn Crag,** which is mainly developed on the North Norfolk coast; but the presence of outlying patches shows that inlets must have extended as far as Norwich. All the divisions of the Icenian Crag yield marine fossils, with the percentage of Arctic molluscs increasing steadily upwards.

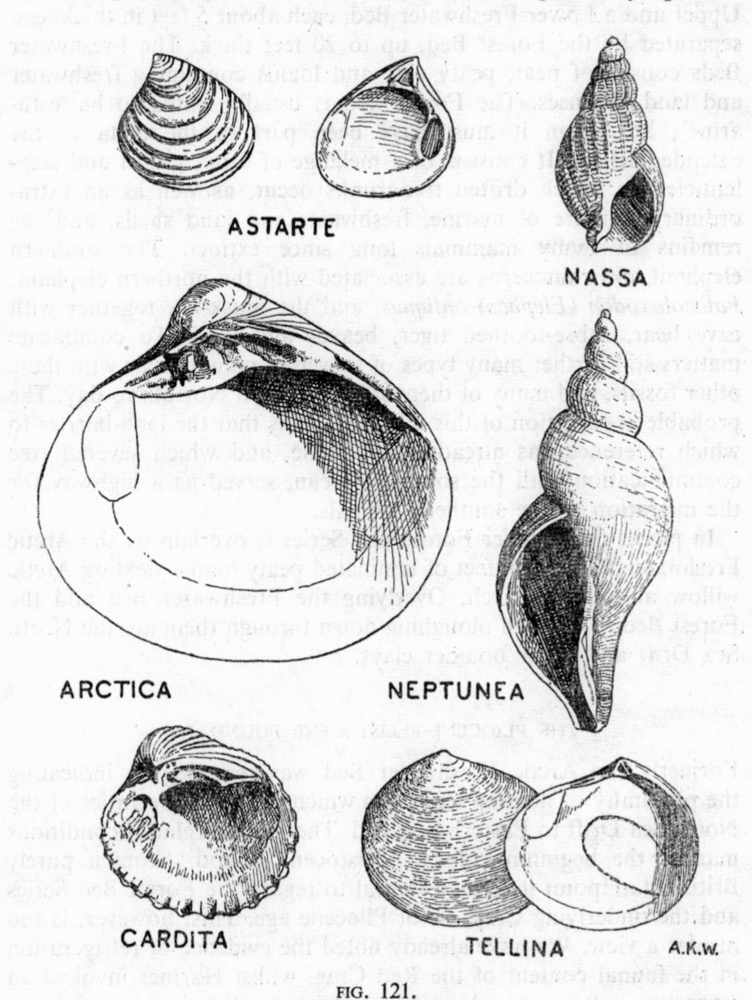


FIG. 121.
Fossils from the Pliocene:
*Astarte omalii*, Corallian Crag.
*Hinia* (*Nassa*) *reticosa*, Red Crag.
*Arctica islandica*, Coralline Crag.
*Neptunea contraria*, Waltonian Crag.
*Cardita senilis*, Coralline Crag.
*Tellina* sp., Red Crag.

The appearance of vast numbers of *Macoma balthica* in the Weybourn Crag is particularly significant.

The 'Crag' succession in Norfolk is overlain by the **Cromer Forest Bed Series,** which outcrops on the east coast and consists of an Upper and a Lower Freshwater Bed, each about 5 feet in thickness, separated by the Forest Bed, up to 20 feet thick. The Freshwater Beds consist of peat, peaty clay and loams containing freshwater and land molluscs. The Forest Bed is usually stated to be 'estuarine'; but again it must have been part of the delta of the extended Rhine. It consists of a mélange of sand, gravel and clay-lenticles, in which drifted tree-trunks occur, as well as an extraordinary mixture of marine, freshwater and land shells, and the remains of many mammals long since extinct. The southern elephant and rhinoceros are associated with the northern elephant, *Palaeoloxodon* (*Elephas*) *antiquus*, and the musk-ox, together with cave bear, sabre-toothed tiger, beaver and wolf. To complicate matters still further many types of flowering plants occur with these other fossils, and many of them still flourish in Norfolk to-day. The probable explanation of this mixed fauna is that the land-barrier to which reference has already been made, and which severed free communication with the southern ocean, served as a highway for the migration of the southern animals.

In places the Cromer Forest Bed Series is overlain by the **Arctic Freshwater Bed,** a few feet of laminated peaty loams yielding Arctic willow and Arctic birch. Overlying the Freshwater Bed and the Forest Beds and often ploughing down through them are the North Sea Drift and other boulder clays.

### THE PLIOCENE-PLEISTOCENE BOUNDARY

Formerly the Arctic Freshwater Bed was regarded as indicating the proximity of floating ice-sheets which carried the erratics of the North Sea Drift to Eastern England. The onset of glacial conditions marked the beginning of the Pleistocene Period. From a purely British standpoint it seemed logical to regard the Forest Bed Series and the underlying Crags as of Pliocene age. This, however, is too insular a view. We have already noted the evidence of refrigeration in the faunal content of the Red Crag, whilst Harmer invoked an extensive polar anticyclone to explain the lithological contrasts between the beds then being deposited in Suffolk and in Belgium. At the International Geological Congress in London in 1948, the question of the best position for the Plio-Pleistocene boundary was thoroughly considered. As is shown more fully in the following chapter, there is unquestionable evidence from many parts of the world of several glacial periods separated by interglacials. In any one region (the Alps, the United States, etc.) it can be shown that the areas covered by the boulder-clays of the different glacial periods varied considerably. It therefore follows that it is extremely unlikely that the lowest boulder-clay is everywhere of the same age. The first ice-sheet to cover Holland might not have extended to East Anglia or vice versa. If, as has been the custom in England, the base of the Pleistocene is drawn beneath the oldest definite glacial deposits of different areas there is a serious risk, indeed the very strong probability, that the base of the Pleistocene System would be strongly diachronous. It was therefore recommended that, as with other systems, the base of the Pleistocene System should be determined by palaeontological criteria. The first major advance of the ice-sheets must have caused a lowering of sea temperatures, and consequently faunal change, over very wide areas.

We have already commented on the marked change between the molluscan fauna of the Coralline Crag (with its Mediterranean affinities), and the Red Crag (showing a marked increase in Arctic forms). In Italy, richly fossiliferous marine beds (Calabrian), showing a comparable incoming of cold-type molluscs, can be traced inland into non-marine strata (Villafrancian) which have yielded many vertebrates. A striking faunal change, marked especially by the incoming of *Bos*, *Equus* and *Elephas*, occurs in the continental beds at the same horizon as the appearance of the cold-water molluscs (*Cyprina islandica*, etc.) in the offshore deposits. In East Anglia *Elephas* has been recorded from the bone-bed beneath the Red Crag and at higher levels, but not from the bone-bed underlying the Coralline Crag. There is, therefore, very strong palaeontological evidence for regarding the Coralline Crag as highest Pliocene and the Red Crag as basal Pleistocene, even though it means drawing a most important boundary, the Tertiary-Quaternary boundary, through the 'Crags', which form a distinctive rock-unit. As we have seen in numerous earlier cases time planes, which are the ideal dividing lines, do not necessarily coincide with the boundaries of rock-formations.

There is no doubt about the reality of the Lenham Beds and the widely traced surface upon which they rest; but there is difficulty in assigning them to a specific level in the stratigraphical column. The palaeontological evidence afforded by a meagre molluscan fauna is inadequate. More than half the forms recorded from Lenham itself occur also in the Coralline Crag. From sands resting on the sub-Lenham surface elsewhere fossils of Red Crag types have been obtained, and these are thought to indicate a Red Crag age. If this correlation is true, the Lenham Beds are younger in the west than in the east, and may actually transgress across the Pliocene-Pleistocene boundary. The surface itself may well be Pliocene. Until more palaeontological evidence is forthcoming, perhaps it is best to use the non-committal term 'Lenhamian', until such time as it is possible to correlate confidently both the Lenham Beds and the underlying erosion surface with the Mediterranean stages.

## REFERENCES

CURRY, D. *Proc. Geol. Assoc.*, **76** (1965), 151. The latest account, with useful diagrams, of the Eocene and Oligocene beds of the London and Hampshire Basins.

DAVIS, A. G., and ELLIOTT, G. F. *Proc. Geol. Assoc.*, **68** (1957), 255. The Palæogeography of the London Clay Sea.

DEARMAN, W. R. *Proc. Geol. Assoc.*, **74** (1963), 265. Effects of mid-Tertiary wrench-faulting in Cornwall and South Devon.

HESTER, S. W. 'Stratigraphy and Palaeogeography of the Woolwich and Reading Beds'. *Bull. Geol. Surv.*, **23** (1965), 117.

HOLLINGWORTH, S. E. *Q.J.G.S.*, **94** (1938), 55. A statistical study of the platforms of western Britain.

KING, W. B. R., and OAKLEY, K. P. *Nature*, **163** (1949), 186. Report of Committee to the XVIII International Geological Congress on the Pliocene-Pleistocene boundary. Evidence from all over Europe is discussed.

STAMP, L. D. *Geol. Mag.*, **58** (1921), 108. First application of the concept of cycles of sedimentation to the British Lower Tertiary strata.

WOOLDRIDGE, S. W. *Proc. Geol. Assoc.*, **37** (1926), 162. Earth-movements in the London Basin during Tertiary times.

WOOLDRIDGE, S. W., and LINTON, D. L. *Proc. Geol. Assoc.*, **49** (1938), 264. Structural Evolution of South-East England in post-Palæozoic times.

WOOLDRIDGE, S. W., and LINTON, D. L. *Structure, surface and drainage in South-East England* (Philips, London, 1955). The history of the area in Tertiary and Pleistocene times treated from a geomorphological aspect.

See also the appropriate *Brit. Reg. Geol.* Memoirs of the Geological Survey.

## CHAPTER XXI

# THE QUATERNARY ERA

### THE PLEISTOCENE

QUATERNARY time is usually regarded as including one complete geological Period, the *Pleistocene*, and the beginning of another, the *Holocene*. In terms of years they are the shortest of all the periods, the Holocene covering a mere 10,000 years or so, the Pleistocene something less than a million. But although the latest, they bristle with unsolved problems, more so than most other Systems. The volume of literature written on different aspects of the Pleistocene Period alone must be almost as great as that dealing with the remainder of geological time. Not only the geologist and the geomorphologist are interested: we must consider, amongst others, the meteorologist. When so many specialists are concerned, it is indeed difficult to present a comprehensive picture that pays due weight to the opinions, often controversial, advanced by experts in various branches of science—opinions which unfortunately are often restricted to one field only.

There are two main reasons for the great interest shown in the Pleistocene Period. It spanned the last great *glacial* episode in the history of the earth. As we have already seen, life evolved most rapidly under the stimulus of climatic change and *Man* is, from many points of view, the most important fossil yielded by the Pleistocene deposits.

It must be realized, however, that whilst the ice-sheets of the Pleistocene covered very considerable areas in both the Northern and the Southern Hemispheres, it is not the only glacial episode known to geologists. Indeed, evidence of an even more extensive glaciation in Permo-Carboniferous times has been described from many places in the Southern Hemisphere. Fossil glacial deposits have been claimed to occur at many other horizons as well; in some part of the world or other, from nearly every geological System. The evidence in some cases is extremely strong and irrefutable, in others very controversial. It is not appropriate here to discuss the many theories that have been advanced to account for the world-wide changes of climate that produced the Pleistocene Glaciation; but any theory that deals only with the most recent glacial episode and does not attempt to take into account, as well, the earlier and well-proven glaciations, such as the Permo-Carboniferous of the Southern Hemisphere, is surely framed on too narrow lines.

The Old Red Sandstone, the Permo-Trias, the Miocene and the Pleistocene are the four great periods of dominantly continental conditions in the British Isles. But there is a great contrast between the two former (which witnessed the wearing away of newly formed mountain-chains under relatively stable climatic conditions, comparable with those of existing deserts) and the two latter. As we have seen, the mid-Tertiary earth-movements affected only the southern part of the British Isles, and their effects, considered in terms of the production of new physical features, were slight. But during the Pleistocene Period, the present very diverse landscape was carved out of a gently undulating surface. The climate of the British Isles changed frequently from Arctic cold to conditions at least as warm as to-day. During the cold episodes, the glaciers and snow-caps were actively etching out the uplands and depositing material in the lowlands. During the warmer episodes, denudation by the normal agents, described succinctly as 'Rain and Rivers', accelerated by considerable changes in sea-level, must have been almost equally active. The debatable question as to the relative effectiveness of glacial and fluviatile erosion is more appropriately considered in geomorphological text-books. We are only concerned here with describing the final results.

We will therefore begin our description of the Pleistocene Period with a brief account of the changes it produced in the pre-Pleistocene landscape of the British Isles. We will then attempt to give a general picture of the stratigraphy of the period comparable with those given for other Systems; but it must be emphasized that the evidence on which to build it is often very scanty and at times controversial. Finally we conclude with an account of the geological history of man; for no book purporting to describe the history of some portion of the earth's surface through Palaeozoic, Mesozoic, Cainozoic and Quaternary times, that is for some 600 million years, can ignore the span of Man's existence on this planet for the last million years or so.

## 1. The Physiographic Effects of the Pleistocene Period

### (*a*) The Glaciated Uplands

In all the mountainous parts of Britain evidence of the great Ice Age is seen on every side. Great semicircular hollows with precipitous walls have been bitten deep into the hillsides. Frequently at the foot of such a **corrie** a deep rock-basin lake lies, hemmed in by a crescentic dam of rock debris. Spectacular examples occur in

Snowdonia and on both sides of the Cader Idris range in North Wales (Fig. 122) in the Lake District and in Scotland. The working back into the hillside of corries until they intersected gave rise to the steep narrow ridges known as **arêtes.** Again, many of the valleys in the uplands were already in existence in pre-Glacial times, though their final shaping was by ice, which in the course of a long tenancy modified the form in two ways: firstly, by straightening the courses of the valleys, this involving the removal of overlapping spurs; and secondly, by converting the V-shaped cross section characteristic of river action into the U-shape typical of the glaciated valley. Glen Rosie and Glen Sannox in Arran, and the Talyllyn Valley in North

FIG. 122.
Corrie on the north face of Cader Idris, North Wales.

Wales (Fig. 123), are among the best examples in this country. The extent to which ice is directly responsible for the over-deepening of main valleys is a disputed point; but the fact that many glaciated valleys are over-deepened is beyond question. The tributaries in hundreds of cases flow in open, relatively mature valleys which hang above the main valley into which the streams plunge as rapids or as actual waterfalls (Fig. 123).

Both on the hilltops and in the valleys the work of ice is proclaimed no less eloquently by the smoothed and polished rock surfaces on which the striations chiselled by hard stones frozen into the ice have stood for many thousand years, and where, protected under peat or soil, they are as clear to-day as when the ice finally retreated. Rocky crags were smoothed and modelled into 'roches moutonnées', while on the valley sides huge blocks are perched in precarious positions to which they were transported on the surface of some glacier and gently lowered into position as the ice melted. The general smoothing and shaping of the rock surfaces dates from the maximum glaciation, but some very distinctive land-forms were produced during the retreat stages. Probably corrie formation, which requires exposure of the bare rock to frost chipping and to alternating periods of freezing and thawing, was most active during the waning of the glacial conditions.

FIG. 123.
Looking down into the over-deepened Talyllyn Valley from the lower slopes of Cader Idris, North Wales.
Note the hanging tributary valley.

### (*b*) The Glaciated Lowlands

Equally characteristic land-forms were produced on the low ground by the deposition of the load carried by the glaciers. Over thousands of square miles the Tertiary and older rocks were buried beneath Pleistocene and, at first glance, the 'drift' edition of a geological map, on which the Pleistocene deposits are shown, often bears little resemblance to the 'solid' edition of the same area, on which the outcrops of the pre-Pleistocene and the Holocene rocks are depicted.

The most extensive type of 'drift' forms the great spreads of **boulder clay** that represent the ground moraines of the ice-sheets deposited on the spot when the ice melted. The boulder clay normally gives rise to a flat monotonous type of landscape, less diversified than the surface on which it rests, for it tends to thicken in the pre-Glacial valleys and to thin over the buried hills. In many parts of the country the boulder clay reaches 150 feet in thickness. It is a stiff tenacious clay which varies widely in appearance, in colour, and in the proportion of clay to imbedded stones, a very small proportion of which show the tell-tale striated facets ground smooth and scratched when frozen into the base of the ice-sheet.

The **boulder clays** contain within themselves evidence of the materials laid under contribution during their formation, and hence of the directions of ice-movement. Erratics, sometimes of enormous size and weight such that no agent other than ice could possibly have effected their transportation, are found many miles from the place where they originated and serve the same purpose. In southern Scotland a black boulder clay with Scandinavian erratics and Arctic shells picked up from the floor of the North Sea is succeeded by a red boulder clay, so coloured by the Old Red Sandstone of Strathmore, and this in turn is succeeded by a grey boulder clay from the Highlands. Thus the general characters of a boulder clay are usually sufficient to indicate the strata which have contributed to its formation; but a much higher degree of accuracy is afforded by certain **indicator erratics.** The Shap granite in Westmorland, for example, although exposed over only about a square mile, has been distributed over hundreds of square miles by the ice which carried it from the Lake District southwards into Lancashire, and eastwards via the Stainmore Pass into Yorkshire where it is distributed all down the coast. Shap granite is quite distinctive and easy to recognize even in a small pebble. Equally distinctive are the Scandinavian rocks referred to above and including the 'rhomb-porphyries', so-called on account of the characteristic shape of the cross-sections of the feldspar crystals they contain. An igneous rock of very rare type, riebeckite-microgranite, sometimes called 'paisanite', builds the small island of Ailsa Craig in the Firth of Clyde and a small hill in Snowdonia, Mynydd Mawr. Both of these rocks are most valuable indicators of the routes followed and the farthest points reached by the ice which passed over their outcrops. Deductions based on the general characters of the boulder clays and of the erratics may be confirmed by observation of the directions of glacial striations on smoothed rock surfaces, especially on the glaciated 'pavements'. The boulder clays themselves are fringed by more or less extensive sheets of sand and gravel laid down by streams issuing from the ice-front and by melt-waters. These accumulations are **outwash fans** when deposited on the land surface, and **outwash deltas** when deposited under water in glacial lakes. The surface of the outwash fan is usually irregular, hummocky and dimpled by depressions (kettle holes) often occupied by ponds and small lakes, and thought to mark the sites of large masses of ice incorporated in the gravel and subsequently melted. The outwash delta, by contrast, has typically a flat surface as it was built up to water-level; it slopes gently downwards on the side away from the ice and has a lobate front. The back of the delta on the other hand is usually very steep as it was the **ice-contact slope.**

In the temporary lakes beyond the deltas finer-grained material was deposited as well-laminated **varve clays,** often showing a beautiful seasonal banding, each pair of laminae being an annual contribution, and comprising a thin, finer and darker-coloured band formed during the dry winter period, and a thicker, coarser, lighter band deposited during the summer when melting was at a maximum. In Sweden and Finland, where these varve clays are exceptionally well developed, they have proved invaluable in deciphering the events of the last 15,000 years. Baron de Geer and his fellow-workers have been able to date in terms of years the striking geographical changes which occurred round the Baltic Sea as the ice-sheets retreated, for the last time, from the shores of south-west Sweden into the Scandinavian mountains. Unfortunately, in the British Isles varve clays are very rarely to be found and there is some doubt as to the correct position in the Scandinavian chronology of those which have been studied.

Locally the surface of the glacial deposits is much more diversified than so far described. **Terminal Moraines,** consisting of a heterogeneous mass of unsorted débris dumped by a glacier, when the ice-front remained stationary for a long period, may be studied in all the heavily glaciated uplands, for example in the Pass of Llanberis in Snowdonia and in the higher parts of the Yorkshire Dales. Such moraines often dam up lakes. Indeed most of the existing British lakes are of glacial origin and fall into two chief categories: some occupy hollows scooped out by the ice; others lie in glaciated valleys behind a dam of glacial drift. In the Lake District, Haweswater is a rock-basin lake, and an example of the first type, while Ennerdale Water is a drift-dammed lake. Corrie lakes of much smaller size really fall into an intermediate class, for they occupy rock-basins, but most, like Llyn-y-Gader on Cader Idris, are moraine-dammed in addition.

Terminal moraines also occur, more locally, on the low ground. Two particularly good examples are the crescentic ridge, crossing the valley of the Ouse, on which York is built (the York moraine), and the prominent ridge immediately to the south of Cromer on the North Norfolk coast (the Cromer moraine).

Another of the most characteristic of the glacial land-forms is the **drumlin**—an Irish term signifying a little hill. Of an elongated egg-like shape in plan, drumlins are usually steeper at the one end than the other (Fig. 124). They were moulded from boulder clay by the ice and, as might be expected, their longer axes lie parallel to the direction of ice-movement to which the steeper end of the drumlin was opposed: this is the opposite to the arrangement in 'roches moutonnées' (Fig. 124). In the latter case the end directed up-stream is gentler than the downstream end, which is often very steep and irregular on account of plucking—the removal from the downstream end of blocks of the solid rock, bounded by joints and fractures, that became frozen into the base of the ice-sheet. Drumlins often occur in groups of rounded grass-covered hills forming the distinctive 'basket-of-eggs topography' so well displayed in Co. Down and other Irish localities. Typical examples occur also in the valley of the Tweed, in the Lake District, in Wensleydale, in

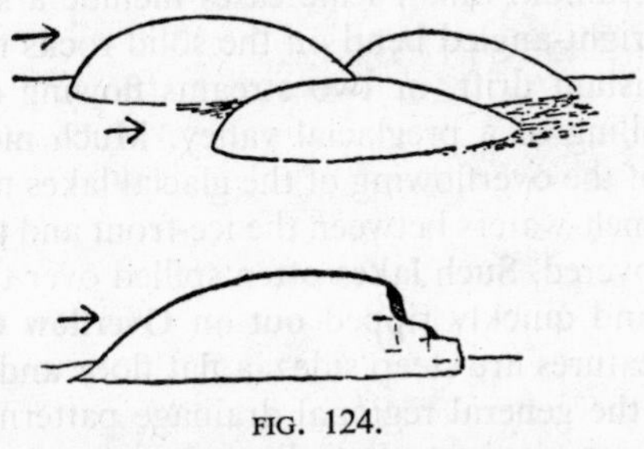

FIG. 124.

Drumlins, the ideal form; and below, a roche moutonnée plucked at the downstream end. The arrows show the direction of ice-movement.

Stainmore and west of Skipton in Yorkshire and elsewhere. They are invaluable to the glaciologist as providing useful evidence of the direction of ice-movement.

More rarely found are **eskers,** sinuous ridges of gravel and sand, trending at right angles to the ice-front and representing either the infilling of tunnels at the bottom of the glacier, or the fans or deltas built at the points of emergence of such subglacial streams from beneath a rapidly retreating glacier. A chain of typical eskers can be studied to the north-west of Wolverhampton. Of different orientation are **kames.** They are ridges of sand and gravel, *not* boulder clay, lying roughly parallel to the ice margin and in most cases they represent confluent fans or deltas of a number of closely spaced subglacial streams. A particularly good example occurs at Carstairs in South Scotland.

As a result of the accumulation of these several types of drift the surface area of the British Isles in relation to the present sea-level was considerably increased. Over wide areas, notably in East Anglia and eastern Yorkshire, the top of the 'solid' rocks is below sea-level, the existing land-surface being entirely composed of 'drift' deposits. Indeed it has been shown that about one-eleventh of England and Wales would be flooded by the sea if the Pleistocene deposits were to be suddenly removed.

One very important effect of the glaciation was the modification of drainage that it produced. The pre-Pleistocene land-surface was largely buried beneath a mantle of drift. As the ice-sheets retreated, the courses of the streams would be determined by the irregularities in relief and composition of the drift surface. Where the drift was thin and incoherent, it would be quickly removed and the streams would rediscover their preglacial courses; but where the drift was exceptionally thick or tenacious, the rivers might find it easier to cut new channels. In all the glaciated areas examples of glacial diversion are common. Small-scale cases include a stream taking a sudden double right-angled bend on the solid rocks round a plug of particularly resistant drift, or two streams flowing down the sides of the drift infilling of a preglacial valley. Much more spectacular are the results of the overflowing of the glacial lakes produced by the ponding-up of melt-waters between the ice-front and the high ground no longer ice covered. Such lakes often spilled over the lowest point of the barrier and quickly ripped out an **Overflow Channel,** whose characteristic features are steep sides, a flat floor and the absence of relationship to the general regional drainage pattern. Once cut, the river tended to remain in such a channel.

A classic example of modification of drainage is the diversion of the River Severn, which in preglacial times flowed into the Irish Sea instead of, as now, into the Bristol Channel. Professor L. J. Wills has shown that the Dee in preglacial times followed a course much the same as its present one through Wales to the place near Llangollen where it breaks through the barrier formed by the Carboniferous Limestone and the Millstone Grit. From this point it formerly swept in a wide curve southwards, eastwards and finally northwards to Bangor-on-Dee, collecting *en route* as tributaries the Ceiriog and the Severn. The Irish Sea ice-sheet, described below, when shrinking northwards, impounded melt-water between the ice-front and the high ground near Bridgnorth, bringing into existence an extensive sheet of water, 'Lake Lapworth', the shores of which lie at about 300 feet O.D., and are clearly seen in a number of localities in the Midlands, though not so well displayed as the successive strand lines of the glacial lake that formerly occupied Glen Roy in Scotland. The overflow from Lake Lapworth ripped out the Ironbridge Gorge into which the Severn was directed when its northern course was blocked by drift. Similarly the Dee was itself diverted into the straight course which it now follows north-eastwards from Llangollen to Bangor-on-Dee. At other points farther up the valley the Dee was diverted through overflow channels which cut across the chords of meanders, thus shortening and straightening the course of the river which now flows through the Berwyn Hills in exceedingly beautiful gorges.

### (*c*) The Periglacial Areas

The most southerly part of Britain lay beyond the limits of the ice-sheets though there is clear evidence that the hills were snow-capped, as might be expected. The limits of the ice-sheets coincided roughly with a line joining the estuaries of the Thames and Severn. In general, the escarpments of the Cotswolds and the Chilterns acted as fenders holding back the ice which piled up behind these barriers, in the latter case to a height of over 400 feet. Some of the gaps through the escarpments were already in existence and through these the ice pressed: through the Stevenage gap, for example, giving access to the low-lying Vale of St Albans behind the escarpment. East of Hitchin the Chalk escarpment is lower and the ineffective barrier was overriden by the ice, which advanced down the dip-slope of the Chalk into the Tertiary uplands where it sent lobes down the valleys now occupied by the tributaries of the Thames, the Lea and Roding, and also into the 'Finchley depression', which is referred to later (Fig. 127).

The distinctive topographical features of the Chalk-lands beyond the ice margin were developed during the Pleistocene Period, but there has been much discussion as to the mode of origin of the **coombes** and the **dry valleys.** Some of the coombes, which cut back into the scarp slopes, are closely similar to corries in all but size, and there is no doubt that they were formed by frost-chipping working back into snow-filled hollows on the hillside. Others resemble overflow channels in form but strike into the hillsides and end blindly in a steep face like the back wall of a corrie. A series of such coombes festoons the South Downs, a striking example being the Devil's Dyke near Lewes, while other good examples occur near Ivinghoe in the Chiltern Hills. According to one view such features were produced by the sapping back of particularly powerful scarp-foot springs. This must have been an important factor in the formation of many of the smaller coombes, for springs must have been flowing much more vigorously during periods of thaw than they do to-day. It is inadequate, however, to account for the largest coombes like the Devil's Dyke. They may have been initiated by spring action, but the main cause that sculptured them must have been the melting of snow caps and névé fields on the hills at their heads. The great quantities of water released must have ripped out these huge gashes into the hillsides—gashes which in cross-section have much the same shape as the unquestioned overflow channel.

Equally characteristic of the Chalk-lands are the **dry valleys** furrowing the dip-slopes. According to one theory they are the products of streams flowing over a surface of frozen Chalk, which would then behave as an impervious rock owing to the joints being sealed with ice. Such conditions must have prevailed for long periods during the glacial episodes. Then the climate of southern England must have been very similar to that of the tundra regions of northern Siberia and Canada to-day, with the soil permanently frozen to a considerable depth, but with the upper few inches thawing out during the summer months. The deposits which are produced under such conditions will be referred to later. But these valleys, which show every sign of having been originally shaped by flowing streams, may have become dry owing to a drop in the water-table, due either to a marked decrease in precipitation, or to the recession of the escarpments and the down-cutting of the main river valleys. The first cause is very difficult of proof; the reality of the second has been demonstrated in the Limpsfield area on the Kent-Surrey border. There it has been shown that the Chalk escarpment has receded northwards for about two miles since the middle of the Pleistocene Period. The level of the water-table beneath the dip-slope is controlled by the height of the spring line on the scarp face. If the latter is worn back down-dip, the height of the spring line must fall and so will the level of the water-table on the dip-slope, with the result that valleys once occupied by flowing streams become at first 'bourne' valleys with springs breaking out only during seasons of abnormally heavy rain, and presently even these fail and the valleys become entirely dry. In the interior of the Chalk down-lands the height of the water-table is controlled largely by the level of the major river valleys. Periods of vigorous downcutting by the rivers will therefore produce a steady lowering of the water-table with the results given above.

In recent years it has been increasingly recognized that the drift deposits of the periglacial areas are just as characteristic and afford just as good evidence of past climatic conditions as does the boulder clay of the glaciated regions. Over large parts of the unglaciated south and to a less extent the glaciated north of England, occur great spreads of unstratified or very poorly stratified drift. The constituents are all of local origin and may be angular, subangular or rounded. These deposits sometimes mantle the high ground, elsewhere they occur on slopes or in the valleys. In the past they have been given a variety of names, such as 'Coombe Rock' in certain Chalk areas, 'Pebbly Clay and Sand' in the Chilterns, 'Head' in Cornwall and 'Angular Chert Drift' on some of the Greensands—names in many cases intended merely to bring out the salient lithological features of the drift. The general name **'Head'** has been suggested to include all deposits of this type and, in future, they are to be depicted, where possible, on the maps of the Geological Survey. These Head deposits must have been formed under tundra conditions by what is called **solifluxion,** that is, the bodily flow, down quite gentle slopes, of the surface layers of the soil, when oversaturated with melt-water from ice and snow. Under such conditions there will be repeated freezing and thawing of the top-soil with considerable volume changes of the various constituents. Deposits, identical with Head in all details of mass composition and structure have been described from the periglacial areas of to-day—that is, from Greenland, Spitzbergen, etc.

The spectacular upstanding isolated tors of the granite areas of South-West England and of the gritstone ridges of the Pennines were most probably developed by the combination of frost action on well-jointed and resistant bed-rock and the removal by solifluxion of the weathered material under wet periglacial climatic conditions.

Another feature of the periglacial areas (particularly of the scarplands of southern England) is the widespread development of landslipping, cambering and other kinds of superficial structures (see p. 356). Such movements cannot be dated with any degree of precision, but many of the landslipped masses must be of considerable antiquity, for the scarp behind them has receded several hundreds of yards since the time of slipping.

To-day the tundras of northern Siberia merge southwards into the arid steppes of northern Mongolia, where wind erosion is dominant and great sheets of **loess** have accumulated. On the Continent a broad belt of loess, lying in the main to the south of the great terminal moraines, stretches westwards from southern Russia across southern and central Germany into northern France. Unquestioned loess has not yet been described from the British Isles, but much of the fine-grained and structureless 'Brick-earth' of southern England is probably of aeolian origin, whilst at a number of localities dreikanter pebbles have been found lying either on the surface of the ground or just beneath it.

Boulder Clay is the product of ground moraine, Head was formed just south of the ice-sheets, loess was laid down still farther south. If, then, in a section one finds, as is often the case on the continent of North-West Europe, a deposit of loess separating two boulder clays, one has evidence of considerable oscillation of the ice margin and of the climatic belts.

Our knowledge of the deposits of the warm interglacial periods is much more scanty, but this is not surprising. An ice-sheet advancing over a countryside will incorporate in its ground moraine any unconsolidated material and, depending on the momentum of the glaciers, much that is consolidated. It is only in specially sheltered areas, such as lake basins, to be described later, that the deposits of an interglacial period may escape the effects of the next advance of the glaciers. In periglacial areas also, the interglacial deposits would tend to be incorporated in the next phase of solifluxion, except where they were exceptionally thick, as were the sands and gravels laid down along the river courses and now, owing to changes in sea-level, forming river terraces.

But it is to the interglacial periods that we must ascribe much of the vast amount of erosion that has taken place in post-Eocene times in the upland areas of Britain. In Scotland, for example, in the Western Isles and the adjacent parts of the mainland, not only have 6000 feet of basaltic lavas been locally completely destroyed, but the underlying plutonic complexes have been so deeply dissected as to expose their roots. It would be futile to claim the whole of this erosion as Pleistocene Interglacial, for the Oligocene, Miocene and Pliocene Periods were also available; but one naturally turns to the Pleistocene with its succession of drastic climatic changes, and particularly to these periods when normal erosion was able to bite quickly into mountains deeply riven by the action of frost and thaw at the close of a glacial episode.

### (*d*) Raised Beaches, River Terraces and Submerged Forests

Raised beaches at several different heights above present sea-level occur along certain stretches of our coastline, and are specially well developed in Scotland at heights of 100, 75, 50 and 25 feet. In southern England and the Channel Islands the most prominent is probably the 25-foot Raised Beach. Submerged Forests are laid bare at exceptionally low tides at many places round our coasts, notably on both shores of the Bristol Channel, and in the English Channel at Hastings, Bexhill and Dover.

Raised beaches and submerged forests have this in common: both resulted from relative changes of sea-level—in the former case a relative rise, and in the latter, a fall. A rising sea-level might be brought about by an increase in the volume of oceanic water; or conceivably by down-warping of the earth's crust due to ice-loading. In the former case the rise would be world-wide or **eustatic**; in the latter case it would be local and practically restricted to the area of the ice-sheets. If eustatic changes of sea-level alone were involved, obviously a high sea-level would imply inter-glacial conditions, and conversely, a low sea-level would correspond with glaciation. This, however, is doubtful, for the submerged forests spread far into regions previously glaciated and are thus demonstrably not glacial. It is tempting to argue, therefore, that periods of high sea-level correspond with glaciation, the highest raised beach correlating with the maximum glaciation, when the ice was thickest and weighed most heavily upon the crust. This is the generally accepted view; but it should be realized that although the phenomena may conveniently be explained as due to crustal warping consequent on ice-loading followed by elastic recovery when the ice melted, this is *not* the whole story, for it does not give adequate consideration to eustatic changes of sea-level.

The alternate freezing up of vast quantities of water to form the ice-sheets, and the subsequent melting during the interglacial periods and when the Glacial Period finally passed, must have been at least in part the cause of the changes in the relative levels of sea and land that constitute the lower treads of the chronological staircase.

It appears that the changes whose effects are so strikingly shown by the phenomena of raised beaches, river terraces and submerged forests were brought about by the interaction of two chief factors which worked in opposition to one another. The facts may be illustrated by reference to two regions, the Thames Valley and southern Scotland. In immediately preglacial times[1] the land must have stood higher, in places considerably higher than at present—or alternatively the sea stood much lower, for the solid rock is encountered under drift at a depth of 300 to 400 feet below present sea-level in the Firths of Forth and Clyde. Farther south along the English coastline the glacial deposits are thick and preglacial valleys with floors at 140 feet below O.D. have been proved by borings. In the London Basin, on the other hand, the preglacial valleys are but slightly entrenched in the 200-foot platform and their floors lie well above sea-level (Fig. 131). Scotland was then loaded with ice to a thickness of several thousand feet, and to redress the balance the land was depressed until the **100-foot Raised Beach** stood at sea-level. It stood at this level sufficiently long for a flat beach to be developed, while varve clays were deposited in the estuaries of the larger rivers. So the 100-foot Raised Beach came into being. Examination of the varve clays has led to the conclusion that it dates from a period about 13,000 years ago and is a late-Glacial feature (Fig. 125). Other less well-developed raised beaches can be traced at 75 and 50 feet above O.D., and represent periods of still-stand during a gradual elevation of the land, some believe due to the

[1] The term 'preglacial' used loosely means the period before the earliest glaciation in any particular area; it does not necessarily mean 'pre-Pleistocene.'

removal by melting of the ice-sheets. This elevation ceased during a period of much milder climatic conditions when the coastal regions were heavily covered with forests of hazel, birch and alder which gradually extended northwards well into the region of maximum glaciation, only to be submerged to a depth of 25 to 30 feet below present O.D. At this level the sea proceeded to cut another bench backed by the remains of sea-cliffs and sea-caves. This is seen to-day as the '25-foot Raised Beach'. Sand and shingle resting on this beach contain an abundant molluscan fauna, including living species of cockles, mussels and oysters together with the remains of seals and whales, the stone implements of early Neolithic (Azilian) man and heaps of shells used in his 'kitchens'. In de Geer's time-scale the 25-foot Raised Beach dates back to 6000 years ago, that is, to a period long after the close of the Pleistocene Period.

In southern England raised beaches are to be seen at a few localities only. Along the Sussex coast, there are two raised beaches: a higher one, the Goodwood Beach, at a height of around 100 feet O.D., and a lower, Brighton Beach, at about 25 feet O.D. In each case the gravels and sands of the beach are overlain by thick Coombe Rock (Head) and therefore both beaches must be older than the last phase of periglacial conditions. In Scotland the raised beach at the same level is demonstrably much younger as it cuts into, and is therefore younger than, the latest boulder clay (Fig. 125). The age difference may be of the order of 200,000 years.

The Boyn Hill Terrace, often called the 100-foot Terrace of the Thames, is graded to the 100-foot Raised Beach of southern England; both date from the period of high sea-level, resulting from the melting of the ice-sheets during the Great Interglacial period.

At first sight it appears anomalous that the submerged forests round the coasts of both Scotland and England are of the same age; but the probable explanation is that crustal warping due to ice-loading and unloading was no longer a factor in producing changes in sea-level. Both the submerged forests and the ensuing 25-foot Raised Beach are almost certainly the effects of eustatic movements.

## 2. The Geological History of the Pleistocene

The details of the geological history of the Pleistocene Period are still being unravelled. Some areas, such as East Anglia and parts of the Thames Valley, have been studied in great detail by many workers; other areas are almost *terra incognita*, as regards their drift deposits. It is impossible, on the basis of existing knowledge, to produce anything but a very small-scale map of the Pleistocene deposits of Britain, for over considerable areas the drift deposits have never been surveyed. Even in the most thoroughly studied areas there is no unanimity as to the geological history, and correlation of the deposits in different parts of the country is still more a matter of opinion. This is due partly to the many and diverse lines of evidence which have to be woven together to give the final complete pattern, and partly to the fact that, in the glaciated areas, each advance of the ice and to a lesser extent, in the periglacial areas, each phase of solifluxion, was likely to incorporate and hence obliterate, any unconsolidated drift lying on the land surface.

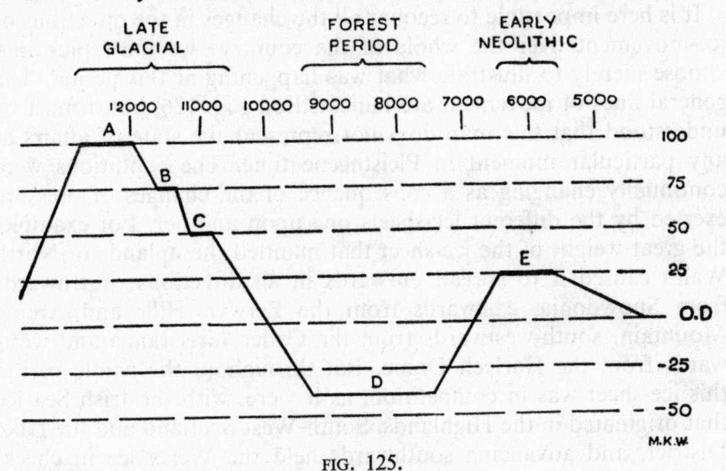


FIG. 125.

Diagram showing the altitudes and chronology of the raised beaches and submerged forest in Scotland.

A. 100-foot raised beach.
B. 75-foot raised beach.
C. 50-foot raised beach.
D. Submerged forest.
E. 25-foot raised beach.

(*After M. and A. Macgregor, in 'Midland Valley of Scotland,' British Regional Geology.*)

In the midst of much uncertainty and difference of opinion on the part of experts, this much at least is certain: in each glaciated area investigated more than one glaciation can be traced. It is impossible in an account of this length to discuss all the conflicting views, especially as regards the correlation of events in the glaciated and the unglaciated areas. The account given below of the sequence of events in certain selected areas will, we know, not find general agreement, but neither does any other known to us. We have tried to paint what seems to us to be a connected picture on the basis of existing knowledge. In doing so, for reasons of both brevity and clearness, we have had to avoid discussing many controversial points, but we are fully conscious of their existence.

As might be expected, each of the existing upland areas in Britain was a centre of ice-dispersal from which the ice-sheets tended to move radially outwards. This is true of the Highlands and the Southern Uplands of Scotland, the Lake District, North Wales and the Black Mountains in mid-South Wales. In addition, the North Sea Basin was occupied by the North Sea ice-sheet, fed mainly by the névé fields of Scandinavia and probably in part floating, as is the Great Ross Barrier in Antarctica to-day.

It is here impossible to recount all the changes in the directions of ice-movement over the whole of the country: we must pick and choose merely to illustrate what was happening at this period. The general lines of movement are indicated on Fig. 126, but it must be understood that this map does not represent the state of affairs at any particular moment in Pleistocene time. The conditions were continually changing as a consequence of the changes of pressure exerted by the different ice-sheets one upon another. For example, the great weight of the ice-sheet that mantled the uplands of North Wales caused it to spread outwards in all directions; northwards from Snowdonia, eastwards from the Berwyn Hills and Arenig Mountain, south-westwards from the Cader Idris range and westwards from the Harlech Dome. But throughout the whole period this ice-sheet was in competition, as it were, with the Irish Sea ice that originated in the Highlands, South-West Scotland and the Lake District, and advancing southwards held the Welsh ice in check. At one period it prevailed to such an extent that shell-laden sand from the floor of the Irish Sea and frozen into the base of the ice-sheet was pushed far up the flanks of the Welsh hills. On Moel Tryfaen, north of Snowdon, these fossiliferous sands (the so-called Shelly Drift) are found as high as 1400 feet above sea-level, also at high levels on the hills near Harlech and at 1000 feet O.D. near Oswestry on the *east* side of the Welsh mountains. On this side the Irish Sea ice advanced as far south as the Longmynd, leaving behind on its retreat a trail of erratics from the Southern Uplands (the Galloway granites), from Ailsa Craig (riebeckite-microgranite) and the Lake District (various well-known igneous rocks). Some particularly interesting conclusions have been drawn by Dr E. Greenly from a study of the erratics in Anglesey where the Drift, in addition to the above, yields debris derived from the Chalk, iron-shot oolite from the Jurassic, red sandstones and green marls containing rock-salt 'pseudomorphs' and dreikanters, obviously derived from the Trias. Taking into consideration the direction of movement of the ice as evidenced by glacial striae, Greenly concludes that the sea-floor north-east of Anglesey must consist in part of Cretaceous and Jurassic rocks.

It is often convenient to draw a distinction between the 'Newer' and the 'Older' Drifts. In the 'Newer Drift' areas of much of Wales, northern England and Scotland, the moraines, eskers, kames, drumlins, overflow channels and the like are beautifully fresh

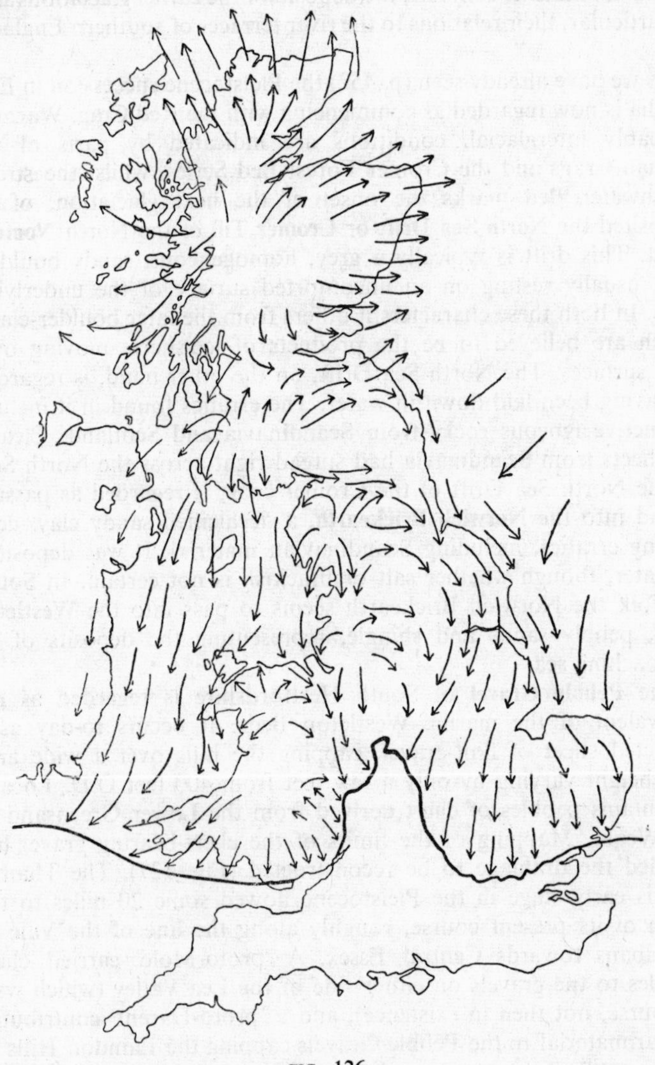

FIG. 126.
Sketch-map showing generalised directions of ice-flow during the Quaternary glaciation.
(*From various sources.*)

land-forms; they were clearly formed during the retreat phases of the last glaciation. In the 'Older Drift' areas of East Anglia and most of the Midlands, the land-forms are much more degraded. This adds to the difficulties of interpreting them, but it is only in such areas that one can study the deposits of the earlier glaciations and, in particular, their relations to the river terraces of southern England.

As we have already seen (p. 452) the Pleistocene succession in East Anglia is now regarded as commencing with the Red Crag. Warmer, probably interglacial, conditions are indicated by parts of the Icenian Crags and the Cromer Forest Bed Series, whilst the Arctic Freshwater Bed marks the onset of the next glaciation, which deposited the **North Sea Drift** or **Cromer Till** of the North Norfolk coast. This drift is typically a grey, homogeneous, sandy boulder-clay, usually resting on an uncontorted surface of the underlying beds. In both these characters it differs from the later boulder-clays, which are believed to be the products of ice-sheets moving over land surfaces. The North Sea Drift, on the other hand, is regarded as having been laid down in water. The erratics found in it include distinctive igneous rocks from Scandinavia and Scotland. Clearly ice-sheets from Scandinavia had spread right across the North Sea.

The North Sea Drift of the Cromer coast is regarded as passing inland into the **Norwich Brickearth,** a decalcified sandy clay, containing erratics, including Scandinavian material. It was deposited in water, though whether salt or brackish is not certain. In South Norfolk the Norwich Brickearth seems to pass into the **Westleton Beds,** pebbly sands and shingle, representing the deposits of an encroaching sea.

The **Pebble Gravel** of South Hertfordshire is regarded as the equivalent of the marine Westleton Beds. It occurs to-day as a dissected sheet of flint-gravel, capping the hills over a wide area at a height varying by only a few feet from 400 feet O.D. Locally it contains pebbles of chert derived from the Lower Greensand of the Weald. Mapping of the limits of the chert-bearing gravel has enabled the drainage to be reconstructed (Fig. 127). The Thames at this early stage in the Pleistocene flowed some 20 miles to the north of its present course, roughly along the line of the Vale of St Albans towards Central Essex. A 'proto-Mole' carried chert pebbles to the gravels on either side of the Lea Valley (which was, of course, not then in existence), and a 'proto-Darent' contributed similar material to the Pebble Gravels capping the Laindon Hills in south-east Essex. Apart from the two narrow belts, aligned north-east to south-west, the Pebble Gravel is devoid of chert pebbles.

In places on the dip-slope of the Chiltern Hills and on hill-tops in

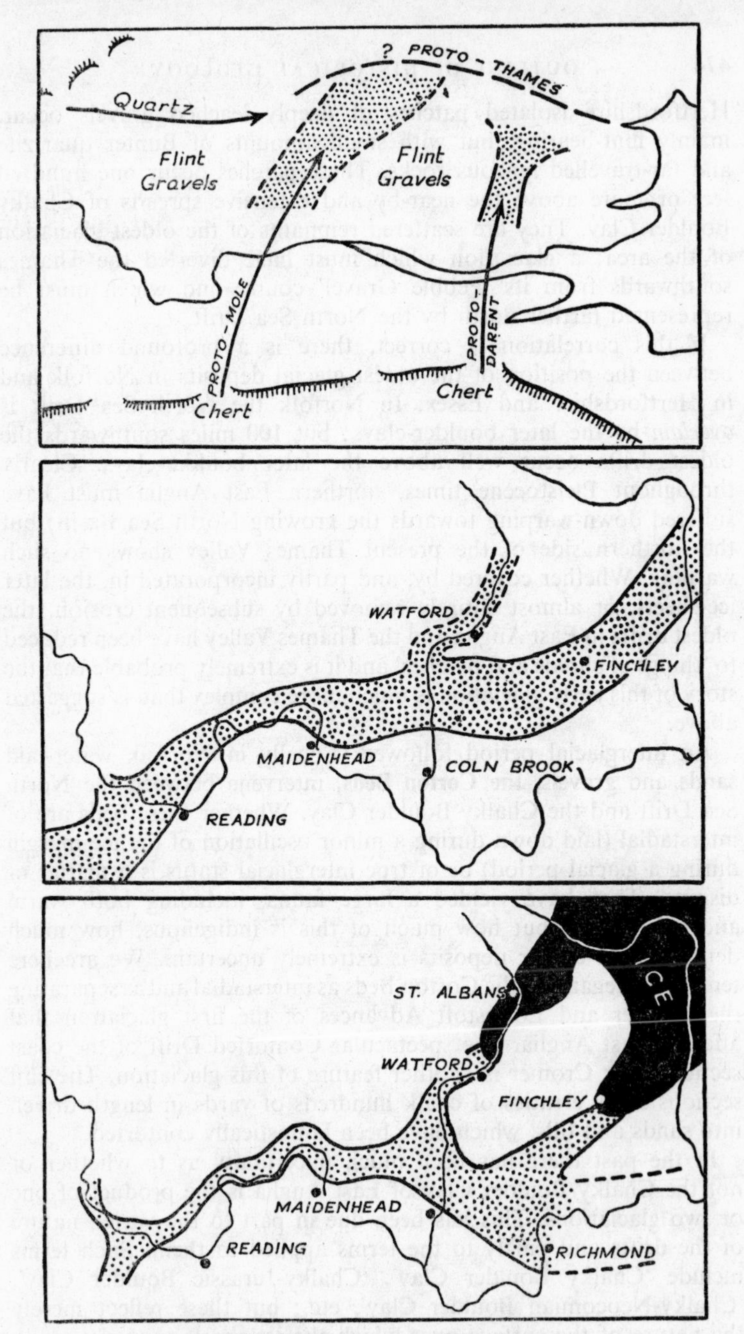


FIG. 127.—Former courses of the Thames.

*Above*—At time of Pebble Gravel phase. Belts of chert-bearing gravel stippled.
*Middle*—In pre-Chalky Boulder Clay times. Probable flood-plain stippled.
*Lower*—Southward deflection consequent on advance of the Great Chalky Boulder Clay ice-sheet.

(*After S. W. Wooldridge.*)

Hertfordshire isolated patches of deeply leached gravels occur, mainly flint-bearing, but with small amounts of Bunter quartzite and far-travelled igneous rocks. These patches occur one hundred feet or more above the near-by and extensive spreads of Chalky Boulder Clay. They are scattered remnants of the oldest glaciation of the area; a glaciation which must have diverted the Thames southwards from its 'Pebble Gravel' course and which must be represented farther north by the North Sea Drift.

If this correlation is correct, there is a profound difference between the position of the oldest glacial deposits in Norfolk and in Hertfordshire and Essex. In Norfolk the North Sea Drift is *overlain* by the later boulder-clays; but 100 miles southwards the oldest drifts occur well above the later boulder-clays. Clearly throughout Pleistocene times, northern East Anglia must have suffered down-warping towards the growing North Sea Basin; but the northern side of the present Thames Valley shows no such warping. Whether covered by, and partly incorporated in, the later ice-sheets, or almost entirely removed by subsequent erosion, the oldest drifts in East Anglia and the Thames Valley have been reduced to 'things of shreds and patches' and it is extremely probable that the story of this early glaciation is much more complex than is suggested above.

An interglacial period followed. Locally in Norfolk water-laid sands and gravels, the **Corton Beds,** intervene between the North Sea Drift and the Chalky Boulder Clay. Whether these beds are of interstadial (laid down during a minor oscillation of the ice margin during a glacial period) or of true interglacial status is a matter of dispute. They have yielded a large fauna, including both warm and cold forms, but how much of this is indigenous, how much derived from earlier deposits is extremely uncertain. We are here tentatively regarding the Corton Beds as interstadial and as separating the Cromer and Lowestoft Advances of the first glaciation that affected East Anglia. The spectacular Contorted Drift of the coast sections near Cromer is another feature of this glaciation. The cliff sections show erratics of chalk hundreds of yards in length driven into sands and tills, which have been fantastically contorted.

In the past there has been much uncertainty as to whether or not the Chalky Boulder Clay of East Anglia is the product of one or two glaciations. This has been due in part to the varied nature of the drifts and partly to the terms applied to them. Such terms include 'Chalky Boulder Clay', 'Chalky-Jurassic Boulder Clay', 'Chalky-Neocomian Boulder Clay', etc.; but these reflect merely the nature of the surface over which the ice-sheets moved and do not necessarily indicate an age-difference. In recent years, however, more and more convincing evidence has been presented to prove that the Chalky Boulder Clay as a whole is the product of *two* separate glaciations. These have been named the **Lowestoft** and the **Gipping** glaciation respectively, following normal geological practice, after type-areas.[1] Such terms as 'Chalky-Jurassic Boulder Clay' can therefore be used as purely lithological terms to describe the relevant parts of either the Lowestoft or the Gipping drift.

Studies of the erratic-content of the tills and also of the long-axis orientation of the stones have enabled the paths of the respective ice-sheets to be reconstructed with considerable confidence (Fig. 128). The fact that the direction of stone orientation is the same in the Cromer and Lowestoft tills suggests that the Corton Beds represent an interstadial rather than an interglacial period.

The Lowestoft ice-sheets advanced into East Anglia from a north-westerly or even westerly direction. In northern Norfolk as the ice was moving from Lincolnshire the Lowestoft boulder-clays are therefore very chalky; but farther southwards they pass into 'Chalky-Jurassic' drift brought by ice travelling across the wide Jurassic outcrops to the south of the Fens.

The Gipping ice-sheets, on the other hand, moving on a more direct course from the north, deposited Chalky drift along the Norfolk-Suffolk border, on top of the Chalky-Jurassic drift of the Lowestoft glaciation. The Gipping ice-sheets do not seem to have covered eastern Norfolk: the boulder-clays there, whether of Chalky or Chalky-Jurassic content, are all of 'Lowestoftian' age.

In many areas the advancing Gipping ice-sheets seem to have removed any interglacial deposits which may have accumulated during the Lowestoft-Gipping interglacial. In sections near Ipswich, for example, the pale-coloured Gipping boulder-clay rests with a very sharp junction on the darker coloured Chalky-Jurassic Lowestoft boulder-clay. But in a few hollows on the surface of the Lowestoft drift, interglacial lacustrine deposits have been preserved. The most famous of these lake-basins is the **Hoxne,** near Diss, on the Suffolk-Norfolk border.

These Hoxne interglacial beds have been recently studied (1956) and very interesting results have been achieved by pollen analysis. By suitable techniques the pollen in the different layers has been isolated and the different kinds of pollen grains have been identified and counted. By such 'palynological' methods it is possible to infer climatic conditions, for the pollen-content of any one layer

[1] There are obvious objections to this usage: place-names, unmodified, cannot be satisfactorily used in a time sense. To the ordinary reader 'Lowestoft drift' means 'the drift at Lowestoft.' 'Lowestoftian' and 'Gippingian' are preferable terms or even C-B-C(1) and C-B-C(2). A.K.W.

reflects the nature of the contemporary flora. The lowest lacustrine muds in the Hoxne succession yield Sea Buckthorn in abundance,

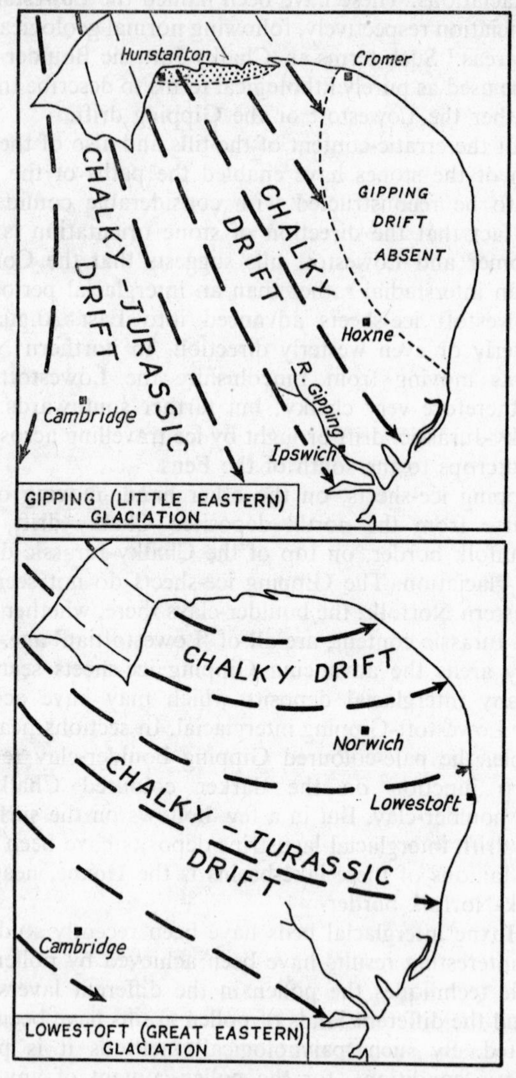


FIG. 128.

Sketch-maps showing variation in erratic-content (and hence directions of ice-movement) in the 'Chalky Boulder Clays' of East Anglia.
The area occupied by the Hunstanton Boulder Clay is stippled on the upper diagram.

*(After D. F. W. Baden-Powell, R. G. West and J. J. Donner.)*

associated with small amounts of birch. This represents a scrub vegetation with scattered clumps of trees, and is a typical late-Glacial flora. The proportion of tree-pollen increases upwards through the incoming first of pine, then at higher levels, of oak, elm and hazel. This pollen sequence indicates an amelioration of climatic conditions culminating in the mild and oceanic conditions required by a 'mixed-oak' forest. At higher levels still there is evidence of a recrudescence of cold conditions: the pollen of the 'mixed-oak' forest gradually diminishes, while that of birch and pine become dominant. Man-made implements of Acheulian type (see Fig. 132) have been obtained from the layers with a high birch-pine pollen content, proving that man was living on the margins of the lake-basin under climatic conditions similar to those now prevailing in northern Scandinavia. The highest lacustrine muds yield pollen of arctic willow and dwarf arctic birch (*Betula nana*) only. This is a typical tundra flora. Overlying these lacustrine muds are disturbed periglacial deposits which indicate the approach of the Gippingian ice-sheets. Thus the evidence of the successive floras, as indicated by pollen counts, presents a singularly clear picture of the advent and departure of an interglacial episode between two cold periods.

All the glacial deposits discussed above belong to the Older Drift. In East Anglia the Newer Drift is found only in the extreme North of Norfolk. A few feet above present sea-level, occurs a distinctive brown boulder clay, the **Hunstanton Boulder Clay,** containing erratics derived from the Cheviot Hills, but practically no Chalk. It is correlated with the lithologically similar **Hessle Boulder Clay** of the Lincolnshire and Yorkshire coasts. Its erratic-content shows that it had been brought in by ice moving from a northerly direction; and it is probable that at this period the edge of the Scandinavian ice-sheet, lying a short distance to the east of the present coast, had deflected southwards the ice-stream flowing out from the hills and mountains of northern Britain.

So far we have concentrated on establishing the Pleistocene chronology for East Anglia. Before dealing with other parts of Britain, it will be well to refer briefly to some wider aspects of correlation. In the early part of this century, Penck and Brückner in classic work on the Eastern Alps established the following sequence of glaciations separated by interglacial periods:

4. Würm.
3. Riss.

Great Interglacial.

2. Mindel.
1. Gunz.

Many workers have attempted to apply this fourfold scheme to Britain; but is it safe to say that no two have agreed in detail on the same correlation table, especially as regards the older, and therefore more fragmentary, drifts. In recent years, however, there has been an increasing tendency to attempt correlation with the sequence of events that has been worked out in Holland and Germany. This sequence comprises three glaciations, separated by interglacial periods which are represented near the coast by marine deposits, and inland by lake beds, sands and gravels, containing molluscs, plants and vertebrates indicating warm conditions. The full sequence is:

5. Weichsel, Würm or Last Glaciation with a complex history of halts in the retreat of the ice-sheets into the Scandinavian mountains.
4. Eemian Interglacial.
3. Saale Glaciation.
2. Holstein Sea or Great Interglacial.
1. Elster Glaciation.

Recent work has shown that the deposits of these two interglacials can be distinguished by the study of their pollen content. The differences are not so much in the genera of plants present, but in their relative abundance and times of appearance. These differences are consistent and provide a valuable tool not only for deciding whether a particular pollen-bearing deposit between two boulder clays represents an interstadial or an interglacial, but enable it to be correlated with the correct interglacial. The pollen-bearing Hoxne deposits yield the Holsteinian pollen spectrum and therefore the Gippingian and Lowestoftian Boulder Clays must be correlated with the Saale and Elster glaciations respectively.

It may seem surprising that the Great Interglacial is represented in East Anglia by only a few small pockets of lake-deposits; but this may be largely due to the removal of loose debris by the Gippingian ice-sheets.

By contrast recent work in the English Midlands has given impressive evidence of the complexity of the changes that occurred during the Great Interglacial and the succeeding Saale Glaciation. The 'Older Drift' yields evidence of two distinct glacial episodes, separated by an interglacial period represented by river gravels containing a temperate fauna. Two separate ice-sheets, the Western and the Eastern, invaded the area during both glaciations. The place of origin of the Western Drift is shown by the distinctive Welsh erratics it contains. At its maximum, during the first glaciation, the Welsh ice-sheets extended down the Severn Valley to the Malvern Hills, Gloucester, the scarp of the Cotswolds and the Vale of Moreton (Fig. 129), whilst a tongue of ice may have

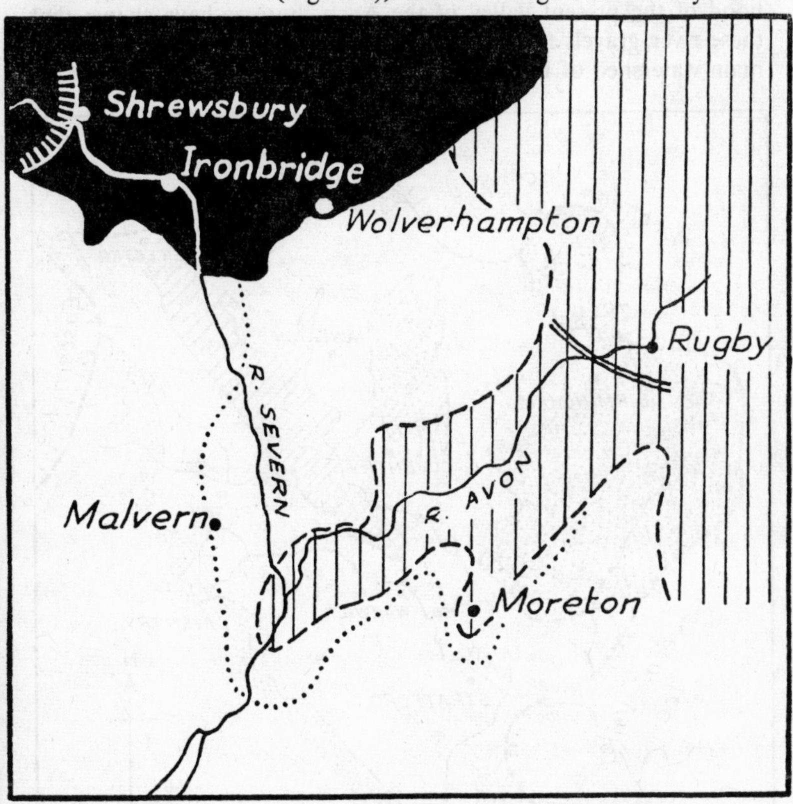


FIG. 129.

The approximate limits of the successive ice-sheets in the English Midlands. (*After L. J. Wills.*)

1. Welsh ice maximum, dotted line; First Eastern (Lowestoft), double line, near 'Rugby.'
2. Second Eastern (Gipping), ruled. Second Western, not shown.
3. Irish Sea Ice, black.
4. Welsh Ice readvance, hachured line near 'Shrewsbury.'

extended down the Evenlode Valley to the neighbourhood of Oxford and beyond, to carry the Bunter quartzites which occur in the high-level drifts of the Oxford neighbourhood and the Chiltern dip-slope. The boulder-clays then deposited are now deeply weathered and occur mainly as scattered patches on high ground. The contemporary Eastern (Lowestoft) ice-sheet only just spread into the Midlands.

Then followed a long period of erosion and weathering. River-terrace gravels were deposited and these have yielded mammalian remains indicating a warm to temperate climate. In the neighbourhood of the present valley of the Avon, borings have shown that these river gravels lie in a valley sloping northwards, and that the main watershed of England, between the rivers flowing northwards

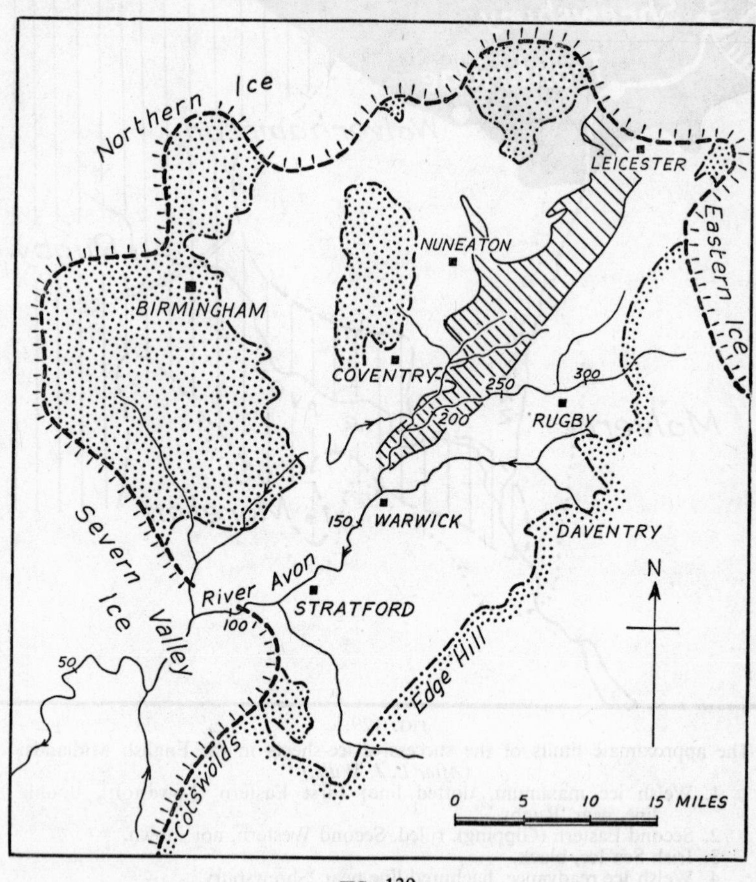


FIG. 130.

Sketch-map of the English Midlands showing 'Lake Harrison' and the Avon river system.
(*After F. W. Shotton.*)

Ground over 400 feet stippled; a pre-Glacial valley draining north-eastwards beneath the Drift indicated by oblique shading; edge of ice-sheets hachured.
Lake Harrison lay between the edge of the ice-sheets and the high ground at 410 feet O.D.
Note the northward shift of the watershed consequent upon glacial modification of the drainage system.

to the North Sea and those draining southwards to the Bristol Channel, was at this period many miles to the southward of its present position (Fig. 130).

These gravels are overlain, and overlapped towards the sides of this sub-Drift valley, by upwards of 50 feet of plastic and sometimes laminated clays with subordinate seams of sand. These clays and sands are interpreted as the deposits of a large pro-glacial lake, 'Lake Harrison', formed between the advancing ice-sheets and the Cotswold scarp (Fig. 128). In the upper part of the clays there are increasing numbers of scattered pebbles, mainly of flint and Bunter quartzite. These pebbles must have been dropped by ice-bergs which had broken away ('calved') from the ice-sheets on the northern side of the lake. The highest level reached by Lake Harrison is shown by a marked bench, at just over 400 feet O.D., that has been traced for 27 miles along the face of the Cotswold scarp from near Moreton to Daventry.

The Gippingian ice-sheet, carrying its load of Chalk, flint and distinctive igneous rocks such as Mountsorrel granite and markfieldite from Leicestershire gradually advanced, though with oscillations, into the lake basin and finally swept right across it depositing Chalky Boulder Clay as far south as Moreton-in-the-Marsh. When the ice-sheet dwindled away, the pile of soft deposits infilling the old valley and lake-basin was attacked with great vigour by a southward-flowing stream, the primitive Avon. Finally the main watershed across England was pushed back from perhaps the neighbourhood of Bredon Hill to between Nuneaton and Coventry, whilst the Avon system, with its southward-sloping river-terraces was incised into the flat surface of the lake deposits and thin cover of Boulder Clay and outwash Gravels.

The Newer Drift of the Midlands is represented by the Irish Sea ice-sheet (Fig. 129), which carried millions of boulders of distinctive Lake District and Southern Scottish rocks into Cheshire and north Shropshire. During the retreat of this ice-sheet a number of glacial lakes were formed between the ice-front and the high ground of the Wenlock-Pennine watershed. The lakes discharged through overflow channels, such as the Ironbridge gorge near Shrewsbury, which cut through high ground, whilst below Ironbridge the greatly augmented Severn cut deeply into spreads of sands and gravels, partly solifluxion deposits and partly the product of spring and summer melt-waters. As a result the Main Terrace of the Severn, which dates from this period, is in places as much as 100 feet above the present river.

The final retreat of the ice-sheets was interrupted by a number of minor cold periods such as the Welsh Readvance, when the Upper Severn Valley glacier extended as far east as Shrewsbury (Fig. 129), and the Scottish Readvance when ice-sheets again reached the coasts of the Irish Sea. The details of the pauses and readvances of the dwindling Newer Drift ice-sheets are gradually being pieced together by local studies of the distribution and height-relations of its beautifully preserved overflow channels, glacial lakes, moraines, etc.

It is now necessary to give further consideration to the periglacial region, particularly the valley of the Thames. It was shown above that the onset of the first glaciation diverted the Thames southwards from its 'Pebble Gravel' course. As the result of a long and complex series of generally southward shifts the Thames finally followed a course from north of Maidenhead across the present suburbs of North London into a deep depression (the Finchley Depression) between the high ground of the Barnet-Totteridge and Hampstead ridges, and so towards Harlow in Essex (Fig. 127). This course is related to a widely traceable erosion level, formerly called the 200-foot platform, but latterly, the Ambersham Surface (Fig. 131). This Surface forms the middle of the five treads of the 'physiographic staircase' of Southern England.

During the second glaciation (the Lowestoft) an almost moribund ice-sheet moved sufficiently far up the Finchley Depression to divert the Thames to a new course over what is now Central London. During the following Hoxnian Interglacial period the river deposited the **Boyn Hill Terrace,** from the gravels of which the remains of Swanscombe Man, together with temperate types of vertebrates and Acheulian flint implements have been obtained. The Boyn Hill Terrace is often referred to as the 100-foot Terrace; but although it is approximately at this level to the east of London, it rises to 175 feet O.D. in the Middle Thames near Slough.

Following this interlude of mild climatic conditions the advance of the Gipping ice-sheet farther north gave periglacial conditions in the area under consideration, causing contortions of the highest levels of the Boyn Hill gravels and the formation of extensive spreads of Coombe Rock.

During the early phases of the ensuing post-Gipping interglacial period the gravels of the **Taplow Terrace** (the '50-foot Terrace') were deposited, and have yielded 'cold' mammals including reindeer and mammoth. Actually the deposits of the Taplow and the younger **Flood Plain Terrace** are complex: neither represents a single uninterrupted phase of aggradation. The Taplow gravels are disturbed and contorted by another phase of solifluxion which is probably represented by peat beds in the Flood Plain Terrace of the Lower Lea Valley. These peats with a $C^{14}$ dating of 28,000 B.C., contain arctic birch and arctic mosses together with tundra and steppe forms of vertebrates and molluscs. The latter indicate a climate similar to that of Lapland to-day. It is tempting to correlate this periglacial phase with the Newer Drifts to the north; but if so, only one short chapter of a long and complicated story is preserved in the Thames Valley. The final episode was the cutting in the Lower Thames Valley of a narrow gorge to a maximum depth of 100 feet below O.D. This **'Buried Channel'** was infilled during the Holocene

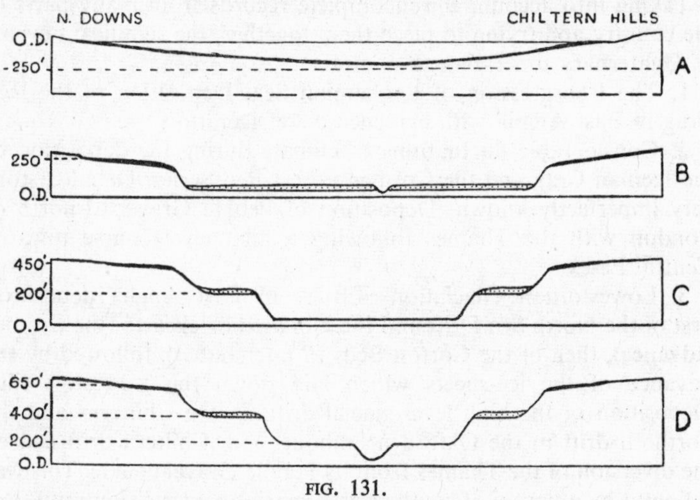


FIG. 131.

Diagrammatic sections showing the effects of changes of level during the Pliocene and Pleistocene Periods.

A. The Lenham Gulf.
B. The Pebble Gravel plain cut in the floor of the Lenham Gulf.
C. The Lenham shelf, Pebble Gravel platform (at 200 feet O.D.) and a lower plain.
D. The Lenham shelf at 650 feet, the Pebble Gravel platform at 400 feet, the 200-foot Platform (Ambersham Surface) trenched by rivers in pre-Chalky Boulder Clay times.

The elevations in D are the existing ones.

(*Based on the work of S. W. Wooldridge.*)

Period, intermittent halts of the rising sea-level being indicated by layers of peat or of tree stumps in the alluvium.

The name **Flandrian Transgression** is often applied to this Holocene rise of sea-level. It is widely traceable along the shores of the English Channel and marks the final severing of England from the Continent, about 7000 B.C. But it must not be thought that the 24-mile-wide Straits of Dover were all cut in the last 9000 years. As we have seen above, there was considerable oscillation of sea-level during the Pleistocene; during the periods of low sea-level (glacial periods) the Chalk ridge joining Kent and Artois would have been undergoing subaerial erosion, with rivers flowing from it towards the

North Sea and the Channel. During the periods of high sea-level (interglacial episodes), marine erosion would have widened the cols worn in the Chalk cuesta. The Straits of Dover are, therefore, of very considerable antiquity, and were opened for the last time and the Chalk cliffs clipped somewhat back by this most recent positive movement of sea-level.

Taking into account the incomplete records from many parts of the country and trying to piece them together, the significant events of Quaternary time seem to comprise:

1. The transgression of Lenhamian Sea. Deposition of the Red Crag in East Anglia with evidence of refrigeration.

2. Considerable fluctuations of climate during the deposition of the Icenian Crag and the Cromer Forest Bed Series. Detailed story very imperfectly known. Deposition of Pebble Gravel to north of London with the Thames following a high level course towards Central Essex.

3. Lowestoftian Glaciation = Elster. In East Anglia deposition first of the North Sea Drift and the Norwich Brickearth (the Cromer Advance), then of the Corton Beds (? interstadial), followed by the advance of the ice-sheets which laid down the Lowestoft tills. Deposition of the high level glacial drifts in the Chilterns and the northern drift in the Oxford neighbourhood. Chiltern drift caused the diversion of the Thames from its Pebble Gravel course. This was followed by a period of southward migration and incision until, just before the advance of Lowestoft ice-sheets, the Thames was flowing through the Finchley depression and then probably towards the Blackwater Estuary. The Lowestoft ice-sheets caused the final southward diversion of the Thames into its present valley. First Welsh Glaciation of the Severn valley.

4. Hoxnian or Great Interglacial. Periods of high sea-level are shown by the Boyn Hill Terrace of the Thames and the Goodwood Raised Beach of Sussex. The Clacton and Nechells Channels were cut during periods of lower sea-level followed by aggradation.

5. Gippingian Glaciation of East Anglia = Saale. The ice-sheets fanned out southwards to deposit the Eastern Drift in the Midlands and to spread across 'Glacial' Lake Harrison. Second Welsh glaciation of the Severn valley. Coombe Rock conditions in South-East England.

6. Ipswichian or last Interglacial (Eemian). Back-cutting of the Avon System and formation of terraces in the Avon and Severn valleys. Taplow and Upper Flood Plain Terrace of Thames. Brighton Raised Beach and Estuarine Deposits of Selsea. Interglacial sites include Trafalgar Square, London and Selsea.

7. Weichselian or Würm Glaciation. Dominance of the Irish

Sea ice. During first stages of its retreat, the emptying of 'Lake Lapworth' and the incision of the Severn into its Main Terrace. Advance of Hessle ice-sheets onto the coasts of Norfolk, Lincolnshire and Yorkshire. Mid-Glacial Sands of Cheshire (57,000 years ago) represent an interstadial. Final retreat stages interrupted by the Scottish Readvance. Stranraer-Lammermuir Moraine, Perth-Aberdeen Readvance (100-foot beach in Scotland), Allerød Interstadial (9,000 B.C.), Highland Readvance (50-foot beach of Scotland). Ponders End Stage in the Lea Valley (28,000 B.C.) and cutting of Buried Channel of Thames.

8. Post-Glacial. Flandrian Transgression or Neolithic Submergence. Infilling of the Buried Channel of Thames, silting up of Fens, etc. Climatic Optimum (Atlantic), *c.* 5000 B.C., when much of upland Britain was covered by forests and the 25-foot Raised Beach of Scotland was cut.

### (3) The Geological History of Man

It is appropriate that this book should conclude with brief reference to the rarest group of fossils—the mammalian genus *Homo* and his ancestors. From the most superficial examination it must be obvious that the structure and functions of the human body are no different in essentials from those of certain other mammals. To the geologist, armed with some knowledge of the succession of faunas and of the onward march of evolution to which they so clearly bear witness, the acceptance of the lower mammalian ancestry of man presents no difficulty, and he accepts the fact without question. There is, or should be, nothing startling or disquieting in the supposition that man and ape have shared a common ancestry and have diverged somewhat from a common stock which flourished in the Tertiary earlier than the Pliocene. Man has been led to rise above the other mammalian stocks by reason of the superior brain with which he has been endowed. In this connection the contrast afforded by the Mesozoic dinosaurs is instructive. Among these animals which dominated the world in the Jurassic and Cretaceous Periods were herbivorous dinosaurs of larger size than any other creature that has ever lived. Among the carnivorous types were some which were more formidably armed with tooth and claw than any other creature, reptile or mammal. Yet these animals, which had reached the acme of development along certain lines, became extinct in the geological Middle Ages, and the commonly accepted reason is that their huge bulk and formidable armament were controlled by wholly inadequate brains. A creature the size of an elephant, weighing several tons, but with the brain of a kitten, was at the outset doomed to extinction in a world where the battle does not always go to the strong, but in the long run to the crafty and the wise. By contrast with the dinosaurs man has a puny physical development, which is more than offset, however, by a large, highly efficient brain.

It is only natural that man should exhibit special interest in the traces of his ancestry, but the data so far collected are too meagre to make a connected story. The number of fossil men and 'missing links' so far discovered is very small; and just as some reptiles are known only by footprints on the bedding planes of certain Permian and Triassic sandstones, so early man is better known by the practically indestructible stone weapons and tools he manufactured than by actual skeletons. In Britain the **stone implements** or artefacts are made almost exclusively of flint, and the study of these has shown a succession of Palaeolithic 'cultures' in which the workmanship steadily improves in technique. Working up the succession the crude implements which even the layman would accept as definitely shaped by man give place in higher layers to tools bearing evidence in their workmanship of a clever control over the medium used. The time arrived in the Upper Palaeolithic Period when the artisan was no longer satisfied with merely chipping his implements to the desired shape, but aimed at a higher class of finish by grinding and polishing. Finally the Stone Age was brought to a close when man discovered the art of smelting and made his implements of bronze and of iron. Now working down the time-scale we meet a difficulty. In the abstract all geologists would agree that well-shaped and obviously worked tools must have been preceded in earlier times by others in which the workmanship was poor and the fact that they were shaped by design not so convincing. Doubtless before the desire to shape stones to his own end was born in the mind of primitive man, he made use of natural stones. Thus the 'worked' grades back into the 'unworked'. The first flints that have been claimed in Britain to have been chipped by man are the **'Eoliths'** or 'rostrocarinates', with a broad, heavy butt and the narrow anterior part curved into a beak, hence the name 'Eagle's beak'. These occur in the Stone Bed at the base of the Crag in Norfolk and Suffolk and in high-level gravels on the North Downs.

Measurements of the 'platform-scar angle' (that is, the angle between the sides of a flake and the 'platform' at the blunt end of the flake, where the blow that detached it was struck), have given readings greater than 90 degrees for more than 60 per cent. of the flakes measured from sub-Crag sites. The percentage of flakes with platform-scar angles greater than 90 degrees from (*a*) sub-Eocene and (*b*) undoubted Palaeolithic sites are 54 and 18 respectively. There can be no question that the flakes from the sub-Eocene sites have been produced by natural (i.e. non-human) causes. The close correspondence of the percentage of flakes with high platform-scar angles from sub-Eocene and sub-Crag sites suggests that the human origin of these eoliths is extremely doubtful. The flaking is much more probably due to natural causes: in the case of the sub-Red Crag eoliths most likely to the grounding of pack-ice which jammed together patches of flints lying on the sea-bed and caused some of them to strike flakes off their neighbours. The hurling of flints against one another by storm waves is now believed to have been responsible for the great 'flint implements' (up to 14 lb. in weight) which have been found on Cromer beach and which were claimed to have been the handiwork of a race of giant 'men of exceptional strength and size of hands'. These flakes have an ochreous patination; but this is no proof of antiquity, for recent studies have shown that such patination can be acquired in a few years on the Cromer coast, possibly due to the action of certain algae.

No question of human design arises in connection with the Abbevillian and later Palaeolithic cultures, which are set out in order below:

Magdalenian, named from La Madeleine in the Dordogne.
Solutrian, from Solutré in France.
Aurignacian, from Aurignac in the South of France.
Mousterian, from Le Moustier in southern France.
Levallois, from Levallois on the Seine.
Acheulian, from St. Acheul near Amiens.
Clactonian, from Clacton in Essex.
Abbevillian (formerly called Chellian), from Abbeville in France.

In both the Abbevillian and the Acheulian cultures, the dominant tool was the hand axe or **coup-de-poing** (see Fig. 132), made by trimming cores, crudely in the case of the Abbevillian, with considerable skill in the case of the Acheulian. It has been suggested that these hand axes were excellent tools for the digging up of roots and grubs from the ground.

Clactonian implements were, however, flakes struck off a core, and with their strong cutting-edges were well adapted for working wood. It is therefore probable that the Clactonian people, who were contemporary with the Abbevillian and the early Acheulian, were a forest race.

Levallois man, on the other hand, was probably a hunter, for a great advance in technique had been made, which enabled the production of implements admirably designed for the cutting and preparing of carcases. In place of the core or flake, which had previously been laboriously trimmed into the required tool, man had learnt the knack of first shaping a nodule into a 'tortoise core', from which a heavy blow would strike a flake, requiring the minimum of subsequent trimming.

The Mousterian culture was characterized by semicircular scrapers and 'Mousterian points' (Fig. 132). Of the people who made these, more will be said later.

Aurignacian implements are very varied in form, but are characterized by the fineness of the marginal flaking and by their symmetrical design. Some of the flint implements were used for the first time for shaping bone and ivory: the artist had arrived and produced drawings and sculpture reminiscent of the work of the South African Bushmen.

The Solutrian implements include types of exceptional thinness and beautiful finish, and represent the peak of attainment in working flint. They include tanged arrow-heads and the characteristic laurel-leaf points (Fig. 132).

The Magdalenian flint implements, by contrast with the preceding, are much cruder in design and execution; but they were probably only a means to an end, being used in the production of distinctive weapons of ivory and bone. These latter are often ornamented in a manner that indicates considerable artistic skill, as do the mural decorations and engravings on bone discovered in the caverns which Magdalenian man used as dwellings.

The 25-foot Raised Beach in Scotland yields implements belonging to the succeeding Azilian and Tardenoisian cultures, placed by some authorities in the Mesolithic (connecting the Palaeolithic with the Neolithic), but by others in the Neolithic. The flint implements characteristic of the Azilian are angular and of small size, being termed 'pigmy flints' (Fig. 132).

Passing now from the implements to the men who made and used them, it is much to be regretted that the fossil men so far discovered are so few in number, and in the case of the oldest ones, so fragmentary and incomplete, though later Palaeolithic man is represented by several whole or nearly whole skeletons.

The oldest humanoids at present known are the *Australopithecinae*, in very hard cave-breccia in South Africa. The work of cleaning off the matrix is exceedingly laborious, but sufficient has been done to reveal the remains of creatures, which were either a very advanced type of ape, though differing from modern anthropoid apes by possessing a number of human-like features, or an exceedingly primitive type of mankind with a brain of only simian capacity. In 1956 undoubted pebble tools were found associated with these remains. Australopithecine remains have been found also in the famous sections at Olduvai, Tanganyika. Potassium/

argon determinations of biotites and sanidines in the associated deposits suggest an age of one million years or perhaps a little greater. At a higher level in the gorge a volcanic tuff overlying a layer yielding Chellean implements and containing a sinanthropine skull was dated by the same method as 360,000 years old.

The oldest unquestionable human remains are those of 'Java

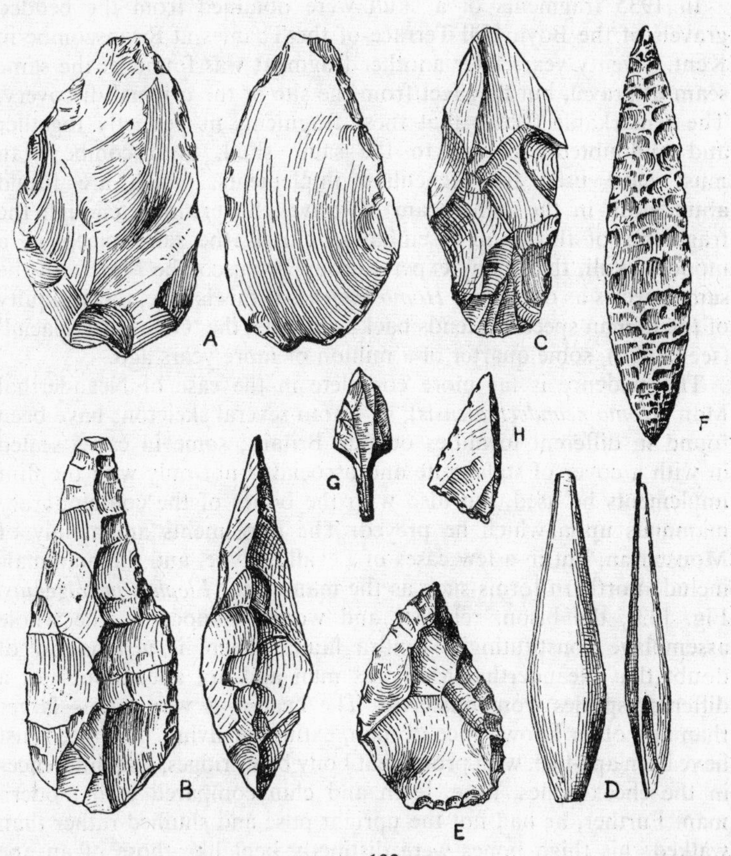


FIG. 132.

Implements manufactured by early man.

A. Abbevillian implement.
B. Acheulian coup-de-poing.
C. Aurignacian keeled scraper.
D. Aurignacian bone point.
E. Mousterian point found with Neanderthal man at Spy, Belgium
F. Solutrian laurel-leaf point.
G. Solutrian tanged arrow-head.
H. Azilian pigmy flint.

(*M. K. W., after Sir A. Smith Woodward and W. B. Wright.*)

Man' and of 'Peking Man'. Recent work has shown that they belong to the same genus, *Sinanthropus*, though to different species, *Sinanthropus erectus* and *S. pekinensis* respectively. Together with the remains of Peking Man were found a number of crudely shaped implements and charred bones of deer, proving that he understood the use of fire.

In 1935 fragments of a skull were obtained from the bedded gravels of the Boyn Hill Terrace of the Thames at Swanscombe in Kent. Twenty years later another fragment was found in the same seam of gravel, but fifty feet from the site of the original discovery. The remarkable fact is that these fragments fit perfectly together and undoubtedly belong to the same skull. Swanscombe Man must have used the Acheulian implements, which are found abundantly in the same seam of gravel. Surprisingly enough the fragments of this skull resemble so closely the same pieces of a modern skull, that many experts group Swanscombe Man with the same species as ourselves, *Homo sapiens*. If this is true, the antiquity of the human species extends back to at least the 'Great Interglacial' (see p. 477), some quarter of a million or more years ago.

The evidence is far more complete in the case of Neanderthal Man (*Homo neanderthalensis*), of whom several skeletons have been found in different localities outside Britain; some in caves sealed in with a cover of stalagmite and associated not only with the flint implements he used, but also with the bones of the contemporary mammals upon which he preyed. The implements are mainly of Mousterian, but in a few cases of Levallois type, and the mammals include northern forms such as the mammoth (*Elephas primigenius*, Fig. 133), the bison, reindeer and woolly rhinoceros, the whole assemblage constituting a tundra fauna. There is no shadow of doubt that Neanderthal Man was man and not ape, though of a different species from ourselves. The head was very large—larger than any other known race of man, extinct or living. The face must have been ape-like, with prominent bony brow ridges, and differences in the cheek-bones, nose, teeth and chin compared with modern man. Further, he had not the upright pose and shuffled rather than walked; his thigh bones were distinctly bent like those of an ape instead of being straight as in modern man. Radio-carbon age determinations on charcoals found at a number of Levalloiso-Mousterian or Mousterian sites have given dates of between 50,000 and 35,000 years ago.

One interesting suggestion, based at present on rather scanty evidence, is that the hand-axe industries (e.g. the Acheulian of Swanscombe) were made by *Homo sapiens* and the flake industries by *Homo neanderthalensis*.

The remains of cave-dwelling men have been found associated with three other cultures, the Aurignacian, Solutrian and Magdalenian, and with much the same types of extinct mammals, though there is evidence that Aurignacian Man lived in the open, under more genial climatic conditions than Neanderthal Man and

FIG. 133.

The mammoth (*Elephas primigenius*), a contemporary of early man in the Pleistocene Period.

(*M. K. W., from a drawing by Alice B. Woodward, issued by the British Museum of Natural History.*)

those who succeeded him. As noted above, Upper Palaeolithic man was sometimes an artist who not only drew and coloured his drawings with ochre, but also produced small sculptured figures, mostly female and presumably based upon the beauties of the period.

There is evidence, by now, of considerable differentiation of the human stock. Associated with Aurignacian and later implements have been found at a number of localities, the remains of a finely built race, *Crô-Magnon Man*, of considerable cranial capacity. The presence of eastern and western types of Crô-Magnon Man has been claimed on both cultural and anthropological evidence. Both types were nomadic, following the migrating herds of game in summer, whilst in winter retiring to the mouths of caves or to rock shelters, though on the open grasslands of southern Russia, semi-underground dwellings had to be constructed. Occasional migration from Africa into Europe is suggested by the discovery in a cave near Mentone of the skeletons of an old woman and a boy (*Grimaldi Race*) which are claimed by many to have distinctly negroid characters. Also there is considerable resemblance between some of the cave art and that of the modern Bushmen. Some of the few human remains that have been found associated with Magdalenian implements show Eskimo-like characters, whilst the general assemblage of the implements including ivory or bone harpoons, needles, spear throwers, etc. shows many similarities to those used by the modern Eskimo. There is, however, much evidence that Magdalenian Man lived under much severer climatic conditions than did Aurignacian Man, so that the resemblances to the Eskimos may be due to adaptation to a similar environment. Certainly these skeletons and implements are associated with a thoroughly arctic fauna characterized by an abundance of reindeer, together with the musk ox, arctic hare and other animals.

Grimaldi and Crô-Magnon Man, like the modern negro, Eskimo and ourselves, are all forms of *Homo sapiens*. The existing types of *Homo sapiens* are divided into a number of races. The archaeological evidence suggests that some of these races are of considerable antiquity.

The study of the implements and remains of fossil man raises many great problems which still await solution, and discussion of which would be out of place in this book. One of the surprising features is the concentration of practically all the Palaeolithic cultures in a single cave, distributed through a score or two feet of cave earth or breccia; while elsewhere they are distributed through the whole succession of river-terrace gravels. One may well be puzzled as to the extent to which the different cultures are really successive, or did they overlap in time? The impression conveyed is that the series of invasions and conquests of the Historical Period by the Romans, the Saxons, the Danes and the Normans commenced far back in time, with Neanderthal Man wiping out the makers of the giant flint implements of Cromer, and being in turn overcome and ultimately exterminated by the more highly civilized Crô-Magnon Man, and so on. The implication of this idea is clearly the co-existence, at first in separate localities, but later for a time in the same areas, of at least two of these races in the role of victors and vanquished. This being so, the value of the implements for correlation, certainly over a wide area, is under suspicion. And yet the careful examination of any implementiferous deposit of any reasonable thickness yields clear evidence of a succession of types as noted above. Thus in Kent's cavern, Torquay, the succession of deposits and of the associated implements is as follows:

The highest deposit—

Black Mould—Early Iron implements
Bronze implements
Neolithic implements
Stalagmite (granular)
Black Band—Magdalenian implements
Cave earth { Solutrian implements
late Aurignacian implements
middle Aurignacian implements
early Mousterian implements
Acheulian hand axes }
Stalagmite (crystalline)
Cave breccia—early Abbevillian.

This was also one of the critical sites for proving Man's antiquity. Dean Buckland claimed that the implements found below the stalagmite layer in beds yielding the bones of extinct animals had been inserted by burial and that therefore man and the extinct animals could not have been contemporary. In 1858 the nearby Windmill Hill Cave at Brixham was excavated. The same sequence as at Kent's Cavern was found there. Sir Charles Lyell and other eminent geologists were convinced that there was no evidence of disturbance.

Thus these deposits, expressed in terms of the implements they contain, epitomize the rise of man almost from his earliest decipherable beginnings through the period when he was a nomad and a hunter living a primitive life on the outskirts of the Pleistocene icefields, to the more advanced times in the Neolithic Period when he had begun to master agriculture, to domesticate animals and to build in stone. It is at this point that the geologist hands over his pen to the archaeologist and the historian, perhaps after one glimpse into the future. Some of the animal races we have had occasion to notice did not enjoy a long life—long, that is, in the geological sense. Through some fault in their make-up they suffered extinction; others enjoyed a racial life vastly longer than the short span between man's first appearance and the present. Man is certainly very near to the commencement of what we may call his evolutionary career, from which fact those who are dissatisfied with his actions, thoughts and ambitions may take some comfort.

There can be no doubt that, at the acme of his development, he will both look and act differently, unless in the meantime he has successfully engineered some means of prematurely bringing about his own extinction, as the present course of events leads one to think possible.

## REFERENCES

BADEN-POWELL, D. F. W. *Geol. Mag.*, **85** (1948), 279–296. The Chalky Boulder Clay of East Anglia divided into the Lowestoft and the Gipping drifts.

CHARLESWORTH, J. K. *The Quaternary Era* (Arnold, London, 1957). An encyclopaedic work with very comprehensive bibliography.

DINES, H. G., and others. *Geol. Mag.*, **77** (1940), 198–226. Suggests the use of the term 'Head' for solifluxion deposits and stresses their importance.

KING, W. B. R. *Q.J.G.S.*, **111** (1955), 187–209. A review of the Pleistocene Epoch in England.

LE GROS CLARK, W. E. *History of the Primates*. British Museum (Natural History) (1949).[1]

OAKLEY, K. P. *Man the Tool-Maker*, British Museum (Natural History) (1949).[1]

OAKLEY, K. P. *Proc. Geol. Assoc.*, **63** (1952), 271–300. A comprehensive account of Swanscombe Man.

OAKLEY, K. P. *Antiquity*, **31** (1957), 199–209. Discusses eoliths and Man's earliest tools.

OAKLEY, K. P. *Adv. of Sc.*, **18** (1962), 415–426. Radiometric dating of the emergence of Man.

SHOTTON, F. W. *Phil. Trans. Roy. Soc.* Ser. B., **237** (1953), 209–260. 'Lake Harrison' and the history of Avon system.

TOMLINSON, W. E. 'The Pleistocene Chronology of the Midlands,' *Proc. Geol. Assoc.*, **74** (1963), 187–202.

WEST, R. G. *Proc. Geol. Assoc.*, **74** (1963), 147–186. The correlation and problems of the British Quaternary with particular reference to palynology.

WOOLDRIDGE, S. W. *Proc. Geol. Assoc.*, **71** (1960), 113–129. Summarizes his lifelong study of the history of the London Basin during the Pleistocene.

For details of different areas consult the *Brit. Reg. Geol. Memoirs* or the references given in Charlesworth's volumes.

[1] These two very reasonably priced guides give authoritative and most readable summaries of our knowledge of fossil man, his habits and his implements.

# INDEX